Bridges

Second Edition

to Algebra and Geometry

Mathematics In Context

Developed by:

CORD

Leading Change in Education

Waco, Texas

CORD COMMUNICATIONS

tools for contextual learning

CORD Staff
Program Director: Michael Crawford, Ph.D.
Program Manager: John Souders, Jr., Ph.D., currently Vice President for Academic and Student Affairs,
    Cedar Valley Community College, Texas
Educational Specialist: Lewis Westbrook
Chief Scientist: Leno Pedrotti, Ph.D.
Applications Specialist: Woody Baker
Applications Specialist: Nick G. Carter
Applications Specialist: John Chamberlain
Implementation Specialist: Claudia D. Maness
Technology Specialist: Carolyn Prescott

Project Staff
Project Director: Piers Bateman
Assistant Project Director: Tara Jones
Assistant Project Director: John D. Willome

Consultants

Wes Evans	**Howard L. Rolf, Ph.D.**	**Charles A. Milam**	**Rhonda Jones**
Mathematics Teacher	**Professor Emeritus**	**Mathematics Teacher**	**Mathematics Teacher**
Midway High School	**Mathematics**	**H. P. Miles Middle School**	**Steelville High School**
Waco, Texas	**Baylor University**	**Waco, Texas**	**Steelville, Illinois**

Jim Bohan
Mathematics Coordinator
Manheim Township High School
Lancaster, Pennsylvania

Editorial Services: MATHQueue, Inc.
Production Services and Design: Robb & Associates, Inc.

ISBN 1-57837-341-7
Printed in the United States of America

1 2 3 4 5 6 7 8 9 10 QV 05 04 03 02

800-231-3015
www.cordcommunications.com

CHAPTER 1

Decimals and Problem Solving

CHAPTER 2

Working with Data

CHAPTER 3

Integers

CHAPTER 4

Solving Equations

CHAPTER 5

Rational Numbers

CHAPTER 6

Ratio, Proportion, and Probability

CHAPTER 7

Percent

CHAPTER 8

Graphing on the Coordinate Plane

CHAPTER 9

Introduction to Geometry

CHAPTER 10

Powers and Roots

CHAPTER 11

Measurement

CHAPTER 12

Surface Area and Volume

Bridges

Second Edition

to Algebra and Geometry

Mathematics In Context

CHAPTER 1

WHY SHOULD I LEARN THIS?

You can use the basic properties of algebra to solve many types of problems. For example, the properties are important tools in designing, building, launching, and operating satellites like the Hubble Space Telescope.

DECIMALS AND PROBLEM SOLVING

LEARN HOW TO...

1. **Order numbers using place value and number lines.**
2. **Estimate answers using rounding and compatible numbers.**
3. **Apply the order of operations to evaluate expressions.**
4. **Simplify expressions using the basic properties of addition and multiplication.**
5. **Use the four-step problem-solving plan to solve problems.**

Everyone solves problems. An auto mechanic figures out why a car engine is not working. A carpenter calculates how much lumber is needed for a job. A farmer determines how much seed money is needed for planting. A teenager estimates how much money to save to buy a special gift. Successful people apply the skills of problem solving in many areas of life.

Mathematics helps you solve problems and think logically. Many times you need to assemble facts and use addition, subtraction, multiplication, or division to solve a particular problem.

You also need to be a good estimator. When you are solving a problem, you do not always need an exact answer. Sometimes you need to know if an answer you get is reasonable.

In this chapter, you will review the basic operations of arithmetic, learn how to estimate answers, and use a four-step plan to solve problems.

LESSON 1.1 THE DECIMAL SYSTEM

In the years 600–400 BCE, the Hindus and Arabs developed the symbols we use today to write numbers. This system uses ten **digits** to write a number. Since there are ten digits in the Hindu-Arabic system, it is also called the **decimal** or **base-ten** system.

$$0 \quad 1 \quad 2 \quad 3 \quad 4 \quad 5 \quad 6 \quad 7 \quad 8 \quad 9$$

In the decimal system, one digit is needed to write a **whole number** less than 10. Two digits are needed to write the next ninety whole numbers.

$$10 \quad 11 \quad 12 \ldots 97 \quad 98 \quad 99$$

How many digits are needed to write the next nine hundred whole numbers?

EXAMPLE 1 Writing Money in Decimal Notation

Stacy is collecting money for her soccer team's fund-raiser. She has collected 4 ten-dollar bills, 6 one-dollar bills, 5 dimes, and 7 pennies. How much money has Stacy collected?

SOLUTION

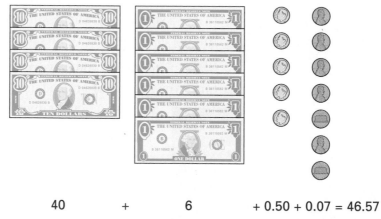

$$40 \qquad + \qquad 6 \qquad + 0.50 + 0.07 = 46.57$$

Stacy collected forty-six dollars and fifty-seven cents, or $46.57.

In decimal notation, a decimal point is used to separate the whole number from the decimal part. In 46.57, 46 is the whole number and 57 is the decimal part. In Example 1, 57 represents a part of a dollar. The decimal 46.57 is read *forty-six and fifty-seven hundredths* or *forty-six point fifty-seven*.

EXAMPLE 2 Writing Decimals

At the equator, the radius of the Earth is 6378.533 kilometers. What is the place value of each digit in this number?

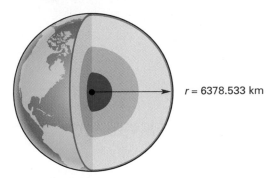

r = 6378.533 km

SOLUTION

Use a place-value chart to write the number.

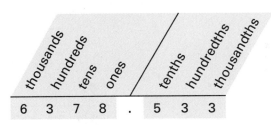

thousands	hundreds	tens	ones		tenths	hundredths	thousandths
6	3	7	8	.	5	3	3

Digit	Place Value	
6	thousands	6000
3	hundreds	300
7	tens	70
8	ones	8
5	tenths	0.5
3	hundredths	0.03
3	thousandths	0.003
	Total	6378.533

ONGOING ASSESSMENT

Write the value of each underlined digit.

a. 34.2<u>8</u>7   **b.** 8071.35<u>4</u>   **c.** 75.<u>0</u>

You can use a number line to represent the numbers between any two whole numbers. For example, if you divide the segment between 2 and 3 into ten equal parts, each of the divisions is one-tenth (0.1) of a unit.

The number 2.4 is located four-tenths (0.4) of a unit to the right of 2.

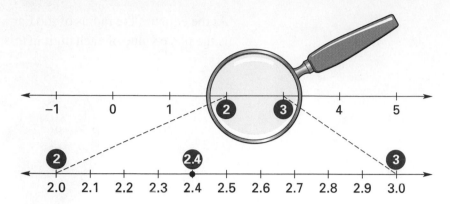

You can use the same number line to locate 2.67. Divide the number line between 2.6 and 2.7 into ten equal parts. The result is a division of the number line into hundredths. Each division is one-hundredth (0.01) of a unit. The number 2.67 is located between 2.6 and 2.7.

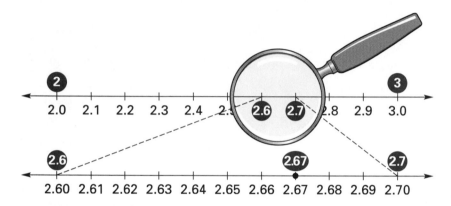

Critical Thinking Explain how to locate 2.635 on the number line above.

ACTIVITY   **Comparing Decimals**

A video game rental costs $5.38. A movie rental costs $5.34.

1 Draw a number line to show the hundredths from 5.30 to 5.40.

2 Locate 5.38 and 5.34 on your number line. Which number is farther to the right? Which number has the greater value?

3 How can you use a number line to determine the greater of two numbers?

4 Which costs more: the game rental or the movie rental?

On a number line, numbers to the right are **greater than** numbers to the left. Numbers to the left are **less than** numbers to the right. You can use symbols to show this relationship.

Words	Symbols
5.38 is greater than 5.34.	5.38 > 5.34
5.34 is less than 5.38.	5.34 < 5.38

You can also compare two decimals by writing them in place-value form and comparing their digits.

EXAMPLE 3 Comparing Digits

The top two finishers in a slalom race have times of 88.46 seconds and 88.5 seconds. Which skier finished the race in the least time?

SOLUTION

Write out each number to the hundredths place. Remember that 88.5 is the same as 88.50. To compare 88.46 with 88.50, start at the left and compare the digits in each place-value position.

When one of the digits has greater value than the other, the number with this digit has the greater value.

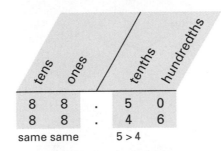

88.5
SECONDS

Since there are more tenths in 88.50,

88.5 > 88.46 or 88.46 < 88.5

The skier with the time of 88.46 seconds completed the race in the least time and is the winner.

Critical Thinking Placing zeros to the right of a whole number changes its value. Placing zeros to the right of the decimal part of a number does not change the value of the number. Explain why.

LESSON ASSESSMENT

Think and Discuss

1 A car's 16.3-gallon fuel tank is empty. You have a 10-gallon container, a 1-gallon container, and a $\frac{1}{10}$-gallon container. Explain how to fill the tank using only full containers.

2 How do you locate 7.41 on a number line?

3 Explain how to use a number line to compare 7.41 and 7.43.

4 Explain how to use place value to compare 245.37 and 245.307.

Practice and Apply

Write the number represented by the base-ten blocks.

5.

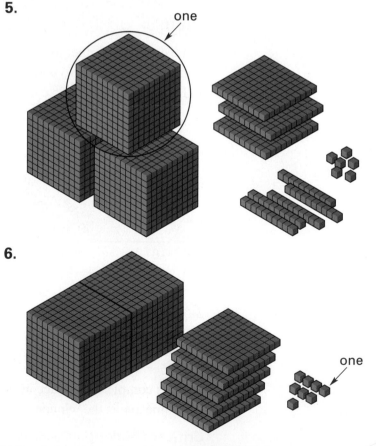

one

6.

one

Write the value of each underlined digit.

7. 56.3<u>5</u>24   **8.** 124. <u>0</u>986   **9.** 50.709<u>2</u>

Use < or > to complete Exercises 10–15.

10. 3.58 ? 3.52

11. 1.49 ? 1.39

12. 4.015 ? 4.105

13. 7.541 ? 7.514

14. 10.025 ? 10.05

15. 0.004 ? 0.0039

For Exercises 16–17, write each decimal in words.

16. The weight of a wrestler is 145.25 pounds.

17. The average length of some bacteria is about 0.0015 centimeters.

For Exercises 18–19, write a decimal for each italicized phrase.

18. Your normal temperature is about *ninety-eight and six-tenths* degrees Fahrenheit.

19. One kilometer is about *six hundred twenty-five thousandths* of a mile.

20. The normal annual precipitation for St. Louis is 37.51 inches. The normal annual precipitation for Kansas City is 37.62 inches. Which city has less normal annual precipitation?

21. The snowfall for a ski resort over a 3-day period was: Monday, 3.14 inches; Tuesday, 3.32 inches; and Wednesday, 3.09 inches. On which day was the snowfall the greatest?

A graduated cylinder measures volume in milliliters (mL).
Draw the scale from 25 milliliters to 35 milliliters. Mark
each measurement in the correct position on the scale.

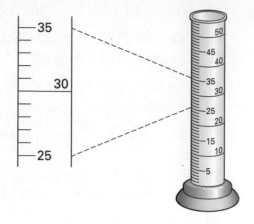

22. 29 mL   **23.** 33 mL

24. 26.5 mL   **25.** 30.5 mL

26. Write the measurements in Exercises 22–25 in order
from least to greatest.

27. The table at the right gives
the times for the first four
swimmers in a swim meet. List
the names of the finishers in
order from first to fourth.

	min:sec
NANCY	1:58.15
MEI	1:57.03
MARY	1:58.17
LANA	1:57.15

Mixed Review

Find each sum or difference.

28. 124 + 375   **29.** 839 − 157

30. 120.4 − 91.5   **31.** 52.64 + 691.8

32. 528 + 28,676   **33.** $431.28 − $274.09

Find each product or quotient.

34. 16 × 8   **35.** 450 ÷ 5

36. $128 ÷ 4   **37.** $203 × 9

38. 18 × 15   **39.** 24 × $196

LESSON 1.2 ROUNDING DECIMALS

OBJECTIVES

➤ Round whole numbers and decimals using number lines and place value.

Latisha is the treasurer of the Lincoln Theatre Club. The club president asks how many people will be attending Saturday's performance. Latisha replies, "There will be about 160 people at the performance."

Day	Tickets Sold	Amount Collected
Monday	17	$118.25
Tuesday	36	$250.30
Wednesday	47	$326.65
Thursday	21	$145.95
Friday	34	$229.45

Latisha **estimated** the number of tickets sold. She knew the president did not need an exact number; so she gave an **approximate** answer. There are many ways to estimate a number. One method uses **rounding.**

You can use a number line to help visualize the rounding process.

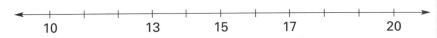

The number 17 is closer to 20 than to 10. If you round 17 to the nearest ten, the result is 20.

Similarly, the number 13 is closer to 10 than 20. If you round 13 to the nearest ten, the result is 10.

How would you round 15 to the nearest ten? The number 15 is halfway between 10 and 20. Would you choose 10 or 20? Since two different answers lead to confusion, this book will always round up numbers that are halfway between two numbers. Thus, 15 rounded to the nearest ten is 20.

To summarize, when rounding to the nearest ten,

13 is **rounded down** to 10 because 13 is closer to 10 than 20,

17 is **rounded up** to 20 because 17 is closer to 20 than 10, and

15 is **rounded up** to 20 because 15 is halfway between 10 and 20.

ACTIVITY 1   Rounding Whole Numbers

Use the number line below to round Latisha's ticket sales numbers to the nearest ten.

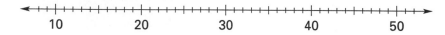

1 Locate 36 on the number line. Is 36 nearer 30 or 40? What is 36 rounded to the nearest ten?

2 Use the number line to round 47, 21, and 34 to the nearest ten.

3 Find the sum of the rounded numbers of tickets sold.

4 Find the sum of 17, 36, 47, 21, and 34.

5 Explain why the sum you found in Step 3 is a good estimation for the total number of ticket sales.

Rounding numbers is a skill used in many situations. Businesses use rounding to estimate profits and expenses. Census workers round to estimate the population of a state. A medical technician rounds a calculated percentage to record test results on a patient's chart.

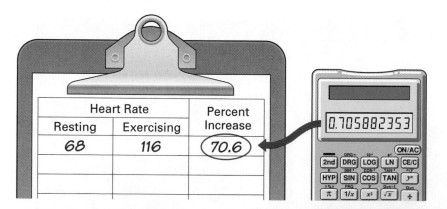

Heart Rate		Percent Increase
Resting	Exercising	
68	116	70.6

0.705882353

EXAMPLE 1 Steps to Rounding

Antonio keeps track of his business expenses with a spreadsheet. Each quarter (three-month period) he reports his expenses to the nearest hundred dollars. What should Antonio report for the first quarter?

1999 Expenses		
	A	**B**
1	**Month**	**Expenses ($)**
2	Jan	2938
3	Feb	2978
4	March	2850

SOLUTION

Round each month's expenses to the nearest hundred. You can use a number line or you can also use place value as shown below.

Step 1 Underline the digit at the place value you want to round.

$$\$2\underline{9}38 \qquad \$2\underline{9}78 \qquad \$2\underline{8}50$$

Step 2 Look at the digit to the right of the underlined digit.

If the digit is less than ($<$) 5, round down. If the digit is greater than or equal to ($\geq$) 5, round up.

$\$2\underline{9}38$	$\$2\underline{9}78$	$\$2\underline{8}50$
$3 < 5$	$7 \geq 5$	$5 \geq 5$
Round Down	Round Up	Round Up
$\$2900$	$\$3000$	$\$2900$

Antonio should report $2900, $3000, and $2900.

EXAMPLE 2 Rounding Decimals

Round the following weights to the nearest tenth.

a. 118.24 lb   **b.** 89.65 oz   **c.** 53.029 g

SOLUTION

	a.	**b.**	**c.**
1. Underline the tenths place.	118.$\underline{2}$4	89.$\underline{6}$5	53.$\underline{0}$29
2. Check the digit to the right of the underlined digit. If this digit is less than 5, round down. If this digit is greater than or equal to 5, round up.	$4 < 5$	$5 \geq 5$	$2 < 5$
	118.2 lb	89.7 oz	53.0 g

Day	Tickets Sold	Amount Collected
Monday	17	$118.25
Tuesday	36	$250.30
Wednesday	47	$326.65
Thursday	21	$145.95
Friday	34	$229.45

1 Use rounding to estimate (to the nearest dollar) each amount collected by the Lincoln Theatre Club.

2 Approximately how much was collected for the week?

3 Use a calculator to find the total amount collected. Round this number to the nearest dollar.

4 For Step 2, you rounded the daily amounts and then added. For Step 3, you added the daily amounts and then rounded. Do both methods result in the same total?

LESSON ASSESSMENT

Think and Discuss

1 Give an example of a situation where an approximate answer can be used instead of the exact answer.

2 How do you round a number to the nearest hundred? How do you round a number to the nearest hundredth?

3 Two people use rounding to estimate the sum of a set of numbers. Explain how they might get different answers.

Practice and Apply

Round each number to (a) the nearest tenth and (b) the nearest hundredth.

4. 7.516   **5.** 13.049   **6.** 23.375

7. 0.357   **8.** 0.096   **9.** 8.4863

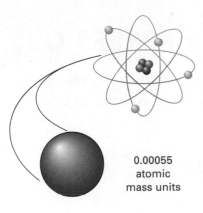

0.00055
atomic
mass units

10. In geometry, the value of π is about 3.14159. Round π to the nearest thousandth.

11. In physics, the mass of an electron is approximately 0.00055 atomic mass units. To which place is the mass rounded?

Find each sum or difference on a calculator. Round the answer to the nearest tenth.

12. 73.31 ft + 109.67 ft + 88.7 ft

13. 87.95 + 158.38 − 76.15

14. $136.08 − $95.75

15. 3.78 s + 8.0235 s + 7.166 s

16. Rhoda's savings account has $2415.35. During the month, she makes a deposit of $116.72 and a withdrawal of $53. To the nearest dollar, how much does Rhoda have in her account?

17. To make a load of concrete, you mix 22.71 kilograms of cement, 45.46 kilograms of water, and 68.24 kilograms of sand. To the nearest tenth of a kilogram, what is the weight of the concrete?

18. Casey jogs 5.2 kilometers on Monday, 7.5 kilometers on Wednesday, and 4.8 kilometers on Friday. To the nearest kilometer, about how far does Casey jog for these three days?

Mixed Review

Give the value for each underlined digit.

19. 23.93<u>4</u>6 **20.** 9.7<u>0</u>54 **21.** 11.868<u>2</u>

Replace the ? with < or >.

22. 4.56 ? 4.64 **23.** 236.938 ? 236.97

24. The diameters of three large washers measure 2.346 centimeters, 2.367 centimeters, and 2.364 centimeters. List the diameters in order from least to greatest.

LESSON 1.3 VARIABLES AND EXPRESSIONS

OBJECTIVES

➤ **Use variables to write expressions from word expressions.**
➤ **Use the order of operations to simplify expressions.**

Marcos is saving for a CD player that costs $108. He earns money by washing cars. For each car he washes, Marcos earns $9. The chart shows Marcos' earnings.

Cars Washed	Computation	Money Earned In Dollars
1	9×1	9
2	9×2	18
3	9×3	27
⋮	⋮	⋮
n	$9 \times n$	$9n$

Numerical and Algebraic Expressions

After three cars, Marcos earns 9×3 dollars. The multiplication 9×3 is an example of a *numerical expression*. A **numerical expression** contains only numbers and operational symbols.

The operational symbol $\times$ means to multiply the numbers or variables to the left and right of the $\times$. A center dot or parentheses also indicate multiplication. Thus, you can write 9 times 3 with any of the following numerical expressions.

$$9 \times 3 \qquad 9 \cdot 3 \qquad 9(3) \qquad (9)(3) \qquad (9)3$$

After n cars, Marcos earns $9 \times n$ dollars. In the expression $9 \times n$, n is a *variable*. It is a **variable** because its value can vary or change. In algebra you solve problems using variables to represent unknown quantities.

You can also write $9 \times n$ as $9n$. The expression $9 \times n$ or $9n$ is called an *algebraic expression*. An **algebraic expression** contains at least one variable.

EXAMPLE 1 Translating Expressions

Translate each word expression into an algebraic expression.

a. six divided by y **b.** twelve dollars plus the sales tax m

a. $6 \div y$ or $\dfrac{6}{y}$ **b.** $\$12 + m$

ONGOING ASSESSMENT

Translate each word expression into an algebraic expression.

a. the time t decreased by 5 minutes

b. the height h multiplied by 12 meters

EXAMPLE 2 Replacing a Variable

Will Marcos have enough money for the CD player after washing 6, 9, or 12 cars?

SOLUTION

Find the value of $9n$, when n is replaced by

a. 6   **b.** 9   **c.** 12
    $9(6) = 54$ $9(9) = 81$ $9(12) = 108$

Marcos will have $108 after washing 12 cars.

ACTIVITY

Evaluating Algebraic Expressions

1 Evaluate $m + n$, when m is replaced by 15 and n is replaced by 8.

2 Evaluate $m + n$, when m is replaced by 10 and n is replaced by 13.

3 What is the relationship between the answers to Steps 1 and 2?

An equal sign is used to show that two expressions are **equivalent**. Expressions such as $15 + 8$ and $10 + 13$ are equivalent because they represent the same number.

$$15 + 8 = 10 + 13$$

$$23 = 23$$

When you simplify $15 + 8$ and $10 + 13$, replace each expression with 23.

Sometimes an expression contains parentheses. When this happens, you perform the operations inside the parentheses first.

Order of Operations

How do you simplify $5 + 3 \cdot 2$? If you add 5 and 3 first, the result is $8 \cdot 2$ or 16. But if you multiply 3 times 2 first, the result is $5 + 6$ or 11. To get the same results, you must use the same **Order of Operations**.

Order of Operations
1. Simplify all expressions inside parentheses first.

2. Then multiply and divide from left to right.

3. Then add and subtract from left to right.

If you apply the Order of Operations to $5 + 3 \cdot 2$, the result is 11. To get a result of 16, you must insert parentheses.

$$(5 + 3) \cdot 2 = 8 \cdot 2 = 16$$

EXAMPLE 3 Simplifying an Expression

a. Simplify $6 \cdot (5 + 2)$.   **b.** Simplify $\dfrac{12}{4 + 2}$

c. Evaluate $15 \div (c - p)$ when $c = 10$ and $p = 7$.

SOLUTION

a. Always perform the operations within the parentheses first. Since $5 + 2 = 7$,

$$6 \cdot (5 + 2) = 6 \cdot 7 = 42$$

b. The line separating 12 from $4 + 2$ is used as a division symbol. $\dfrac{12}{4 + 2}$ is the same as $12 \div (4 + 2)$. To simplify an expression containing a division line, first simplify the expressions above and below the division line. Then divide.

$$\frac{12}{4 + 2} = \frac{12}{6} = 2$$

c. Substitute 10 for c, 7 for p, and simplify.

$$15 \div (c - p) = 15 \div (10 - 7)$$
$$= 15 \div 3$$
$$= 5$$

Evaluate each expression when $r = 6$.

a. $12 + (r \div 2)$ **b.** $(12 + r) \div 2$

EXAMPLE 4 Using the Order of Operations

Marcos wants to buy the CD player for $108 and eight CDs for $14 each. He has washed 27 cars and earns $9 per car

How much money will he have left after his purchases?

Marcos can write two expressions to calculate the amount remaining.

Amount earned	−	Amount spent on CD player	−	Amount spent on CDs

a. 9×27 − 108 − 8×14

Amount earned	−	Total amount spent

b. 9×27 − $(108 + 8 \times 14)$

Show that both numerical expressions simplify to the same result.

SOLUTION

a. There are no parentheses. First complete the multiplications from left to right. Then subtract from left to right.

$$9 \times 27 - 108 - 8 \times 14 = 243 - 108 - 112$$
$$= 135 - 112$$
$$= 23$$

b. First simplify the expression inside the parentheses. Then complete the remaining operations.

$$9 \times 27 - (108 + 8 \times 14) = 9 \times 27 - (108 + 112)$$
$$= 9 \times 27 - 220$$
$$= 243 - 220$$
$$= 23$$

By either method, Marcos will have $23 left over.

LESSON ASSESSMENT

Think and Discuss

1 Look up the word *variable* in a dictionary. How does the definition compare to the way *variable* is used in this lesson?

2 The cost of a flat of bedding plants is $15. How can you use a numerical expression to describe the cost of 6 flats? How can you use an algebraic expression for the cost of *b* flats?

3 How do you know when an expression is simplified?

4 Explain how to evaluate the expression $12 \div (d + 2)$ when $d = 4$.

Practice and Apply

Translate each word expression into an algebraic expression.

5. *p* increased by eight.   **6.** The product of six and *b*.

7. The amount of sales tax *s* added to a bill of eighteen dollars.

8. The number of inches in *q* feet.

Simplify each expression.

9. $3 + 5 \cdot 8 + 6 \div 2$ **10.** $4 \cdot 5 + 3 \cdot 5 - 6 \cdot 5$

Insert parentheses to make the expression equal 20.

11. $18 \div 4 + 5 \cdot 7 + 6$ **12.** $7 + 3 \cdot 3 - 1 + 7$

Evaluate each expression when $x = 2$, $y = 3$ and $z = 6$.

13. $y + 8$ **14.** $z - 6$ **15.** $5x$

16. $(2y) + 4$ **17.** xz **18.** $\dfrac{z}{y}$

19. $x(y + 5)$ **20.** $\dfrac{z}{yx}$ **21.** xyz

22. $\dfrac{xy}{z}$ **23.** $(xy) + (xz)$ **24.** $5y \div (z - y)$

For Exercises 25–27, write your answer as a numerical expression, then simplify the expression.

25. Chun collects 96 eggs and packages them in cartons of one dozen eggs each. How many cartons will Chun need?

26. Rochelle started a college savings account with a $200 deposit. She added $25 per week for 8 weeks. How much has she deposited in her account at the end of 8 weeks?

27. If the sales tax rate is *r* and the purchase price is *p*, the amount of sales tax is *rp*. How much is the sales tax on a pair of shoes priced at $74.99 if the sales tax rate is 0.085?

Give the value for each underlined digit.
28. 135.<u>6</u>85   **29.** 17.0<u>0</u>85   **30.** 65.56<u>3</u>

Which number is greater?
31. 2.031 or 2.301   **32.** 78.085 or 78.02

33. In a 100-m dash Paula's time was 12.45 seconds, Mary's time was 12.42 seconds, and Nita's time was 12.52 seconds. List the times from greatest to least.

Rothchild Turf Farm measures the amount of rain that falls on its fields. During the summer, the fields need at least 1.0 inch of water per week. If the total amount of rainfall is less than 1.0 inch for any week, the farm must irrigate the field to make up the difference. The rainfall measured for the first week of July is shown below.

Date	Precipitation (inches)
7/1	0.00
7/2	0.14
7/3	0.17
7/4	0.00
7/5	0.33
7/6	0.09
7/7	0.00

34. What is the total rainfall for the first week in July, rounded to the nearest tenth of an inch?

35. Should the turf farm irrigate the fields this week? If so, how much water should be added?

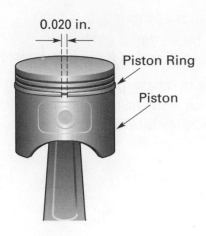

0.020 in.

Piston Ring

Piston

Juan is an apprentice service technician in a shop that rebuilds truck engines. One of his responsibilities is to install piston rings, and to adjust the gap between the ends of each ring. The proper ring gap is 0.020 inch.

If a ring gap is greater than 0.020 inch, the ring cannot be used and must be discarded. If a gap is less than 0.020 inch, Juan can remove material from the ends of the ring to make the gap the proper size.

The following table shows the results of piston gap measurements for an engine with six pistons.

Copy the table.

Piston	Ring Gap Measurement	Action Taken
a	0.016 in.	
b	0.020 in.	
c	0.021 in.	
d	0.019 in.	
e	0.022 in.	
f	0.020 in.	

36. Complete your copy of the table by filling in the Action Taken for each piston. Write "Discard" if the piston ring cannot be used, "Use as is" if no adjustment is required, or "Remove ___ of material" (fill in the blank with the correct length) if Juan can make the gap the proper size.

Jill is helping her father remodel a room. He measures two lengths of ceiling molding needed for a corner of the room. He asks Jill to cut one length of molding one hundred fifty-eight and two tenths centimeters, and one length one hundred fifty-eight and six tenths centimeters.

37. Write each length as a decimal.

38. Jill's father asks her to cut the shortest length of molding first. Which length should Jill cut first?

Lian is the scorekeeper for the basketball team. One of her responsibilities is to calculate free-throw percentages and rank the players in order from highest to lowest percentage.

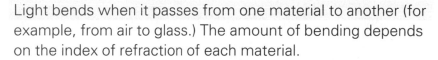

Player	Free-Throw Percentage (%)
Billy	75.92
Michael	76.50
Tony	83.42
Manuel	85.12
Trevor	83.45
Keegan	77.08
Kent	76.09

39. To what place value does Lian round the free-throw percentages?

40. Rank the seven players listed from highest to lowest percentage.

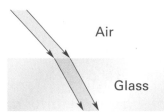

Air

Glass

Light bends when it passes from one material to another (for example, from air to glass.) The amount of bending depends on the index of refraction of each material.

In a laser optics experiment, Brittany passes laser light from a fiber optic cable to a piece of silicon dioxide. She can use fiber A or fiber B in the cable, but the index of refraction of the fiber must closely match that of the silicon dioxide. The index of refraction of the silicon dioxide is 1.471; for fiber A it is 1.4783; and for fiber B it is 1.4767.

41. Does fiber A or B have the greater index of refraction?

42. Which fiber has an index of refraction closest to that of the silicon dioxide?

43. In order for Brittany to use one of the fibers, the difference between its index of refraction and that of the silicon dioxide must be less than five thousandths. Can she use fiber A? Can she use fiber B?

LESSON 1.4 PROPERTIES OF ADDITION

OBJECTIVES
➤ Use basic properties of addition to evaluate expressions.

Raymond is a musher who competes in Alaskan races. In a 20-mile race, he uses two teams of dogs, Team *m* and Team *n*. Team *m* can race 8 miles. Team *n* can race 12 miles. Does it matter which team Raymond uses first?

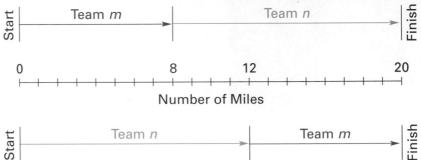

ACTIVITY 1   The Commutative Property of Addition

1 Evaluate the expression $m + n$ for $m = 8$ and $n = 12$.

2 Evaluate the expression $n + m$ for $m = 8$ and $n = 12$.

3 What is the relationship between $m + n$ and $n + m$ for $m = 8$ and $n = 12$?

4 Suppose *m* and *n* are any two whole numbers. What is the relationship between $m + n$ and $n + m$?

You can add numbers in any order and still get the same result. This is the **Commutative Property of Addition**.

> **Commutative Property of Addition**
> Changing the order of two addends does not change their sum.
>
> $$a + b = b + a$$

The Commutative Property of Addition is one of the **basic properties** of algebra. A basic property is *true* for any replacement of the variables. The following bills demonstrate the Commutative Property of Addition.

+ = $15

+ = $15

Critical Thinking   Is there a Commutative Property for Subtraction? Explain your answer.

In another race, Raymond uses three different teams to complete the race. Team p races 5 miles, Team q races 8 miles, and Team r races 7 miles. What is the length of the race?

ACTIVITY 2   The Associative Property of Addition

1   Evaluate the expression $(p + q) + r$ for $p = 5$, $q = 8$, and $r = 7$.

2   Evaluate the expression $p + (q + r)$ for $p = 5$, $q = 8$, and $r = 7$.

3   What is the relationship between $(p + q) + r$ and $p + (q + r)$ for $p = 5$, $q = 8$, and $r = 7$?

4   Suppose p, q, and r are any three whole numbers. What is the relationship between $(p + q) + r$ and $p + (q + r)$?

One definition of the verb *associate* is to join or connect together. Why do you think the different groupings in this Activity are called the **Associative Property of Addition?**

Associative Property of Addition
Changing the grouping of three addends does not change their sum.

$$(a + b) + c = a + (b + c)$$

Critical Thinking   Is there an Associative Property for Subtraction? Explain your answer.

Replace the _?_ to make a *true* statement.

a. $24 + (\underline{\,?\,} + 32) = (24 + 16) + 32$

b. $\$10 + (\$5 + \$1) = (\$5 + \$1) + \underline{\,?\,}$

c. $(x + y) + z = (y + \underline{\,?\,}) + z$

SOLUTION

a. Use the Associative Property. $24 + (\underline{16} + 32) = (24 + 16) + 32$

b. Use the Commutative Property. $\$10 + (\$5 + \$1) = (\$5 + \$1) + \underline{\$10}$

c. Use the Commutative Property. $(x + y) + z = (y + \underline{x}) + z$

You can use the Commutative and Associative Properties to rearrange the addends. Sometimes, rearrangement simplifies mental arithmetic. Look for combinations of 10 in the ones place.

For example, to mentally find the sum $(68 + 89) + 32$, it is easier to change the grouping and ordering of the addends to $(68 + 32) + 89$. Now you can add 68 and 32 to get 100 and then add 100 and 89 to get 189.

ONGOING ASSESSMENT

Use the Commutative and Associative Properties to find each sum.

a. $5 + 37 + 15$ b. $\$64 + (\$36 + \$75)$

Zero is a special number. Whenever you add zero to another addend, the sum is identical to the addend. For this reason, zero is called the **additive identity**.

Identity Property of Addition
The sum of any number and zero is the original number.

$$a + 0 = a \quad \text{and} \quad 0 + a = a$$

ONGOING ASSESSMENT

Name the property illustrated in each problem.

a. $3 + (9 + 0) = 3 + (0 + 9)$ b. $(0 + r) + s = r + s$

LESSON ASSESSMENT

Think and Discuss

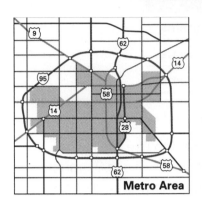

Metro Area

1 One definition of the verb *commute* is to travel back and forth regularly. For example, many workers commute between the suburbs and the city. How is this similar to the Commutative Property of Addition?

2 How can you use the Associative Property to simplify mental math?

3 Why is zero called the additive identity for addition?

4 Explain why the sum $x + (y + z)$ is the same as the sum $z + (y + x)$.

Practice and Apply

Replace the ? with a number that makes a *true* statement.

5. $4 + (3 + \underline{?}) = (4 + 3) + 5$

6. $15 + 18 = \underline{?} + 15$

7. $25 + \underline{?} = 25$

8. $(19 + 0) + 24 = (0 + \underline{?}) + 24$

Name the property illustrated by each of the following.

9. $3 + (5 + 8) = (3 + 5) + 8$

10. $8 + 0 = 8$

11. $(9 + 6) + 0 = 9 + 6$

12. $x + y = y + x$

13. $(x + y) + z = x + (y + z)$

14. $(a + 3) + b = b + (a + 3)$

15. $[x + (y + 4)] + z = x + [(y + 4) + z]$

16. $t + (p + d) = t + (d + p)$

Use the Commutative and Associative Properties to find each sum mentally.

17. $18 + 4 + 6$ **18.** $91 + 6 + 9$

19. $17 + 9 + 3 + 11$ **20.** $35 + 48 + 65$

21. $47 + 25 + 53 + 75$ **22.** $4528 + 3689 + 472$

A weather-monitoring satellite must fire three thrusters to maneuver. The amount of fuel used by each thruster is shown in the table.

Thruster	Fuel Used
A	17 grams
B	12 grams
C	9 grams

23. What is the total amount of fuel used in the maneuver?

24. A second maneuver is programmed to use the same total amount of fuel. However, Thruster A will use 9 grams and Thruster B will use 17 grams. How many grams of fuel will Thruster C require?

Satellite

Earth

25. A third maneuver uses the same total amount of fuel. However, Thruster A uses 17 grams and Thruster B uses 21 grams. How many grams of fuel does Thruster C require?

Mixed Review

Round each number to the nearest tenth.
26. 345.73   **27.** 216. 26   **28.** 0.07

Round each number to the nearest hundredth.
29. 7.834   **30.** 0.635   **31.** 119.081

Evaluate each expression when $c = 4$, $d = 6$, and $e = 9$.
32. $c + d$ **33.** de **34.** $e - c$

35. $(5c) \div 10$ **36.** $e(c + d)$ **37.** $\dfrac{ce}{d}$

38. cde **39.** $e(2d - 3c)$ **40.** $\dfrac{2d + 4e}{6c}$

LESSON 1.5 ESTIMATING SUMS AND DIFFERENCES

In many situations, estimates are preferred over exact values. You would probably use an estimate to answer any of the following:

- The movie starts at one o'clock. What time should I leave?

- How much money should I take for the ticket, popcorn, and a soda?

- How many people will be in line for tickets?

The most common method of estimating is rounding. In Lesson 1.2, you learned how to round decimals.

Day	Tickets Sold	Amount Collected
Monday	17	$118.25
Tuesday	36	$250.30
Wednesday	47	$326.65
Thursday	21	$145.95
Friday	34	$229.45

Recall the amount collected by the Lincoln Theatre Club. If you round the daily amounts to the nearest hundred dollars, you can add the rounded numbers mentally.

Day	Amount Collected	Rounded Amount
Monday	$118.25	$100
Tuesday	$250.30	$300
Wednesday	$326.65	$300
Thursday	$145.95	$100
Friday	$229.45	$200

The sum of the rounded numbers is $1000. When you add the exact daily amounts, the sum is $1070.60. Thus, the sum of the rounded amounts is close to the exact amount and is a *reasonable estimate*.

El Paso
485 Miles

EXAMPLE 1 Estimating Sums

During a trip from Texas to California, Mr. Sanchez drove 485 miles on Monday, 618 miles on Tuesday, and 523 miles on Wednesday. Estimate to the nearest hundred the number of miles Mr. Sanchez drove on the trip.

SOLUTION

Round each day's mileage to the nearest hundred.

485 rounds to 500   618 rounds to 600   523 rounds to 500

Add the rounded numbers.

$$500 + 600 + 500 = 1600$$

Thus,

$$485 + 618 + 523 \approx 1600$$

The symbol $\approx$ means *is approximately equal to*.

Mr. Sanchez drove about 1600 miles.

It is always a good idea to use estimation to make sure calculator answers are reasonable.

ONGOING ASSESSMENT

Estimate the sum by rounding. Tell whether the calculator answer is reasonable or unreasonable.

a. $837.85 + $1165.40 = $\boxed{2003.25}$

b. 672.36 + 239.05 + 915.6 = $\boxed{182.701}$

ACTIVITY   Estimating Differences

A sweater costs $38.50 and pants cost $29.95. How much more does the sweater cost than the pants?

1   Round the cost of the pants to the nearest ten dollars.

2   Round the cost of the sweater to the nearest ten dollars.

3   Find the difference between the answers to Step 2 and Step 1.

4   Use your calculator to find the difference in cost between the sweater and the pants.

5   Is your calculator answer reasonable?

EXAMPLE 2 Using Estimation

Yolanda's PC has about 483 megabytes (MB) of hard disk free space. She wants to install computer games that will use about 256 megabytes. To the nearest hundred megabytes, how much free space will remain after Yolanda installs the games?

SOLUTION

Estimate 483 − 256 by rounding to the nearest hundred.

Round 483 to 500. Round 256 to 300.

483 − 256 ≈ 500 − 300 or 200.

Yolanda estimates her PC will have about 200 MB of free space.

LESSON ASSESSMENT

Think and Discuss

1 Explain how to use rounding to estimate the sum of two numbers.

2 Explain how to use rounding to estimate the difference between two numbers.

3 When you estimate a sum, you can round the addends and then add. You can also add the addends and then round. Will you get the same result either way? Show examples.

4 Calculators and computers can find sums and differences quickly and accurately. Why is estimation a useful skill when using these technology tools?

Practice and Apply

Use rounding to estimate each sum or difference to the nearest hundred or to the nearest ten dollars.

5. $12.75 + $18.19 + $25.78

6. $98.50 − $36.70

7. 45.87 + 38.6 + 74.35

8. 857.279 − 382.76

9. 3783 + 7869

10. 253.18 + 467.4 + 845.92

11. $4315.85 − $2484.28

12. $346.12 + $854.10 + $98.65

Item	Cost
Cereal	$3.49
Bananas	$0.85
Milk	$2.39
Lunch meat	$6.75
Bread	$1.39
Soup	$4.59

BEST BURGER
Menu of the Day

Hamburger $2.15
Baked Beans.... $1.40
Fruit Juice $0.95
Salad $2.45
Egg Roll $1.70
Ice Cream $1.65

For Exercises 13–16, use the table at the left to estimate each answer.

13. About how much more is the cost of the most expensive item on the list than the least expensive item?

14. If you have $10, can you buy cereal, bananas, and soup?

15. If you have $20 and buy all the groceries on the list, about how much change will you receive?

16. If you have $15, do you have enough money to buy all the items except the soup?

The Best Burger restaurant has its menu placed in the front window.

17. Estimate the cost of a salad, egg roll, ice cream, and fruit juice.

18. List the three-item combinations you can purchase for less than $5.50 if one of the items is a hamburger or salad.

In Exercises 19–22, estimate each answer. Then use your calculator to find the exact answer. Make sure the calculator answer is reasonable.

19. Charlie has a balance of $156.38 in his checking account. He wrote a check for $81.49. How much does he have left in his account?

20. Keisha has four pledges for the walkathon. They are for $13.65, $8.30, $12.80, and $15.25. How much will Keisha earn for the walk-a-thon?

21. Taylor had $17.50 when he went to the arcade. He spent $7.25 on video games, $4.85 on food, and $2.95 on drinks. How much did Taylor have when he left the arcade?

22. Amy is a personal trainer at a health club. She is helping Karl reach his workout goal of 150 minutes per week. The first four days, Karl works out 26 minutes, 28 minutes, 30 minutes, and 32 minutes. How many minutes does Karl need to work out the fifth day to meet his goal?

Write a decimal for each italicized phrase.

23. A microsecond is *one-millionth* of a second.

24. The amount of debt is *six million three hundred fifty-six thousand, eighty-five dollars.*

Write in order from least to greatest.

25. 17.018, 17.108, 17.088   **26.** 0.0307, 0.03, 0.032

Evaluate each expression when $m = 12$ and $n = 6$.

27. $m(n + 3)$

28. $\dfrac{mn}{m + n}$

Name the property illustrated by each of the following.

29. $4 + 0 = 4$ **30.** $5 + (8 + 4) = (5 + 8) + 4$

31. $j + k = k + j$ **32.** $(0 + 7) + 3 = 3 + (0 + 7)$

Cumulative Problem Solving

Kenneth's electric utility bill shows that July's energy cost is $0.07901 per kilowatt-hour (kWh). The bill also includes a table showing the energy cost for the previous five months. Kenneth uses the July bill to estimate his costs for August.

Month	Cost per Unit of Energy
March	$0.08252
April	$0.08259
May	$0.07966
June	$0.08174
July	$0.07901

33. Which month was Kenneth's lowest energy cost?

34. Which month was Kenneth's highest energy cost?

35. Draw a number line like the one below. Round each energy cost to the nearest ten-thousandth, and locate the five costs on the number line. Draw a dot to represent each point on the number line.

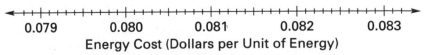

Energy Cost (Dollars per Unit of Energy)

36. When the five points are arranged in order, the point in the middle is called the **median**. Kenneth uses the median to estimate his cost per kilowatt-hour for August. What estimate should he use?

Custom Metal Works has a milling machine, lathe, and welder. The machines use electrical current as shown below.

Machine	Current
Milling machine	17.5 amps
Lathe	11.5 amps
Welder	43 amps

The machines are connected to an electrical circuit that can handle a total of 80 amps.

37. If all three machines are operating at the same time, what is the total amount of current used?

38. The company wants to add an electrical furnace that will use 61 amps. An electrician proposes adding a 60-amp circuit so that all four machines can operate at the same time. Which machines should be connected to the new circuit, and which should be connected to the old circuit, so that neither circuit is overloaded?

Tonika's lawn-care business depends on her ability to estimate costs accurately. She is estimating the cost of fertilizing a customer's lawn. The lawn is divided into three sections. She measures the sections and uses a formula to calculate their areas. The results are 3863.60 square feet, 6233.22 square feet, and 2986.58 square feet.

39. Round each area to the nearest hundred square feet. Use the rounded numbers to estimate the total area Tonika will fertilize, to the nearest hundred square feet.

40. Tonika buys fertilizer in bags that cover 5000 square feet. She cannot buy a portion of a bag. How many bags are needed for this job?

Jelani needs five pounds of ground meat for a chili recipe. At the supermarket's meat counter, he finds seven packages of ground meat with the following weights in pounds (lb).

0.86, 1.03, 1.06, 1.31, 1.45, 1.67, 1.80

41. Round each of the weights to the nearest tenth of a pound.

42. Which combination of packages of meat should Jelani select for his chili if he wants to buy the fewest number of packages?

The Wilson High School girls basketball team averages 68 points per game. Tonight they play Jefferson High. The players on Jefferson's team are listed on a roster, with their average points per game.

Player	Average
Anne	12
Hallie	17
Beth	6
Hillery	3
Katherine	3
Mindy	9
Juanita	10
Marsha	4
Stefani	5
Leanne	6

43. Estimate Jefferson's total average points per game.

44. Compare this estimate to the sum found with a calculator.

45. With no other information, which team would be favored to win tonight's game?

LESSON 1.6 PROPERTIES OF MULTIPLICATION

➤ Use basic properties of multiplication to evaluate expressions.
➤ Apply the distributive property to simplify expressions.

In Lesson 1.4, you learned three basic properties for addition. They are the Commutative, Associative, and Identity Properties. Do these same properties hold for multiplication?

Sylvia sells fresh eggs to restaurants and bakeries. She delivers the eggs in flats that hold six rows and five columns of eggs. How many eggs are in each flat?

ACTIVITY 1   Commutative Property of Multiplication

1 Evaluate the expression $m \cdot n$ for $m = 6$ and $n = 5$.

2 Evaluate the expression $n \cdot m$ for $m = 6$, and $n = 5$.

3 What is the relationship between $m \cdot n$ and $n \cdot m$ for $m = 6$ and $n = 5$?

4 Suppose m and n are any two numbers. What is the relationship between $m \cdot n$ and $n \cdot m$?

> **Commutative Property of Multiplication**
> Changing the order of two factors does not change their product.
>
> $$a \cdot b = b \cdot a$$

At a delivery stop, Sylvia stacks three flats. How many eggs does she deliver at this stop?

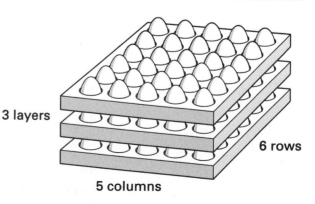

3 layers

6 rows

5 columns

1 Evaluate $(m \cdot n) \cdot k$ for $m = 6$, $n = 5$, and $k = 3$.

2 Evaluate $m \cdot (n \cdot k)$ for $m = 6$, $n = 5$, and $k = 3$.

3 What is the relationship between $(m \cdot n) \cdot k$ and $m \cdot (n \cdot k)$ for $m = 6$, $n = 5$, and $k = 3$?

4 Suppose m, n, and k are any three numbers. What is the relationship between $(m \cdot n) \cdot k$ and $m \cdot (n \cdot k)$?

Associative Property of Multiplication
Changing the grouping of three factors does not change their product.

$$(a \cdot b) \cdot c = a \cdot (b \cdot c)$$

In multiplication, one is a special number. What happens when you multiply a number by one? One is called the **multiplicative identity**.

Identity Property of Multiplication
The product of any number and one is that number.

$$a \cdot 1 = a \quad \text{and} \quad 1 \cdot a = a$$

EXAMPLE 1 Using the Basic Properties of Multiplication

Rewrite each expression using the Commutative Property.

a. $5 \cdot 7$ **b.** $p \cdot q$

Rewrite each expression using the Associative Property.

c. $(45 \cdot 20) \cdot 6$ **d.** $s \cdot (t \cdot u)$

Simplify each expression.

e. $3(4x)$ **f.** $5x(2)$

g. Use mental math to evaluate $(st)u$ when $s = 25$, $t = 15$, and $u = 4$.

SOLUTION

a. $5 \cdot 7 = 7 \cdot 5$ **b.** $p \cdot q = q \cdot p$

c. $(45 \cdot 20) \cdot 6 = 45 \cdot (20 \cdot 6)$ **d.** $s \cdot (t \cdot u) = (s \cdot t) \cdot u$

e. $3(4x) = (3 \cdot 4)x = 12x$ **f.** $5x(2) = (5 \cdot 2)x = 10x$

g. Substitute for the variables.

$$(st)u = (25 \cdot 15) \cdot 4$$

Use the Commutative and Associative Properties to rearrange the factors and simplify. Multiply 25 by 4 to get 100. That is,

$$(25 \cdot 15) \cdot 4 = 4 \cdot (25 \cdot 15) = (4 \cdot 25) \cdot 15 = 100 \cdot 15$$

Multiply 100 by 15 to get 1500.

You can sometimes use addition and multiplication in the same expression. Remember to complete the operations inside the parentheses first.

ACTIVITY 3   **The Distributive Property**

1 Simplify the expressions in each column. How do they compare?

Column A	Column B
a. $5(3 + 8)$	$(5 \cdot 3) + (5 \cdot 8)$
b. $7(2 + 4)$	$(7 \cdot 2) + (7 \cdot 4)$
c. $5(9 - 6)$	$(5 \cdot 9) - (5 \cdot 6)$
d. $4(8 - 3)$	$(4 \cdot 8) - (4 \cdot 3)$

2 Use variables to represent the pattern you found in Step 1.

One definition of the verb *distribute* is to divide among several. For example, a fruit juice distributor distributes cases of grape juice to several stores. Why do you think the pattern in Activity 3 is called the **Distributive Property**?

> **Distributive Property**
> For all numbers a, b, and c,
> $$a(b + c) = (a \cdot b) + (a \cdot c)$$
> $$a(b - c) = (a \cdot b) - (a \cdot c)$$

Critical Thinking   What properties can you use to write $(5 + 6)3 = (3 \cdot 5) + (3 \cdot 6)$?

EXAMPLE 2 Using the Distributive Property

The Freshman Chorus is sponsoring a trip to an amusement park. The chorus needs to purchase 15 adult tickets at $6 each and 15 student tickets at $4 each. How much money will the chorus need for tickets?

SOLUTION

The expression that models the problem is $(15)(6) + (15)(4)$. You can use the Distributive Property to simplify the expression.

$$(15)(6) + (15)(4) = 15(6 + 4)$$
$$= 15(10)$$
$$= 150$$

The Freshman Chorus needs $150 to purchase the tickets.

ONGOING ASSESSMENT

Name the property illustrated by each of the following.

a. $(4 \cdot 1) = 4$

b. $(9 \cdot 8) \cdot 4 = 9 \cdot (8 \cdot 4)$

c. $(4 \cdot 9) - (4 \cdot 8) = 4(9 - 8)$

d. $(9 - 8)4 = 4(9 - 8)$

You can use the Distributive Property to simplify mental math. For example, to multiply $8 \cdot 24$, you can use place value to rewrite 24 as $20 + 4$. Thus,

$$8 \cdot 24 = 8(20 + 4)$$
$$= (8)(20) + (8)(4)$$
$$= 160 + 32$$
$$= 192$$

LESSON ASSESSMENT

1 How is the Commutative Property of Multiplication similar to the Commutative Property of Addition?

2 How is the Associative Property of Multiplication similar to the Associative Property of Addition?

3 Why is 1 called the multiplicative identity?

4 Talma earns $8 an hour. He works 5 hours on Friday and 6 hours on Saturday. Explain how Talma can use the Distributive Property to find the total earnings for the two days.

Practice and Apply

Replace the ? with a number that makes a *true* statement.

5. $8 \cdot 3 = \underline{?} \cdot 8$

6. $(7 \cdot \underline{?}) + (7 \cdot 5) = 7(4 + 5)$

7. $34 = 34 \cdot \underline{?}$

8. $26 \cdot (10 \cdot \underline{?}) = (26 \cdot 10) \cdot 18$

Name the property illustrated by each of the following.

9. $(4 \cdot 6) \cdot 3 = 4 \cdot (6 \cdot 3)$

10. $8(6 - 3) = (8 \cdot 6) - (8 \cdot 3)$

11. $1 \cdot 8 = 8$

12. $9(4 + 5) = (4 + 5)9$

13. $7(ab) = (7a)b$

14. $(15 \cdot 1)x = 15x$

15. $(rs) + (rm) = r(s + m)$

16. $7(ab) = 7(ba)$

Use the basic properties and mental math to simplify each expression.

17. $9 \cdot 1 \cdot 8$

18. $14(8) + 14(2)$

19. $8(5q)$

20. $(8d)(6)(5)$

21. $46 + 93 + 54$

22. $14(15) - 4(15)$

Use the Distributive Property to find each product.

23. $7 \cdot 18$

24. $9 \cdot 56$

25. $48 \cdot 3$

26. $6 \cdot 215$

27. $452 \cdot 5$

28. $4 \cdot 3527$

29. In the morning, the Martins filled their ski boat with 16 gallons of gas. In the afternoon, they needed 14 more gallons. If gas costs $1.319 per gallon, how much did the Martins pay for gas that day?

The volume of a rectangular carton is the product of its length, width, and height. Use this information to complete Exercises 30–31.

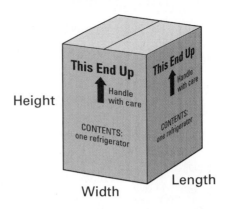

30. A refrigerator is delivered in a carton with dimensions 6 feet by 4 feet by 3 feet. What is the volume of the carton in cubic feet? In calculating this volume, does it matter which numbers you use for its length, width, or height? Why or why not?

31. In a warehouse, nine of the refrigerator cartons are stored side-by-side. How many cubic feet of storage volume are taken up by these cartons?

Mixed Review

Give the place value of the underlined digit.
32. 2<u>0</u>4.18   **33.** 63.8<u>6</u>3   **34.** 0.603<u>2</u>8

In Exercises 35–36, estimate the answer, then use your calculator to find the exact answer.
35. The elevation of King Mountain in the Yukon is 16,971 feet. The elevation of Mount McKinley in Alaska is 20,320 feet. What is the difference in the elevation of the two mountains?

36. Marla bought 2 sweaters and a shirt. She gave the clerk a $100 bill. How much change did Marla receive?

SALE
TODAY ONLY
Sweaters $23.79
Shirts $18.49

LESSON 1.7 ESTIMATING PRODUCTS AND QUOTIENTS

OBJECTIVES

➤ Use mental math to multiply and divide by powers of 10.

➤ Use compatible numbers to estimate multiplication and division problems.

You will often use multiplication or division to solve problems involving numbers with many digits. You can compute answers for these problems using pencil and paper or a calculator.

In either case, it is easy to make a mistake. For example, you can press a wrong key on your calculator or put a decimal point in the wrong place. When this happens, the answer usually does not make sense. It is always a good idea to use estimation to make sure your answers are reasonable.

Chen earns $8.35 an hour making compact discs. In one week, Chen works 38 hours. How much will Chen earn that week? Use a pencil and paper or a calculator to find the answer.

$$\begin{array}{r} 8.35 \\ \times\, 38 \\ \hline ? \end{array}$$

| 8.35 | × | 38. | = | ? |

To make sure the answer is reasonable, use mental math to find an estimate. Using the rules for rounding, round 8.35 to the nearest whole number and 38 to the nearest ten.

Since 8×40 is 320, your calculated answer should be close to 320. Is your answer reasonable?

ONGOING ASSESSMENT

Use your calculator to find the answer. Use estimation to see if your answer is reasonable.

a. The tax rate for a business is 5.425 dollars per thousand dollars in assessed value. What is the tax due on a business that is assessed at 240.6 thousand dollars?

b. It takes 1.9 hours to manufacture a pair of inline skates. How many pairs of skates can be manufactured in 35.5 hours?

You can simplify estimates of products and quotients if one of the numbers can be rounded to 10, 100, 1000 or any other multiple of 10. The number of zeros determine where to place the decimal point in the answer. Use the following place value chart to help you complete the activity.

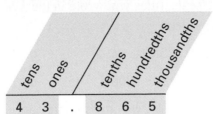

Each place is 10 times greater than the place to its right.

Each place is 0.1 times as great as the place to its left.

Multiplying and Dividing by 10, 100, 1000, and 10,000

1 Copy and complete the table using your calculator.

$$10 \cdot 43.865 = \underline{?}$$
$$100 \cdot 43.865 = \underline{?}$$
$$1000 \cdot 43.865 = \underline{?}$$
$$10,000 \cdot 43.865 = \underline{?}$$

2 What effect does each multiplication have on the original position of the decimal point? Compare the number of positions the decimal moves to the number of zeros in 10, 100, or 1000. Does the decimal point move to the left or the right?

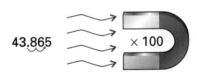

3 Write a rule for multiplying a decimal by 10, 100, 1000, and 10,000.

4 Copy and complete the following table. Use your calculator.

$$43.865 \div 10 = \underline{?}$$
$$43.865 \div 100 = \underline{?}$$
$$43.865 \div 1000 = \underline{?}$$
$$43.865 \div 10,000 = \underline{?}$$

5 What effect does each division have on the original position of the decimal point? Compare the number of positions the decimal moves to the number of zeros in 10, 100, or 1000. Does the decimal point move to the left or the right?

6 Write a rule for dividing a decimal by 10, 100, 1000, and 10,000.

Use the rules you wrote in the Activity to find each product or quotient.

a. $0.325 \cdot 10$ **b.** $1500 \div 100$

c. $0.018 \div 1000$ **d.** $1.05 \cdot 10,000$

The easiest way to estimate quotients is to use *compatible numbers*. **Compatible numbers** are numbers that divide evenly.

EXAMPLE 1   Dividing Decimals

At the end of each work day, Tamara fills her delivery truck with diesel fuel. One day she drives the truck 233.8 miles. The truck averages 13.3 miles to a gallon of fuel. About how many gallons of fuel will Tamara need?

SOLUTION

To find the number of gallons, divide 233.8 by 13.3. Use approximations that are close to 233.8 and 13.3 and divide evenly.

$$233.8 \approx 240 \qquad\qquad 13.3 \approx 12$$
$$240 \div 12 = 20$$

Tamara needs about 20 gallons of diesel fuel.

ONGOING ASSESSMENT

Use your calculator to find the number of gallons of fuel Tamara needs in Example 1. Suppose you accidentally enter 2338 on your calculator. What result would your calculator display? How would you know you made an error?

EXAMPLE 2   Estimating Multiplication and Division

a. Estimate the quotient $79.4 \div 21.1$.

b. Estimate the product 28.23×8786.8.

SOLUTION

Use compatible numbers.

a. $79.4 \approx 80$ $21.1 \approx 20$

Thus, $80 \div 20 = 4$

b. $28.23 \approx 30$ $8786.8 \approx 9000$

Thus, $30 \times 9000 = 270,000$

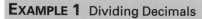

CULTURAL CONNECTION

Multiplication can be a difficult process using only paper and pencil. In the tenth or eleventh century, early Hindu mathematicians devised the lattice method for simplifying multiplication. This method was used in eighteenth century American classrooms and is very much like the method used today.

Follow Steps 1-4 to see how the lattice method works in finding 2.46 × 37.

Step 1
Place 246 along the top of the lattice. Place 37 along the right side of the lattice.

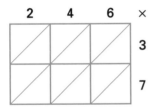

Step 2
Fill in the lattice by multiplying the top and right hand side digits.

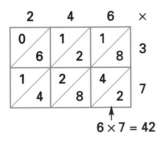

$6 \times 7 = 42$

Step 3
Add diagonally. Carry the tens digit of the sum to the next diagonal. For example, in the diagonal with 8 + 4 + 8 = 20, the 0 is placed at the bottom of the diagonal and the 2 is carried over to the top of the next diagonal.

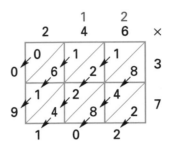

Step 4
Write the numbers from the diagonal addition from upper left to lower right. That is 09102.

Thus, 246 × 37 = 9102. Since 246 ÷ 100 = 2.46, move the decimal point two places to the left.

$$2.46 \times 37 = 91.02$$

Use the lattice method to find each product.

1. 536 × 97
2. 836 × 249
3. 12.75 × 86
4. 41.25 × 2.7
5. 112 × 10.4
6. 303 × 99
7. 1037 × 243

LESSON ASSESSMENT

1 Explain how to estimate 4.5 · 9.8.

2 Explain how to estimate 365.25 ÷ 18.8.

3 Write a rule for multiplying and dividing a number by one million.

Estimate each product or quotient.

4. 38.9 × 8.75   **5.** 17.098 ÷ 7.4

6. 35.23 ÷ 125.57   **7.** $27.38 × 35

8. 7.921 × 36.23   **9.** $250 ÷ 22.5

Use a calculator to find an exact answer for each problem. Then estimate the answer. Compare your estimate to the exact answer to make sure your solution is reasonable. An inventory of flowers is shown below. Find the cost for each order of flowers.

Flower	Inventory Cost
Geraniums	$2.50
Pansies	$1.79
Impatiens	$4.25
Mums	$3.88

10. 857 geraniums

11. 1043 pansies

12. 512 impatiens

13. 815 mums

14. Paul earns $6.18 per hour. Rashad earns 3.2 times as much as Paul. How much does Rashad earn per hour?

15. To raise money for a charity, Tom and Cathy sold banners for $0.75 each. Together they earned $204.75. How many banners did they sell?

Tawana has 57 customers on her newspaper route. In 6 months she has earned $461.70.

16. What is Tawana's average monthly earnings?

17. What is Tawana's average earnings per customer per month?

It takes a planet one year to orbit the sun. One year on Mars is about 1.9 years on Earth.

18. How many years on Mars is 15.6 years on Earth?

19. How many years on Earth is a century on Mars?

One inch is approximately 2.54 centimeters.

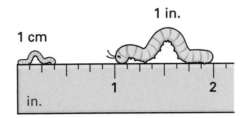

20. How many centimeters are equivalent to 123.19 inches?

21. How many inches are equivalent to 500 centimeters?

Leon is reimbursed $0.33 per mile for travel expenses. The following chart shows Leon's mileage for one week.

Day	Mileage
Monday	138
Tuesday	214
Wednesday	283
Thursday	315
Friday	196

22. How many miles did Leon drive for the week?

23. How much will Leon be reimbursed for the week's travel expenses?

Write each number in words.

24. The diameter of the Earth is 8250 miles.

25. The world record for the men's 100-meter dash is 9.78 seconds.

26. One sheet of paper is 0.008 centimeters thick.

27. The following chart gives the population of four large countries. List the population of each country in order from least to greatest.

Country	Population (Billions)
China	1.203
India	0.937
Russia	0.149
United States	0.263

Name the property illustrated by each of the following.

28. $(5 \cdot 18) + 0 = 5 \cdot 18$

29. $17 \cdot (22 \cdot 8) = (17 \cdot 22) \cdot 8$

30. $(43 + 29) + 16 = 16 + (43 + 29)$

31. $9 \cdot 36 = (9 \cdot 30) + (9 \cdot 6)$

32. $(x + y)z = z(x + y)$

33. $(a + b) \cdot 1 = a + b$

LESSON 1.8 A PROBLEM-SOLVING STRATEGY

OBJECTIVES
➤ Use the four-step problem-solving plan.
➤ Solve a nonroutine problem about patterns.

People solve problems every day. But have you ever thought about *how* they go about solving them? Most successful problem-solvers follow a four-step strategy.

1. Understand the problem

2. Develop a plan

3. Carry out the plan

4. Check the results

EXAMPLE 1 Using the Problem-Solving Plan

The athletic department needs to put a temporary fence around a practice field. The sides of the field measure 420 feet, 395 feet, 375 feet, and 385 feet. The fencing comes in 50-foot rolls. How many rolls are needed to enclose the field?

SOLUTION

Step 1 Understand the problem
Read the problem carefully.

What do you need to find? Make sure you know what question you are trying to answer.

   Find: The number of rolls of fencing needed.

What facts are you given? Are they enough to solve the problem? Do you need more information? Do you need all the information? Can you figure out other facts from the ones you are given?

Given: The practice field has four sides.

The sides measure 420 feet, 395 feet, 375 feet, and 385 feet.

A roll contains 50 feet of fencing.

Organize the information so you can work with it. For example, you might draw a diagram or make a list. For this problem, draw a diagram of the practice field.

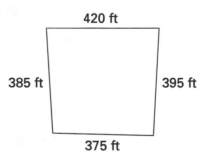

420 ft

385 ft   395 ft

375 ft

Step 2 Develop a plan

There are usually several ways to solve a problem. You may see how to solve it right away. If not, ask yourself:

- Have I seen a problem like this before? Can I solve the problem in the same way that I have solved a similar one?

- Is there a trend or pattern in the given information? A table, graph or formula may help answer this question.

- What calculations are needed to solve the problem?

- Can I find the answer by working backward?

Remember, there are many ways to solve a problem. The more problems you solve, the easier it will be to develop a plan.

For the practice field problem, try working backward. You need to complete the following statement:

_____?_____ rolls of fencing are needed to enclose the practice field.

Let the variable *m* represent the number that completes the statement. The variable, *m* is the total length of fencing needed divided by the length of fencing in each roll. Since each roll contains 50 feet, you can calculate *m* with the following formula.

Fencing 50 ft

Fencing 50 ft

$$m = \frac{\text{Total length of fencing needed in ft}}{50 \text{ ft per roll}}$$

The total length of fencing needed is the distance around the practice field. This is the sum of the lengths of its four sides, or its **perimeter**. So, find this sum and divide by 50 to find m.

Step 3 Carry out the plan

This is the action step of the plan.

- Find the distance around the practice field.

$$420 \text{ ft} + 395 \text{ ft} + 375 \text{ ft} + 385 \text{ ft} = 1575 \text{ ft}$$

- Substitute 1575 into the equation from Step 2.

$$m = \frac{1575}{50}$$

$$= 31.5$$

To enclose the practice field, 31.5 rolls of fencing are needed.

Step 4 Check the results

Think about your answer. Ask questions like these:

- What is a good estimate for the answer? Use rounding to estimate the quotient, $1575 \div 50$. Are the calculated values close to the estimated values?

- Have you answered the original question?

- Does the answer make sense? Can you buy half a roll of fencing? Do you need 31 or 32 rolls?

ONGOING ASSESSMENT

Use the four-step problem-solving plan to solve the following problem.

Jerry is building a backyard patio. The completed patio will measure 24 feet by 18 feet. Jerry will use concrete patio stones that measure 12 inches by 18 inches. A home improvement store sells patio stones for $0.95 each. How many patio stones should Jerry buy? How much will the stones cost?

The problems above require only computation to find the answers. There are other problems in mathematics that are not computational. These problems are called **nonroutine problems**.

EXAMPLE 2 Solving a Nonroutine Problem

Examine the pattern as the number of dots in each square increases.

Square 1   Square 2   Square 3   Square 4

How many dots are in Square 20?

SOLUTION

Use the four-step problem-solving plan.

Step 1 Understand the problem

This is a visual problem showing a series of squares increasing in size.

> **Find:**   The number of dots in Square 20.
>
> **Given:**   As you move from left to right, the sides of each square increase by 1 dot.

Step 2 Develop a plan

There are several strategies you can use to solve this problem. One strategy is to create a table and find a pattern.

Square number	1	2	3	4	$\cdots$	20
Number of dots	1	4	9	16	$\cdots$	?

Step 3 Carry out the plan

Notice that the number of dots is the same as the square number multiplied by itself. That is, $1 \times 1 = 1$, $2 \times 2 = 4$, $3 \times 3 = 9$, and $4 \times 4 = 16$. If this pattern continues, the number of dots in square 20 will be 20×20 or 400.

Step 4 Check the results

Check the result by drawing a square with 20 dots on each side.

ONGOING ASSESSMENT

Use the four-step problem-solving plan to solve the following problem:

A science book and a math book are placed side-by-side on a bookshelf. The front and back covers of each book are 0.125 inch thick. The thickness of each book without the covers measures 2 inches. What is the total shelf width occupied by the books?

PROBLEM SOLVING

USING THE FOUR-STEP PLAN

On April 14, 1970, the astronauts aboard the *Apollo 13* spacecraft were faced with a very serious problem on their way to the moon. An explosion caused their service module to lose its oxygen supply, water, power, and propulsion system. NASA and the three astronauts aboard *Apollo 13* had to quickly develop problem-solving strategies in order to bring the astronauts back alive.

Research the *Apollo 13* accident, and study one of the problems encountered. You can view the movie *Apollo 13*, visit the library, or use the Internet. Describe how each of the following steps were applied to solve the problem successfully.

Step 1 Understand the Problem
State a problem encountered by the *Apollo 13* astronauts or NASA. Did the astronauts or the people on the ground have enough information to solve the problem? Did they have more information than needed?

Step 2 Develop a Plan
What plan was developed to solve the problem? What strategy was used? Strategies might include looking for a pattern, making a table or diagram, working backward, or using an equation.

Step 3 Carry Out the Plan
How was the plan carried out?

Step 4 Check the Results
How did the astronauts or NASA know the problem was solved?

LESSON ASSESSMENT

1 Describe four steps you can follow in solving a problem.

2 Why should you check the results when you solve a problem?

3 How is a nonroutine problem different than a routine problem?

Use the four problem-solving steps to solve each of the following.

4. Electricians at Reliable Electric earn $550 per week and $25 per hour of overtime. Over a period of 4 weeks, one electrician works 14 hours overtime. What are the electrician's earnings for the four weeks?

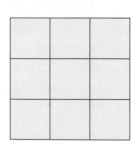

5. A car rental company charges $34 per day and $0.35 per mile. On a trip that takes 5 days, Juanita drives a rental car 320 miles. How much does it cost Juanita to rent the car?

6. A vending machine takes exact change only. The machine takes only quarters, dimes, and nickels. List all the ways that you can put coins into the machine for a 40¢ item.

7. In January, Amanda saves $1. In February, she saves $2; in March, $4; in April, $8; and so on. At this rate, how many months does it take to save a total of $1000?

8. Write the numbers from 1 to 9 in the squares so that the sum of each row, each column, and each diagonal is 15.

9. Tickets to a concert cost $28.50 for adults and $12.75 for children. If 118 adult tickets and 47 children's tickets were sold, how much money was collected?

10. The sum of the digits of a two-digit number is 6. The number is six times its ones digit. What is the number?

11. Mario earns $4.75 after taxes at his part-time job. He is saving all of his income to buy a watch that costs $185.95. So far this month, Mario has worked 20 hours. How much more must Mario save to buy the watch?

12. Gail is the purchasing agent for a computer firm. She must purchase full boxes of computer disks. One large box of 200 disks costs $450. One small box of 75 disks costs $225. What is the maximum number of disks Gail can order and stay under her budget of $1250?

13. Gail must also decide whether to lease or buy a copy machine. Leasing a copy machine costs $110 per month and $0.025 per copy. Purchasing a copy machine costs $125 per month for 3 years and $0.015 per copy. If the office expects to run 100,000 copies per year, which is the least expensive plan?

14. Six cubes form a 3-step staircase. How many cubes are needed for a 9-step staircase?

15. Kwame bought a TV for $329 and a VCR for $189. The sales tax is $30.10. If Kwame pays for his purchase in six equal payments, how much is each payment?

16. Ronald is working on a production line that manufactures key chains. He is filling boxes with 235 key chains each. How many boxes will Ronald need to hold 3538 key chains?

17. Sarah is placing flowers into vases. She wants to put the same number of flowers in each vase. When she separates the flowers into twos, threes, fours, fives, or sixes there is always one left over. What is the least number of flowers Sarah has?

18. There are eight football teams in the Mid-Valley Conference. Each team plays every other team once. How many games are played in the Mid-Valley Conference?

19. Linda has been hired to distribute advertising flyers in her neighborhood. She will be paid $8 per day and $ 0.04 for each flyer she places on a front door. How many flyers must Linda distribute to earn $44.80 in two days?

20. There are six people in a room. Each person shakes hands with all the others in the room. How many handshakes take place?

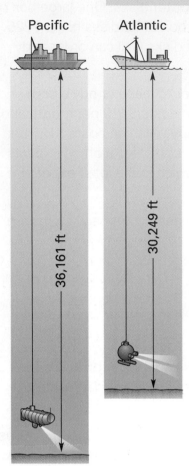

Pacific   Atlantic

36,161 ft

30,249 ft

Use < or > to complete Exercises 21–22.

21. 5.679 _?_ 6.769   **22.** 104.34 _?_ 104.3402

23. List the following measurements in order from least to greatest.

a. 48.24 cm   **b.** 49.36 cm   **c.** 48.78 cm   **d.** 49.45 cm

Round each number to (a) the nearest tenth and (b) the nearest hundredth.

24. The diameter of a small washer is 1.056 centimeters.

25. The length of fiber optic cable is 45.967 meters.

Evaluate each expression when $p = 3$, $q = 2$, and $r = 10$.

26. $p(r - q)$ **27.** $\dfrac{pqr}{q + r}$

Estimate each answer. Use your calculator to find the exact answer.

28. The greatest depth of the Atlantic Ocean is 30,249 feet. The greatest depth of the Pacific Ocean is 36,161 feet. What is the difference in the greatest depths of the two oceans?

29. Latoya can work part time for 23 hours each week. If Latoya wants to earn $125 each week, how much must she earn per hour?

30. It cost $0.06 to make one photocopy at The Mail Store. Tricia made 75 copies on Monday, 115 copies on Tuesday, and 105 copies on Wednesday. How much did it cost Tricia to make all the copies?

You have volunteered to provide pizzas for an after-game party for 12 people. You need to determine how many pizzas to order and how much to charge each person to cover the cost.

31. Listed below, in random order, are 6 steps you might take to solve this problem. Reorder the steps in the most logical order, from 1 to 6. You learn from the restaurant manager that a medium pizza serves three people and costs $8.64 with tax.

• I need to charge each person enough to cover the cost of the pizzas.

- To find the total cost, multiply the number of pizzas ordered by the cost per pizza.

- If everyone comes to the party, will the money I collect pay for the pizzas?

- To find the number of pizzas to order, divide the number of people at the party by the number of people fed per pizza.

- Calculate [(12 ÷ 3) • 8.64] ÷ 12.

- To find the cost per person, divide the total cost by the number of people at the party.

32. For each step in your ordered list, state which of the four problem-solving steps it is a part of: understand the problem, develop a plan, carry out the plan, or check the results.

Thirty-two students in the Lincoln Theatre Club are going to a play. Latisha must determine how many adults can accompany the students. The school has budgeted $425 for the trip. The cost per person is $12.

33. Let x represent the number of adults going on the trip. Write an algebraic expression for the total number of people going on the trip.

34. Write an algebraic expression for the total cost of the trip with 32 students and x adults. Use the Distributive Property to write your answer without parentheses.

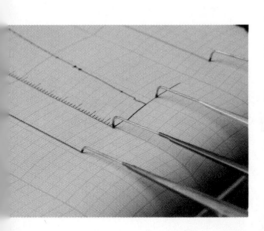

35. Evaluate the expression in Exercise 34 for one, two, three, and four adults. What is the maximum number of adults that can go on the trip?

Gerald is a technician working in a hospital's physiology department. When he runs a test on a patient, he uses a recording instrument called a *kymograph*. The kymograph prints data on chart paper. Gerald needs to estimate the amount of paper needed for a heart stress test. The test will last 14.75 minutes, and the kymograph will use paper at a rate of 0.25 meters per minute.

36. Round the testing time to the nearest minute. Round the paper use rate to the nearest tenth meter per minute.

37. About what length of chart paper will Gerald need for the test?

Carbon dioxide (CO_2) is a "greenhouse effect" gas, thought by many scientists to have the potential for causing global climate changes. Automobile engines produce CO_2 when they burn gasoline. About 18 pounds of CO_2 are produced per gallon of gasoline burned. Therefore, if a car's fuel mileage is g miles per gallon and it is driven y miles per year, the number of pounds of CO_2 produced is given by the algebraic expression

$$(y \div g) \cdot 18$$

The average American car gets about 20 miles per gallon and is driven about 12,000 miles per year.

38. About how many pounds of CO_2 does an average American car produce each year? Round your answer to the nearest thousand pounds.

39. Ethanol is a mixture of gasoline and ethyl alcohol. When an automobile burns ethanol, it produces about 70% of the amount of CO_2 produced when burning gasoline. Using your answer to Exercise 38, estimate the number of pounds of CO_2 produced per year by a car when it burns ethanol.

A store sells CDs for $12.99 each. Ann-Marie estimates the cost of a CD plus tax to be $14.30. She selects nine CDs. The clerk tells Ann-Marie her bill is $157.18.

40. Use rounding to determine if this is a reasonable total.

41. How can Ann-Marie explain to the clerk she has been overcharged?

Theresa is considering buying a collection of coins at a show and sale. The collection has ten coins. Theresa estimates five are worth $7 each and five are worth $3 each.

42. Show how Theresa can use the Distributive Property to find the value of the collection with a mental calculation.

43. The seller is asking $35 for the collection. If Theresa buys the coins, is she getting a good deal?

MATH LAB

Equipment Meter stick with scale markings of 1 mm
Masking tape
String
Marker

Problem Statement

Sometimes a distance measurement requires an estimation.

You will estimate distances to the nearest whole, tenth, and thousandth meter.

Procedure

a Your teacher will mark two locations on the floor with masking tape. Use the marker to label one piece of tape *A* and the other *B*.

b About how many lengths of the meter stick will fit between *A* and *B*? Your answer is an estimate of the distance between *A* and *B* to the nearest meter.

Record your estimate in a data table similar to the following one. If there is more than one estimate in your group, record all the estimates.

Measurement Precision	Measurement
Estimated to nearest meter	
Measured to nearest meter	
Measured to nearest $\frac{1}{10}$th meter	
Measured to nearest $\frac{1}{100}$th meter	
Measured to nearest $\frac{1}{1000}$th meter	

c Stretch the string between *A* and *B* so that it overlaps the tape. Tape the string to the floor.

d Place the end of the meter stick at the point where the string crosses the inside edge of the tape at *A*. Mark the string at the other end of the meter stick. What is the distance between the mark and *A*?

e Move the meter stick along the string and mark a point 1 meter from the first mark. Continue marking the string at 1-meter intervals until the meter stick overlaps the inside edge of the tape at *B*. Leave the meter stick in this position.

f How many whole meters did you measure between *A* and *B*? Is there more or less than one-half meter between the last mark on the string and the point where the string crosses the inside edge of the tape at *B*? Record the distance you measured between *A* and *B* to the nearest meter.

g Find the marks on the meter stick that divide it into tenths. To the nearest tenth of a meter, what is the distance from the last mark on the string to the point where the string crosses the inside edge of the tape at *B*? Record the distance between *A* and *B* to the nearest tenth of a meter.

h Find the marks on the meter stick that divide it into hundredths. To the nearest hundredth of a meter, what is the distance from the last mark on the string to the point where the string crosses the inside edge of the tape at *B*? Record the distance between *A* and *B* to the nearest hundredth.

i Find the marks on the meter stick that divide it into thousandths. Record the distance between *A* and *B* to the nearest thousandth of a meter.

Discussion Questions

1. How close was your distance estimate to the distance from *A* to *B*?

2. How does the string increase the accuracy of your measurements?

3. Instead of a meter stick with scale markings, suppose you had three sticks with no marks on them. One stick is one meter long, another is one-tenth meter long, and the third is one-hundredth meter long. How can you measure the distance between *A* and *B* using these sticks? To what place value would you record the distance?

Equipment   Road map showing the United States
                 interstate highway system
                 Calculator

Problem Statement

When a truck driver plans a cross-country delivery of cargo, he or she must estimate the travel time and fuel usage for the trip. From the travel time, the driver can tell the customer the estimated time of arrival of the cargo. From the fuel usage, the driver can predict the cost of the trip.

Procedure

a Your teacher will assign your group a departure city and a delivery city. You will complete a planning log, similar to the one below. The log will show a plan for hauling a load of washing machines from the manufacturer at the departure city to a customer's warehouse at the delivery city. Your departure date and time are Monday, December 3rd, at 7:00 a.m. Fill in the first four boxes of the planning log.

TRUCKER'S PLANNING LOG	
[1] Description of Load:	[2] Departure Date and Time:
[3] Depart From:	[4] Deliver To:
[5] Estimated Total Mileage:	[6] Estimated Fuel Usage:
[7] Estimated Date and Time of Arrival:	
[8] Special Considerations:	
Instructions: Complete and sign planning log. Fax copies to pick-up and delivery warehouses. Submit original to dispatcher.	Driver's Signature:

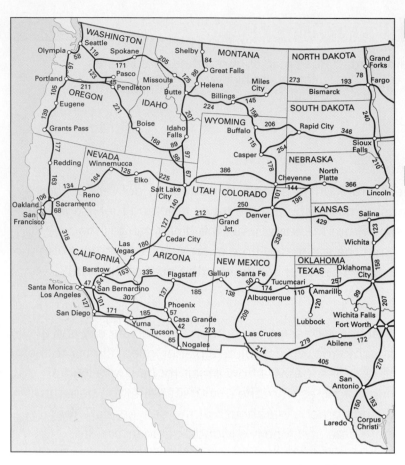

b Identify the route you will drive from the departure city to the delivery city. The route must use the interstate highways, and should be the shortest possible distance between the two cities.

c Make a list of the cities along the route you have chosen, beginning with the departure city and ending with the delivery city. If two highways intersect where no city is labeled, write "INT" on your list. Beginning with the second city on the list, write the mileage between each pair of cities. For example, the list for a route from Las Vegas to Denver would look like this:

Las Vegas	
Cedar City	180
INT	127
Grand Junction	212
Denver	250

d Round each distance on your list to the nearest hundred miles. Using mental math, what is the approximate total mileage of the route? Add the exact distances on the list. Based on your estimate, is this total reasonable? Round the exact total to the nearest hundred miles, and enter this value in the planning log.

e Let d represent the estimated total mileage. Your truck averages 8 miles per gallon of fuel. Therefore, you can calculate the approximate number of gallons of fuel g required for the trip with the formula

$$g = d \div 8$$

Substitute the value for *d* into this formula and find *g*. Enter the estimated amount of fuel required to the nearest ten gallons.

f Let *h* represent the estimated number of hours of driving required. You will average 60 miles per hour on the interstate. Therefore, you can calculate *h* from the formula

$$h = d \div 60$$

Substitute the value for *d* into this formula and find *h* rounded to the nearest hour.

g For every ten hours of driving, you will have one rest stop. How many rest stops will you have? A rest stop lasts 10 hours (this includes time for sleeping, refueling, and eating). How many hours will be spent in rest stops?

h To the nearest hour, how many total hours will be required for the trip?

i Estimate the date and time of arrival at the delivery city. Enter this information in the planning log.

Discussion Questions

1. For the return trip, from the delivery city to the departure city, you do not need a planning log. The distance is the same. What property of addition allows you to reach this conclusion?

2. You estimate the cost of diesel fuel to be $1.35 per gallon. What is the approximate fuel cost for the round trip?

Activity 3: Step-by-Step

Equipment   Tape measure
Masking tape
Stop watch
Calculator

Problem Statement

You will calculate your average step length and walking speed. Then you will use these averages to estimate distances. Record your data in tables similar to those on the next page.

Measured Values

	Number of Steps	Time (seconds)
Trial 1		
Trial 2		
Trial 3		
Average number of steps, a_s		
Unknown distance, x feet		

Calculated Values

Average step length, d feet	
Average speed, v feet/minute	
Unknown distance, x feet	

Procedure

a Use the tape measure to mark a 100-foot length in a place identified by your teacher. Mark the ends of the 100-foot length with masking tape.

b Stand on one of the pieces of masking tape, with the toe of your shoe on the tape. Step off the distance to the other piece of masking tape. Walk with normal steps and at a normal speed. Count the number of steps needed to walk the 100-foot distance. At the same time, have another group member time the walk with the stop watch. Record the number of steps for Trial 1 to the nearest whole step. Record the time to the nearest second.

c Repeat Step **b** two more times, and record the results for Trials 2 and 3 in the data table. Make sure the same group member is the "walker" each time.

d Calculate the average number of steps for the 100-foot distance for the three trials. Let a_s represent this average. You can find the average step length d with the formula

$$d = 100 \div a_s$$

Use rounding to estimate the value of d. Find d with your calculator. Based on your estimate, is the calculator result reasonable? Record the average step length to the nearest tenth of a foot in the Calculated Values table.

e Calculate the average time to the nearest tenth of a second for the 100-foot distance for the three trials. Let a_t represent this average. Since a_t is in seconds, you can find the average walking speed v in feet per minute, with the formula

$$v = 100 \cdot (60 \div a_t)$$

Use rounding to estimate the value of v. Find v with your calculator. Based on your estimate, is the calculator result reasonable? Record the average speed to the nearest tenth of a foot per minute in the data table.

f Now use your data to estimate the length of another unknown distance identified by your teacher. Step off the distance, counting and timing as in Step **b**. Round the number of steps n to the nearest whole step and the time t to the nearest second. Record the data in the table.

g The unknown distance x can be calculated with two formulas. Using the number of steps and step length,

$$x = n \cdot d$$

Using time and speed,

$$x = (t \div 60) \cdot v$$

Calculate x using both formulas. If the calculated values are different, discuss the values within your group, and decide what value to report. Record x to the nearest foot.

Discussion Questions

1. Compare your results with other groups in the class. Did each group have the same values for average step length d and average speed v? Explain.

2. Did each group have the same values for the unknown distance? Explain any differences.

3. One mile is 5280 feet. Bernardo Segura from Mexico is a world champion race walker. In a 20-kilometer race (about 12.4 miles), Segura can walk the first 10 miles in about 63 minutes. Estimate his speed in feet per minute.

CHAPTER 1 ASSESSMENT

Communicate

1. Explain how to use a number line to compare two numbers.

2. Describe how to round a number to a given place value.

3. When you simplify a numerical or algebraic expression, what order of operations do you follow?

4. Explain how to estimate sums and differences by rounding.

5. What are the four steps in problem solving? Briefly explain each step.

Skills

6. Write twelve and twenty-four thousandths as a decimal.

7. Write 9.1086 in words.

8. Evaluate the expression $3p + t$ when $p = 5$ and $t = 7$.

9. Rewrite the expression $5x + 5y$ using the Distributive Property.

Estimate the answer. Then use your calculator to find the exact answer.

10. $36.18 + 12.085 + 48.9$ **11.** $\$8.12 \times 19$

Applications

Solve each of the following problems. Use estimation to see if your answer is reasonable.

12. Tom filled his car with 11.7 gallons of gas. The tank holds 16 gallons. How much gas was in the tank before it was filled?

13. Lisa bought six CDs for $68.94. What was the average price for each CD?

Solve each problem.

14. A surround-sound stereo system can be purchased for $950 cash or $45.30 per month for 24 months. If you buy the stereo system on the monthly plan, how much more will you pay?

15. You can either buy or lease a new car. The cost of a new car is $15,500 and you can sell it after 3 years for $6800. To lease the same car for 3 years, you must make an initial payment of $1500. The monthly payments are $189. Which plan costs the least? How much does it save over the other plan?

16. How many rectangles will there be in the next figure?

1 rectangle   3 rectangles   6 rectangles   _____?_____

Math Lab

17. The distance between two pieces of tape is two meters, four tenths of a meter, nine hundredths of a meter, and one thousandth of a meter. Write the distance as a decimal. Is the distance closer to 2 meters or 3 meters?

18. A truck driver records the following distances (in miles) for a trip from Fort Worth to Albuquerque.

$$207 \quad 257 \quad 110 \quad 174$$

What is the total distance, d to the nearest hundred miles? The truck averages 8 miles per gallon of fuel. Use the formula $g = d \div 8$ to find the estimated number of gallons of fuel g needed for the trip.

19. In a math lab, a person walks for t seconds at a speed v feet per minute. The distance walked x is given by the formula $x = (t \div 60)v$. If the person's speed is 400 feet per minute and the walk lasts 30 seconds, how many feet did the person walk?

CHAPTER 2

WHY SHOULD I LEARN THIS?

Statistics provide important information to leaders in business, school, entertainment, and sports. How might you use statistics to determine if racing in one of the middle lanes in a swim meet is an advantage?

Contents: Working with Data

WORKING WITH DATA

LEARN HOW TO...

1. Calculate the mean, median, and mode of a set of data.
2. Construct the following displays of data:
   - line plots
   - frequency tables
   - stem-and-leaf plots
   - box-and-whisker plots
   - bar graphs
   - histograms
   - line graphs
3. Understand the misuse of statistics.

Data are facts expressed as numbers. This chapter deals with collecting, organizing, displaying, and interpreting data to help make decisions. **Statistics** is the branch of mathematics that deals with collecting, organizing, and analyzing data. Here are just a few places where you can find statistics.

Internet	Textbooks	News broadcasts
Newspapers	Encyclopedias	Library references
Owner manuals	Magazines	Computer data banks

Data is usually presented in tables and graphs. To help you solve problems and make informed decisions, you need to read and interpret the following presentations of data.

Stem-and-leaf plots	Line graphs
Bar graphs	Frequency tables
Histograms	Line plots
Box-and-whisker plots	

Tables and graphs are useful when they clearly and accurately present data. In some cases, graphs can be misleading. This chapter will help you identify the misuse of graphs and measures of central tendency.

LESSON 2.1 MEASURES OF CENTRAL TENDENCY

OBJECTIVES

➤ Find the mean, median, and mode of a data set.

Danielle needs to buy new computers for her travel agency. One supplier, Network Service, quotes a price of $1410 per computer. How can Danielle determine if this is a good price for new computers?

Danielle collects the data shown below. She compares the quoted price to the prices of the six other suppliers. The prices form a **data set**. Each price is a **data value**.

Supplier	Price
Network Service	$1410
Discount Electronics	$1380
Outlet Computer	$1490
Department Store	$1630
Office Supply	$1510
Warehouse Club	$1470
Mail Order	$1380

To help her make a decision, Danielle uses *measures of central tendency*. A **measure of central tendency** is a single value that describes a data set. Three measures of central tendency are the **mean**, **median**, and **mode**.

ACTIVITY 1   Finding the Mean of a Data Set

1 Find the sum of the seven computer prices in Danielle's data set.

2 Divide the sum by the number of prices.

3 The result of Step 2 is the average, or **mean**, price. Is $1410 a good price compared to the mean?

Mean

The mean of a data set is the sum S of the data values divided by the number of data values N.

$$\text{Mean} = \frac{S}{N}$$

ACTIVITY 2 Finding the Median of a Data Set

1 List the seven computer prices in order from *least to greatest*.

2 What data value is located in the *middle* of the ordered data set?

3 The result of Step 2 is the **median** price. Is $1410 a good price compared to the median?

> ### Median
> The median is the middle value of an ordered set of data. For an even number of values, the median is the average of the two middle values.

ONGOING ASSESSMENT

Is the following statement *true* or *false*?

Half the data values in a data set are greater than the median and half are less than the median.

ACTIVITY 3 Finding the Mode of a Data Set

1 In the list of computer prices, which data value or values occur most often?

2 The result of Step 1 is the **mode** of the data set. Is $1410 a good price compared to the mode?

> ### Mode
> The mode of a data set is the data value that occurs most often. A data set may have one mode, no mode, or several modes.

Critical Thinking In Danielle's data set, replace the mail order price with $1381. Describe the change in each measure of central tendency.

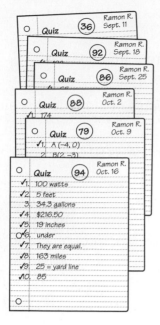

EXAMPLE Finding the Mean, Median, and Mode

Ramon received the scores at left for six quizzes in math.

Find the mean, median, and mode of Ramon's quiz scores.

SOLUTION

a. To find the mean, add the quiz scores and divide by 6.

$$\text{Mean} = \frac{36 + 92 + 86 + 88 + 79 + 94}{6} \approx 79.2$$

The mean of Ramon's quiz scores is approximately 79.2.

b. To find the median, list the scores in order from least to greatest.

$$36 \quad 79 \quad 86 \quad 88 \quad 92 \quad 94$$

The values 86 and 88 are located in the middle of the data set. Since there are an even number of scores, the median is the average of 86 and 88.

$$\text{Median} = \frac{86 + 88}{2} = 87$$

The median of Ramon's quiz scores is 87.

c. Since no score occurs more than once, there is no mode.

Critical Thinking In the data set for Ramon's quiz scores, 36 is an *outlier*. An **outlier** is a data value that is much higher or lower than most of the other data values. Calculate Ramon's mean score without the outlier. What effect does an outlier have on the mean of a data set?

ONGOING ASSESSMENT

A pollster takes a survey to find how many hours a group of boys and girls watch TV during one school week.

Find the mean, median, and mode of each data set. Which group watches more TV?

Hours of TV Watched									
Boys:	7	9	9	8	7	8	8	10	6	12
Girls:	6	8	8	5	7	9	10	9	7	5

LESSON ASSESSMENT

Think and Discuss

1 What are three measures of central tendency? How do you find each one?

2 Which measure of central tendency is affected most by an outlier? Why does an outlier affect this measure and not the other two?

3 Explain why the mean and median might not be actual data values in a set.

4 Which measure of central tendency would you use to find how much money most students spend on entertainment over a weekend? Explain your answer.

Practice and Apply

Find the mean, median, and mode for each set of data.

5. Noontime temperatures for ten days:

78° 86° 88° 93° 87° 84° 88° 88° 86° 85°

6. Prices of athletic shoes sold at the Fast Foot Store during one day:

$58.75 $63.89 $58.25 $75.59 $65.79 $63.98 $58.25

7. Figure skating scores for the top skater:

5.4 5.6 5.3 5.4 5.5 5.4 5.7 5.3

8. Number of minutes for each long-distance telephone call in one week:

15 17 3 6 9 8 12 8 9 16 7 6 14 6 10

During one grading period, your test scores are:
83 79 92 86 93

9. Find the mean, median, and mode of the test scores.

10. Which measure of central tendency would give you the highest final grade?

11. There is one more test during the grading period. What score do you need on this test to raise your average to 88?

Sherri and Carri own a shoe shop employing ten people. The payroll for the ten employees includes one who earns $25,000, three who earn $22,000 each, two who earn $20,000 each, and four who earn $16,000 each. You are one of the persons earning $20,000.

12. Find the mean, median, and mode for the ten employees' salaries.

13. Which of the measures found in Exercise 12 is the highest?

14. Describe your position in the payroll relative to each measure of central tendency.

Dominique scored the following number of points in six consecutive basketball games:

16   15   18   20   18   17

15. What is the mean, median, and mode of the points scored?

16. How would you use measures of central tendency to answer the following question?

About how many points does Dominique score per game?

Evaluate each expression when $a = 1$, $b = 5$, and $c = 8$.

17. $ab + c$ **18.** $\dfrac{4c + 3a}{b}$ **19.** $3c \div (3b - 3a)$

Use rounding to estimate each sum or difference. Then use your calculator to find the exact answer.

20. $245.9 + 189.25 + 367.4$ **21.** $\$3095.39 - \$1838.75$

Solve each of the following problems.

22. A car repair bill is $145.50. The bill includes charges for 2.5 hours of labor and $33 for parts. What is the hourly charge for labor?

23. Suppose you have 3 nickels, 4 dimes, and 2 quarters. List all the ways you can give a friend 50¢.

A video store made $1358 for rentals on Friday and $2183 for rentals on Saturday.

24. Estimate how much the video store made for the two days.

25. Estimate how much more the video store made on Saturday.

26. The average cost of renting a video is $4. About how many videos were rented for the two days?

27. The average yearly rainfall of three cities is given in the table. List the cities from least to greatest rainfall.

City	Amount (in.)
A	17.31
B	17.3
C	17.28

28. In 1920, a gasoline-powered racing car set a speed record of 155.046 miles per hour. In 1997, a jet-propelled car set a speed record of 763.04 miles per hour. Find the difference in the two records.

29. Nita had the recommended 15,000-mile maintenance service performed on her car 8 months after purchasing it new. Estimate the average number of miles she drives the car each month.

LESSON 2.2 FREQUENCY TABLES

OBJECTIVES

➤ Read and create line plots.
➤ Read and make frequency tables.
➤ Calculate measures of center from a frequency table.

Justin is taking an aerobics class to improve his fitness level. During each class, the students count their heartbeats for a 10-second period. Justin's counts for his first ten classes are shown below.

20 17 19 19 19 18 19 17 20 21

You can display this data set in a **line plot.**

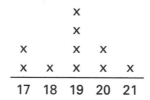

```
            x
            x
  x         x    x
  x    x    x    x    x
  ――――――――――――――――――――
  17   18   19   20   21
```

Each time a particular count occurs, an X is placed above it. For example, on four occasions, Justin's 10-second heartbeat was 19. Use the line plot to complete the following activity.

ACTIVITY 1   Reading a Line Plot

1 What was Justin's lowest heartbeat count? What was his highest heartbeat count?

2 The difference between the highest data value and the lowest data value is the **range** of the data. What is the range of Justin's heartbeat counts?

3 Find the mean, median, and mode of the data. Which measure of central tendency can be found by just looking at the line plot?

The data can also be displayed in a **frequency table**.

Heartbeat Counts	Tally	Frequency
17	||	2
18	|	1
19	||||	4
20	||	2
21	|	1

A **tally mark** represents each time a particular heartbeat count occurs. The sum of the tally marks in each row is the **frequency** of the counts.

ACTIVITY 2 **Finding the Measures of Central Tendency**

1 Copy the frequency table in Activity 1.

2 Add a column to the frequency table as shown. Complete the table by multiplying each heartbeat count *n* by the frequency *f* of that count.

Heartbeat Counts (*n*)	Tally	Frequency (*f*)	*nf*
17	||	2	?
18	|	1	?
19	||||	4	?
20	||	2	?
21	|	1	?

3 The mathematical symbol for finding a sum of numbers is the Greek letter *sigma* Σ. Find the sum of the frequencies, Σf by adding the frequency column. Find the sum of the fourth column, Σnf.

4 Calculate the mean using the formula

$$\text{Mean} = \frac{\Sigma nf}{\Sigma f}$$

5 Use the frequency table to find the median and mode.

Critical Thinking   What part of the definition of mean from Lesson 2.1 corresponds to Σnf? What part corresponds to Σf?

ONGOING ASSESSMENT

In the fourth month of Justin's aerobics class, he records the following heartbeat counts on eleven consecutive days:

19 21 22 21 22 20 20 19 19 21 23

Display the data in a line plot and a frequency table. Find the mean, median, and mode of the heartbeat counts. Which measures of central tendency show that the intensity of Justin's exercise has increased?

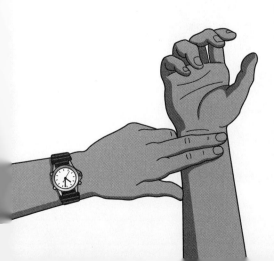

LESSON ASSESSMENT

1 How do you calculate the range of a data set?

2 Explain how to find the median and mode from a line plot.

3 Explain how to find the mean from a frequency table.

Construct a line plot for each set of data. Find the mean, median, and mode for each set.

4. 20 23 22 23 22 21 24 22 23 24 21 22

5. 7 11 10 8 9 8 10 9 11 7 8 9 9 10 11

Make a frequency table for each set of data. Find the mean, median, and mode for each set.

6. Heights of students in inches: 69 64 70 65 65 68 67 67 66 69 64 70 66 65 64

7. Ages of club members: 15 16 13 14 15 16 13 14 15 13 15 15 16 15 13 14 14 14 16 13 14 16 14 15 14

8. Miles per gallon: 12.6 13.5 13.3 12.8 13.5 12.8 13.2 12.6 13.5 12.8 13.3 13.2 13.3 13.5

9. Distances cycled in kilometers: 10 4 6 6 9 7 6 7 9 7 7 10 10 8 6 7 9 10 7

10. Make a survey to collect data from your class on the total number of brothers and sisters each student has. Arrange the data in a frequency table.

11. Find the median and mode for your data set.

Mixed Review

Write a decimal for each italicized word.

12. The sun is approximately *one hundred fifty million* kilometers from the Earth.

13. A computer chip contains *four hundred-thousandths* of a gram of gold.

Use < or > to show the inequalities in Exercises 14 and 15.
14. 67.076 _?_ 67.067   **15.** 0.0003 _?_ 0.00003

Translate each word expression in Exercises 16 and 17 into an algebraic expression.

16. The number of centimeters in m meters

17. The amount earned in h hours at $8 per hour

18. Evaluate $2s + 5$ when $s = 7$.

19. Evaluate $0.3d - 2.1$ when $d = 8.5$.

20. Evaluate $m + mn + n$ when $m = 3$ and $n = 4$.

21. Evaluate $3a + 4b$ when $a = 5$ and $b = 2$.

22. Evaluate $ab + bc$ when $a = 1.5$, $b = 4$, and $c = 2.5$.

23. Evaluate $3.5m \cdot 2n$ when $m = 9$ and $n = 0.5$.

24. Evaluate $st \div 3.2$ when $s = 1.6$ and $t = 4$.

Simplify each expression.
25. $8(ab)2$ **26.** $3(6x - 9)$

LESSON 2.3 STEM-AND-LEAF PLOTS

- Construct and interpret stem-and-leaf plots.

In Lesson 2.2, you learned how to display data using line plots and frequency tables. These displays help you visualize and obtain information such as the measures of central tendency. A **stem-and-leaf plot** is another kind of display that shows data in a structured form. This plot is useful in finding the median and mode.

To construct a stem-and-leaf plot, represent each number in a data set by a stem and a leaf. The leaf is the first digit on the right. The stem is the remaining digit or digits. Thus, for the number 624,

The stem is 62 ⌐   ⌐ The leaf is 4

6 2 4

ACTIVITY

Constructing a Stem-and-Leaf Plot

Office Temp Inc. places workers in businesses needing part-time office workers. In one week, 20 part-time employees worked the following number of hours:

41	26	27	33
18	27	30	31
31	33	6	41
40	28	39	29
40	9	40	8

Construct a stem-and-leaf plot for the data.

1 The leaves are the ones digits and the stems are the tens digits for each data value. First write the stems in a column, from least to greatest.

0
1
2
3
4

2 Draw a vertical line to the right of the column. Write the leaf of each data value in a row to the right of its stem. The first three data values are shown as examples.

Stems	Leaves
0	
1	
2	6 7
3	
4	1

Stems	Leaves
0	6 8 9
1	
2	
3	
4	

3 Complete the stem-and-leaf plot by rearranging the leaves for each stem in order from least to greatest. The first row is shown as an example.

4 Use the stem-and-leaf plot to find the median and mode of the Office Temp Inc. data set.

Critical Thinking   Is the following criticism fair? Explain why or why not.

Office Temp Inc. should not be called a *part-time* personnel business because more of its employees work 40 hours per week than any other number of hours.

You can also use stem-and-leaf plots to display decimal data values.

EXAMPLE Data from a Stem-and-Leaf Plot

Batting Averages	
0.29	3 4 5 9
0.30	0 1 8
0.31	6 7
0.32	8
0.33	4 5 5 6
0.34	1 7 9
0.35	4 4 7

a. What is the lowest batting average? What is the highest batting average? What is the range?

b. How many hitters have a batting average greater than 0.334?

c. What is the median batting average?

d. What is the mode of the batting averages?

SOLUTION

a. The lowest batting average is 0.293. The highest is 0.357. The range is $0.357 - 0.293 = 0.064$.

b. There are 9 hitters with batting averages greater than 0.334.

c. Since there is an even number of leaves, the median is the average of the two middle data values.

$$\frac{0.328 + 0.334}{2} = 0.331$$

The median batting average is 0.331.

d. The batting average data has two modes: 0.335 and 0.354.

ONGOING ASSESSMENT

The grade point averages of ten students applying for a scholarship are 3.85, 3.75, 3.66, 3.96, 3.68, 3.76, 3.89, 3.95, 3.87, and 3.75.

1. Construct a stem-and-leaf plot for the grade point averages.

2. What is the median? What is the mode?

LESSON ASSESSMENT

1 Explain how to construct a stem-and-leaf plot.

2 The minimum and maximum values of a set of data are 14.36 and 14.63. If you draw a stem-and-leaf plot of the data, what place value would you use for the leaves?

3 Explain how to find the median and mode from a stem-and-leaf plot.

Practice and Apply

Use the stem-and-leaf plot to answer Exercises 4–8.

Books Borrowed from the Library Each Day

10	0 1 2 5 5 7
11	3 3 3 6 8
12	1 5 6 7 7 8

Key: 10|1 means 101

4. What place values make the stem of the plot?

5. What place values make the leaves of the plot?

6. Find the range of the data.

7. Find the median of the data.

8. Find the mode of the data.

The average monthly temperature for two cities are given below.

	Jan	Feb	Mar	Apr	May	Jun	July	Aug	Sept	Oct	Nov	Dec
Average Monthly Temperature °F												
Martin	41	49	52	60	62	64	78	82	79	65	59	50
Grayson	53	58	60	65	68	70	73	74	73	65	62	51

9. Construct a stem-and-leaf plot for each city.

10. Which city has the smallest range of temperatures?

11. Which city has more average monthly temperatures greater than 50° Fahrenheit?

12. Which city has the highest median temperature?

The ages of thirty employees of a company are given below.

$$60 \quad 62 \quad 40 \quad 28 \quad 33 \quad 38 \quad 54 \quad 46 \quad 26 \quad 27$$
$$54 \quad 56 \quad 29 \quad 32 \quad 68 \quad 57 \quad 47 \quad 48 \quad 33 \quad 33$$
$$63 \quad 62 \quad 41 \quad 29 \quad 27 \quad 38 \quad 55 \quad 50 \quad 54 \quad 30$$

13. Construct a stem-and-leaf plot for the data.

14. Find the range of the data.

15. Find the median of the data.

16. Find the mode of the data.

Rob's bowling scores for his last 15 games are shown in the stem-and-leaf plot.

Rob's Bowling Scores

13	0 5 5 8
14	0 1 1 5 5 5 5
15	1 6 6 9

Key: 13|5 means 135

17. What is the lowest score Rob bowled? highest?

18. Find the range of Rob's scores.

19. Find the mean, median, and mode of Rob's scores.

Mixed Review

Write the value of the underlined digit.
20. 25609.007   **21.** 17.080776

List the numbers in order from least to greatest.
22. 34.078 34.087 34.008   **23.** 0.0045 0.005 0.0005

For Exercises 24–25, estimate the answer. Then find the answer using a calculator.
24. During one week, Antawn made deposits of $154.79, $216.75, and $196.37. He also made a withdrawal of $109.35. What was the net increase in Antawn's account during the week?

25. It is 78 miles from Austin to San Antonio. A company's trucks make 35 round trips between Austin and San Antonio each week. How many miles are driven for these trips each week?

Gas Mileage, mpg

29	0 1
28	0 4 4 4 6
27	5 5 8

Key: 27|5 means 27.5

Damon keeps a record of his car's gas mileage to help him plan a long trip. After 10 refuelings, he calculates the miles per gallon shown on the stem-and-leaf plot at left.

26. What is the range of the data?

27. Does the data contain any outliers?

28. What place value is used as the leaves?

29. What is the mean of the data?

30. What is the median of the data?

31. What is the mode of the data?

32. What value for gas mileage should Damon use in estimating the cost of gas for the trip? Explain your answer.

= 10 stores

Region

Northeast, Southeast, Midwest, South, Northwest, Southwest, West

You are considering purchasing a franchise from a company that sells children's clothing through retail outlet stores. In its annual report, the company uses the graph at left to display the number of stores it owns.

33. In which region of the country does the company own the most stores?

34. Approximately how many stores does the company own in all?

35. Is the mode the best measure of central tendency to use to decide the number of stores in each region?

36. Your first choice for the location is the region with the fewest number of stores. Which regions do you consider first?

Lane Number	Number of Winners
1	2
2	4
3	3
4	5
5	4
6	7
7	4
8	6

The finals of a state swim meet were held after several days of qualifying races. Lane assignments of the 35 winners of the finals are shown in the table on the left.

37. Construct a line plot to display the data.

38. The fastest qualifiers were assigned to the middle lanes for the finals. Did the fastest qualifiers also win the most number of finals? Explain your answer.

LESSON 2.4 BOX-AND-WHISKER PLOTS

OBJECTIVES
➤ Identify quartiles and outliers.
➤ Create and interpret box-and-whisker plots.

High school coaches rank the state's athletic teams by voting. Before casting their votes, the coaches review each team's statistics. These statistics can be displayed with **box-and-whisker plots**.

A box-and-whisker plot divides a data set into four regions. Each region contains 25 percent of the data values in the set. These plots are especially useful in comparing two data sets.

ACTIVITY 1   Identifying Quartiles

Player	Number of Hits
Andrews	35
Bocci	21
Cappeletti	44
Downs	29
Rodriguez	27
Harris	18
Isaacs	35
Jordan	39
King	37
Nu	48
Posey	13
Robisch	17
Rossi	32
Washington	59
Wheeler	15

The table shows the number of hits for players on the Washington High School baseball team.

1 List the data from least to greatest.

2 What is the median? This value divides the data in half. The median is the **second quartile**, Q_2.

3 Look at the data set of values less than Q_2. What is the median of this set? This value is the **first quartile**, Q_1.

4 Look at the data set of values greater than Q_2. What is the median of this set? This value is the **third quartile**, Q_3.

5 What is the least value of the data set? What is the greatest value of the data set? These values determine the **whiskers** of the graph.

EXAMPLE 1 Drawing a Box-and-Whisker Plot

Draw a box-and-whisker plot to display the Washington High School baseball data.

SOLUTION

1. Draw a number line that includes the least and greatest values. Mark the quartiles on the number line.

2. Draw a box with ends at Q_1 and Q_3.

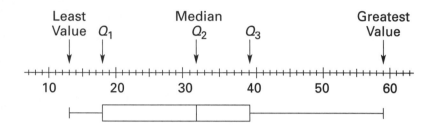

Draw a vertical line through the box to mark the median, Q_2.

3. Draw the whiskers from each end of the box to the least and greatest values.

ONGOING ASSESSMENT

Use the box-and-whisker plot to complete Exercises **a** and **b**.

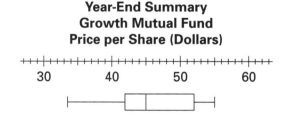

a. Over the year, what was the lowest, highest, and range of the price per share of the Growth Mutual Fund?

b. What are the median, first quartile, and third quartile prices per share?

Critical Thinking Can you find the mean from a box-and-whisker plot? Explain.

Use the box-and-whisker plots to compare the number of hits for the Washington High School and Springfield High School baseball teams.

Number of Hits
Washington High School (WHS)
Springfield High School (SHS)

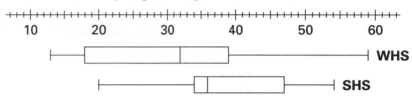

1 Compare the highest and lowest values, medians, and "middle 50 percent" of the data (defined as the data set within the box) for the two teams.

2 Which team appears to have the best hitters?

3 If you were voting for the state baseball ranking, would you vote for Springfield over Washington? Explain your reasoning.

SPORTS

| June 9 | THE STAR | Section D |

Springfield Pounds Washington, 14–8

The Stallions smoothed over their rough pitching yesterday by hammering away at the plate. Not exactly Major League-style baseball, but an effective tool nonetheless.

Shut out for the first time in 50 games the previous week, the Stallions made up for lost at-bats by erupting for a season-high 18 hits and scoring their highest number of runs this season,

Tom Smith of the Springfield Stallions

ONGOING ASSESSMENT

Use the box-and-whisker plot below.

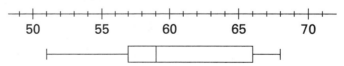

a. Find the median.

b. Find the lowest and highest values.

c. What does 57 represent?

d. What is Q_3?

If a data set contains an outlier, show the outlier with an asterisk and draw the whisker to the next or previous data value.

The table below shows the number of airplanes taking off each hour for a 10-hour period. Make a box-and-whisker plot for the data.

Number of Take-offs from Los Angeles International Airport

Time	Number of Take-offs
7:00 – 7:59	34
8:00 – 8:59	41
9:00 – 9:59	27
10:00 – 10:59	40
11:00 – 11:59	44
12:00 – 12:59	12
1:00 – 1:59	32
2:00 – 2:59	37
3:00 – 3:59	30
4:00 – 4:59	38

SOLUTION

1. List the data in order and find the quartiles.

$$12 \quad 27 \quad 30 \quad 32 \quad 34 \quad 37 \quad 38 \quad 40 \quad 41 \quad 44$$

$$Q_1 = 30 \quad Q_2 = \frac{34 + 37}{2} = 35.5 \quad Q_3 = 40$$

2. Draw a number line that includes the least and greatest values.

3. Draw the box and mark the median.

4. The value 12 is much lower than the other values, and is an outlier. Mark the outlier with an asterisk.

5. Draw the whiskers to show the extent of the other values.

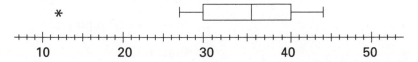

LESSON ASSESSMENT

1 How do you find the first, second, and third quartiles for a data set?

2 Is the following statement *true* or *false*? Explain your reasoning.

In a box-and-whisker plot, half the data are contained in the box.

3 How does an outlier affect the size of the box of a box-and-whisker plot?

4 The box-and-whisker plot for data set A has a much longer box than the plot for data set B. Describe the difference in the data values for the two data sets.

Practice and Apply

For each set of data in Exercises 5–8: **(a)** List the highest and lowest value; **(b)** List the quartiles; **(c)** Name any apparent outliers.

5. 24 28 18 20 35 25 32 24 32

6. 115 108 112 158 110 104 108 112

7. 70 70 88 75 79 83 74 72 88 78 70

8. 5.9 2.9 3.2 3.8 2.0 3.1 6.0 2.6 4.6

Use the data below to complete Exercises 9–15.

Weekly Summer Income							
Hakeem	$34	$37	$40	$30	$25	$37	$44
Kevin	$40	$35	$42	$35	$28	$46	$42

9. Make a box-and-whisker plot for Hakeem's income.

10. Make a box-and-whisker plot for Kevin's income.

11. Who has the highest one-week income? What is this income?

12. Who has the greater range of income? What is this range?

13. Who has the higher median? What is this median?

14. Who has the lowest first quartile? What is this value?

15. Write a paragraph explaining how the middle half of Hakeem's and Kevin's incomes compare.

The data below show the scores for the Lions and their opponents.

	A	B	C
1	**Game**	**Lions**	**Opponents**
2	1	60	52
3	2	68	59
4	3	52	63
5	4	50	66
6	5	81	65
7	6	59	62
8	7	66	60
9	8	64	67
10	9	63	65

16. Make a box-and-whisker plot showing both sets of data on the same number line.

17. Mark any outliers with an asterisk.

18. What are the quartiles for each set of data?

19. What is the range for each set of data?

20. Write a paragraph about the comparisons you can make using the box-and-whisker plot.

Mixed Review

List the numbers in order from least to greatest.
21. 23,079   23,753   23,508   **22.** 0.0621   0.2065   0.532

Evaluate each expression for $x = 2.5$ and $y = 1.8$.
23. $3y + x$ **24.** $xy + 3x - y$ **25.** $6(x - y) + 4(x - y)$

Use the pattern below to complete Exercises 26–27.

```
Row 0              1
Row 1            1   1
Row 2          1   2   1
Row 3        1   3   3   1
Row 4      1   4   6   4   1
```

26. What is the sum of the numbers in each row?

27. What is the sum of the numbers in row 5? In row 6?

LESSON 2.5 BAR GRAPHS AND HISTOGRAMS

OBJECTIVES
> Read and construct bar graphs and histograms.

A **bar graph** is one of the most common ways to display data. In the horizontal-bar graph below, the lengths of the bars model the data taken in a survey.

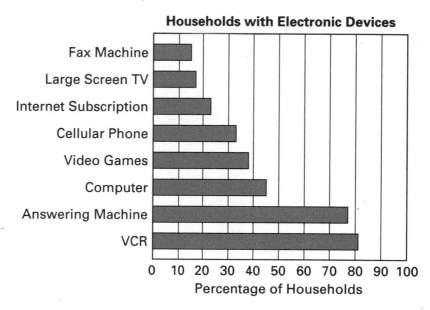

Households with Electronic Devices

ACTIVITY

Reading a Horizontal-Bar Graph

1 A bar graph has vertical and horizontal axes. In the bar graph above, which axis is labeled with a numerical scale? The **interval**, the distance between two entries, on this scale is 10.

2 What electronic device is owned by most households according to the survey?

3 What electronic device was found to be owned by the least number of households?

4 Estimate the percentage of households with cellular phones.

5 About what percentage of the households have computers, but do not subscribe to the Internet?

ONGOING ASSESSMENT

Explain why data taken from a bar graph are usually estimates.

EXAMPLE 1 Reading a Vertical-Bar Graph

The table below shows 4 months of sales data for fax machines at Discount Electronics. Construct a vertical-bar graph to display this data.

Sales of Fax Machines

Month	Fax Machines Sold
Oct	12
Nov	25
Dec	46
Jan	8

SOLUTION

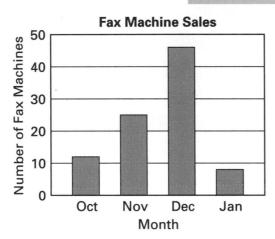

Fax Machine Sales

1. Use vertical bars. The lengths of the bars model the sales data.

2. Use a numerical scale on the vertical axis.

3. Since the maximum data value is 46, use a maximum value of 50 for the scale, and an interval of 10.

Critical Thinking   Can you estimate the mean, median, or mode using a bar graph? Explain how.

A **double-bar graph** compares two sets of data side by side. A legend on the graph shows which data set corresponds to each type of bar.

ONGOING ASSESSMENT

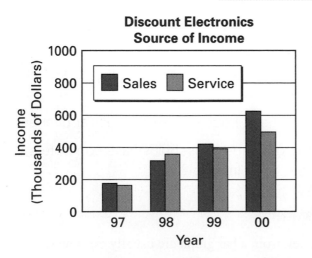

Discount Electronics Source of Income

1. What do the blue bars represent?

2. Estimate Discount Electronics' total income for 1999.

3. In what year did income from service exceed income from sales?

4. Estimate how much more income Discount Electronics received from sales in 1999 then in 1998.

5. Did Discount Electronics' income from service increase each year for the years shown in the graph?

A **histogram** is a bar graph that shows the frequency of data from the heights of the bars. The width of the bars is the interval used to display the data. A histogram has no space between the bars. To construct a histogram, first make a frequency table from the data.

EXAMPLE 2 Constructing a Histogram

The scores on a math test are listed.

Construct a histogram to display the test scores. Use five equal-size intervals.

Math Test Scores

75 67 93 99 81
85 92 50 80 94
51 96 85 73 84
82 91 87 77 78
73 86 71 77 85

SOLUTION

Scores	Tally	Frequency
50 – 59	||	2
60 – 69	|	1
70 – 79	⊬⊬ ||	7
80 – 89	⊬⊬ ||||	9
90 – 99	⊬⊬ |	6

First find the interval size by dividing the range by the number of intervals. The lowest score is 50 and the highest is 99. The range is $99 - 50 = 49$. For five equal-size intervals, each interval should be $49 \div 5 \approx 10$.

Now make a frequency table using an interval size of 10.

Construct the histogram from the frequency table. Show the test score intervals on the horizontal axis and the frequencies on the vertical axis.

Draw a bar for each interval.

The length of each bar models the frequency of the scores for that interval.

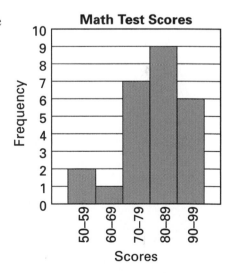

ONGOING ASSESSMENT

In Example 2, which interval has the greatest frequency? What is different about your answer compared to the mode of the data set?

LESSON ASSESSMENT

Think and Discuss

1 Which measure of central tendency can you easily obtain from a bar graph?

2 When is a double-bar graph used?

3 How do you construct a frequency table?

4 Explain how to construct a histogram from a frequency table.

Practice and Apply

The science club kept a record of the hours of sunshine during one week in November. Use the bar graph below to complete Exercises 5–9.

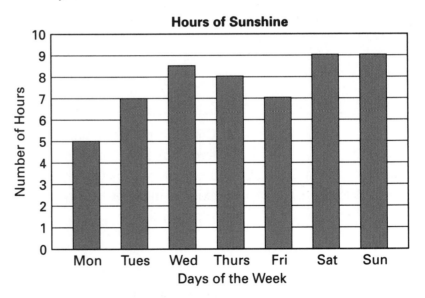

Hours of Sunshine

5. Which day had the least amount of sunshine?

6. Which days had 9 hours of sunshine?

7. How many hours of sunshine were there on Wednesday?

8. Find the mean, median, and mode for the data.

9. If you change the intervals on the vertical axis from 1 hour to 2 hours, how will the appearance of the graph change?

The volleyball coach recorded the number of serves for each player during a game.

Paula 5	Natalie 6
Vikki 8	Yolanda 5
Clarissa 7	Celia 4

10. Use the data to construct a bar graph.

11. Find the mean, median, and mode.

A police department technician constructed a double-bar graph to compare battery performance in radar guns. Use the graph to complete Exercises 12–15.

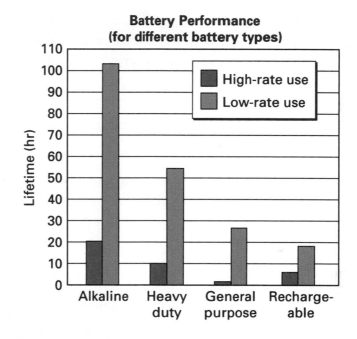

Battery Performance (for different battery types)

12. Which type battery lasted the longest for either high-rate or low-rate use?

13. How do the heavy-duty batteries compare to the other types of batteries shown on the graph?

14. The police department needs batteries to last through an 8-hour shift of high-rate use. Which battery types meet this requirement?

15. Under conditions requiring occasional low-rate use, batteries should last at least 48 hours. Which battery types meet this requirement?

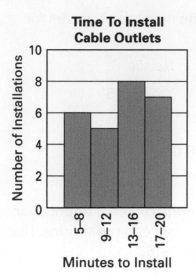

Time To Install Cable Outlets

Number of Installations (vertical axis): 0, 2, 4, 6, 8, 10
Minutes to Install (horizontal axis): 5–8, 9–12, 13–16, 17–20

The histogram to the left shows the number of minutes spent installing cable outlets.

16. What is the size of each interval on the horizontal axis?

17. What does the length of each bar represent?

18. How many installations took less than 17 minutes?

19. How many installations took more than 8 minutes?

In an 8-week boating class, Mr. Thompson recorded how many minutes it takes the boys and girls to sail around a course. Mr. Thompson calculated the average number of minutes for each group.

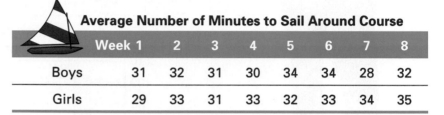

	Average Number of Minutes to Sail Around Course							
	Week 1	2	3	4	5	6	7	8
Boys	31	32	31	30	34	34	28	32
Girls	29	33	31	33	32	33	34	35

20. Construct a double-bar graph showing the averages.

21. How many weeks did the girls have a higher average?

Use intervals of 28–30, 31–33, and 34–36 to construct each of the following.

22. A frequency table for the boys.

23. A histogram for the boys.

24. A frequency table for the girls.

25. A histogram for the girls.

26. Which interval on each histogram has the greatest frequency?

Mixed Review

Give the value of each underlined number.

27. 0.008<u>9</u>3   **28.** 14.6<u>0</u>45   **29.** 2<u>3</u>5,986.1

Name the property illustrated.

30. $25 + (7 + 18) = (7 + 18) + 25$

31. $(m \cdot 1) + 12 = m + 12$

32. $6(2n) = (6 \cdot 2)n$

33. $7x - 4x = x(7 - 4)$

On a three-day business trip, Rozene spent $106 each night for lodging, $35 each day for transportation, and $95 each day for food. Estimate the answers to Exercises 34–36. Then use your calculator to find the answer.

34. How much more did Rozene spend on food and transportation than on lodging each day?

35. What was Rozene's daily business expense?

36. How much did Rozene spend on lodging, food, and transportation for the entire business trip?

37. Terrance is saving his money to buy a pair of in-line skates that cost $99.95. He has already saved $26.50. He saves $4.25 per week from his allowance. How many more weeks will Terrance need to save before he can buy the skates?

Cumulative Problem Solving

Amber is unpacking a shipment of cookies for a school fund-raiser. Her school ordered 100 cases. There are five varieties of cookies—mint, chocolate chip, peanut butter, oatmeal, and shortbread. The school ordered an equal number of cases of each variety.

38. Draw a bar graph showing the number of cases of each variety that should be in the shipment. Leave space to the right of each bar for a second type of bar.

When Amber unpacks the first ten cases from the shipment, she finds the following number of cases of each variety of cookie:

> 5 cases of mint
> 3 cases of chocolate chip
> 1 case of peanut butter
> 1 case of oatmeal
> 0 cases of shortbread

39. On the bar graph from Exercise 38, draw a second set of bars showing the number of cases of each variety that Amber has unpacked. You have drawn a double-bar graph.

40. Should Amber suspect there is an error in the shipment? Explain why or why not.

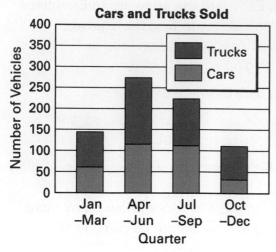

Cars and Trucks Sold

Delia is the purchasing manager of an automobile dealership. At the beginning of each year, she determines the inventory of cars and trucks for the new year. Last year, she kept approximately half the dealership's inventory in cars and half in trucks. The sales data from the previous four quarters are displayed in a **stacked bar graph.**

41. Approximately how many vehicles were sold the previous year?

42. Approximately how many cars were sold the previous year? How many trucks?

43. Should Delia continue to keep equal numbers of cars and trucks in the inventory? Explain your answer.

A person's basal metabolic rate (BMR) is the amount of energy his or her body uses when at rest. A pediatric research team is studying the BMRs of 10-year-old males. The team measures the following rates, in calories per day, of 16 boys:

1373	1242	1068	1183
1149	1324	989	1317
902	1370	2197	1245
1232	1070	1027	1290

44. Construct a box-and-whisker plot of the data.

45. The research team will perform follow-up tests on the boys in the upper 25 percent of the data values. Which rates are in the upper 25 percent?

46. The normal BMR for a 10-year-old is about 1050 calories per day. The research team will test someone for a hyperthyroid condition if they have a BMR that is 2100 calories per day or higher. Should the team test any of the 10-year-olds in the study? If so, which ones?

47. Describe how an outlier affects the appearance of a box-and-whisker plot.

48. What is the median BMR for the 10-year-olds tested?

A consumer research group publishes ratings of electronic devices. The group interviews users of the devices, and asks them to rate the devices on a scale from 1 (lowest) to 10 (highest). The results of one survey are shown on the following box-and-whisker plot.

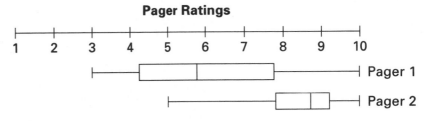

Pager Ratings

49. Which pager had the lowest rating? Which had the highest rating?

50. Which pager had the greatest range of ratings?

51. Which pager would you buy, based on these ratings? Explain your reasoning.

Lucia is a city traffic engineer considering a request to install larger speed limit signs on Oakmont Avenue. The speed limit is 35 mph. She decides to measure the speeds of cars traveling on Oakmont. If at least one-half the cars are going over 35 mph, she will approve the request. Car speeds are measured for one hour during the morning and one hour during the afternoon. The results are displayed on a histogram.

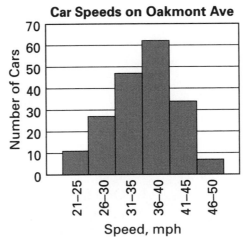

52. How fast were most cars traveling on Oakmont Ave?

53. Should Lucia approve the request for larger speed limit signs? Explain why or why not.

LESSON 2.6 LINE GRAPHS

OBJECTIVES

➤ Read and construct line graphs.
➤ Make predictions from a line graph.
➤ Read and construct frequency polygons.

The planting date of cotton affects how well plants grow during the summer and how much the plants produce in the fall. The planting date depends on soil temperature.

Every day in the spring at 10 a.m., Edwin measures soil temperature at a depth of 3 inches. He will plant cotton seed when the soil temperature reaches 65° F. He records the measurements on a spreadsheet.

	A Day of the Year	B Temp (°F)
1	Day of the Year	Temp (°F)
2	120	62
3	121	62
4	122	61.5
5	123	62.5
6	124	63
7	125	63
8	126	63.5
9	127	64

On a spreadsheet, a **cell** is the box where a row and a column meet. For example, cell A2 contains a value of 120. This value represents the 120th day of the year (April 30). On this day, Edwin measured a temperature of 62°F as shown in cell B2.

Edwin can observe how the soil temperature changes from day to day by displaying the data on a **line graph**.

EXAMPLE 1 Drawing a Line Graph

Construct a line graph to display Edwin's soil temperature data.

SOLUTION

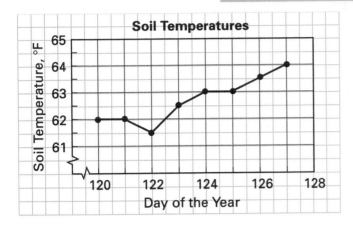

Draw horizontal and vertical axes on graph paper. Use line breaks on the axes to show the least values are not zero.

Plot the data values from Edwin's spreadsheet. Connect the points with line segments. Label the axes, and write the title above the graph.

Use the line graph from Example 1 to complete Activity 1.

ACTIVITY 1   **Predicting from a Line Graph**

1   When you look at the line graph and see how the values change, you are observing a **trend**. Is the trend for the soil temperature increasing, decreasing, or remaining the same?

2   When you use the trend to extend a line graph beyond the data given, you are **extrapolating**. What is a reasonable extrapolation for the temperature on day 128?

3   Predict what day Edwin should plan to plant cotton seed.

ONGOING ASSESSMENT

Cassandra is a student pilot who must keep track of her flight hours. Use Cassandra's records to construct a line graph. Title the graph and label the horizontal and vertical axes.

Month	Flight Hours
October	8
November	9
December	10
January	9
February	12
March	14

Lakeview High School Weights of Football Players

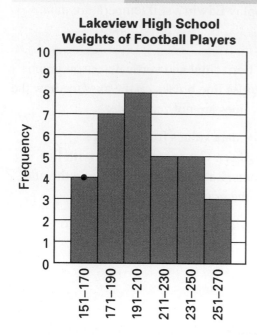

The following histogram shows the weights of the players on the Lakeview High School Football team.

1 Copy the histogram on a sheet of paper.

2 Mark the midpoint of the top of each bar. The first midpoint is marked as an example.

3 Draw a line graph on the histogram. Start the graph at the left end of the horizontal axis. Continue the graph through each midpoint marked. End the graph at the right end of the horizontal axis.

4 Why do you think this line graph is called a **frequency polygon**?

EXAMPLE 2 Reading a Frequency Polygon

The Williams Company keeps a record of gas mileage for their fleet of company cars. The data are shown on a frequency polygon.

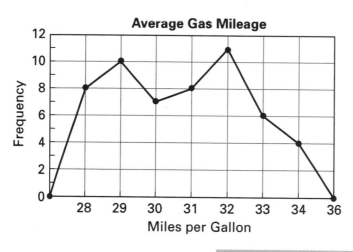

a. How many cars average 33 miles per gallon (mpg)?

b. How many cars average less than 30 miles per gallon?

c. How many cars are in the Williams Company fleet?

d. What is the mode of the gas mileage data?

SOLUTION

a. Six cars average 33 mpg.

b. Eighteen cars average less than 30 mpg.

c. There are 54 cars in the fleet.

d. The mode is 32 mpg.

Critical Thinking How can you estimate the mean of a data set if you are given a frequency polygon similar to the one in Example 2?

USING THE FOUR-STEP PLAN

You are a nurse in a hospital's neonatal care unit. You are caring for a premature baby who must be fed by a nasal-gastric tube—a tube through the baby's nose into his stomach. Doctor's orders are to gradually reduce feeding through the tube until the baby is fed only by mouth.

You feed the baby a total of 780 cubic centimeters (cc) of formula per day. At each feeding, you feed the baby as much as he will take by mouth, and the remainder by tube. You record the amount fed for the first five days on a spreadsheet.

	A	B	C	D	E	F	G
1	Time	Fed By	Day 1	Day 2	Day 3	Day 4	Day 5
2	Morning	Tube	115 cc	100 cc	55 cc		
3		Mouth	15 cc	30 cc	45 cc	45 cc	75 cc
4	Mid-morning	Tube	100 cc	70 cc	120 cc		
5		Mouth	30 cc	60 cc	10 cc	75 cc	110 cc
6	Noon	Tube	85 cc	100 cc	115 cc	140 cc	75 cc
7		Mouth	45 cc	30 cc	45 cc		
8	Afternoon	Tube	120 cc	85 cc	100 cc		
9		Mouth	10 cc	45 cc	30 cc	30 cc	60 cc
10	Evening	Tube	100 cc	55 cc	100 cc		
11		Mouth	30 cc	75 cc	30 cc	75 cc	100 cc
12	Night	Tube	110 cc	115 cc	115 cc	415 cc	360 cc
13		Mouth	20 cc	15 cc	15 cc		

The doctor wants to see the data to determine if feeding by mouth is succeeding. She also wants your estimate of the number of days until the feeding tube can be removed.

Step 1 Understand the Problem
What questions must be answered for the doctor? What must happen before the feeding tube can be removed?

Step 2 Develop a Plan
Problem-solving strategy: Use a graph. How can you display the data? What type of graph can you use?

Step 3 Carry Out the Plan
Create the graph. Write answers to the Step 1 questions.

Step 4 Check the Results
Does the graph support your answers? Are they reasonable?

LESSON ASSESSMENT

1 When drawing a line graph, how do you determine the scale to use on an axis?

2 What is extrapolation?

3 How is a frequency polygon constructed?

The district water authority keeps a weekly record of the depth of a reservoir.

4. Use the following 8-week record to construct a line graph.

5. Is the 8-week trend in the water depth increasing, decreasing, or remaining constant?

6. Make a reasonable prediction of the water depth on week 9.

Week	Water Depth (ft)
1	16.5
2	18
3	17
4	18.5
5	20
6	19
7	18
8	19.5

Use the graph to complete Exercises 7–13.

7. What does the graph display?

8. What does the vertical scale represent? What does 20 on the vertical scale represent?

9. Why is there a break in one axis and not the other?

10. In which year did the profit decrease from the previous year?

11. What was the profit in 1999?

12. What was the profit in 2000?

13. If the trend in the profit from 1996–2000 continues, predict the profit in the year 2001.

The In-Line Skate Company experienced a rapid growth in sales. As a result, inventory in the warehouse declined. The manufacturing plant increased production and raised inventory to acceptable levels. The graphs of the sales and inventory for this period are shown on a **double-line graph.**

14. What does the scale on the vertical axis represent?

15. Between which two weeks did the highest growth in sales take place?

16. When did the inventory reach its lowest point? During this week, how many units was inventory above sales?

17. Following this low point, how many weeks did it take for the inventory to return to a level of nearly 200 units above the number sold per week?

18. Suppose the trend between week 5 and week 8 continued for both sales and inventory. Predict what week the inventory would drop below the number of sales.

A survey was taken to find out how much families spend for a meal at a restaurant. Use the survey responses to complete Exercises 19–21.

$59 $50 $57 $47 $56 $52 $60 $43

$49 $51 $57 $40 $45 $56 $55 $60

$57 $53 $46 $54 $48 $52 $50 $50

19. Find the mean, median, and mode for the data.

20. Construct a frequency table for the data collected. Use intervals of $40–$42, $43–$45, and so on.

21. Construct a frequency polygon for the data in the table. Title your graph and label the axes.

Use the following double-line graph to complete Exercises 22–29.

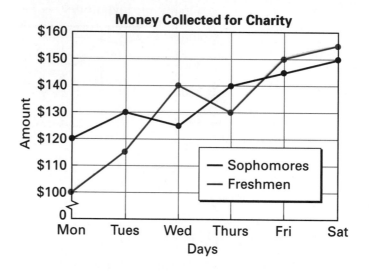

22. On which days did the sophomore class collect more money than the freshmen?

23. On which days did the sophomores collect more than $130?

24. On which days did the freshmen class collect more than $130?

25. Which class collected the most money on Wednesday? How much did they collect?

26. What is the median of the amount collected by the freshmen class?

27. Does either classes' collection have a mode? Explain your reasoning.

28. What is the median of the amount collected by the sophomore class?

29. If the trends in collections continue, predict the Sunday collections for both classes.

Use the following table to complete Exercises 30–33.

River	Length in Miles
Amur	2744
Mississippi	2340
Congo	2718
Volga	2290
Niger	2590
Madeira	2013
Parana	2485
Missouri	2315

30. List the rivers in order from longest to shortest.

31. Find the difference in length between the longest and shortest rivers.

32. Find the average length of the eight rivers.

33. Find the median length of the rivers.

LESSON 2.7 MISUSES OF STATISTICS

OBJECTIVES

➤ Analyze data and graphs.
➤ Determine misleading graphs.
➤ Determine misleading measures of center.

People sometimes use graphs and statistics to persuade others to see things in certain ways. For example, a mayor running for reelection claims the city's median family income has increased dramatically during her first 4-year term. Her opponent claims the increase has not been significant.

ACTIVITY 1   Using Graphs to Persuade

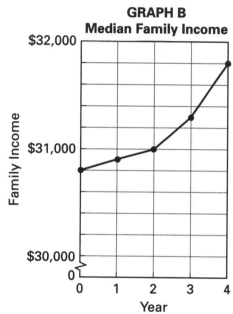

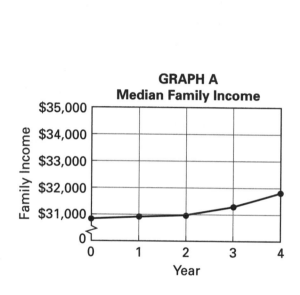

1 What is different about the two graph's axes? What is the same?

2 Do both graphs display the same data?

3 What effect does the difference in the vertical scales have on the appearance of the two graphs.

4 Which graph would the mayor use to support her argument? Which graph would her opponent use?

ACTIVITY 2   Analyzing Graphs

Sal's Pizza Palace claims a slice of its pepperoni pizza contains much less fat than its competitor's. Sal's uses a bar graph to support their claim.

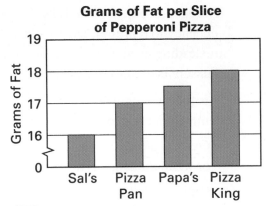

Grams of Fat per Slice of Pepperoni Pizza

1 How do you know there is a gap in the vertical scale of the graph?

2 Which of the four pizzas contains the least amount of fat per slice?

3 The length of the bar for Sal's is one-half the length of the bar for Pizza Pan. Is the fat content per slice of Sal's pizza one-half that of Pizza Pan's? Explain your answer.

4 Is the graph misleading? Explain.

ONGOING ASSESSMENT

Redraw the bar graph in Activity 2 to support the claim that there is little difference in the number of grams of fat in the four pizzas.

ACTIVITY 3 **Analyzing Data**

The price of a sport utility vehicle is listed in a newspaper advertisement. Off-roader's Car Barn has 10 Megamite sport utility vehicles in stock. The prices are shown on the computer printout below.

Off-roader's Car Barn Slashes Prices
NEW Megamites

STK#165412

$19,100

MMSV Stock Number	Price
165412	$19,100
031411	$25,500
021654	$25,500
154005	$25,500
054184	$25,500
165005	$27,200
135498	$27,200
065403	$27,200
846518	$28,500
065874	$28,500

1 Is $19,100 a good representation of the prices of Megamite sport utility vehicles at Off-roader's Car Barn?

2 Does the mean, median, or mode best represent the prices?

3 What is a better representation of the prices?

The advertisement in Activity 3 does not use a measure of central tendency to represent the price data. However, statistics can be misleading even with a measure of central tendency, if the *wrong* measure is used to represent the data set.

The following guidelines can help you choose the best measure of central tendency to use in many situations.

- Outliers affect the mean. Use the mean when there are no outliers or when the range is not great.

- Outliers have little effect on the median. Use the median when there are outliers and when the range is great.

- When there are many repeated data values, the mode usually best represents the data.

EXAMPLE Misleading Measures of Central Tendency

Why are the following conclusions misleading? What would be a better measure of central tendency to use in each case?

a. A hospital patient's temperature is recorded every 2 hours.

98.4°F   98.6°F   98.6°F   98.7°F   102.2°F

Conclusion: Since the mean is 99.3, the patient's typical temperature is 99.3°F.

b. A band director records the sizes of band uniforms.

Size	Number of Uniforms Needed
Extra Small	6
Small	6
Medium	4
Large	10
Extra Large	4

Conclusion: Since the median size is medium, the typical band member is a size medium.

SOLUTION

a. The temperature data contains an outlier. In this case, the median value 98.6°F is a better representation of a typical temperature.

b. Most band members need a size large. In this case, the mode is a better representation of the data.

CULTURAL CONNECTION

Counting large numbers of people requires a number system that allows you to deal with a lot of data. The earliest known census of people and animals was taken by the Babylonians as early as 3800 BCE.

The Egyptians and the Romans also took an annual census. The Egyptians used a number system that involved pictographs. The Romans used the more familiar Roman numerals to record numbers. In the tables below, the symbols used in the Egyptian and Roman systems are compared to our current Arabic numerals used today.

1. Work in pairs or small groups to take a census of a group in your school. Use either Egyptian or Roman numerals to record your census.

2. Take a census of another group using Arabic numerals.

3. Compare the number systems you used. Which is easier to use? What made it easier? What are the advantages and disadvantages of each system?

Arabic	Egyptian Numeric Notation
1	│
10	∩
100	℮
1000	𐦀
10,000	∕
100,000	🐊
1,000,000	👤

Some examples of Egyptian numbers:

🐊 ///// ℮℮ ∩∩ || = 130,434
        ℮℮ ∩∩ ||

𐦀𐦀 ℮ ∩∩ |||| = 2,328
        ℮ ||||

Arabic	Roman Numeric Notation
1	I
5	V
10	X
50	L
100	C
500	D
1000	M

A letter placed after one of equal or greater value adds its value:
II = 2 and LX = 60.

A letter placed before one of greater value subtracts its value:
IV = 4, XL = 40, and CD = 400.

A bar over the letter indicates "multiply by 1000": $\overline{X}$ = 10,000

LESSON ASSESSMENT

Think and Discuss

1 What are some of the ways data can mislead an individual who is viewing a bar graph?

2 How can a line graph be used in an advertisement to mislead the reader?

Practice and Apply

Use Graphs A and B to complete Exercises 3–6.

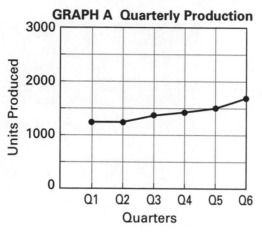

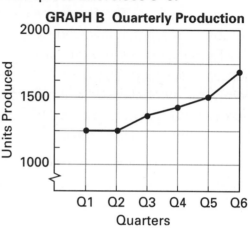

3. Is the trend increasing or decreasing?

4. Do both graphs display the same data?

5. Which graph is misleading? Explain why.

6. Why is Graph B better than Graph A for a presentation?

Tell whether the mean, median, or mode best summarizes each of the following data sets.

7. Grade point averages:

3.95   3.91   3.65
3.50   3.29   3.14

8.

New Home Prices
$ 62,000
$ 71,000
$ 83,000
$ 92,000
$ 97,000
$193,000

9.

Song Lengths on a CD	
Minutes : Seconds	Frequency
1 – 1:59	3
2 – 2:59	5
3 – 3:59	8
4 – 4:59	4
5 – 5:59	2

Find an example of a graph in a newspaper or magazine that might be misleading. Use it to complete Exercises 10–11.

10. Explain why the graph is misleading.

11. How can you reconstruct the graph so that it is not misleading?

Gather data from a newspaper, magazine, or the Internet. Use the data to complete Exercises 12–14.

12. Construct a bar graph that makes the data appear to vary widely.

13. Construct a line graph that makes the data appear to show little variation.

14. For each graph, write a statement that someone might support with the graph.

The monthly snowfall at a mountain resort follows. Use the data to complete Exercises 15–16.

Nov: 23 in.   Dec: 28 in.   Jan: 25 in.   Feb: 26 in.

15. Construct a misleading bar graph that shows there is one month with an exceptionally large amount of snowfall.

16. Construct a bar graph that shows the snowfall is fairly consistent.

Mixed Review

17. Round 56.894 to the nearest tenth.

18. Round 134,568 to the nearest thousand.

19. Round $215.87 to the nearest ten dollars.

20. Find the value of $3x - 4y$ when $x = 12$ and $y = 3$.

21. Find the value of $2ab + (b + c) \div 3$ when $a = 0$, $b = 7$, and $c = 5$.

Let $m = 25$, $x = 7$, $y = 8$, and $z = 5$. Use these values to complete Exercises 22–23.

22. Find the value of $mx + my - mz$.

23. Find the value of $m(x + y - z)$.

24. How do the answers for Exercises 22 and 23 compare? What property is demonstrated?

25. Shirts are on sale for $18.25. Jeans are on sale for $25.95. Estimate the cost of 5 shirts and 3 pairs of jeans.

26. Miguel is vacationing in Washington, D.C. He plans to visit the Washington Monument (W), the Lincoln Memorial (L), and the Jefferson Memorial (J). In how many different orders can he visit these sites? List the orders.

Cumulative Problem Solving

The graphs below show the average yards per carry for the six leading rushers in the conference at the end of the football season.

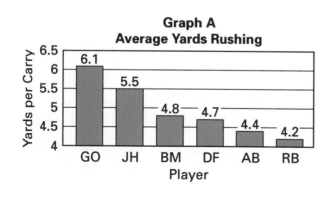

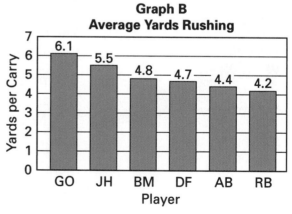

Explain your answers for Exercises 27–29.

27. Which graph would Gary Outlaw's (GO) coach use to persuade the sports writers to select Gary for the All-Conference team?

28. Which graph would Billy Motkin's (BM) coach use to persuade the sports writers to vote for Billy?

29. Is either graph incorrect? How could someone use Graph A to mislead sportswriters?

You are the Director of Sales for a company that markets video games. The president of the company asks, "How much did She-Boom sales decline from January to December last year?" To help you answer the president's question, one of your sales associates produces Graph A. Another produces Graph B.

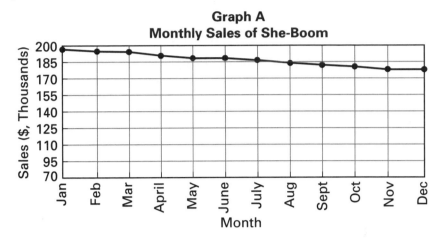

Graph A
Monthly Sales of She-Boom

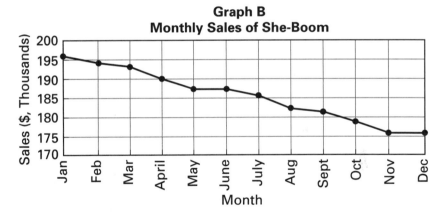

Graph B
Monthly Sales of She-Boom

30. Do both graphs display the same data? How are the graphs different?

31. Describe the trend in sales over the last year.

32. How would you answer the president's question? Which graph is easier to use to find the answer?

33. To reduce inventory, you will reduce the price of She-Boom when sales drop below $170,000 per month. Predict the month in which you will reduce the price.

34. Is either graph misleading? Explain your answer.

Colorado has 54 mountain peaks over 14,000 feet (4267 meters) high. Julia is attempting to climb all of them before she graduates from high school. She keeps a tally of the number of peaks she has climbed and their altitudes on a histogram.

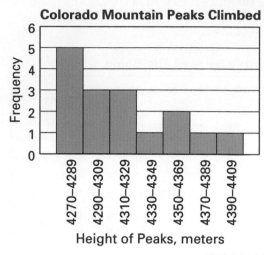

Colorado Mountain Peaks Climbed

35. How many peaks over 14,000 feet has Julia climbed?

36. In which interval is the altitude of the tallest peak she has climbed?

37. The altitudes of the peaks of most mountains Julia has climbed lies within what interval?

38. The mean altitude of the mountain peaks Julia has climbed cannot be exactly determined from the histogram. But the mean can be estimated. Explain how.

Yokio is planning a January trip to Sydney, Australia. He uses the graph below to help select clothing for the trip.

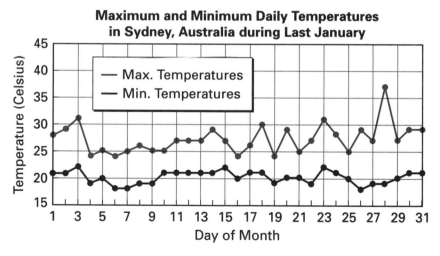

Maximum and Minimum Daily Temperatures in Sydney, Australia during Last January

39. What was the highest maximum temperature recorded in Sydney last January?

40. What was the range of the minimum temperatures last January?

41. For what temperature high and low should Yokio plan?

MATH LAB

Equipment   Unshelled pecans, peanuts, green
                beans, or other objects, 1 per student
                Centimeter ruler
                Graph paper

Problem Statement

Manufactured products have some variations in size, though
the variations are usually small. Objects in nature also vary in
size but to a greater degree than manufactured objects. In
agriculture, statistics of the sizes of produce are important.
Statistics are used to design equipment and packaging and to
set produce prices.

In this lab, you will measure the lengths of unshelled pecans
(or peanuts, green beans, or other produce items supplied by
your teacher). You will use several graphs to show the
variation in length for the pecans.

Procedure

a   Each group member should measure the length of at least
one pecan. Record each measurement to the nearest
millimeter.

b   Record your group's data on the board. Use the class-
combined data for the remainder of the activity.

c   Construct a stem-and-leaf plot from the data.

d   What is the second quartile, Q_2? What is the first quartile,
Q_1? What is the third quartile, Q_3?

e   Construct a box-and-whisker plot from the data.

f   What is the range of the data? Use the range to divide the
data into five to eight equal-sized intervals. Make a frequency
table for the data.

g   Construct a histogram from the frequency table.

Discussion Questions

1. What is the length of most pecans measured by your class? Which plot did you use to find this length?

2. Between what two lengths are the middle 50 percent of the pecans measured by your class? Which plot did you use?

Activity 2: Spreadsheet Statistics Calculations

Equipment Spreadsheet computer program
Stop watch or a watch that measures seconds

Problem Statement

You will use a spreadsheet program to record data values and calculate measures of central tendency.

Your spreadsheet program may not have the same function names as those used in these instructions. If so, your teacher will supply the correct names to use as replacements.

Procedure

a Designate a timer for the group. Each group member will estimate a one-minute time period, without the use of a watch or clock. The timer will say "start" and start the watch. The person being timed will say "stop" when they think exactly one minute has passed. The timer will record the actual amount of time elapsed to the nearest second. When everyone in the group has been timed, another group member should time the timer.

b In cell A1 of the spreadsheet program, enter the label *Time, sec.* List the data values from your group in column A, beginning in cell A2. An example for a group of five follows.

$$= A2 + A3 + A4 + A5 + A6$$

	A	B	C
1	**Time, sec**		
2	48		
3	68		
4	53	Grp Sum	
5	81	Grp Mean	
6	64		

$$= C4/5$$

c Enter the label *Grp Sum* in cell B4. In cell C4, enter a formula to add the data values for your group. In a spreadsheet, formulas are preceded by an = sign, and can perform operations on values in cells. For the example above, the following formula is entered in cell C4:

$$= A2 + A3 + A4 + A5 + A6$$

After you enter the formula, the result of the calculation, not the formula, is displayed in the cell. Where is the formula displayed?

d Enter the label *Grp Mean* in cell B5. In cell C5, enter a formula to calculate the mean of your group's data. The mean is the sum displayed in cell C4 divided by the number of data values. For the example above, the formula is =C4/5. The symbol / means to divide.

e Enter the data for the rest of your class in column A beginning with the first cell after your group's data. If there are 25 students in your class, you should have data values in cells A2 through A26.

f Enter the label *Class Mean* in cell B24. In cell C24, enter a formula to calculate the mean of your class's data. This time use the built-in spreadsheet function for calculating the mean or average. This function is called AVERAGE or AVG. After the function name, enter the range of cells containing the data, enclosed by parentheses and separated by a colon. For example, if there are 25 students in the class, enter the following in cell C24:

$$= AVERAGE (A2:A26) \quad or \quad = AVG(A2:A26).$$

g In cell B25 enter the label *Min*, and in cell B26 enter the label *Max*. In cell C25 enter the function =MIN(A2:A26) and in cell C26 enter=MAX(A2:A26). These spreadsheet functions find the minimum and maximum values of the specified data set.

h In cell B27 enter the label *Median*, and in cell B28 enter the label *Mode*. In cells C27 and C28, enter

$$= MEDIAN(A2:A26) \quad and \quad = MODE(A2:A26)$$

These spreadsheet functions find the median and mode of the specified data set.

i Print your spreadsheet.

j Change a data value in the data set by clicking on a cell containing a value and entering a different number. Change several data values. How does the spreadsheet respond?

Discussion Questions

1. What are the advantages of using a spreadsheet instead of calculating measures of central tendency by hand?

2. What are the advantages of using the functions built into the spreadsheet?

Activity 3: Graphing Height and Arm Span

Equipment	Metric tape measure
	Graph paper
	Straightedge

Problem Statement

You will measure the height and arm span of each member of your group. You will plot the data for your group and the rest of the class. Then you will use the plot to predict the arm span of your teacher.

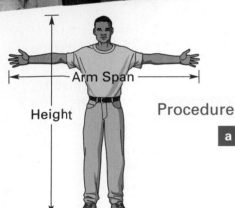

Procedure

a Make a data table similar to the one below to record your group's data.

Height (cm)	Arm Span (cm)

b Measure each group member's height and arm span. Record each pair of measurements in the table. Each row in the data table contains an **ordered pair** of measurements. The ordered pairs can be written as (height, arm span).

c Draw horizontal and vertical axes on a sheet of graph paper. Use *Height in Centimeters* for the horizontal axis and *Arm Span in Centimeters* as the vertical axis. Neither axis will start at zero. Choose beginning scale values less than the minimum data values and convenient intervals for the scales. Make sure the axes are long enough for the range of your data. An example is shown below. Adjust the length and scale intervals of the axes for your data.

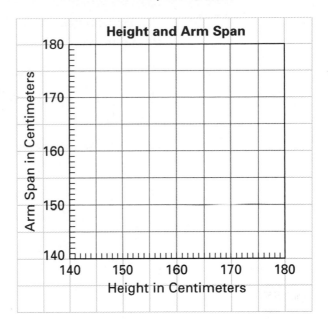

d Plot the ordered pairs from your group on the axis system. Combine your data with the other groups, and plot the ordered pairs for the entire class.

e You have constructed a **scatter plot**. Each point on the scatter plot represents an ordered pair. Is there a trend in the scatter plot? If so, describe the trend.

f Use the straightedge to draw a single straight line through the points. If you cannot draw a straight line that contains all the points, draw the line so there are as many points above the line as below it. This line is called a **fitted line**.

g Measure your teacher's height. Use the fitted line to estimate your teacher's arm span. Measure his or her arm span, and compare your estimate to the measurement.

Discussion Questions

1. Compare your group's fitted line to other groups. Did everyone draw exactly the same line to fit the data points? Explain why or why not.

2. Explain how to use the fitted line to predict someone's height if you know their arm span.

CHAPTER 2   ASSESSMENT

Communicate

1. Explain how to find three measures of central tendency for a set of data.

2. How do you create a frequency table?

3. Which measures of central tendency can be read directly from a line plot and a stem-and-leaf plot?

4. List the steps required to construct a histogram from a frequency table.

5. How do you find the first, second, and third quartiles from a box-and-whisker plot?

6. What are some ways people misuse statistics?

Skills

Use the following set of data to complete Exercises 7–9.

38 32 36 39 31 32 37

7. Find the range of the data.

8. Find the mean, median, and mode of the data.

9. Suppose the data represents the number of hours you work each week during the summer. Which measure of central tendency would you use to convince your friends that you worked many hours during the week?

Use the bar graph to complete Exercises 10–12.

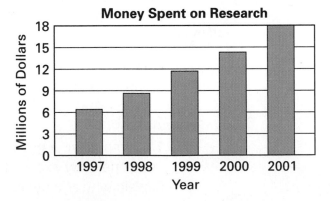

About how much money was spent on research
10. in 1999?   **11.** in 2000?   **12.** over the 5 years?

The data listed on the racecar shows the miles per gallon for 13 different automobiles. Use the data to complete Exercises 13–16.

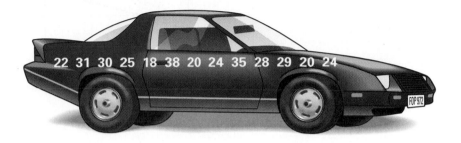

22 31 30 25 18 38 20 24 35 28 29 20 24

13. Construct a stem-and-leaf plot.

14. Construct a box-and-whisker plot.

15. Construct a frequency table using intervals of 18–21, 22–25, and so on.

16. Use the frequency table in Exercise 15 to construct a histogram.

17. Which of the plots in Exercises 13–16 can be used to find the mean of the data given? the median? the mode? the range?

The stem-and-leaf plots below shows the kilometers recorded for a charity bike-a-thon.

Bike-a-thon, km	
15	3 6 7 9 9 9
16	1 1 2 3 5 5
17	0 2 2 4
18	4 5 8 9

Key: 18|5 means 18.5

18. How many people participated in the bike-a-thon?

19. How many of the participants rode more than 17 kilometers?

20. Find the mean, median, mode, and range of the data.

Graph A and Graph B show two different pictures of an employee's expenses for four months. Use the graphs to complete Exercises 21–23.

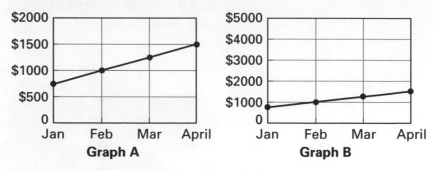

Graph A

Graph B

21. What is the difference in the two graphs?

22. How are the graphs alike?

23. Which graph would someone use to support each of the following arguments?

a. Expenses have only reached $1500 and are not excessive.

b. Expenses have doubled in only three months and must be carefully controlled.

24. This chart shows Standardized Test scores of the students in Ms. Morris' fifth period math class.

82	115	92	103	103	112	90	92
79	87	104	128	110	101	104	93
99	104	109	107	93	105	98	

Construct a frequency table displaying the data using intervals of 70-79, 80-89, and so on.

Math Lab

25. A spreadsheet contains the data shown.

	A	B	C	D
1				
2		51		
3		49		
4		60		
5		56		
6				

You enter in cell C5:   =B2 + B3 + B4 + B5

You enter in cell C6:   =C5/4

What is displayed in cell C5? In cell C6? What measure of central tendency is displayed in cell C6?

26. Use the data in the scatter plot to estimate the height of someone whose arm span is 155 centimeters.

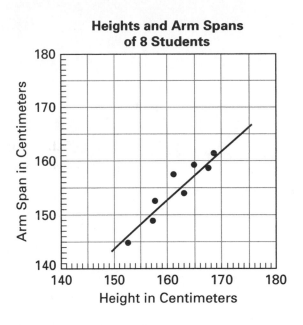

Heights and Arm Spans of 8 Students

27. A manufacturing plant produces automobile brake rotors with three diameters:

Model I	Diameter = 8.125 inches
Model II	Diameter = 8.625 inches
Model III	Diameter = 8.875 inches

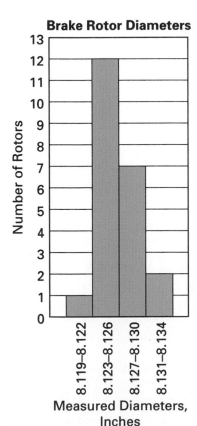

Brake Rotor Diameters

During a production run, a quality control technician measures rotor diameters and constructs the histogram at the left from the data.

Which model is being manufactured in the production run?

CHAPTER 3

WHY SHOULD I LEARN THIS?

You need to use integers to represent quantities that can be positive, negative, or zero. For example, in a hot air balloon race a pilot uses integers to predict the temperatures at various altitudes.

Contents: Integers

INTEGERS

LEARN HOW TO...

1. **Graph positive and negative integers on a number line.**
2. **Find the opposite and absolute value of an integer.**
3. **Model addition and subtraction with vectors on a number line.**
4. **Use positive and negative integers to solve problems involving addition, subtraction, multiplication, and/or division.**

In Chapters 1 and 2, you solved problems that used whole numbers. Whole numbers are members of the set {0, 1, 2, 3, 4, . . .}. You can use whole numbers to show distance, like altitude above the ground. But, suppose you are flying a hot air balloon whose altitude *changes* by 50 feet. The whole number 50 tells you the amount of change but it does not tell you whether you rose or descended 50 feet.

In this chapter, you will work with integers. The set of integers includes the whole numbers and their opposites: {. . ., –4, –3, –2, –1, 0, 1, 2, 3, 4, . . .}. To show that your balloon rises 50 feet, you can use a positive number such as +50. To show that your balloon descends 50 feet, you can use a negative number such as −50.

You will solve addition, subtraction, multiplication, and division equations with positive and negative integers. You will also solve application problems with integers, such as: the amount of money in a bank account, the number of yards gained or lost in a football game, and the amount of electrical current from a battery.

LESSON 3.1 GRAPHING INTEGERS

OBJECTIVES
- Use integers and a number line to solve problems.
- Simplify absolute value expressions.

Marta changes engine coolant in her car every two years. The coolant is a mixture of antifreeze and water. It protects the engine from overheating when Marta drives the car. The antifreeze prevents the coolant from freezing during cold weather.

If Marta wants to prevent the coolant from freezing at a temperature of 30 degrees below zero Fahrenheit, what mixture of antifreeze and water should she use?

You can write 30 degrees below zero as $-30°F$. The mark in front of 30 is a called a **negative sign**.

-30 is read *negative thirty*.

You can write 30 degrees above zero as either $+30$ or 30. The mark in front of 30 is a called a **positive sign**.

$+30$ is read *positive thirty*.

30 is read *positive thirty* or *thirty*.

ACTIVITY 1   Data Containing Negative Values

This bar graph shows the freezing points of five antifreeze-water mixtures. A mixture of 0% is pure water. A mixture of 100% is pure antifreeze.

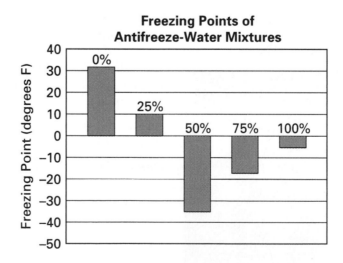

Freezing Points of Antifreeze-Water Mixtures

1. What is the freezing point of pure water?

2. Which mixtures have freezing points below zero?

3 Which mixtures have freezing points above zero?

4 What is the freezing point of pure antifreeze?

5 Which mixtures should Marta use to prevent the coolant from freezing at −30°F?

The set

$$\{\ldots -5, -4, -3, -2, -1, 0, 1, 2, 3, 4, 5, \ldots\}$$

is called the set of **integers.**

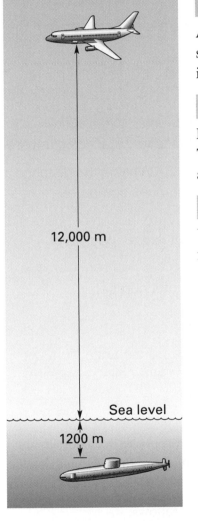

12,000 m

Sea level

1200 m

EXAMPLE 1 Using Integers

An airliner flies at an altitude of 12,000 meters above sea level. A submarine cruises at a depth of 1200 meters below sea level. Use integers to represent the altitude and depth.

SOLUTION

Let zero represent sea level. Let altitude be a positive quantity. Then the airliner flies at 12,000 meters and the submarine cruises at −1200 meters.

ONGOING ASSESSMENT

Use positive and negative integers to represent each of the following quantities.

a. Ten seconds before lift-off and twelve seconds after lift-off.

b.  A deposit of $350 and a withdrawal of $48.

c. A loss of 4 yards and a gain of 8 yards.

d. Walk down 6 stairs and climb 9 stairs.

e. A tax hike of 5% and a tax reduction of 2%.

In Chapter 1, you located numbers as points on a number line. On a horizontal number line, negative integers are to the left of zero, and positive integers are to the right of zero.

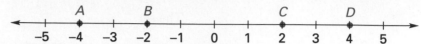

Four points, *A* through *D*, are graphed on the number line. The numbers represented by the points are called the **coordinates** of the points.

1 Which points are positive? What are the coordinates of these points?

2 Which points are negative? What are the coordinates of these points?

3 The distance from zero to *A* is four units. What is the distance from zero to *D*? How do these distances compare?

4 What is the distance from zero to *B*? What is the distance from zero to *C*? How do these distances compare?

5 Numbers the same distance from zero, but on opposite sides of zero are called **opposites**. What is the opposite of 4? What is the opposite of −2?

6 How would you find the opposite of a number *n*?

> **Opposites**
> Two numbers that are the same distance from zero, but on opposite sides of zero, are called opposites. The opposite of zero is zero.

A negative sign is used to indicate the opposite of a number. For example, you can write a negative sign in front of 2 to indicate its opposite −2.

The opposite of −4 can be written as follows.

$$-(-4) = 4$$

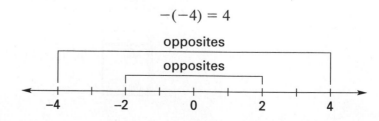

EXAMPLE 2 Finding Opposites

Find the opposite of

a. -6 **b.** 7 **c.** 0

SOLUTION

a. The opposite of -6 is 6. That is, $-(-6) = 6$.

b. The opposite of 7 is -7. That is, $-(7) = -7$.

c. The opposite of 0 is 0. That is, $-(0) = 0$.

Critical Thinking   Inside and outside are opposites. Suppose positive integers are inside and negative integers are outside. Every inside integer has an opposite outside integer. Is zero inside or outside?

On a number line, the distance from a number to zero is called the **absolute value** of the number. Since distance is a positive quantity, the absolute value of a number is never negative. For example, -4 is four units from zero. Thus, the absolute value of -4 is 4. Vertical bars $|\,\,|$ are used to represent absolute value.

$$|-4| = 4 \qquad\qquad |4| = 4$$

Absolute Value
The absolute value of a number is the distance the number is from zero on the number line.

EXAMPLE 3 Absolute Value

Simplify.

a. $|-15|$ **b.** $|14 - 6|$ **c.** $|-(15 - 9)|$

SOLUTION

a. $|-15| = 15$

b. $|14 - 6| = |8| = 8$

c. $|-(15 - 9)| = |-(6)| = |-6| = 6$

ONGOING ASSESSMENT

Simplify.

a. $|21|$ **b.** $|-(35 - 15)|$ **c.** $|16 - 16|$

LESSON ASSESSMENT

1 How can integers be used to describe

  a. a change in someone's weight?

  b. a change in the price of an airline ticket?

  c. the number of students who add or drop a class?

2 How do you write two integers that are opposites?

3 Two opposites, x and $-x$, are graphed on a number line. Write an expression for the distance between the two coordinates.

4 Can the absolute value of a number be negative? Explain your reasoning.

Practice and Apply

Write an integer to represent each situation described in Exercises 5–12.

  5. Meiko is 3 points ahead of Miriam.

  6. Renee's check register shows a $10 deposit.

  7. It is 7 degrees below zero.

  8. The linebacker returned the fumble 4 yards.

  9. The baby has grown 8 inches.

  10. The jet has lost 1000 feet in altitude.

  11. Tisha withdrew 55 dollars from her savings account.

12. The opposite of falling 20 centimeters.

Write the opposite of each of the following.

13. 18   **14.** −7   **15.** (12 − 8)

16. −1   **17.** 0   **18.** −(21 − 19)

Simplify.

19. $|23|$ **20.** $|-38|$ **21.** $|35-16|$

22. $|-28|$ **23.** $|2-2|$ **24.** $|-(17-8)|$

25. During one month, Camisha made the following deposits and withdrawals from her checking account.

		PLEASE BE SURE TO DEDU				PLY TO YOUR ACCOUNT	
NUMBER	DATE	CHECKS ISSUED TO OR DESCRIPTION OF DEPOSIT	(−) WITHDRAWAL		(+) DEPOSIT		BALANCE
	11/1	Deposit			38	00	
	11/8	Deposit			47	00	
1701	11/12	Super market	22	00			
	11/20	Deposit			30	00	
1702	11/25	Animal Hospital	42	00			
	11/30	Deposit			36	00	

Use the data to construct a bar graph showing each deposit and withdrawal.

Mixed Review

Monthly Cost of Gasoline

2	4 6 6 7 9
3	4 5 6 8 8 8
4	0 1 2 6 8
5	0 1 3

Key: 3|4 means $34.00

Premium   Regular

Use < or > to complete Exercises 26–28.

26. 27 _?_ 30   **27.** 0.03 _?_ 0.004   **28.** 6.54 _?_ 6.455

Use the stem-and-leaf plot at the left to complete Exercises 29–36.

29. What is the place value of the stems?

30. What is the place value of the leaves?

31. What is the range of the data?

32. For how many months did gas cost more than $30?

33. For how many months did gas cost less than $42?

34. What is the median?

35. What is the mode?

36. What is the mean?

LESSON 3.2 INTEGERS AND INEQUALITIES

OBJECTIVES

➤ Compare integers using a number line.
➤ Determine the inequality of expressions including absolute values.

Sean is responsible for publishing a ski area's weather advisory on the Internet. Skiers use the advisory to determine what clothing to wear for the conditions at the ski area.

Wind chill is a key factor in the advisory. Wind causes people to feel colder than the actual air temperature. For example, on a day the temperature is 10°F and the wind is blowing 20 miles per hour, the wind chill is −24°F. A person skiing on this day feels as if the temperature is 24°F below zero.

At the ski area, weather conditions are monitored at five locations. The wind speed, temperature, and wind chill are shown below. If Sean reports the lowest wind chill in the weather advisory, which value should he use?

Location	Wind, mph	Temperature, °F	Wind Chill, °F
Lift 1	10	15	−3
Lift 4	15	25	2
Lift 8	22	20	−10
Midway	15	17	−8
Powderhaus	10	23	7

Recall when two integers are graphed on a horizontal number line, the integer to the right is greater than the integer to the left.

1 Draw a number line showing the integers from −10 through 10.

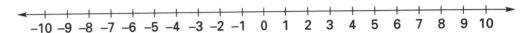

2 Circle the integers corresponding to the wind chills for the five locations shown on the chart from the ski area.

3 Which integer is greater, 2 or 7? Replace the _?_ with an inequality sign to make the following *true*: 2 _?_ 7

4 Which integer is greater, 2 or −3? Replace the _?_ with an inequality sign to make the following *true*: 2 _?_ −3

5 List the integers for wind chills in order from least to greatest. What wind chill should Sean report for the ski area's advisory?

6 Which location would feel the warmest?

ONGOING ASSESSMENT

Replace the ? with an inequality sign to make each of the following *true*. You can use the number line from Activity 1.

a. 4 _?_ 5   **b.** 0 _?_ −2   **c.** −1 _?_ 1

d. −4 _?_ −5   **e.** 0 _?_ 2   **f.** 3 _?_ −3

EXAMPLE Ordering Integers

The wind chill values for a four-day period were recorded as follows:

Monday: −17°F   Tuesday: −13°F

Wednesday: −15°F   Thursday: −16°F

Write the wind chill values in order from least to greatest.

SOLUTION

Graph the wind chill values on a number line.

$$\xleftarrow{\quad} \overset{\bullet}{-19} \quad -18 \quad \overset{\bullet}{-17} \quad \overset{\bullet}{-16} \quad \overset{\bullet}{-15} \quad -14 \quad \overset{\bullet}{-13} \quad -12 \xrightarrow{\quad}$$

List the integers as they appear from left to right.

$$-17, -16, -15, -13$$

In Lesson 3.1, you learned:

- The absolute value of a number is the distance the number is from zero on a number line.

- Two numbers that are opposites are the same distance from zero.

Therefore, the absolute values of two opposites are equal. For example,

$$|-1| = |1| \quad \text{and} \quad |3| = |-3|$$

In general, if m is any number, $|m| = |-m|$.

How do you compare the absolute value of two numbers that are not opposites?

ACTIVITY 2   Comparing Absolute Values

A traffic management system uses radar to determine the location of cars. The system's computer assigns negative coordinates to cars that are approaching the radar and positive coordinates to cars going away from the radar.

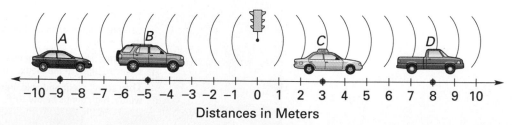

Distances in Meters

1 The locations of four cars are graphed on the number line at *A*, *B*, *C*, and *D*. Which is farther from zero, *A* or *D*? Replace the ? with an inequality sign to make the following *true*: $|-9|$ _?_ $|8|$

2 Which is farther from zero, *C* or *B*? Replace the ? with an inequality sign to make the following *true*: $|3|$ _?_ $|-5|$

3 List the absolute values in order from least to greatest.

$$|-9|, \quad |-5|, \quad |3|, \quad |8|$$

ONGOING ASSESSMENT

Replace the ? with an inequality or equal sign to make each of the following *true*.

a. $|5|$ _?_ $|4|$

b. $|2|$ _?_ $|-2|$

c. $|-5|$ _?_ $|4|$

d. $|-2|$ _?_ $|0|$

Critical Thinking   Is the following statement *true* or *false*? Explain your reasoning.

If $|a| > |b|$, then the absolute value of the opposite of *a* is greater than the absolute value of the opposite of *b*.

LESSON ASSESSMENT

Think and Discuss

1 Explain how integers are ordered on a number line.

2 Suppose *p*, *q*, and *r* are integers. If $p < q$ and $q < r$, what is the relationship between *p* and *r*? Explain your answer.

3 You are given that $|m| = |n|$. Can you conclude that $m = n$? Explain your answer.

Practice and Apply

Write <, >, or = to make a *true* statement.

4. 8 _?_ 15

5. $|-8|$ _?_ -4

6. 0 _?_ -6

7. -9 _?_ -7

8. $-(-3)$ _?_ -3

9. $5 + 3$ _?_ $14 - 9$

10. $|8|$ _?_ $|-8|$

11. $-(9 - 4)$ _?_ -5

12. $-|8 + 2|$ __?__ -6 **13.** $|12|$ __?__ $|-5|$

14. -26 __?__ $-(-26)$ **15.** $|18 - 18|$ __?__ -18

Write each set of numbers in order from least to greatest.
16. $-4, |2|, -1, |-3|, 0$ **17.** $2, -5, 8, -6, -3, 4$

18. List the locations on this elevation chart from the highest elevation to the lowest elevation.

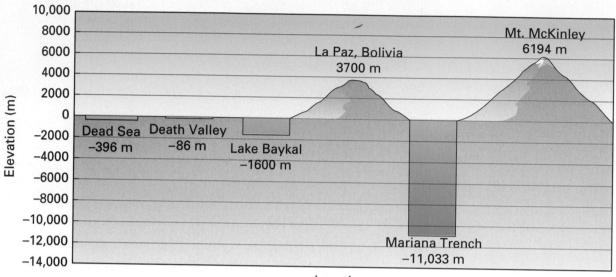

19. Write an inequality that compares the temperatures of Detroit and Peoria.

City	Temperature
Anchorage	5° F
Detroit	15° F
Madison	−5° F
Peoria	10° F
Wichita	−10° F

20. Write an inequality that compares the temperatures of Anchorage and Wichita.

21. Write an inequality that compares the temperatures of Wichita and Madison.

22. List the cities in order from lowest to highest temperature.

Let $x = 5$, $y = 4$, and $z = 2$. Find the value of each expression.

23. $x(y + z)$ **24.** $xz \cdot x + y$ **25.** $x + y \div z$

Estimate each answer. Then use your calculator to find the answer.

26. $234.96 + 118.7$ **27.** $32{,}228 \div 28$

28. $924 \cdot 89$ **29.** $2397.5 - 912.7$

Pamela drives a delivery van from Anders to Sachville to Hernden and back to Anders each day. Use the mileage chart to complete Exercises 30–32.

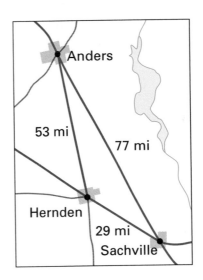

30. Pamela drives the route 5 days each week. How many miles does she drive each week?

31. Pamela's delivery van averages 26 miles per gallon. How many gallons of gas does she use each week?

32. Pamela pays an average of $1.19 per gallon of gas. How much does she spend on gas each week?

For Exercises 33–35, write each number as a decimal.

33. Six hundred three and four tenths.

34. Twelve and seven thousandths.

35. Eighty and eight tenths.

LESSON 3.3 ADDING INTEGERS

OBJECTIVES

- Add integers.
- Identify zero pairs and use to simplify expressions.

You can model integer addition with Algeblocks or unit blocks. You will need a mat like the one shown below and 10 Algeblocks or 10 unit blocks.

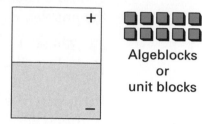

Algeblocks
or
unit blocks

Base mat

The basic mat is divided into two equal parts. The top part is labeled positive and the bottom part negative. Positive and negative integers are modeled by placing blocks on the mat.

Suppose Alicia and Bob use two mats to keep score in a card game. Blocks on the positive side of the mat represent points won in the game. Blocks on the negative side represent points lost.

In the first round of the game, Alicia wins 3 points and Bob loses 2 points. Alicia's score is recorded as $+3$ and Bob's score is recorded as -2.

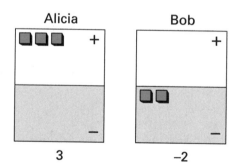

Alicia   Bob

3   -2

ACTIVITY 1   **Using Blocks to Add Integers with Like Signs**

1 Place 3 blocks on the mat to model Alicia's score in round 1. In the second round, Alicia scores 2 points. Add 2 blocks to the positive half of the mat. How many points does Alicia have now? You have used unit blocks to model the equation $3 + 2 = 5$.

2 Place 2 blocks on the mat to model Bob's score in round 1. In the second round, Bob scores -1 point. Add 1 block to the negative part of the mat. How many points does Bob have now? Write the equation modeled by the blocks.

3 Use blocks to model each equation. Find each sum.

a. $3 + 5 = $ __?__

b. $1 + 4 = $ __?__

c. $2 + 2 = $ __?__

d. $-3 + (-5) = $ __?__

e. $-1 + (-4) = $ __?__

f. $-2 + (-2) = $ __?__

4 All the integers in **a**, **b**, and **c** are positive. They have the same sign. All the integers in **d**, **e**, and **f** are negative. They also have the same sign. Explain how to use blocks to add two integers with the same sign.

5 In Step 3 **a** and **d** you found

$$3 + 5 = 8 \quad \text{and} \quad -3 + (-5) = -8$$

Compare the sum of the absolute values of the integers on the left hand side of each equation. Compare the signs of the integers with the sign on the right hand side.

6 Write a rule for adding two integers with the same sign. Test your rule with the other equations from Step 3.

An **algorithm** is a step-by-step procedure for solving a certain type of problem. An algorithm for adding two integers with the same sign is shown below.

> ### Adding Integers with the Same Sign
> To add two integers that have the same sign,
>
> 1. add the absolute values of the integers;
>
> 2. then write the sum with the same sign as the integers.

ONGOING ASSESSMENT

Use the algorithm above to find each sum.

a. $12 + 8$ **b.** $-11 + (-13)$ **c.** $9 + 10$ **d.** $-7 + (-4)$

This mat shows a score of 3 points followed by a score of −3 points. When you add 3 points and take away 3 points the net result is 0. The blocks model the equation 3 + (−3) = 0.

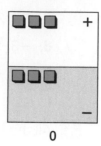

0

1 Use blocks to model each equation. Then find the sum.

a. 2 + (−2) = _?_   **b.** 5 + (−5) = _?_

c. −2 + 2 = _?_   **d.** −5 + 5 = _?_

2 Each equation in Step 1 is a sum of opposites. What is the sum of any two opposites?

The result of Activity 2 demonstrates an important property in algebra.

Addition Property of Opposites
If a and b are opposites, then $a + b = 0$.

If $a + b = 0$, then a and b are opposites. That is, $a = -b$ and $b = -a$.

ACTIVITY 3   Using Zero Pairs to Add Integers with Different Signs

Since the sum of opposites is zero, they are called a **zero pair**. You can add or take away zero pairs without altering the scores shown on the mat.

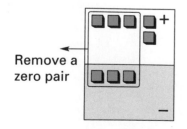

Remove a zero pair

1 Set up a mat to show a round 1 score of 5 and a round 2 score of −3. Since 3 and −3 form a zero pair, you can remove them from the mat without affecting its value. How many blocks are left on the mat? You have modeled the equation 5 + (−3) = 2.

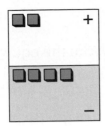

2 Set up a mat to show a round 1 score of −4 and a round 2 score of 2. What is the largest zero pair you can make with the blocks? Remove that pair from the mat. What is the sum of −4 and 2? Write the equation modeled by the blocks.

3 Use blocks to model each equation. Find each sum.

a. 3 + (−5) = _?_ **b.** −6 + 4 = _?_ **c.** 3 + (−4) = _?_

d. 2 + (−3) = _?_ **e.** −4 + 6 = _?_ **f.** −2 + 7 = _?_

Use the following algorithm to check your answers in Step 3.

Adding Integers with Different Signs
To add two integers with different signs,

1. subtract the smaller absolute value from the larger absolute value;

2. then write the difference with the sign of the integer with the larger absolute value.

ONGOING ASSESSMENT

Use the algorithm for adding integers with different signs to find each sum.

a. 8 + (−9) **b.** −17 + 3 **c.** 12 + (−8) **d.** −5 + 20

Critical Thinking Someone explains how to add two integers with different signs as follows:

Subtract the smaller integer from the larger integer and write the answer with the sign of the larger integer.

Why is this explanation incorrect?

LESSON ASSESSMENT

Think and Discuss

1 Explain how to add two integers with the same sign.

2 Explain how to add two integers with different signs.

3 Why are m and $−m$ called a zero pair?

4 Suppose a and b are both positive and $a > b$. Is $−a + b$ positive or negative? Explain your reasoning.

Use Algeblocks to find each sum. Write the equation that you model.

5. $-8 + (-3)$ **6.** $-6 + 2$ **7.** $4 + (-1)$

8. $2 + 5$ **9.** $-3 + (-7)$ **10.** $-8 + 8$

Find each sum.

11. $-35 + 20$ **12.** $50 + (-50)$ **13.** $117 + (-213)$

14. $13 + 24$ **15.** $-8 + (-31)$ **16.** $-92 + 94$

17. $110 + (-83)$ **18.** $-28 + (-35)$ **19.** $154 + 29$

20. $34 + (-18) + (-24)$ **21.** $-29 + (-54) + (-46)$

22. $235 + (-187) + 175$ **23.** $-312 + 215 + (-248)$

24. $-38 + 50 + 8$ **25.** $63 + (-63) + (-159)$

JULIUS CAESAR
100 BC – ?

Which of the following statements is always *true*? If the statement is not always *true,* tell why not.

26. The sum of two integers with different signs is always negative.

27. If the sum of two integers is zero, then the integers have the same absolute value.

28. The sum of three negative integers is greater than zero.

29. If the sum of two integers is positive, then both integers are positive.

Write an addition equation to model Exercises 30–35. Find the sum.

30. Julius Caesar was born in 100 BC. He died when he was 56 years old. In what year did Caesar die?

31. Arlin deletes a 7 MB file from a data disk. Then he saves a 4 MB file on the disk. What is the total change in the number of megabytes stored on the disk?

32. The temperature rose 6 degrees in the morning. It fell 9 degrees in the evening. What was the net change in temperature for the day?

33. The price of a share of Big Time stock is $25 on Monday. On Tuesday, the price dropped $8. On Wednesday, the price rose $4. On Thursday, the price dropped $3. On Friday, the price stayed the same. What is the price of Big Time stock at the end of the week?

34. Umeko delivers mail in an office building. She begins her delivery on the eighth floor. She takes an elevator down 2 floors, then up 5 floors, and finally down 3 floors. Which floor is Umeko on at the end of her delivery?

35. Shea lost 2 yards on his first carry in a football game. He gained 8 yards on his second carry, and on his third carry, lost 4 yards. What was Shea's net gain or loss of yards?

Mixed Review

Evaluate each expression when $p = 5$, $q = 7$, and $r = 3$.

36. $p \cdot r - q$ **37.** $p + q \cdot r$ **38.** $(p + q) \div r$

39. $q + pr - r$ **40.** $pq + pr - p$ **41.** $\dfrac{3p}{r + q}$

Beginning with a full tank of gas, Satinka drove her car 375.9 miles during a 4-day period. At the end of the 4-day period, she filled the tank with 16.2 gallons. The fuel cost $1.179 per gallon.

42. What was the average number of miles driven each day?

43. Estimate the average number of miles per gallon.

44. Estimate the cost of filling the car's tank.

Almeda earned the following scores on her math tests:

$$86 \quad 85 \quad 93 \quad 82 \quad 95 \quad 86 \quad 87$$

45. Find the mean of the scores.

46. Find the mode of the scores.

47. Find the median of the scores.

48. Suppose Almeda scored 86 on the eighth test. Which measure of central tendency would change? Would this measure increase or decrease?

When your heart beats, it causes the blood to exert pressure on the walls of your arteries. The pressure exerted when your heart contracts is called systolic blood pressure (SBP). It is measured in units called millimeters of mercury (mmHg).

Jakeem's average SBP is 160 mmHg. His doctor has placed Jakeem on a diet and exercise program to reduce his blood pressure. Jakeem's goal is to reduce his SBP by 10 mmHg.

49. Write a negative integer to represent the goal Jakeem has set for the change in his SBP.

50. At the end of 6 months, Jakeem has reduced his average SBP by 12 mmHg. Use absolute value to write an inequality that compares Jakeem's actual SBP change to his goal.

51. Did Jakeem meet or exceed his goal? Explain

In the 1950s and the 1960s, the Soviet Union and the United States were in a race to explore the surface of the moon. The table below shows important milestones for the exploration, the missions that achieved the milestones, and the dates they were launched.

Milestone	USA		USSR	
	Mission	Launch Date	Mission	Launch Date
Earth Orbit	Explorer 1	17 March 1958	Sputnik 1	4 Oct 1957
Lunar Flyby	Pioneer 4	3 March 1959	Luna 1	2 Jan 1959
Lunar Impact	Ranger 4	23 April 1962	Luna 2	12 Sept 1959
Lunar Landing	Surveyor 1	30 May 1966	Luna 9	31 Jan 1966
Lunar Orbit	Lunar Orbiter 1	10 Aug 1966	Luna 10	31 March 1966
Manned Lunar Orbit	Apollo 8	21 Dec 1968		
Manned Lunar Landing	Apollo 11	16 July 1969		

52. Draw a time line from 1957 to 1970. On the time line, show the missions for both countries and the dates they were launched.

53. What are the advantages of presenting the information in the article on a time line instead of a table?

A remote botanical research facility uses five wind turbines and a set of batteries as the primary source of electricity for its greenhouse. If a turbine generates more electrical current than needed by the greenhouse, the batteries are charged by the excess current. When this happens, a meter in the greenhouse shows a positive current reading for that turbine. A negative reading means the greenhouse is using more electrical current than the turbine is generating, and the batteries are being discharged.

A technician runs a test on the electrical network. The meters in the greenhouse read as shown at the left.

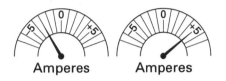

54. Write each of the readings from the meters as a positive or negative current. Current is measured in amperes.

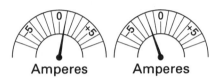

55. What is the total current for the test? Are the batteries being charged or discharged with all five turbines combined?

Courtney needs to find the balance of her checking account to see if she has enough money to buy a $120 parka.

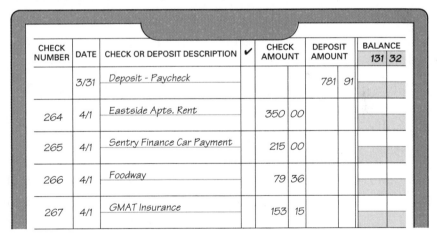

CHECK NUMBER	DATE	CHECK OR DEPOSIT DESCRIPTION	✔	CHECK AMOUNT		DEPOSIT AMOUNT		BALANCE 131 32	
	3/31	Deposit - Paycheck				781	91		
264	4/1	Eastside Apts. Rent		350	00				
265	4/1	Sentry Finance Car Payment		215	00				
266	4/1	Foodway		79	36				
267	4/1	GMAT Insurance		153	15				

56. Which transactions should Courtney represent as positive amounts? Which should she represent as negative amounts?

57. What is Courtney's balance after she writes check number 267? Does she have enough money in her account to buy the parka?

LESSON 3.4 SUBTRACTING INTEGERS

OBJECTIVES

→ Model subtraction of integers using manipulatives or diagrams.
→ Subtract integers.

In the last lesson, you modeled addition with unit blocks. To show addition, you add blocks to the mat. You can model subtraction by taking blocks away from the mat.

To model $4 - 3$, place four blocks on the positive side of the mat. Then take three blocks away from the mat. You have modeled the equation $4 - 3 = 1$.

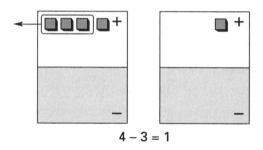

$$4 - 3 = 1$$

ACTIVITY 1 Using a Model to Subtract Integers

1 Use blocks to model $-4 - (-3)$. Start with four blocks on the negative side of the mat. Then take away three blocks from the negative side of the mat. Write the equation to show the result.

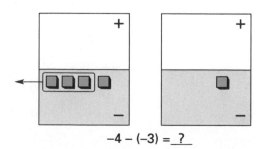

$$-4 - (-3) = \underline{\ ?\ }$$

2 Use blocks to model each subtraction. Write an equation to show each result.

a. $4 - 1$ **b.** $5 - 3$

c. $2 - 2$ **d.** $-4 - (-1)$

e. $-5 - (-3)$ **f.** $-2 - (-2)$

You modeled each subtraction in Activity 1 by taking away blocks that represented the subtracted integer. What happens if there are not enough blocks to take away?

ACTIVITY 2   Adding Zero Pairs to Subtract

1 Use blocks to model $3 - 4$. Start with three blocks on the positive side of the mat. You need to take away four blocks from the positive side. However, there are not enough blocks. How many blocks do you have to add to the positive side so you can take away 4?

2 Remember, you can add a zero pair and not change the value represented on the mat. Add the zero pair 1 and -1 to the mat.

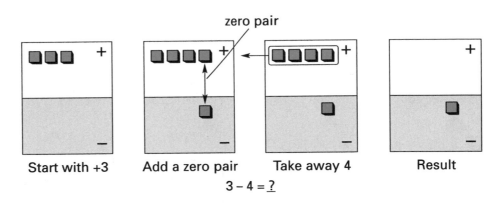

Start with +3   Add a zero pair   Take away 4   Result

$3 - 4 = \underline{?}$

3 Now take away four blocks from the positive side of the mat. Write the equation to show the result.

4 Use blocks to model each subtraction. Write an equation to show each result.

a. $4 - 6$ **b.** $3 - 5$

c. $1 - 2$ **d.** $-4 - (-6)$

e. $-1 - 3$ **f.** $-2 - 2$

1 Copy and complete this table. Use blocks to find $a - b$ and $a + (-b)$.

a	b	a − b	a + (−b)
5	7	?	?
−4	3	?	?
8	−2	?	?
−6	−3	?	?

2 What is the relationship between $a - b$ and $a + (-b)$ for each pair of a, b values?

3 How does subtracting an integer compare with adding the opposite of that integer? Use this relationship to find each difference without using blocks.

a. $20 - (-8)$ **b.** $-15 - 15$ **c.** $-50 - (-75)$

The relationship you discovered in Activity 3 results in the following way to subtract integers:

Subtracting Integers

Subtracting an integer is the same as adding its opposite.

If a and b are integers,

$$a - b = a + (-b).$$

EXAMPLE 1 Subtracting Levels

Ali has parked his car in the only available space in a parking garage, underground on the bottom level.

When he returns for his car, Ali enters the garage on the second level below ground. The parking attendant tells Ali he needs to go down three levels to get to his car. How many parking levels are there below ground?

SOLUTION

Let 0 represent the ground level. Let -2 represent two levels below the ground. Since Ali starts at -2 and needs to go down 3 more, the bottom level can be modeled by the expression $-2 - 3$.

$$-2 - 3 = -2 + (-3) = -5$$

The garage has five levels below ground.

ONGOING ASSESSMENT

Write a subtraction expression for the following problem. Then find the difference.

> The temperature at noon is 16°F. By 6 P.M., the temperature has dropped 26 degrees. What is the temperature at 6 P.M.?

You can use your calculator to subtract integers. On most calculators a [+/−] key changes the value of a number to its opposite. For example, to find $8 - (-3)$

8 [−] 3 [+/−] [=] 11

EXAMPLE 2 Evaluating Expressions

Use a calculator to find the value of each expression when $p = -335, q = 873$, and $r = -597$.

a. $p - r$ **b.** $(r - q) - p$ **c.** $q + r - p$

SOLUTION

a. $p - r = -335 - (-597)$

[335] [+/−] [−] [597] [+/−] [=] [262]

b. This time add opposites to simplify $-p$. This eliminates a keystroke.

$$(r - q) - p = (-597 - 873) - (-335)$$
$$= -597 - 873 + 335$$

[597] [+/−] [−] [873] [+] [335] [=] [-1135]

c. $q + r - p = 873 + (-597) - (-335)$

$$= 873 - 597 + 335$$

[873] [−] [597] [+] [335] [=] [611]

LESSON ASSESSMENT

Think and Discuss

1 Write an algorithm for finding the difference between two integers.

2 Explain why the result of subtracting opposites is not zero.

3 Give an example that shows subtraction of integers is not commutative.

4 When you subtract two integers, you can add the opposite of one of the integers. Which opposite should you use? Give an example to explain why.

Practice and Apply

Simplify each expression.

5. $-4 - 5$

6. $8 - (-2)$

7. $-12 - (-12)$

8. $23 - 48$

9. $-37 - (-28)$

10. $19 - 17$

11. $-15 + 12 - (-9)$

12. $-21 - 36 - (-24)$

13. $34 - 45 - 38$

14. $42 - (-38 - 27)$

Let $x = -10$, $y = -2$, and $z = -7$. Evaluate each expression.

15. $x + y - z$

16. $z - (y - x)$

Write a subtraction expression for each problem. Then find the difference.

17. Your score in a game is 5. In the next play, you lose 8 points. What is your score now?

18. The temperature on the moon can vary from around 130°C to −150°C. How many degrees does the temperature vary on the moon?

19. The height of Mt. McKinley is 20,320 feet. The average depth of the Pacific Ocean is 12,925 feet. What is the difference between the height of Mt. McKinley and the average depth of the Pacific Ocean?

20. A diver is located at 25 feet below sea level. He then descends to 65 feet below sea level. What is the difference in the two depths?

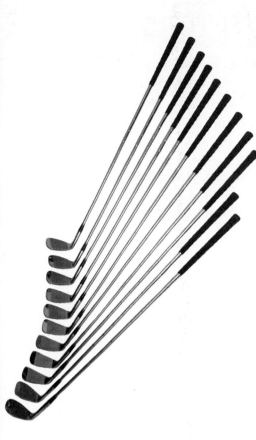

In golf, a *par* is the standard number of strokes for a hole. If par for a hole is 5 strokes, and it only takes you 4 strokes, your score for that hole is −1, or 1 stroke under par.

On April 13, 1997, Tiger Woods became the youngest player ever to win the Masters, one of golf's most prestigious tournaments. His total scores for each of the 18 holes follow.

Tiger Woods' Scorecard: 1997 Masters

	Hole	1	2	3	4	5	6	7	8	9	Total Front-9	
Masters Golf Tournament	Tiger Woods Four-Round Score	+1	−3	+1	+2	−2	0	0	−2	+1		Attest
	Hole	10	11	12	13	14	15	16	17	18	Total Back-9	Scorer
	Tiger Woods Four-Round Score	−1	−2	−1	−4	−2	−4	0	−1	−1		Date

21. What was Tiger Woods' total score on the first nine holes? What was his score on the second nine holes?

22. What was Tiger Woods' total score for the tournament?

23. The Masters Tournament is played on a golf course with a par of 72 strokes. So, in four rounds, par is 4 · 72, or 288 strokes. How many strokes did Tiger Woods take for the four rounds?

24. Tiger Woods won the tournament by 12 strokes. This was the greatest margin of victory ever recorded in a Masters. What was the score of the second place finisher?

Mixed Review

You are considering two earnings options for a job.

      I. $100 cash plus $5.00 per hour
     II. $7.50 per hour

25. If the job will take 30 hours, which option would pay you the most? Explain your answer.

26. How many hours would you have to work before Option II pays the same as Option I?

27. If the job will take more than 40 hours, which option would pay you the most?

LESSON 3.5 INTEGERS AND VECTORS

OBJECTIVES

➤ Model addition of integers using vectors and a number line.
➤ Demonstrate commutative property of addition using a number line.

In football, when a team moves forward toward the goal line, they *gain* yardage. Sometimes, they move backward, and *lose* yardage. You can graph the team's gains and losses with arrows on a number line. For example, a gain of 3 yards is graphed below.

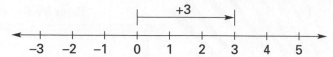

The arrow that represents the gain is called a *vector*.

A **vector** has both *magnitude* and *direction*. The **magnitude** of the vector is the length of the arrow. Magnitude is similar to absolute value. It is never negative. The vector shown above has a magnitude of 3. The arrow points in the **direction** of the vector. On a number line, vectors can point in the positive or the negative direction.

EXAMPLE   A Gain and a Loss

A football team gains 5 yards on the first play and loses 7 yards on the second play. Show the gain and loss with vectors on a number line. What is the net gain or loss of the two plays?

SOLUTION

Draw a vector from 0 to 5. This vector represents the first play. It has magnitude 5 and points in the positive direction.

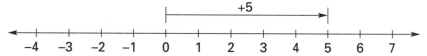

To show how vectors are added, start the second vector at 5. Draw the vector 7 units long to the left. The second vector has magnitude 7 and points in the negative direction.

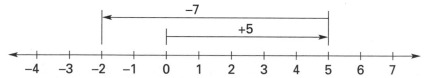

The second vector ends at the sum of the two vectors, -2. The vectors model the equation

$$5 + (-7) = -2$$

After two plays, the team has lost 2 yards.

1   Draw a number line from −10 to 10.

2   Above the number line, draw vectors representing the sum 2 + 3. Above these vectors, draw a single vector from 0 to the arrowhead of the +3 vector. This new vector is called the **resultant**. What is the magnitude of the resultant vector? Compare the magnitude of the resultant vector to the sum of the magnitudes of the +2 and +3 vectors.

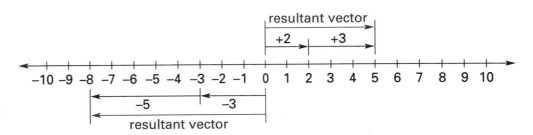

3   Below the number line, draw vectors representing the sum −3 + (−5). Draw the resultant vector from 0 to the arrowhead of the −5 vector. Compare the magnitude of the resultant vector to the sum of the magnitudes of the −3 and −5 vectors.

4   Use a number line and vector addition to show the following sums. In each case, compare the direction of the resultant vector to the direction of the addend vectors. Then compare the magnitude of the resultant vector to the sum of the magnitudes of the addends.

     a. 3 + 4   **b.** −2 + (−4)   **c.** 7 + 1   **d.** −6 + (−3)

5   In Steps 2–4, you added two vectors that point in the same direction. Write an algorithm for finding the magnitude and direction of the resultant vector from the magnitudes and direction of the addend vectors.

6   Compare your algorithm to the one on page 141 for adding two integers that have the same sign.

Activity 1 shows how you can model integer addition using vectors. If the addend integers have the same sign, the addend vectors point in the same direction.

The following Activity shows that you can also use vectors to model integer addition if the addends have opposite signs.

1 Draw a number line from −10 to 10.

2 Above the number line, draw vectors representing the sum 2 + (−7). Draw the resultant vector from 0 to the arrowhead of the −7 vector. What is the magnitude of the resultant vector? Compare the magnitude of the resultant vector to the difference between the magnitudes of the +2 and −7 vectors.

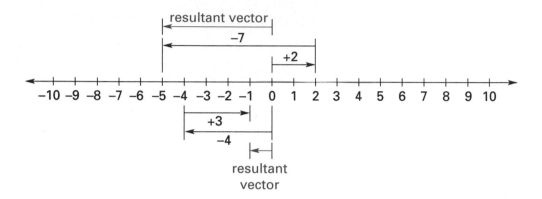

3 Below the number line, draw vectors representing the sum −4 + 3. Draw the resultant vector from 0 to the arrowhead of the +3 vector. Compare the magnitude of the resultant vector to the difference between the magnitudes of the −4 and +3 vectors.

4 Use a number line and vector addition to show the following sums.

   a. 3 +(−4)   **b.** −2 + 8   **c.** 7 + (−1)   **d.** −6 + 3

In each case, compare the magnitude of the resultant vector to the difference between the magnitudes of the addend vectors. The resultant always points in the direction of which addend?

5 In Steps 2–4, you added two vectors that point in opposite directions. Write an algorithm for finding the magnitude and direction of the resultant vector from the magnitudes and directions of the addend vectors.

6 Compare your algorithm to the one on page 143 for adding two integers that have different signs.

1 Draw a horizontal line with a straightedge. Label point 0 near the center.

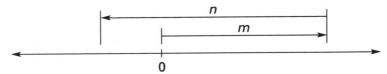

2 Draw a vector with magnitude *m* beginning at 0.The variable *m* can be any value that fits on your paper and can point in either the positive or the negative direction.

3 Draw a vector with magnitude *n* beginning at the arrowhead of *m*. The variable *n* can have any magnitude and can point in either the positive or the negative direction.

4 Your drawing models the expression $m + n$. Use a ruler to measure the lengths of *m* and *n*.

5 On the same horizontal line, draw vectors to model $n + m$. Use the lengths measured in Step 4.

6 Explain how your drawing demonstrates the Commutative Property of Addition.

ONGOING ASSESSMENT

Use three vectors on a number line to demonstrate the Associative Property of Addition.

Critical Thinking   Show that vector addition works even if you do not begin one of the addends at 0: use vectors and a number line to add $-5 + 8$. Start the first vector at 2.

LESSON ASSESSMENT

Think and Discuss

1 What is a vector?

2 What is a resultant vector?

3 Explain how you can use vectors to find the sum of two integers that have the same sign.

4 Explain how you can use vectors to find the sum of two integers that have different signs.

Write the addition equation modeled by the vectors. Find each sum.

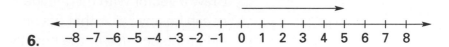

5. −8 −7 −6 −5 −4 −3 −2 −1 0 1 2 3 4 5 6 7 8

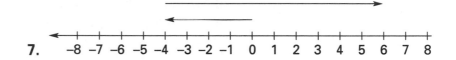

6. −8 −7 −6 −5 −4 −3 −2 −1 0 1 2 3 4 5 6 7 8

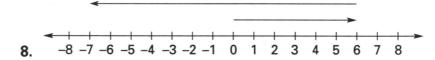

7. −8 −7 −6 −5 −4 −3 −2 −1 0 1 2 3 4 5 6 7 8

8. −8 −7 −6 −5 −4 −3 −2 −1 0 1 2 3 4 5 6 7 8

Use vectors to find each of the following.

9. $5 + (-3)$ **10.** $-4 + (-6)$ **11.** $2 + 4$

12. $-8 + 7$ **13.** $9 + (-9)$ **14.** $-6 + 0$

15. $-3 + 8 + (-6)$ **16.** $4 + (-7) + 9$

17. $-5 + (-2) + (-3)$ **18.** $-4 + (-3) + 8$

Name the property illustrated by each of the following.

19. $3 + (-4) = -4 + 3$ **20.** $(-8 + 0) + (-5) = -8 + (-5)$

Nancy's Bike Shop sold 3 bikes on Monday, bought 2 bikes Tuesday, and sold 1 bike Wednesday.

21. Use integers to express the number of bikes Nancy sold or bought each day.

22. Use vectors to find the change in the number of bikes in the shop.

23. Write an addition equation to model Nancy's bike sales and purchases.

The first Monday, Patrick deposited $15 into his account. The second Monday, he deposited $10. The third Monday, he withdrew $12.

24. Use integers to express each amount that Patrick deposited or withdrew.

25. Use vectors to find the net change in Patrick's account.

26. Write an addition equation to model Patrick's deposits and withdrawals.

27. On the number line above, point *x* is 3 units from point *B*, and 2 units from point *A*. What is the coordinate of point *x*?

28. Point *y* is 7 units from point *A* and 2 units from point *B*. What is the coordinate of point *y*?

Mixed Review

Write the value of the underlined digit.
29. 34.<u>0</u>67   **30.** 0.412<u>2</u>3   **31.** 12<u>8</u>,456,901

A frequency polygon is used to record the heights of the girls on the Wildcats' basketball team.

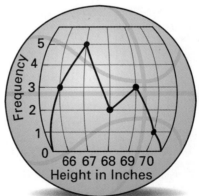

32. How many girls are 67 inches tall?

33. How many girls are over 67 inches tall?

34. How many girls are on the team?

35. Find the mean height of the girls.

36. Find the median height of the girls.

37. Find the mode height of the girls.

Benjamin and Maxwell are planning an around-the-world balloon flight. They will launch their balloon from Albuquerque which has an altitude of 5000 feet above sea level. They plan to fly at altitudes between 5000 and 20,000 feet. The graph shows the expected temperatures at altitudes above sea level.

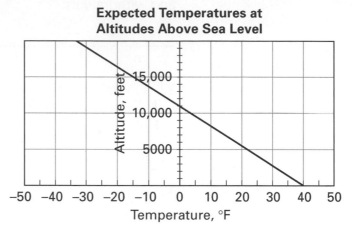

Expected Temperatures at Altitudes Above Sea Level

38. What is the expected temperature in Albuquerque? When the balloon climbs from 5000 feet, what happens to the temperature?

39. Benjamin and Maxwell must adjust their fuel load for the expected temperature change from 5000 to 20,000 feet. How much will the temperature change between these two altitudes?

40. Approximately what temperature can they expect if they climb to 22,000 feet?

Shelby is setting up a three-way videoconference for the executive officers of her corporation. One officer is in Columbia, South Carolina, where Shelby works. One is in Seattle, Washington, and the third is in London, England. Shelby wants to schedule the videoconference between 8:00 A.M. and 5:00 P.M. local time at each of the three locations.

The time in Seattle is three hours earlier than Columbia's time. The time in London is five hours later than Columbia's time.

41. Write a negative integer to represent the time difference between Columbia and Seattle. Write a positive integer to represent the time difference between Columbia and London. How many hours difference are there between London and Seattle?

42. Shelby can schedule the videoconference at 10:30 A.M., 11:15 A.M., or 1:30 P.M. local time in Columbia. Which time should she schedule?

Jonathan Whitebear is Director of Marketing for the Greater Metro Business Directory. For the end-of-year report he calculates the change in advertising sales from the previous year. Jonathan sells three ads: half-page, quarter-page, and eighth-page. The sales income from each size ad is shown in the diagram at the left.

Jonathan finds the number of sales of half-page ads decreased by 12 from the previous year. The number of quarter-page ads increased by 18. The number of eighth-page ads increased by 9.

43. Use integers to write expressions for the changes in sales income from the previous year for half-, quarter-, and eighth-page ads.

44. What is the total change in sales income from the previous year?

In golf, par is the standard number of strokes for a hole. The names of other scores are:

Bogey—one stroke over par
Double Bogey—two strokes over par
Birdie—one stroke under par
Eagle—two strokes under par

45. A par score has a numerical value of 0. Write an integer for each of the other scores.

46. On the first nine holes of a golf game, Cory scores a bogey, par, birdie, double bogey, birdie, eagle, par, bogey, and birdie. How many strokes above or under par is Cory's score after the first nine holes?

47. Cory's best score on 18 holes is four under par. How many strokes above or under par does he need on the second nine holes to beat his best score?

Eighth-
page ad
$350

Quarter-
page ad
$450

Half-page ad
$600

LESSON 3.6 MULTIPLYING INTEGERS

➤ Multiply integers.

The Young Marketeers investment club invests in stocks. At each monthly meeting, the club reviews changes in prices of stocks owned by the club. The club uses positive numbers to represent price increases and negative numbers to represent price decreases.

The price of Captain Tires stock decreases $3 per share. Young Marketeers owns four shares of Captain Tires. What is the change in total value of the club's shares of Captain Tires?

ACTIVITY 1 — Multiplying Integers with Different Signs

1 Write an integer to represent the change in price of one share of Captain Tires stock. What is the sign of the integer?

2 To find the change in total value, use the integer from Step 1 as an addend four times. What is the sign of the sum?

3 Adding the same integer 4 times is the same as multiplying by 4. Use the result from Step 2 to complete the following equation.

$$4(-3) = \underline{\ ?\ }$$

4 Use the algorithm for adding integers with the same sign to complete the following equations.

    a. $3(-6) = -6 + (-6) + (-6) = \underline{\ ?\ }$ **b.** $5(-3) = \underline{\ ?\ }$

    c. $2(-5) = \underline{\ ?\ }$ **d.** $4(-4) = \underline{\ ?\ }$

5 Recall that you can use the Commutative Property of Multiplication to change the order of the factors without changing the value of the product. Use the Commutative Property and the results of Step 4 to complete the following equations.

    a. $-6(3) = 3(-6) = \underline{\ ?\ }$ **b.** $-3(5) = 5(-3) = \underline{\ ?\ }$

    c. $-5(2) = 2(-5) = \underline{\ ?\ }$ **d.** $-4(4) = 4(-4) = \underline{\ ?\ }$

6 When you multiply two integers with different signs, what is the sign of the product?

ACTIVITY 2 Multiplying Two Negative Integers

1 Complete the first four rows of the table.

Factor	•	Factor	=	Product
4	•	−3	=	?
3	•	−3	=	?
2	•	−3	=	?
1	•	−3	=	?
0	•	−3	=	?
−1	•	−3	=	?
−2	•	−3	=	?
−3	•	−3	=	?
−4	•	−3	=	?

2 Observe the pattern established by the products. Continue the pattern, and complete the table.

3 When you multiply two negative integers, what is the sign of the product? When you multiply two positive integers, what is the sign of the product?

4 When you multiply two integers that have the same sign, what is the sign of the product?

The results of Activity 1 and Activity 2 lead to the following rule of signs.

Multiplying Integers

The product of two integers with the same sign is positive.

The product of two integers with different signs is negative.

$$(+) \cdot (+) = +$$
$$(-) \cdot (-) = +$$
$$(+) \cdot (-) = -$$
$$(-) \cdot (+) = -$$

Without computing, tell whether each product is positive or negative.

a. $-97(-6)$ **b.** $4(-84)$ **c.** $-52(107)$

d. $-2(24)(-5)$ **e.** $-6(-16)(-8)$ **f.** $(4)(78)(-5)$

Use your calculator to find the products. Remember, you use the $\boxed{+/-}$ key to change the sign of the factors.

EXAMPLE Losing Money Is a Negative Result

By the next monthly meeting of Young Marketeers, the price of Captain Tires stock further decreases $2 per share. What is the total change in value of the club's four shares of stock over the two months?

SOLUTION

In the first month, the stock's value changed by $4(-3)$, and in the second month, the value changed by $4(-2)$. The total change is the following sum.

$$4(-3) + 4(-2)$$

Use the Distributive Property to find the sum.

$$4(-3) + 4(-2) = 4[-3 + (-2)]$$
$$= 4(-5) = -20$$

The club's investment lost $20 over the two months.

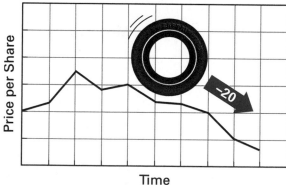

Captain Tire Stock

ONGOING ASSESSMENT

Let $x = -3$, $y = 2$, and $z = -4$. Evaluate each of the following.

1. $xy - z$ **2.** $xy - xz$ **3.** $x(y - z)$

USING THE FOUR-STEP PLAN

You are a computer engineer for a satellite launch. The launch time has been delayed from 9:30 P.M. to 11:45 P.M.

You need to reschedule the beginning and ending times of three programs that the satellite's computer will automatically run before and after the launch. The beginning times and the durations for each program are shown in the table.

Program	Beginning Time	Program Duration
Computer memory test	T – 15 minutes	3 minutes, 15 seconds
Launch safe hold	T – 8 minutes	15 minutes, 0 seconds
Separation from launch vehicle	T + 28 minutes	1 minute, 45 seconds

The beginning times of the programs are given relative to liftoff time T. The minutes and seconds before liftoff are negative, the minutes and seconds after liftoff are positive. For example, *T minus 30 seconds* is 30 seconds before liftoff.

Step 1 Understand the Problem
What do you need to find? What are you given?

Step 2 Develop a Plan
Draw a diagram. Use a number line to plot the beginning and ending times for each program relative to T.

Step 3 Carry Out the Plan
Plot the times on the number line. How will you convert each time relative to T to the new time of the launch?

Step 4 Check the Results
Did you answer the questions? Are the answers reasonable? Do they make sense?

LESSON ASSESSMENT

1 Write an algorithm for finding the product of two integers that have different signs. Demonstrate your algorithm with an example.

2 The temperature falls at a constant rate of 2°C per hour. What multiplication expression can be used to find the change in temperature over 5 hours?

3 The product of four integers is a negative integer. How many of the factors are negative?

Practice and Apply

Find each product.

4. $-8(7)$ **5.** $6(-9)$ **6.** $4(12)$

7. $-3(-15)$ **8.** $-13(5)$ **9.** $-15(0)$

10. $4(-6)(-3)$ **11.** $-2(28)(-5)$ **12.** $(-3)(-3)(-3)$

Which of the statements in Exercises 13–16 is always *true*? If a statement is not always *true,* tell why not.

13. The product of two negative integers is greater than zero.

14. The product of an odd number of negative integers is a negative integer.

15. The product of two integers is either positive or negative.

16. The multiplicative identity for integers is -1.

Evaluate each expression.

17. $2m - 3n$ when $m = -5$ and $n = 2$

18. $s(t - 2u)$ when $s = -4$, $t = 8$, and $u = 5$

19. $a - 2b + 3c$ when $a = 5$, $b = -4$ and $c = -6$

Identify any numbers that represent negative quantities in each problem. Write a multiplication expression to model the problem. Then find the product.

20. The temperature has been dropping at a constant rate of 2°F per hour. How many degrees does the temperature change in 3 hours?

21. An elevator descends 10 feet every second. How far will the elevator move in 6 seconds?

22. Each time you use an ATM to withdraw money, your account is charged 75¢. What is the change in your account balance due to ATM charges after 7 withdrawals?

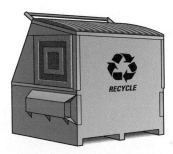

23. An investor earned $4 on each share of Cosmo stock. If the investor had 150 shares, what was his total profit?

24. A recycling center buys aluminum for $0.35 per pound. If you recycle 50 pounds of aluminum, how much money will you receive?

25. A truck backs up at the constant rate of 10 feet per minute. Describe the truck's location 8 minutes ago.

Mixed Review

Use the data below to complete Exercises 26–31.

76 63 81 77 62 87 77 68 75

26. What is the range of the data?

27. What is the mean of the data?

28. What is the mode of the data?

29. What is the median of the data?

30. What are the first and third quartiles of the data?

31. Create a box-and-whisker plot from the data.

LESSON 3.7 DIVIDING INTEGERS

OBJECTIVES
➤ Divide integers.

Elaine's riding club membership dues are $240 per year. Her dues are divided into 12 equal monthly payments and are automatically deducted from her checking account each month. What should Elaine's checking account statement show each month for the dues?

Since the $240 yearly dues are a deduction, it is a negative number. There will be 12 equal deductions. Thus, Elaine needs to find the answer to: "What do I multiply by 12 to get −240?"

Multiplication and division are **inverse operations**. An inverse operation *undoes* the original operation. The inverse relationship between multiplication and division can be expressed in two ways.

$$\text{If } ab = c, \text{ then } \frac{c}{b} = a.$$

$$\text{If } \frac{c}{b} = a, \text{ then } ab = c.$$

Elaine can use this inverse relationship to find the amount that will be deducted from her checking account.

Use the first expression above: If $ab = c$, then $\frac{c}{b} = a$.

$a \to$ Elaine's monthly deduction
$b \to 12$
$c \to -240$

$$\text{If } a\,(12) = -240, \text{ then } \frac{-240}{12} = a.$$

Since $-20\,(12) = -240$, a must be equal to -20. Thus,

$$a = \frac{-240}{12} = -20$$

The negative sign indicates a deduction. Elaine will have $20 deducted from her checking account each month.

You can use this inverse relationship to determine the sign of the quotient when you divide two integers.

ACTIVITY — The Sign of the Quotient

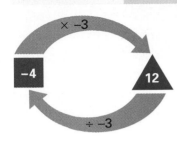

1 Complete each division equation.

a. $(-6)(3) = -18$

$$\frac{-18}{3} = \underline{\;?\;}$$

b. $-4(-3) = 12$

$$\frac{12}{-3} = \underline{\;?\;}$$

2 What is the sign of the quotient when you divide two integers with different signs?

3 Complete each division equation.

a. $2(5) = 10$

$$\frac{10}{5} = \underline{\;?\;}$$

b. $8(-3) = -24$

$$\frac{-24}{-3} = \underline{\;?\;}$$

4 What is the sign of the quotient when you divide two integers with the same signs?

Dividing Integers

The quotient of two integers with the same sign is positive.

The quotient of two integers with different signs is negative.

$$\frac{(+)}{(+)} = + \qquad \frac{(-)}{(-)} = + \qquad \frac{(+)}{(-)} = - \qquad \frac{(-)}{(+)} = -$$

ONGOING ASSESSMENT

Without computing, tell whether the quotient is positive or negative.

a. $\dfrac{-348}{-6}$ **b.** $\dfrac{240}{-16}$ **c.** $\dfrac{-135}{9}$ **d.** $\dfrac{244}{14}$

Use your calculator to find each quotient. Check your answer by multiplication.

EXAMPLE 1 Evaluating Division Expressions

Evaluate $\dfrac{a}{b - c}$ when $a = -36$, $b = 8$, and $c = 17$.

SOLUTION

$$\frac{a}{b - c} = \frac{-36}{8 - 17} = \frac{-36}{-9} = 4$$

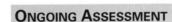
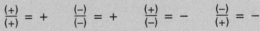

58

EXAMPLE 2 Division Expressions Containing Zero

Find each quotient.

a. $\dfrac{0}{4}$ **b.** $\dfrac{4}{0}$

SOLUTION

Start with the inverse relationship:

$$\text{If } \frac{c}{b} = a, \text{ then } ab = c.$$

a. If $\dfrac{0}{4} = a$, then $a(4) = 0$. The only number a for which this is true is 0. Thus,

$$\frac{0}{4} = 0$$

b. If $\dfrac{4}{0} = a$, then $a(0) = 4$. Since any number multiplied by 0 is 0, $a(0) = 4$ gives $0 = 4$, which is impossible. There is no number a such that $a(0) = 4$. Division by zero is *undefined*.

EXAMPLE 3 Division by 1 and −1

Simplify each expression.

a. $\dfrac{x}{1}$ **b.** $\dfrac{y}{-1}$

SOLUTION

Multiplication is the inverse of division.

a. Since $x \cdot (1) = x$, $\dfrac{x}{1} = x$. Any number divided by 1 is that number.

b. Since $-y\,(-1) = y$, $\dfrac{y}{-1} = -y$. Any number divided by -1 is the opposite of that number.

In Lesson 2.1, you found the mean of a set of data by adding all the numbers and dividing this sum by the number of items in the set. You can also find the mean by using the **assumed mean** method.

Steps 1–4 show how to use this method to find the mean of a data set containing the following numbers:

$$19 \quad 18 \quad 18 \quad 14 \quad 12 \quad 11 \quad 11 \quad 9$$

Step 1 Assume 12 is the mean.

Step 2 Find the difference between each number in the data set and the assumed mean.

$$19 - 12 = 7 \qquad 18 - 12 = 6 \qquad 18 - 12 = 6 \qquad 14 - 12 = 2$$
$$12 - 12 = 0 \qquad 11 - 12 = -1 \qquad 11 - 12 = -1 \qquad 9 - 12 = -3$$

Step 3 Find the average of the differences.

$$\frac{7 + 6 + 6 + 2 + 0 + (-1) + (-1) + (-3)}{8} = \frac{16}{8} = 2$$

Step 4 Add the average of the differences to the assumed mean.

$$12 + 2 = 14. \text{ The mean of the data is } 14.$$

CULTURAL CONNECTION

Zero is part of the Hindu-Arabic numeration system. The word *zero* is of Arabic origin and means *something empty.* Symbols for zero have been found in the writing of many early civilizations. However, the symbol always meant the absence of number. Even in the early Greek and Roman days, the zero symbol was not used in computation. In Far Eastern countries, the abacus was used for computation, but zero was only used to mean the absence of number.

1. Complete the following pattern:

$$\frac{6}{1} = 6$$

$$\frac{6}{0.1} = 60$$

$$\frac{6}{0.01} = \underline{?}$$

$$\frac{6}{0.001} = \underline{?}$$

2. Is the divisor increasing or decreasing?

3. Is the quotient increasing or decreasing?

4. Find the meaning of the word *infinity* or the mathematical symbol ∞.

5. Explain why the following statement makes sense.

You can never divide by zero, but as the divisor gets closer and closer to 0, the quotient approaches positive ∞.

LESSON ASSESSMENT

1 Write two division equations from the multiplication equation $pq = r$.

2 Explain how to find the sign of the quotient when you divide two nonzero integers.

3 Use your calculator to find $\dfrac{8}{0}$. Explain the answer given by your calculator.

Practice and Apply

Find each quotient.

4. $\dfrac{-25}{-5}$ **5.** $\dfrac{-21}{7}$ **6.** $\dfrac{49}{-7}$ **7.** $\dfrac{-48}{12}$

8. $\dfrac{0}{-3}$ **9.** $\dfrac{84}{21}$ **10.** $\dfrac{144}{0}$ **11.** $\dfrac{-625}{25}$

Evaluate each expression.

12. $\dfrac{m + n}{r}$ when $m = 7$, $n = 5$, and $r = -2$.

13. $\dfrac{2a - b}{-3c}$ when $a = 5$, $b = 1$, and $c = -1$.

14. $\dfrac{s + 2t}{s - 2t}$ when $s = 4$ and $t = -2$.

15. $\dfrac{f \cdot g}{g + h}$ when $f = -3$, $g = 2$, and $h = -4$.

Use the assumed mean method to find the average of each set of data.

16. 37 46 39 38 40   **17.** 152 148 145 153 157

Write a division expression to model the problem. Then find the quotient.

18. During a 4-week period, the depth of a reservoir was measured at

-127 feet, -138 feet, -134 feet, and -133 feet.

What was the average depth of the reservoir during the 4-week period?

19. The price of a stock increases $4 per month. How long will it take for the price of the stock to gain $20?

20. Jason's watch lost the same amount of time each day. After 10 days, Jason's watch has lost 18 minutes. How many minutes did the watch lose each day?

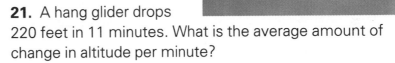

21. A hang glider drops 220 feet in 11 minutes. What is the average amount of change in altitude per minute?

22. After four rounds of golf, Raef's total score was 8 over par. What was Raef's average score per round?

Mixed Review

List each set of numbers in order from least to greatest.
23. 0.515, 0.505, 0.550, 0.551   **24.** −3, −1, 2, 1, −2

List each set of numbers in order from greatest to least.
25. 0.615, 0.651, 0.650   **26.** −12, −15, −13, −18, −9

Solve each problem. Use estimation to make sure your answer is reasonable.
27. A marine biologist weighs a sea lion pup on a scale. The scale reads 13.6 kg. What is the weight of the pup to the nearest kg?

28. Rounded to the nearest 10 kg, the weight of an adult sea lion is 130 kg. Write a weight that could be the actual weight of the sea lion.

29. The price of a shirt is $28. The price of a pair of shorts is $35. What is the cost of 3 shirts and 2 pairs of shorts?

30. LySchale earns $8 per hour. If she works over 40 hours, she makes an additional $4 per hour. One week LySchale worked 46 hours. How much did she earn?

Cumulative Problem Solving

Jenna recruits volunteers to work on a Habitat for Humanity project. Her goal is a total of 100 volunteer hours. She signs up three volunteers to work 8 hours each; five to work 4 hours each; and four to work 6 hours each.

31. Write an expression for the total number of volunteer hours Jenna has recruited.

32. How many more hours are needed to reach her goal?

Lucinda is Director of Operations at an Army Corps of Engineers flood control lake. She monitors the depth of the lake with a gauge. The normal reading on the gauge is 16 feet. After several days of heavy rain, the lake crests at a depth-gauge reading of 37 feet.

Lucinda orders a release of water from the lake to return the depth to normal. During the release, the depth-gauge reading decreases 9 inches per day (or 0.75 foot per day.) Lucinda needs to calculate the number of days it will take for the water depth to return to normal.

33. Write the rate of change of the lake's depth.

34. What is the change in depth needed for the lake to return to normal?

35. Lucinda uses the following quotient to calculate the number of days required to return the depth of the lake to normal.

$$\frac{\text{Change in depth (feet)}}{\text{Rate of change (feet per day)}}$$

How many days will it take for the lake to return to normal depth?

Martha participates in the parent's volunteer program at her daughter's school. Her boss lets her miss work to do this. However, she must make up the time lost. During one month, Martha left work for 90 minutes of volunteer work three different times. To make up the time missed, Martha has already worked 30 minutes extra for 5 days and 15 minutes extra for 6 days.

36. Represent each length of time that Martha misses work by a negative number. Write an expression to determine the total number of minutes Martha has left work to volunteer.

37. Represent each length of time that Martha works extra by a positive number. Write an expression to determine the total number of minutes Martha has worked extra.

38. Does Martha still need to work extra this month? If so, how long?

A consumer research group tests the accuracy of 5 watches over a 5-week period. At the end of each week, the time displayed by each watch is compared to the standard time announcement from the U.S. Naval Observatory. The number of seconds of deviation from the standard time is recorded, and the watches are reset to the standard time. A record of the deviations is shown in this table.

39. Find the mean of the weekly deviations for each watch brand.

40. Find the range of the weekly deviations for each watch brand.

41. Based on the weekly deviations, rate the watches from highest (most accurate) to lowest (least accurate). Explain your ratings.

42. Use the means you calculated in Exercise 39 to estimate the number of seconds each watch will gain or lose in one year if it is not reset.

Weekly Deviations of Watches (Seconds)

Week	Watch Brands				
	A	B	C	D	E
1	−5	−14	2	−6	−17
2	−4	2	−1	−1	−44
3	6	−4	3	−6	−27
4	−3	−7	4	−3	5
5	1	−5	−1	−4	−28

MATH LAB

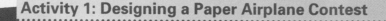

Equipment Tape measure with metric scale
Masking tape
Paper

Problem Statement

Your class is helping design a paper airplane contest for young children. The children will build their own airplanes and fly them in several tests. One test is for accuracy. Each child will launch an airplane from one line to a target line five meters away. Points are awarded for how close to the target line the nose of the airplane lands.

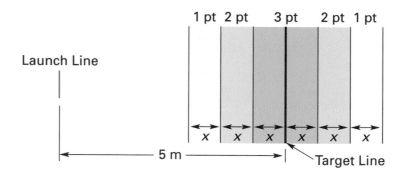

You will use statistical methods to determine appropriate distances x for the 3-, 2-, and 1-point regions. The contest designer wants approximately half the children to score 2 or 3 points.

Procedure

a Have each member of the group construct a paper airplane.

b Place strips of masking tape on the floor for launch lines and target lines. Make sure the target and launch lines are 5 meters apart.

c Have each group member stand behind the launch line and launch the airplane toward the target line.

d Measure the distance from the nose of each airplane to the target line. Record the measurements to the nearest 10 centimeters in a table similar to the one below.

If the airplane lands over the target line, record a *positive* measurement. If the airplane lands short of the target line, record a *negative* measurement.

Trial 1	Launch	Distance Over (+) or Short of (−) Target Line	Trial 2	Launch	Distance Over (+) or Short of (−) Target Line
	1			1	
	2			2	
	3			3	
	4			4	
	5			5	

e Repeat Steps **c** and **d** for a second trial for each group member.

f Combine your group's data with the rest of the class. Graph the class data on a number line. If two or more data points have the same coordinate, stack the points at the coordinate similar to a line plot.

g Beneath the number line, construct a box-and-whisker plot of the class data.

h What are the coordinates of Q_1 and Q_3? Find the difference $Q_3 - Q_1$. Divide this difference by 4. Use this value for the distance x. If the value is negative, use its opposite for x.

i Make a sketch showing the launch line, target line, and 3-, 2-, and 1-point boundary lines. Label the distances on the sketch. How far from the target line are the 3-point boundaries? the 2-point boundaries? the 1-point boundaries?

Discussion Questions

1. Why were Q_1 and Q_3 used in Step **h**?

2. Use an inequality or an equality to compare the absolute value of the median of your group's data to the absolute value of the class median. Was your group or the class more accurate in the airplane tosses?

3. Suppose the median of a data set with an even number of values is zero. What is the relationship between the two middle values of the data set?

4. Explain how you used opposites to decide on the locations of the boundary lines.

Activity 2: The 50-mm Noodle

Equipment   Uncooked spaghetti noodles (about 5 per group)
                   Centimeter ruler

Problem Statement

A manufacturing plant produces many copies of the same part. The lengths of the parts vary slightly, but must be close to a specified length called the **spec length**. The plant's Quality Control Department measures actual lengths of manufactured parts.They find the differences between the actual lengths and spec lengths. This difference is called the **deviation from spec**.

You will break spaghetti noodles to simulate manufactured parts. The spec length of the noodles is 50 millimeters. You will find the deviation from spec for the noodles and create the quality control statistics.

Procedure

a Have each member of the group break off a piece of spaghetti as close as possible to 50 millimeters in length. Do not use a ruler when breaking the noodles.

b Use the ruler to measure the length of each of the pieces to the nearest millimeter. Record the actual lengths under Method 1 in a table similar to the one on the opposite page.

Part Number	Method 1		Method 2	
	Actual Length (mm)	Deviation from Spec (mm)	Actual Length (mm)	Deviation from Spec (mm)
1				
2				
3				
4				
5				
Mean				
Median				
Mode				
Range				

c Calculate the deviation from spec for each piece of spaghetti:

Deviation from spec = Actual length − Spec length

Record the deviations for Method 1.

d Find the mean, median, mode, and range of the deviations. Record these values in the table.

e Bundle five (or one for each group member) noodles together. Have one person break the bundle as close as possible to 50 millimeters in length. It may be easier to break the bundle against the edge of a desk. Repeat Steps **b–d**, and record the data in the table under Method 2.

f Draw two identical number lines. Construct line plots of the deviations from spec recorded for Method 1 and for Method 2.

Discussion Questions

1. Which method produced spaghetti noodles with a mean length closest to 50 mm? Which method produced spaghetti noodles with a median length closest to 50 mm? Which method had the greatest range of deviation from spec?

2. The measures of central tendency can be negative, but the range cannot be negative. Use the rule for subtracting integers to explain why not.

3. A coworker says that if the mean deviation is zero, then all the noodles measure 50 millimeters. Is the coworker correct? Explain why or why not.

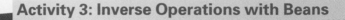

Activity 3: Inverse Operations with Beans

Equipment   Uncooked beans (about one cup)
Scoop that holds approximately
10 beans

Problem Statement

You will count the number of beans that fill a scoop. Then you will use the inverse relationship between multiplication and division to predict the total number of beans as additional scoops are taken.

Procedure

a Have each member of the group fill a scoop with beans level to the top. Count the number of beans in the scoop. Record the data in a table similar to the one following.

	Number of Beans
1st scoop	
2nd scoop	
3rd scoop	
4th scoop	
5th scoop	
Total number of beans N	
Average number of beans per scoop $a = \frac{N}{n}$	

b Add the numbers of beans in all the scoops and enter the total. Calculate the average number of beans per scoop. Round the average to the nearest whole bean per scoop, and record the value in the table.

c Let *n* represent the number of scoops, *N* represent the total number of beans in all the scoops, and *a* represent the average number of beans per scoop. Then

$$\frac{N}{n} = a$$

Write an expression to complete the following:

$$\text{If } \frac{N}{n} = a, \text{ then } N = \underline{\ ?\ }$$

d Use the equation for *N* in Step **c** to predict the number of beans in 2, 4, 6, 8, and 10 scoops. Record your predictions in a table similar to the one below.

Number of Scoops, *n*	Predicted Number of Beans	Actual Number of Beans	Variation
2			
4			
6			
8			
10			

e Fill the scoop with beans *n* times, for *n* = 2, 4, 6, 8, and 10. Count the total number of beans for each value of *n* and record the totals.

f For each value of *n*, calculate and record the variation in the number of beans observed.

$$\text{Variation} = \begin{array}{c}\text{Actual number} \\ \text{of beans}\end{array} - \begin{array}{c}\text{Predicted number} \\ \text{of beans}\end{array}$$

g What is the relationship between the actual number of beans and the predicted number if the variation is positive? If the variation is negative? If the variation is zero?

Discussion Question

A processing plant packages beans in containers that each hold 100 scoops. Predict the number of beans in a container. Suppose you count the beans in one of the containers and calculate the variation as in Step **f**. Approximately what value would you expect for the variation? Use your data to explain your answer.

CHAPTER 3   ASSESSMENT

Communicate

1. Why do two numbers that are opposites have the same absolute value?

2. Two integers with opposite signs are added. How do you determine the sign of the sum?

3. Explain how to rewrite a subtraction expression as an addition expression.

4. How do you determine the sign of the product of two integers?

5. Explain the meaning of the following statement: *Multiplication and division are inverse operations.*

Skills

Write an integer to represent each situation.

6. An English class adds three students.

7. You lose one hour of sleep when you change your clock for Daylight Savings Time.

Simplify.

8. $|-22|$ 9. $|12-7|$

Replace ? with $<$, $>$, or $=$ to make each statement *true*.

10. $-6 \underline{\ ?\ } -4$ 11. $2 \underline{\ ?\ } -(-2)$

Simplify.

12. $-16+23$ 13. $7-(-8)$ 14. $6(-11)$

Evaluate each expression when $x=-3$, $y=-2$, and $z=5$.

15. $xy+z$ 16. $x(y-z)$ 17. $\dfrac{-2z}{x+y}$

Applications

Write an expression to model each problem. Solve the problem.

18. The net change in Widget stocks at the end of a trading day is $-\$2$. The change in Gizmo stock is $-\$3$. Write an inequality that compares the absolute value change in Widget stock to the absolute value in Gizmo stock.

19. A jet increases its altitude 3800 feet and then descends 4100 feet. What is the net change in the altitude of the jet?

20. An oil well is drilled 280 feet below ground. A geologist estimates the well must be drilled 70 feet deeper to reach oil. At what depth will oil be reached?

21. The highest point in Asia is Mt. Everest at 29,028 feet. The lowest point in Asia is the Dead Sea at −1312 feet. Find the difference between the two points.

22. South Bridge Middle School enrolled 7 new students the first week of school. The second week of school, 5 students withdrew. Use vectors to model the net change in the number of students during the first two weeks of school.

23. A submarine is diving at a constant rate of −55 feet per minute. How far will it descend in 8 minutes?

24. The Fine Apparel store had $30,000 in business losses during the year. What was the average business loss per month?

Math Lab

25. Your class uses trial tosses to determine the appropriate target distance for a paper airplane contest. After constructing a box-and-whisker plot of the data, you find $Q_1 = -100$ centimeters and $Q_3 = 140$ centimeters. What is the range of the distance for which half the trial tosses landed?

26. The spec length of noodles is 52 millimeters. The actual length is 43 millimeters. Find the deviation from spec using the formula:

Deviation from spec = Actual length − Spec length

27. When scooping and counting beans, the average number of beans per scoop a is given by the formula:

$$\frac{N}{n} = a$$

where n is the number of scoops and N is the total number of beans in all the scoops. If the average is 17 beans per scoop, predict the number of beans in 8 scoops.

Chapter 4

Why Should I Learn This?

Successful business people write and solve equations to make decisions. For instance, how many trips between a quarry and construction site are needed to make a profit?

SOLVING EQUATIONS

LEARN HOW TO...

1. **Define variables and write equations to model and solve problems.**
2. **Use the Properties of Equality to solve addition, subtraction, multiplication, and division equations.**
3. **Solve equations using the Distributive Property to combine like terms.**
4. **Solve problems involving formulas.**

Writing and solving equations is one of the most common problem-solving strategies. In this chapter, you will see how equations can be used to solve problems that arise in everyday situations. Examples will include: planning a trip to Orlando, storing computer files, paying a restaurant bill, researching plant growth, and setting up a beach volleyball court.

Throughout the chapter, you should practice writing and solving equations following these steps:

- Define a variable for the unknown quantity.

- Write an equation that models the problem.

- Solve the equation using the Properties of Equality.

- Check the solution by substituting into the original equation.

An equation is solved when the variable is isolated on one side of the equal sign. You will learn to isolate the variable using the Properties of Equality, the Distributive Property, and the other properties from previous chapters.

You will also use formulas to solve problems. A formula is an equation that relates two or more variables. You can isolate any variable in a formula using the same properties.

Lesson 4.1 Addition and Subtraction Equations

OBJECTIVES

→ Solve equations using addition and subtraction properties of equality.

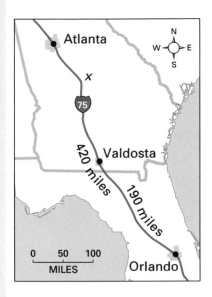

Colby is planning a trip from Atlanta to Orlando. According to his map, Atlanta is 420 miles from Orlando. Colby plans to stop for gas in Valdosta. Orlando is 190 miles from Valdosta. How far is Atlanta from Valdosta?

Let x represent the distance between Atlanta and Valdosta. The equation that models the distances is $x + 190 = 420$. This is an **addition equation** because 190 is added to the variable. How can Colby solve this equation?

You can model an addition equation with a pan balance. When the weight in the left pan equals the weight in the right pan, the pans are in balance. In the same way, an equation is "balanced" because both its sides are equal. This pan balance models the equation $5 = 3 + 2$.

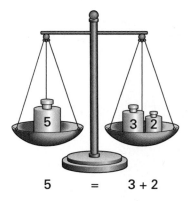

$$5 \quad = \quad 3 + 2$$

ACTIVITY 1   Solving Addition Equations

1 Add an unknown weight to the left pan. Call this weight x grams. The pans are no longer balanced. Write an expression for the total weight in the left pan.

2 The pans rebalance when an additional 3 grams are added to the right pan. Now what is the total weight in each pan? Write the equation modeled by the balance.

3 To find the unknown weight in the left pan, remove 5 grams from each side. Are the pans still balanced? Write the equation modeled by the balance. What is the unknown weight?

In Activity 1, you solved $x + 5 = 8$ by subtracting 5 from both sides of the equation. You can subtract the same amount from both sides of an equation and the equation will stay balanced. This result is called the **Subtraction Property of Equality.**

> **Subtraction Property of Equality**
>   For any numbers a, b, and c,
>
> $$\text{If } a = b, \text{ then } a - c = b - c.$$

To **solve** an equation, you find the value (or values) of the variable that makes the equation *true*. A value that makes an equation *true* is called a *solution*. To solve an equation, use the properties of algebra to **isolate** the variable on one side of the equal sign. Then make sure the solution is correct, by substituting it in the original equation.

EXAMPLE 1 Using the Subtraction Property of Equality

Solve Colby's addition equation $x + 190 = 420$.

SOLUTION

Subtraction is the inverse of addition. Using the Subtraction Property of Equality, subtract 190 from both sides of the equation. The equation will stay balanced and the variable will be isolated on the left side of the equal sign.

$x + 190 = 420$	Given
$x + 190 - 190 = 420 - 190$	Subtraction Property
$x + 0 = 230$	Simplify
$x = 230$	Identity Property of Addition

Check the solution in the original equation:

$$230 + 190 = 420 \quad \checkmark$$

The distance from Atlanta to Valdosta is 230 miles.

Critical Thinking Explain why the equations $420 = x + 190$ and $190 + x = 420$ also model the problem in Example 1. Explain how to solve each equation.

ONGOING ASSESSMENT

Write and solve an addition equation for the following problem.

Renaldo needs to save $250 to buy a new mountain bike. He has already saved $160. How much more does he need to save?

In a **subtraction equation**, a number is subtracted from the variable. Since addition is the inverse of subtraction, use addition to solve a subtraction equaton.

ACTIVITY 2   **Solving Subtraction Equations**

1 Start with the equation $15 - 6 = 9$. Add 6 to both sides of the equation. Is the equation still balanced?

2 Start with the equation $x - 6 = 9$. Add 6 to both sides of the equation. What is the value of the right side? How does the left side show that the equation is solved? What is the solution of the equation $x - 6 = 9$?

3 Explain how to use inverse operations to solve $x - 3 = 7$.

In Activity 2, you solved subtraction equations by adding the same number to both sides of the equation. You can add the same amount to both sides of an equation, and the equation will stay balanced. This is called the **Addition Property of Equality**.

Addition Property of Equality
For any numbers a, b, and c,

$$\text{If } a = b, \text{ then } a + c = b + c.$$

EXAMPLE 2 Using the Addition Property of Equality

Colby is planning a budget for his trip to Orlando. He estimates that gas and food will cost $150. After deducting this amount from the total budget, he wants to have $100 left for a visit to a theme park. Write and solve a subtraction equation for Colby's total budget.

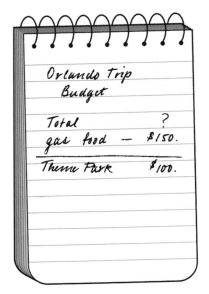

Orlando Trip
Budget

Total   ?
gas food — $150.
Theme Park $100.

SOLUTION

Total budget	−	Amount needed for gas and food	=	Amount left over for a theme park
x	−	150	=	100

$$x - 150 = 100 \qquad \text{Given}$$
$$x - 150 + 150 = 100 + 150 \qquad \text{Addition Property}$$
$$x + 0 = 250 \qquad \text{Simplify}$$
$$x = 250 \qquad \text{Identity Property of Addition}$$

Check the solution in the original equation:

$$250 - 150 = 100 \quad \checkmark$$

Colby needs a total budget of $250.

ONGOING ASSESSMENT

Solve each equation. Check your solution.

a. $7 = c + (-5)$ **b.** $q - (-3) = -8$ **c.** $45 + x = -18$

d. Write and solve a subtraction equation for the following problem.

e. A store reduced the price of all sweaters by $25. Nancy bought a sweater for $80. What was the original price of the sweater?

LESSON ASSESSMENT

1 A pan balance has the same amount of weight in each pan. You add 5 grams to each pan. Are the pans still balanced? What Property of Equality is modeled?

2 How are inverse operations used to solve addition and subtraction equations?

3 To solve a subtraction equation, how can you tell what number to add to both sides?

4 Explain how to solve $c + 5 = -8$.

5 Describe how to check the solution of an equation.

Practice and Apply

Solve each equation. Show each step.

6. $t + 16 = -5$ **7.** $2.8 = x - 1.5$

8. $34 + m = 24$ **9.** $r - (-32) = 46$

Solve each equation.

10. $129 = a + 93$ **11.** $-15 = s - 39$

12. $5.7 + x = 4.7$ **13.** $y + (-74) = 63$

14. $-49 = p - 65$ **15.** $q - (-31) = 34$

16. $u + (-18) = -27$ **17.** $-63 = d + 88$

18. $-23 = z - (-10)$ **19.** $-3.6 + n = -5.4$

For Exercises 20–25, define a variable. Write an addition or subtraction equation. Then solve the equation.

20. A theater seats 436 people. On Friday night, 375 people attended the theater. How many empty seats were in the theater?

21. Maurice spent $64 on CDs. He has $25 left. How much did Maurice have before he bought the CDs?

22. A box containing washers weighs 550 grams. The box weighs 35 grams when it is empty. What is the weight of the washers?

23. During one growing season, an orchard lost 21 trees due to cold temperatures. If the orchard has 190 trees at the end of the growing season, how many trees did it have at the beginning of the season?

24. During 2 weeks, Raul drove his car 588 miles. The second week, Raul drove 326 miles. How many miles did Raul drive the first week?

25. Robin's paycheck was $144 after $36 was deducted for taxes. What was the amount of Robin's pay before taxes?

Mixed Review

List the numbers in order from least to greatest.

26. 0.4457 0.445 0.4465

27. 23,465 23,654 23,546

This stem-and-leaf plot shows the weekly fuel use for a fleet of service vans. Use the data to complete Exercises 28–30.

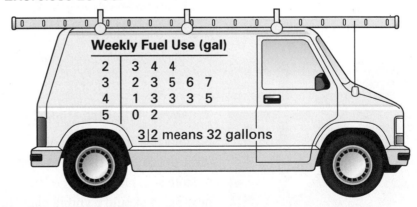

Weekly Fuel Use (gal)	
2	3 4 4
3	2 3 5 6 7
4	1 3 3 3 5
5	0 2

3|2 means 32 gallons

28. What is the range of the data?

29. How many vans use less than 35 gallons per week?

30. Find the mean, median, and mode of the data.

31. Find the value of $\frac{10m + 5}{5m}$ when $m = 1.2$.

32. Find the value of $3c - 2d$ when $c = -4$ and $d = -5$.

LESSON 4.2 MULTIPLICATION AND DIVISION EQUATIONS

OBJECTIVES
- - - - - - - -
➔ Solve equations using multiplication and division properties of equality.

In Lesson 4.1, you learned to solve addition and subtraction equations using inverse operations. Just like addition and subtraction, multiplication and division are inverse operations.

ACTIVITY 1   The Division Property of Equality

1. Start with the equation $5 \cdot 3 = 15$. Divide both sides of the equation by 5. Simplify both sides of the equation. Is the new equation *true*?

2. Start with the equation $5y = 15$. This is a **multiplication equation** because the variable is multiplied by 5. Divide both sides of the equation by 5. Simplify both sides of the equation. How does the left side show the equation is solved?

3. What is the solution of $5y = 15$?

In Activity 1, you solved the multiplication equation $5y = 15$ by dividing both sides of the equation by 5. You can divide both sides of an equation by the same nonzero number, and the equation stays balanced. This is called the **Division Property of Equality**.

> ### Division Property of Equality
> For any numbers a, b, and c, where $c \neq 0$,
>
> $$\text{If } a = b, \text{ then } a \div c = b \div c.$$

EXAMPLE 1 Solving Multiplication Equations

Cynthia has an after-school job as a clerk in a law office. Her directory in the office filing system has four folders. Cynthia wants to store an equal number of files in each folder. If she has 212 files, how many should Cynthia place in each folder?

SOLUTION

Let y represent the number of files in each folder. Since each of the four folders contains y files, the total number of files is represented by $4y$. Thus, Cynthia needs to solve a multiplication equation.

Number of folders		Number of files per folder	=	Total number of files
4	·	y	=	212

$$4y = 212 \quad \text{Given}$$
$$\frac{4y}{4} = \frac{212}{4} \quad \text{Division Property}$$
$$1y = 53 \quad \text{Simplify}$$
$$y = 53 \quad \text{Identity Property of Multiplication}$$

Check the solution in the original equation:

$$4 \cdot 53 = 212 \quad \checkmark$$

Cynthia should place 53 files in each folder.

ONGOING ASSESSMENT

Solve each equation. Check your solution.
a. $5g = -225$ **b.** $96 = -8h$ **c.** $-18x = -2080$

d. Define a variable, write a multiplication equation, and solve the following problem: The cost of a coat is $147. This is 3 times the cost of a pair of slacks. What is the cost of the slacks?

ACTIVITY 2 The Multiplication Property of Equality

1 Start with the equation $\frac{63}{9} = 7$. Multiply both sides of the equation by 9. Simplify both sides of the equation. Is the new equation still *true*?

2 Start with the equation $\frac{y}{9} = 7$. This is a **division equation** because the variable is divided by 9. Multiply both sides of the equation by 9. Simplify both sides of the equation. How does the left side show the equation is solved?

3 What is the solution of $\frac{y}{9} = 7$?

In Activity 2, you solved a division equation by multiplying both sides of the equation by the same number. You can multiply both sides of an equation by the same number, and the equation will stay balanced. This is called the **Multiplication Property of Equality**.

> **Multiplication Property of Equality**
> For any numbers a, b, and c,
> $$\text{If } a = b, \text{ then } a \cdot c = b \cdot c.$$

EXAMPLE 2 Using the Multiplication Property of Equality

Joan needs to make copies of a letter to place in 23 folders. She will divide the total number of copies so that four are placed in each folder. Write and solve a division equation to find the number of copies of the letter Joan needs to make.

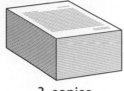

_?_ copies

23 folders

4 copies per folder

SOLUTION

Since multiplication is the inverse of division, you can use the Multiplication Property of Equality. Let y represent the number of copies.

$$\boxed{\frac{\text{Number of copies}}{\text{Number of folders}}} = \boxed{\text{Number of copies per folder}}$$

$$\frac{y}{23} = 4 \qquad\qquad \text{Given}$$

$$\frac{y}{23} \cdot 23 = 4 \cdot 23 \qquad\qquad \text{Multiplication Property}$$

$$y \cdot 1 = 92 \qquad\qquad \text{Simplify}$$

$$y = 92 \qquad\qquad \text{Identity Property of Multiplication}$$

Check the solution in the original equation:

$$\frac{92}{23} = 4 \quad \checkmark$$

Joan needs to make 92 copies of the letter.

ONGOING ASSESSMENT

Solve each equation. Check your solution.

a. $\dfrac{p}{8} = -25$ **b.** $\dfrac{f}{-6} = 12$ **c.** $-8 = \dfrac{x}{-9}$

LESSON ASSESSMENT

1 Why are multiplication and division inverse operations?

2 To solve a multiplication equation, how can you tell what number to use as a divisor?

3 Explain how to solve $\frac{c}{2} = 1$. What property of equality do you use?

Practice and Apply

Solve each equation. Show each step.

4. $-2x = 16$

5. $\frac{x}{7} = -8$

6. $-5 = \frac{x}{-5}$

7. $-135 = 1.5x$

Solve each equation.

8. $4.5 = 9m$

9. $\frac{x}{-8} = 4$

10. $-12 = \frac{y}{12}$

11. $-16b = 1.6$

12. $21r = -336$

13. $0 = \frac{d}{-7}$

14. $-3.3n = -6.6$

15. $324 = -18x$

16. $\frac{c}{2.4} = -6$

17. $-1 = \frac{z}{-12}$

For Exercises 18–23, define a variable. Then write a multiplication or division equation. Solve the equation.

18. A computer technician earns $630 in one week. If the technician works 35 hours, how much does the technician earn per hour?

19. The population of the Austin metro area is about 900,000. This is about 6 times the population of Waco. What is the approximate population of Waco?

20. The weight of an object on the moon is its weight on Earth divided by 6. If a rock weighs 22.5 pounds on the moon, how much does it weigh on Earth?

21. A package of photographic paper contains 250 sheets and is 6 centimeters thick. What is the thickness of one sheet of paper?

22. Sol divided a set of game pieces among 5 people. Each person received 12 game pieces. How many game pieces did Sol have before they were divided?

23. The toll for driving between two cities is $2. How many cars must drive between the two cities to collect a toll of $450?

ALL CARS
STOP - PAY TOLL
$2.00

Mixed Review

Write the value of the underlined digit.

24. <u>1</u>4,678

25. 2,<u>4</u>56,735

26. 0.062<u>0</u>8

27. Round 23,944 to the nearest hundred.

28. Round 0.5472 to the nearest hundredth.

Evaluate $5x - y$ for each value of x and y,

29. when $x = -2$ and $y = 10$

30. when $x = 2.5$ and $y = 12.7$

31. when $x = -1.3$ and $y = -3.8$

32. The temperature dropped 2 degrees each hour for 4 hours. Write an expression to model the temperature drop. Simplify the expression.

Cumulative Problem Solving

Jarrod is collecting money from 7 of his friends for tickets to an NHL game. The 8 tickets cost $160 plus a $2-per-ticket service charge for the first 5 tickets.

33. What is the total amount for the tickets and service charge?

34. Let x represent the amount each person must pay if the cost is shared equally. Write a multiplication equation Jarrod can use to determine how much each person should pay.

35. Solve the equation. How much should Jarrod collect from each person?

Rick is considering a contract for hauling limestone rock to a construction site.

36. The contractor will pay $5.30 per thousand pounds of limestone delivered. Let x represent the number of pounds (in thousands) Rick hauls in each delivery. Write an expression for the payment Rick receives to deliver x pounds of limestone.

37. Rick estimates it will take 75 gallons of fuel to deliver a load of limestone to the construction site. Fuel costs $1.35 per gallon. What is Rick's estimated fuel cost per load of limestone?

38. Write an equation for which Rick's fuel cost is equal to his payment received for each delivery. Solve the equation for x. How many thousand pounds of limestone must Rick deliver to pay for his fuel? This is called the **break-even** point.

39. Rick's truck can haul 40,500 pounds. If each delivery is a full load, what profit will he make on each delivery?

Tyler's bowling team competes in a league. Each bowler in the league has a handicap that is determined from the bowler's average score. In competition, each team bowls 3 games. The team's scratch score in a game is the total number of pins knocked down. The handicaps are added to the scratch scores, and the team with the highest total handicap score for all 3 games is the winner of the match.

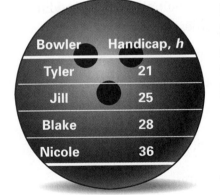

Bowler	Handicap, h
Tyler	21
Jill	25
Blake	28
Nicole	36

Handicap score	=	Scratch score	+	Handicap
t	=	s	+	h

Tyler's team has handicaps as shown in the table at left.

40. Tyler had a handicap score of 643 in his match. What was his scratch score?

41. What is Tyler's team handicap for one game? What is the team handicap for 3 games?

42. In a match, their opponent's team makes a handicap score of 2358. What scratch score does Tyler's team need to win the match?

LESSON 4.3 TWO-STEP EQUATIONS

OBJECTIVES
- Solve two-step equations.
- Solve equations using the distributive property.

After winning a soccer game, 5 players decide to celebrate by eating at a restaurant. The total cost of the dinner is $43.50. The players decide to share the cost equally. The group has a $6 discount coupon. How much should each person pay for the dinner?

Let x represent the amount each person pays. Write an equation for the cost of the dinner.

Amount paid by all 5 players if each pays x	$+$	Amount of the coupon	$=$	Total cost of the dinner
$5 \cdot x$	$+$	6	$=$	43.50

$$5x + 6 = 43.50$$

EXAMPLE   Solving a Two-Step Equation

Solve $5x + 6 = 43.50$.

SOLUTION

This equation involves two operations: multiplication and addition. To isolate x, you must use two properties of equality.

$5x + 6 = 43.50$	Given
$5x + 6 - 6 = 43.50 - 6$	Subtraction Property
$5x = 37.50$	Simplify
$\dfrac{5x}{5} = \dfrac{37.50}{5}$	Division Property
$x = 7.50$	Simplify

Check the solution in the original equation:

$$5 \cdot 7.50 + 6 = 37.50 + 6$$
$$= 43.50 \checkmark$$

Each person should pay $7.50.

To solve an equation that involves two operations, you must use two steps. These are called **two-step equations**.

ACTIVITY 1   Solving Two-Step Equations

Supply the missing properties or the reasons that justify each step in solving $\frac{h}{5} - 2 = 1$.

1 $\frac{h}{5} - 2 = 1$ Given

2 $\frac{h}{5} - 2 + 2 = 1 + 2$ <u> ? </u>

3 $\frac{h}{5} = 3$ <u> ? </u>

4 $\frac{h}{5} \cdot 5 = 3 \cdot 5$ <u> ? </u>

5 $h = 15$ <u> ? </u>

ONGOING ASSESSMENT

Solve each equation. Show each step and provide a reason. Check your solution.

a. $8y - 12 = -40$ **b.** $\dfrac{x}{-6} + 5 = -3$

ACTIVITY 2   Using the Distributive Property

You can solve some equations with more than one method.

Method 1 Use the Distributive Property First

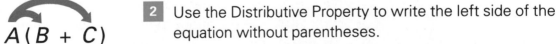

1 Start with $3(x - 2) = 12$.

2 Use the Distributive Property to write the left side of the equation without parentheses.

3 Solve the resulting two-step equation.

4 What two properties of equality are required?

Method 2 Use the Division Property First

1 Start again with $3(x - 2) = 12$.

2 Use the Division Property of Equality to eliminate 3 from the left side of the equation.

3 Solve the resulting subtraction equation.

4 Which method uses fewer steps?

PROBLEM SOLVING

USING THE FOUR-STEP PLAN

Writing an equation is an important strategy for solving many types of problems. Work through the four-step process to set up an equation to solve the following problem.

Lauren buys 9 used paperback books and Mason buys 7. Each book costs the same. The total cost of the books is $24. What is the cost of each book?

Step 1 Understand the Problem

What is the problem about? List the facts you are given. Summarize the goal of the problem in a few words.

Step 2 Develop a Plan

Problem-solving strategy: Use an equation. Assemble the facts into one or more "word equations" similar to the following:

The total cost of the books   is $24.

Lauren's cost plus Mason's cost equals $24.

$$\underline{\quad ? \quad} + \underline{\quad ? \quad} = 24$$

What other facts can be used to complete the equation? What quantity is *unknown*? Define a variable for the unknown.

Step 3 Carry Out the Plan

Write the equation with the variable. Solve the equation.

Step 4 Check the Results

Does the solution make sense? Make sure your solution is the solution to the equation. Does the solution answer the problem stated?

LESSON ASSESSMENT

Think and Discuss

1 Write an algorithm for solving $3x + 9 = 15$.

2 Does the order in which you use inverse operations to solve two-step equations affect the results? Explain.

3 How can you solve $3x + 9 = 15$ using mental math?

4 Describe two methods for solving $4(x - 2) = 16$.

Practice and Apply

Solve each equation. Show each step.

5. $\dfrac{x}{2} + 7 = 8$

6. $8x - (-13) = 21$

7. $15 = -4x - 5$

8. $\dfrac{x}{7} + (-3) = 8$

Solve each equation.

9. $9.6 + \dfrac{x}{-12} = 3.4$

10. $-60 = 4(x - 5)$

11. $21 = 3t + 8$

12. $2.6n - 1 = 14.08$

13. $\dfrac{p}{-2} + 8 = 15$

14. $4 = \dfrac{x + 16}{4}$

15. $-0.8 + \dfrac{a}{8} = -4$

16. $8(t + 7) = -24$

17. $\dfrac{q - 26}{3} = 16$

18. $40 = 8m - 40$

For Exercises 19–23, define a variable. Then write an equation and solve.

19. Twana paid $190 for 3 sweaters and a jacket. The jacket costs $55. If each sweater costs the same amount, what is the cost of each one?

20. To buy a new car, you must make a down payment of $2000 and pay 48 equal monthly payments. The total amount paid is $17,360. What is your monthly payment?

21. Mr. Broglio is planning a budget for a 6-day business trip. If he divides the total amount needed by the number of days and deducts $115 per day for hotel expenses, he wants to have $35 per day left over for meals. What total amount should Mr. Broglio budget for the trip?

TRAVEL EXPENSES	
September 4	**Amount**
Breakfast	
Lunch	
Dinner	
Hotel/Motel	
Trans: Plane	
Railroad	
Taxi/Bus	
Rental	
Baggage	
Entertainment	
Gifts	
Tips	
Telephone	
Auto: Gas/Oil	
Repairs	
Tires	
Insurance	
Taxes	
Parking/Tolls	
Other	
TOTAL	

22. It costs $135 to join a flying club and $15 per month for dues. Brenda has paid the flying club $240. How many months has Brenda been a member of the flying club?

23. An electronics store sells a TV set for $45 less than 3 times the cost to the store. The TV set sells for $270. What is the cost of the TV set to the store?

Brandon has 3 fewer cards than Adoette, and Ebony has 4 times as many cards as Brandon.

24. If Adoette has *m* cards, write an expression that represents the number of cards Brandon has.

25. Write an expression using *m* for the number of cards Ebony has.

26. If Ebony has 8 cards, how many do Adoette and Brandon each have?

Mixed Review

Use rounding to estimate the answer to the nearest hundred.

27. $25,184.5 + 16,487.25 + 19,815.7$

Use rounding to estimate the answer to the nearest ten dollars.

28. $\$783.75 + \$1536.82 - \$625.13$

Evaluate each expression when $s = 4$, $t = -6$, and $u = -5$.

LESSON 4.4 ADDING AND SUBTRACTING EXPRESSIONS

OBJECTIVES
- Combine like terms.
- Solve equations that have like terms.

Some equations contain addition and subtraction of algebraic expressions. For example, how would you solve the following equation?

$$2x - 3x = 5.4$$

You can model addition and subtraction of algebraic expressions with Algeblocks. A rectangular block represents a variable. The algebraic expressions $2x$ and $-3x$ are modeled below.

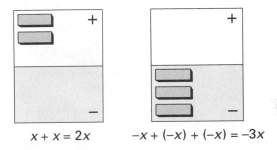

$$x + x = 2x \qquad -x + (-x) + (-x) = -3x$$

ACTIVITY 1   Adding Algebraic Expressions

Follow these steps to model and simplify $2x + (-3x)$.

1 Place two x-blocks on the mat to model $2x$. Add three x-blocks to the negative side of the mat to model $-3x$. $2x$ and $-3x$ are called the **terms** of the expression $2x + (-3x)$. Since the variable, x, is the same in both terms, they are also called **like terms**.

2 Remember, you can remove a zero pair from the mat without changing the value on the mat. What is the largest zero pair you can make with the blocks? Remove that pair from the mat. What single expression is equivalent to $2x + (-3x)$?

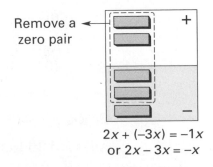

Remove a zero pair ←

$$2x + (-3x) = -1x$$
$$\text{or } 2x - 3x = -x$$

3 You can also simplify $2x + (-3x)$ by **combining like terms**. This is an application of the Distributive Property. Complete:

$$2x + (-3x) = [2 + (-3)]x = \underline{\ ?\ }$$

4 Use Algeblocks to model and simplify each algebraic expression. Then simplify each expression by combining like terms. Do you get the same answer using both methods?

a. $2x + 3x$ **b.** $-3x + x$ **c.** $4x - 3x$ **d.** $-x - 4x$

EXAMPLE 1 Solving Equations Containing Like Terms

Anita and Bridget are members of a bicycle racing team. When they train together, they pedal at the same speed, and take turns leading.

The distance around one lap of their training course measures 5.4 kilometers (km). Their schedule for one lap calls for Anita to lead for 7 minutes and then for Bridget to lead for 3 minutes. At what speed should they travel around the course to meet this schedule?

SOLUTION

Distance traveled is the product *time · speed*. Let x represent the unknown speed in kilometers per minute.

Distance traveled with Anita leading		Distance traveled with Bridget leading		Distance around the course
	$+$		$=$	

$$7 \text{ min} \cdot x\,\frac{\text{km}}{\text{min}} \quad + \quad 3 \text{ min} \cdot x\,\frac{\text{km}}{\text{min}} \quad = \quad 5.4 \text{ km}$$

$7x + 3x = 5.4$ Given

$10x = 5.4$ Combine like terms

$\dfrac{10x}{10} = \dfrac{5.4}{10}$ Division Property

$x = 0.54$ Simplify

Check: $7(0.54) + 3(0.54) = 3.78 + 1.62 = 5.4$ ✓

Anita and Bridget should pedal at 0.54 kilometers per minute.

Solve each equation.

a. $8a + 4a = -36$ **b.** $40 = 2m + 5m + 3m$

Critical Thinking   In the variable expression $3x$, 3 is called the
coefficient of the variable x. When you combine like terms, what do
you do with the coefficients? Use your answer to explain why
$3x + (-3x)$ does not equal x.

ACTIVITY 2   **Using Algeblocks**

Follow the steps to model and simplify $(3x + 2) + (-x + 1)$.

1 Place three x-blocks and two unit blocks on the mat to model
$3x + 2$. Add one x-block and one unit block to model $-x + 1$.

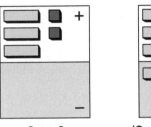

$3x + 2$ $(3x + 2) + (-x + 1)$

2 What is the largest zero pair you can make with the blocks?
Remove that pair from the mat. What single expression is
equal to $(3x + 2) + (-x + 1)$?

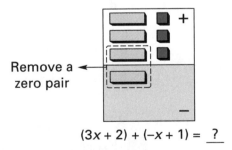

Remove a
zero pair

$(3x + 2) + (-x + 1) =$ __?__

3 You can also simplify the expression by **rearranging** the
terms. Give the missing reasons for the following steps.

$(3x + 2) + (^-x + 1)$	Given
$3x + 2 + (-x) + 1$	__?__
$3x + (-x) + 2 + 1$	__?__
$2x + 3$	__?__

EXAMPLE 2 Combining Like Terms to Solve Equations

Solve $-14 = 5y - 2(y + 1)$.

SOLUTION

$-14 = 5y - 2(y + 1)$	Given
$-14 = 5y - 2y - 2$	Distributive Property
$-14 = 3y - 2$	Combine like terms
$-14 + 2 = 3y - 2 + 2$	Addition Property
$-12 = 3y$	Simplify
$\dfrac{-12}{3} = \dfrac{3y}{3}$	Division Property
$-4 = y$	Simplify

Check:

$$5(-4) - 2(-4 + 1) = -20 - 2(-3) = -20 + 6 = -14 \quad \checkmark$$

ONGOING ASSESSMENT

Solve and check each of the following equations.

a. $3(t - 2) + t = -2$

b. $2a - 3(1 - a) = 12$

c. $6 = \dfrac{x + 4}{3} + 1$

d. $\dfrac{-2x + 3}{2} = -10$

LESSON ASSESSMENT

Think and Discuss

1 Explain how to use Algeblocks to simplify $(2x + 3) + (-5x + 1)$.

2 Write an algorithm for simplifying $2(x - 3) + (-5x + 1)$ algebraically.

3 Make a list of all the properties you can use to simplify expressions and solve equations.

4 What property do you use when you combine like terms?

Simplify each expression.

5. $7e + 3e + 5e$

6. $9p - 3p + 7p$

7. $4n - 3(2n - 6n)$

8. $6.25r - 7.08 - 3(9.13 + r)$

Solve each equation.

9. $12t + 13t = -50$

10. $2.5d - 2.6d = -4.2$

11. $-4y + 9 + 2y = -11$

12. $-5s + 3s - 2s = 48$

13. $48 = 9a - (3a + 12)$

14. $7(3.4x - 5.3x) = -84.5$

15. $-(5.6q - 6.5q) = -8.3$

16. $\dfrac{15x + 9x}{-2} = -48$

17. $5(2x + 3) - 8x = 7$

18. $-8 = 2(-3b + 8b) - (9b - 1)$

For Exercises 19–27, define a variable. Then write an equation and solve.

19. Sita and Alicia earn the same amount of money per hour. Sita worked 16 hours and Alicia worked 20 hours. Together, they earned $315. How much do Sita and Alicia each earn per hour?

20. There are 56 kilobytes of data in two computer files. The second file contains 12 kilobytes more than the first. How many kilobytes of data are in each file?

21. There are 560 students in Fairview School. There are 26 fewer boys than girls. How many girls are in Fairview School?

22. Susan delivers the paper to 5 times as many customers as Arthur. Together they have 312 customers. How many customers does Arthur have?

23. Kris and Yassin own 315 shares of stock together. Yassin owns 15 less than twice the number of shares owned by Kris. How many shares does Kris own?

24. The sum of two consecutive integers is 73. What are the integers?

25. Isako collects 42 pounds of aluminum cans and Stacy collects 56 pounds. When they redeem the cans for recycling, they receive $34.30 altogether. How much did they receive for each pound of aluminum cans?

26. A 48-inch board is cut into 3 smaller boards. One board is 2 inches longer than the shortest board. The other is 4 inches longer than the shortest board. What is the length of the shortest board?

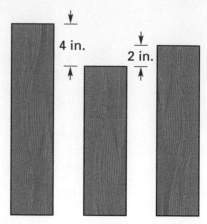

27. In gym class, Lamont, Trey, and Devon ran a total of 50 minutes. Lamont ran twice as many minutes as Trey. Devon ran 2 minutes more than Trey. How many minutes did Trey run in gym class?

Mixed Review

Replace the __?__ with $<$, $>$, or $=$ to make a *true* statement.

28. $3.01 + 5.8$ __?__ $4(2)$ **29.** $74.5 - 48.9$ __?__ $2(12.9)$

30. $3.2(1.6)$ __?__ 5.5 **31.** $\dfrac{19.3}{2}$ __?__ $4.2 + 4.45$

Find the value of $3a - 2b + 5c$ when

32. $a = 8$, $b = 4$, and $c = -2$.

33. $a = -3$, $b = -2$, and $c = -5$.

34. $a = -1.3$, $b = 3.6$, and $c = 0.2$.

Cumulative Problem Solving

Cerissa is planning a trip to Washington for the Richfield High School band. The total cost of the trip is $16,000. The school pays $2500, and the remaining cost is divided equally among 78 band members and sponsors going on the trip.

35. Let *c* represent the cost per person. Write an equation Cerissa can use to determine how much each person going on the trip should pay.

36. Solve the equation. How much should Cerissa collect from each person?

Tano owns The Business Print Shop. A customer needs 1500 copies of a 25-page document. Tano has two printers. One prints 250 pages per minute and the other prints 180 pages per minute. He will run both printers at the same time for the job. Tano needs to tell the customer how much time it will take to print the documents.

37. What is the total number of pages to be printed?

38. Let t represent the time required to print the pages. How many pages are printed in t minutes by the faster printer? How many by the slower printer? Write an expression for the total number of pages printed in t minutes when both printers run at the same time.

39. Write an equation for the number of pages to be printed for the customer. Solve the equation for t. How many minutes will it take to print the pages?

40. How many pages will Tano print on the faster printer? How many on the slower printer?

Ana feeds her new puppy a mixture of canned and dry food. The veterinarian recommends 65 grams of protein per day in the puppy's diet. The puppy gets 30 grams of protein per day from the canned food. The dry food contains 3.2 grams of protein per ounce. Ana needs to determine how much dry food to mix with the canned food.

41. Let z represent the number of ounces of dry food. How many grams of protein will the puppy get from z ounces of dry food?

42. Write an equation for the total number of grams of protein the puppy will get from the canned and dry foods if Ana follows the veterinarian's recommendation.

43. Solve the equation for z. How much dry food should Ana feed the puppy per day?

Micah buys 4 dozen petunias. He wants to plant an equal number of the petunias in 3 planters in his yard. He also wants to plant 6 of the petunias in a pot.

44. Define a variable and write an equation Micah can use to determine the number of petunias to plant in each planter.

45. Solve the equation. How many petunias should Micah plant in each planter?

Amelia walks 4 days a week as part of her exercise program. She writes her walking schedule in a weekly planner. Amelia's goal is to burn 1700 calories for the week.

WEEKLY PLANNER				
Monday April 11	Tuesday April 12	Wednesday April 13	Thursday April 14	Friday April 15
Walk	*Walk*		*Walk*	*Walk*
1 mile	*$1\frac{1}{2}$ miles*		*$1\frac{1}{2}$ miles*	*1 mile*

46. Let *c* represent the number of calories per mile Amelia burns while walking. Write an expression for the number of calories she burns walking for the week shown.

47. Equate Amelia's goal to the number of calories she burns walking for the week shown in the schedule. Solve the equation for *c*. How many calories per mile must Amelia burn to meet her goal?

48. The chart shows the average number of calories per mile burned by a person of Amelia's weight while walking at three speeds. At what speed should Amelia walk to burn 1700 calories for the week?

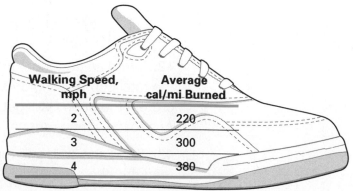

Walking Speed, mph	Average cal/mi Burned
2	220
3	300
4	380

LESSON 4.5 EQUATIONS WITH VARIABLES ON BOTH SIDES

Margaret is a scientist studying the impact of different fertilizers on the growth rates of corn. She uses Type A fertilizer in Field 1 and Type B fertilizer in Field 2. When the corn plants reach the same average height in both fields, Margaret will take samples and analyze them. When should Margaret take the samples?

The following diagram shows the fields on the day the corn plants in Field 1 have an average height of 6 centimeters (cm).

Field 1

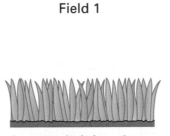

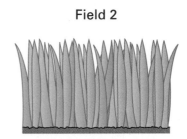

Field 2

Average height = 6 cm
Average growth rate = 1.3 $\frac{cm}{day}$

Average height = 12 cm
Average growth rate = 0.9 $\frac{cm}{day}$

In her data book Margaret records the average height of each field. She records her first measurements in the row for Day 0. She records one day's growth in Day 1, and so on.

Day	Height of Plants in Field 1 (cm)	Height of Plants in Field 2 (cm)
0	6	☐
1	6 + 1.3	☐
2	6 + 2(1.3)	☐
3	6 + 3(1.3)	☐
⋮		
n	?	?

ACTIVITY 1   **Writing Equivalent Expressions**

1 Copy Margaret's table.

2 What is the average height of the plants in Field 2 on Day 0? Enter this value in the table.

3 The first day, the plants in Field 1 grow an average of 1.3 cm. Thus, their average height is 6 cm + 1.3 cm. Write an expression for the average height of the plants in Field 2 on the first day. Enter this expression in the table.

4 The second day, the plants in Field 1 grow an average of 1.3 cm. Thus, their average height is 6 cm + 1.3 cm + 1.3 cm, or 6 + 2(1.3) cm. Write an expression for the average height of the plants in Field 2 on the second day. Enter this expression in the table.

5 If the pattern continues, what is the average height of the plants in Field 1 on the nth day? What is the average height of the plants in Field 2 on the nth day? Enter these expressions in the table.

6 The variable n can be replaced by any number greater than or equal to zero. Calculate the average heights of the plants in Field 1 and in Field 2 on Days 5, 10, and 15. Are the heights equal on any of these days?

In Activity 1, you modeled plant heights with algebraic expressions. Set these two expressions equal to each other.

$$6 + 1.3n = 12 + 0.9n$$

The value of n that makes the equation *true* is the day Field 1 and Field 2 corn plants have the same average height. To solve the equation, isolate the variable.

ACTIVITY 2   **Solving Equations with a Variable on Both Sides**

Supply the reasons for each step in the solution.

1 $6 + 1.3n = 12 + 0.9n$ Given

2 $6 + 1.3n - 0.9n = 12 + 0.9n - 0.9n$ _?_

3 $6 + 0.4n = 12$ _?_

4 $6 - 6 + 0.4n = 12 - 6$ _?_

5 $0.4n = 6$ _?_

6 $\dfrac{0.4n}{0.4} = \dfrac{6}{0.4}$ _?_

7 $n = 15$ _?_

Critical Thinking To solve $x + 10 = 6x$ you can isolate the variable on the left side or the right side of the equal sign. Which method requires the fewest steps?

ONGOING ASSESSMENT

Solve each equation.

a. $3m - 2 = 2m + 5$ **b.** $2n + 1 = 2(5n - 1)$

c. In the following problem, define a variable. Write an equation to model the problem. Solve the equation.

Rosie and Andrew are hiking in a Volksmarch. Rosie has hiked 5 miles and is covering 4 miles each hour. Andrew has hiked 8 miles and is covering 3 miles each hour. If they continue at these rates, in how many hours will Rosie and Andrew have hiked the same distance?

So far, the equations you have solved have had exactly one solution. This is not the case for all equations.

EXAMPLE   Many Solutions or No Solutions

Solve each equation.

a. $2(x + 1) = x + 2 + x$ **b.** $6 + x = 2x + 3 - x$

SOLUTION

a. Simplify each side.

$2(x + 1) = x + 2 + x$	Given
$2x + 2 = 2x + 2$	Distributive Property; Combine like terms
$2 = 2$	Subtraction Property

This result is always *true*. Any number you use as a replacement for x makes the original equation *true*. The solution is the set of all numbers. Such an equation is called an **identity**.

b. Simplify each side.

$6 + x = 2x + 3 - x$	Given
$6 + x = 3 + x$	Combine like terms
$6 = 3.$	Subtraction Property

This result is never *true*. There is no replacement for x that makes the original equation *true*. Thus, there is no solution.

CULTURAL CONNECTION

Some of the earliest examples of equation solving are found in the Rhind Papyrus now located in the British Museum. The Rhind Papyrus is a problem-solving handbook that dates back to the time of the Egyptian scribe Ahmes about 1650 BCE. The Rhind Papyrus presents a method that was later known as **false position.**

The following steps show how to solve $x + 2x = 30$ using the method of false position.

Step 1 Guess a solution and substitute your guess in the left-hand side of the equation. Suppose you guess 2. Then

$$2 + 2(2) = 6$$

Step 2 Let a represent a multiplication factor for the left-hand side of the equation. Solve a multiplication equation for a using the value from Step 1 and the original equation.

$$6a = 30$$
$$a = 5$$

Step 3 Multiply your guess by the factor. The product is the solution to the original equation. Thus,

$$2 \cdot 5, \text{ or } 10 \text{ is the solution.}$$

Use the method of false position to solve each equation.

1. $5x + 4x = 81$

2. $7x - 3x = 48$

3. Start with $3x + 6x = 36$. Let your guess be represented by g. Use the method of false position to show the solution is ga where $a = \frac{4}{g}$.

Lesson Assessment

Think and Discuss

1 When you solve an equation with variables on both sides, which of the following should you do?

    a. Use the properties of algebra as reasons for the steps.

    b. Keep the equations balanced.

    c. Isolate the variable on one side of the equation.

    d. Check your answer by substituting it into the original equation.

    e. All of the above.

2 What first step would you use to solve each equation? Explain why.

    a. $8t - 3 = 2t + 9$ **b.** $3(2 - x) = x$

3 Describe the result of solving an equation that is an identity.

4 Describe the result of solving an equation with no solution.

Practice and Apply

Solve each equation.

  5. $5x = 20 - 3x$ **6.** $8a - 6 = 2a + 42$

  7. $c - 10 = 4c$ **8.** $5p = p - 4.8$

  9. $8y = 2y + 30$ **10.** $5d = -2d - 24$

11. $7.5r + 4.3 = 4.1r + 8.4$ **12.** $5k - 10 = 2k + 17$

13. $8q + 18 = -q$ **14.** $8m = 7m - 8 + m$

15. $8t + 15 - 10t = -7t$ **16.** $7z + 2z + 6 = 3(3z + 2)$

17. $3.5(n + 4) = -2.9(n + 9)$ **18.** $5x - (x + 12) = -4(3 - x)$

Define a variable, write an equation, and solve.

19. Two car companies offer Naliake a job as a sales associate. The first company pays $2000 per month and a commission of $50 for each car she sells. The second company pays $1500 per month and a commission of $75 for each car she sells. How many cars per month must Naliake sell to earn the same amount from each company?

20. Diam must equalize the temperatures of two furnaces in a semiconductor manufacturing plant. The temperature of one furnace is 1500°C. It can be cooled at a rate of 10°C per minute. The temperature of the other furnace is 800°C. It can be heated at a rate of 15°C per minute. How many minutes will it take Diam to make the temperatures in the furnaces the same?

21. Awanda and Ryan are stamp collectors. Awanda needs 150 stamps to have the same number as Ryan. Ryan has 3 times as many stamps as Awanda. How many stamps does Awanda have?

22. An airplane has 2,250 gallons of fuel in the left-wing tank, and 3,100 gallons in the right-wing tank. Fuel is pumped from the right tank to the left tank at a rate of 50 gallons per minute. How long will it take until both tanks have the same amount of fuel?

Mixed Review

Name the property illustrated by each of the following.

23. $7(8 - 3) = (8 - 3)7$

24. $9 \cdot (2 \cdot 5) = (9 \cdot 2) \cdot 5$

25. $a + (b + 0) = a + b$

26. $12 + (-12) = 0$

Use the Distributive Property to find each product.

27. $9 \cdot 15$

28. $35 \cdot 22$

Write the next two numbers in each sequence.

29. 1, 3, 6, 10

30. $-7, 14, -21, 28$

31. Find the value of $3c + 4a$ when $a = -2$ and $c = -5$.

32. Find the value of $\frac{-9a}{b + c}$ when $a = 5$, $b = -3$, and $c = 7.5$.

33. A cake is placed in the oven at 5:20 P.M. If the cake takes 45 minutes to bake, when should the cake be removed from the oven?

LESSON 4.6 FORMULAS

OBJECTIVES

- Use formulas and units to solve problems.
- Solve a literal equation.

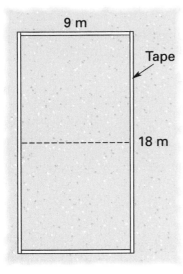

9 m

Tape

18 m

Spencer is setting up a court for a beach volleyball tournament. The court is a 9-meter by 18-meter rectangle. Spencer uses nylon tape to mark the boundary of the court. What length of tape does he need?

The distance around the rectangle is its **perimeter.** You can find the perimeter with the following *formula.*

$$P = 2l + 2w$$

A **formula** is an equation that shows how two or more quantities are related. The quantities are represented by variables. In the formula for the perimeter of a rectangle, P is the perimeter, l is the length, and w is the width.

EXAMPLE 1 Using a Formula

What length of tape does Spencer need for the volleyball court?

SOLUTION

Substitute the values $l = 18$ and $w = 9$ in the formula for perimeter.

$$P = 2l + 2w$$
$$= 2(18) + 2(9)$$
$$= 36 + 18$$
$$= 54$$

Spencer needs a tape 54 meters in length.

ACTIVITY   Rewriting Formulas

Suppose you know the perimeter of a rectangular flower bed is 40 feet and the width is 8 feet. How would you calculate the length? Try these two methods.

Method 1 Substitute, then Isolate

1 Start with the formula $P = 2l + 2w$. Substitute the given values for P and w.

2 Solve the resulting equation for l.

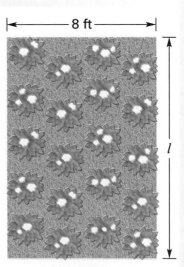

8 ft

l

$P = 40$ ft

Method 2 Isolate, then Substitute

1 Start again with the formula $P = 2l + 2w$. Isolate l on one side of the equation.

2 Substitute the given values for P and w. Solve the equation for l.

Which method would you use if you needed a formula for l to enter in a spreadsheet?

In formulas, the variables represent quantities. When you replace variables in a formula with numerical values, you must use consistent units of measure.

For example, if you measure the length l of a rectangle in feet and the width w in meters, the formula $P = 2l + 2w$ will not work. To calculate perimeter, you can use either feet or meters, but not both.

The distance D traveled while moving at a rate r during a time t, is given by the distance formula.

$$D = rt$$

If you know two of the variables, you can calculate the third. But make sure you use a consistent set of units.

EXAMPLE 2 Using Units in a Formula

On Colby's trip from Atlanta to Orlando, he will drive about 420 miles or about 676 kilometers. He estimates that he will average 60 miles per hour or about 96.5 kilometers per hour. He needs to estimate the number of hours of driving time t. Which of the following equations show the distance formula with consistent units?

a. $676 = 60t$ **b.** $420 = 60t$

c. $420 = 96.5t$ **d.** $676 = 96.5t$

SOLUTION

In **b,** the units are miles and miles per hour. In **d,** the units are kilometers and kilometers per hour. Colby can use either **b** or **d.**

A **literal equation** is an equation in which the constants are represented by letters. For example, $ax + b = c$ is a literal equation with variable x and constants a, b, and c. You can solve a literal equation for the variables.

EXAMPLE 3 Solving a Literal Equation

a. Solve the equation $ax + b = c$ for x.

b. What is the value of x when the constants are given by $a = 3$, $b = 5$, and $c = 8$?

SOLUTION

a.

$ax + b = c$	Given
$ax + b - b = c - b$	Subtraction Property
$ax = c - b$	Simplify
$\dfrac{ax}{a} = \dfrac{c - b}{a}$	Division Property, $a \neq 0$
$x = \dfrac{c - b}{a}$	Simplify

b. Substitute the value of each constant.

$$x = \frac{8 - 5}{3}$$

$$= 1$$

LESSON ASSESSMENT

Think and Discuss

The formula for the average A of two numbers a and b is $A = \frac{a + b}{2}$.

1 How can you find the average if you know a and b?

2 How can you find a if you know the average and b?

3 Explain how to solve the equation $\frac{x}{a} - b = c$ for x.

4 Solve $x + a = 3$ for x. Solve $3x + 3a = 9$ for x. What do the solutions tell you about the two equations? Explain your answer.

The distance formula is $D = rt$.

5. Solve the formula for r.

6. If you travel 30 miles at a constant speed (or rate) for 2 hours, what is your speed?

$a + b + c = 180°$

The formula for finding the sum of the measures of the angles of a triangle is $a + b + c = 180°$, where a, b, and c are the measures of the angles.

7. Solve the formula for a.

8. If two angles of a triangle measure 90° and 45°, what is the measure of the third angle?

The formula for simple interest is $I = prt$.

• I is the interest paid.
• p is the principal, or amount deposited in the account.
• r is the annual rate of interest paid in decimal form.
• t is the number of years the principal is left in the account.

9. Solve the simple interest formula for p.

10. If you want to earn $120 in interest in one year from an account that pays an annual rate of 0.06 or 6%, how much principal do you need?

Solve each equation for x.

11. $2m + x = 3m$ **12.** $x - 3c = 9$

13. $-x + s = 2s$ **14.** $x + a = b + c$

15. $2x + 3e = 8e$ **16.** $r = 2x - s$

17. $5t = 3t - 8 + x$ **18.** $2c + 2x = a - b$

19. $5(x + a) = 10$ **20.** $3x = 4(x - c)$

21. The City Cab Company uses the formula $F = 3 + 2(m - 1)$ to compute their cab fare. F is the total fare and m is the miles driven. Solve the formula for m. Find the number of miles driven if the fare is $7.

22. The formula $P = 2(m + 20)$ is used to estimate the profit on each item manufactured by a company. P is the profit and m is the manufacturing cost. Solve the formula for m. Find the manufacturing cost when the profit on each item is $116.

23. Stefani and Brian are cutting paper from a roll to make a banner for a pep rally. The roll is 3 feet wide. They want to put a strip of crepe paper around the perimeter of the banner. They have 72 feet of crepe paper. What is the maximum length of paper they should cut from the roll?

24. You are making a cage for a rabbit. The volume of the cage will be 14 cubic feet. The length is 3.2 feet and the width is 2.5 feet. What is the height? Use the formula

volume = length · width · height

Mixed Review

Use the bar graph to complete Exercises 25–30.

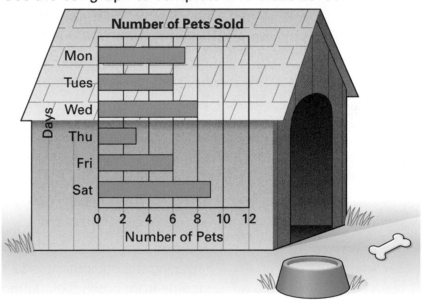

25. How many pets were sold on Thursday?

26. How many more pets were sold on Saturday than on Tuesday?

27. What is the range of the number of sets sold?

28. What is the mean of the number of sets sold?

29. What is the median of the number of sets sold?

30. Construct a frequency polygon for the data.

Complete each of the following statements.
31. The product of two negative integers is ____?____.

32. The absolute value of a negative number is always _____?_____ than zero.

Mr. Anderson, Ms. Bethany, and Ms. Perea are grading final exams. Mr. Anderson grades 4 exams per hour. Ms. Bethany grades 6 exams per hour. She starts 1 hour after Mr. Anderson. Ms. Perea grades 6 exams per hour. She starts 2 hours after Mr. Anderson.

33. Let t represent the number of hours Mr. Anderson grades exams. Write expressions for the number of hours Ms. Bethany and Ms. Perea grade exams.

34. Write expressions for the number of exams completed by Mr. Anderson, Ms. Bethany, and Ms. Perea.

35. In how many hours will Mr. Anderson and Ms. Bethany have the same number of exams graded?

36. In how many hours will Mr. Anderson and Ms. Perea have the same number of exams graded?

37. In how many hours will Ms. Bethany and Ms. Perea have the same number of exams graded?

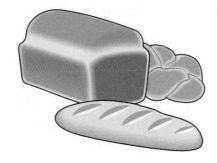

Kim is the Budget Director of a company that makes breads. She must decide whether or not to approve a recommendation to replace the company's production equipment.

The existing equipment produces 5000 loaves of bread a day. The company makes $0.75 per loaf produced. The cost of replacing the equipment is $2 million, including the lost income from production during installation. The new equipment will produce loaves at three times the rate of the existing equipment.

Kim will approve the replacement if the new equipment pays for itself in less than 300 production days. Let w represent the number of production days it will take the new equipment to pay for itself.

38. Write an expression for the amount of money the company makes in w days using the existing equipment.

39. Write an expression for the amount of money the company makes in w days if they install new equipment. This expression should include the amount made from bread minus the cost of the new equipment.

40. Equate the expressions in Exercises 38 and 39. Solve the equation for w.

41. Should Kim approve the replacement of the production equipment? Explain.

Luis operates a laser for cutting sheet metal. He focuses the laser beam to a spot on the surface of the metal. The spot is in the shape of a circle with a radius of 0.1 centimeters (cm). To cut different types of sheet metal, Luis adjusts the power level of the laser. It has four settings:

50 W   100 W

250 W   500 W.

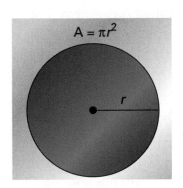

$A = \pi r^2$

For one job, Luis needs an irradiance of $1500 \, \frac{W}{cm^2}$. He uses the formula $I = \frac{P}{A}$. In this formula, I is irradiance, P is power, and A is area. Since the spot is a circle, its area is given by the formula $A = \pi r^2$. The symbol π represents a constant approximately equal to 3.14 (or you can use the π key on your calculator). The variable r is the radius of the spot, and $r^2 = r \cdot r$.

42. Solve the formula $I = \frac{P}{A}$ for P.

43. Which power level setting should Luis use?

Yvonne is considering buying a book of discount coupons to an amusement park. The book costs $30 and contains 10 coupons. Each coupon is worth $5 off the regular admission price to the park for one year. The regular admission price to the park is $36.

44. Let x represent the number of times Yvonne visits the park. Write an expression for the regular cost of admission for x visits.

45. Write an expression for Yvonne's total cost of the book plus x visits to the park with the discount coupons.

46. Equate the expressions in Exercises 44 and 45, and find the number of visits for which the cost of buying the book and using the coupons is the same as the cost of regular admission.

47. If Yvonne buys the book, how many times must she visit the park to save money with the coupons?

MATH LAB

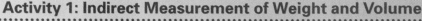

Activity 1: Indirect Measurement of Weight and Volume

Equipment   Spring scale or balance scale, up to 1000 g
100 mL graduated cylinder
400 mL beaker
String (optional)
Water

Problem Statement

Weighing an object directly is not always possible. For example, freshly picked cotton is sold by the pound. To determine the weight of a truckload of cotton, the truck is weighed when it is empty and again when it is full. The weight of the empty truck plus the weight of the cotton equals the weight of the fully loaded truck.

You will use a similar addition equation to determine an unknown weight of water in a container. Then you will use a multiplication equation to calculate the volume of the water.

Procedure

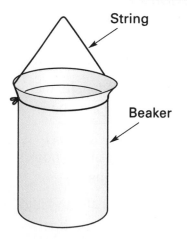

String

Beaker

a   Weigh the empty beaker with the spring scale or balance. If you use a spring scale, tie a string securely around the lip of the beaker as shown in the diagram. Hang the beaker from the scale with the string. Record the weight of the empty beaker in a data table similar to the one below.

Measurement or Calculation	Values
Volume of water added to other group's beaker	mL
Weight of beaker and water, t	g
Weight of empty beaker, b	g
Weight of water, w	g
Volume of water, v	mL

b Exchange beakers with another group. Your teacher will assign your group a volume of water between 100 and 300 milliliters. Use the graduated cylinder to measure your assigned volume of water. Pour this volume of water into the other group's beaker. Record the volume in the data table.

c Do not tell the other group how much water you poured into their beaker. Return the beaker, and retrieve your group's beaker. You will indirectly measure the weight of water in your beaker, and calculate the volume.

d Weigh the beaker and water. Record the measurement in the data table.

e Let b represent the weight of the empty beaker, w represent the weight of water in the beaker, and t represent the measured weight of the beaker and water. Write an addition equation for b, w, and t. Solve the equation for w. What was the weight of the water in your beaker? Enter this amount in the data table.

f The volume v in milliliters (mL), weight w in grams (g), and density d in grams per milliliter $\left(\dfrac{g}{mL}\right)$, of any material are related by the multiplication equation:

$$\boxed{\text{volume}} \quad \cdot \quad \boxed{\text{density}} \quad = \quad \boxed{\text{weight}}$$
$$v \quad \cdot \quad d \quad = \quad w$$

Solve the equation for v.

g The density of water is $1 \dfrac{g}{mL}$. What is the volume of water in your beaker? Record the value in the data table.

h Make two tables on the board. In the first table, write the volume of water each group added to the beakers. In the second table, write the volume calculated by each group. Is there a one-to-one match between the values in the tables? Explain any differences.

Discussion Questions

Salt dissolves in water and forms a solution. A beaker contains a solution of water and salt.

1. Describe how you can use indirect measurement to find the weight of the salt.

2. Define variables and write an addition equation for your method of measurement. Solve the equation for the variable used to represent the weight of salt.

Olive oil does not dissolve in water. When two liquids do not form a solution, the liquid with the lower density floats on the liquid with the higher density. A beaker contains olive oil and water.

3. 50 milliliters of olive oil weighs 45.5 grams. Use the multiplication equation in Step **f** to find the density of olive oil.

4. Does the olive oil float on the water or sink to the bottom of the beaker?

Activity 2: Solving Equations with a Spreadsheet

Equipment   Spreadsheet computer program

Problem Statement

You will use a spreadsheet to solve equations by making the left side equal to the right side.

Procedure

Follow Steps **a–f** to solve the following equation with the spreadsheet program.

$$6x + 1 = 2x - 3$$

a In the first row of the spreadsheet, enter labels for the variable x, the left side of the equation, and the right side of the equation.

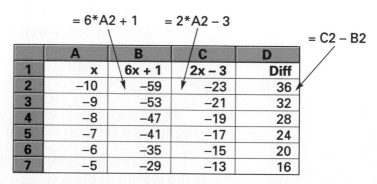

	A	B	C	D
1	x	6x + 1	2x – 3	Diff
2	–10	–59	–23	36
3	–9	–53	–21	32
4	–8	–47	–19	28
5	–7	–41	–17	24
6	–6	–35	–15	20
7	–5	–29	–13	16

= 6*A2 + 1   = 2*A2 – 3   = C2 – B2

b In the column for x, list integer values from -10 to 10.

c In cell B2, enter the formula for the left side of the equation. Copy the formula down the column to the last row (where $x = 10$). In each row, the spreadsheet displays the calculated value of the left side of the equation for the value of x displayed in that row.

d Starting in cell C2, repeat Step **c** for the right side of the equation.

e For what value of x is the left side of the equation equal to the right side? What is the solution to the equation?

f Add a fourth column to calculate the difference between the left side and the right side of the equation for each value of x. What is the difference when x equals the solution?

g Print the spreadsheet. Circle the row that contains the solution.

h Change the labels and formulas in the spreadsheet to find the solutions to the following equations. Print each spreadsheet and circle the solutions.

    1. $-9x + 16 = 15x + 10 - 27x$

    2. $4.6x + 8.3 - 3.4x = -0.9 + 3.5x$

i Change the labels and formulas in the spreadsheet to find the solution to the following equation. Print the spreadsheet.

$$3x + 2 + 2x = -4x + 5 + 9x - 3$$

How can you recognize an identity using the spreadsheet?

j Change the labels and formulas in the spreadsheet to find the solution to the following equation. Print the spreadsheet.

$$6x + 6 - 4x = -2 + 2x$$

How can you recognize an equation that has no solution using the spreadsheet?

k How can you change the spreadsheet to find solutions that are not between -10 and 10? Develop a strategy. Use the strategy to solve the following equation with the spreadsheet.

$$2x - 5 = x + 22$$

I How can you change the spreadsheet to find solutions that are not integers? Develop a strategy. Use the strategy to solve the following equation.

$$x + 3 = 3x + 8.2$$

Discussion Questions

1. You are using a spreadsheet to solve $49x + 441 = 0$. You enter a range of values for x in column A. You enter the formula for $49x + 441$ in column B. What is the value in column B when x equals the solution?

2. You are using a spreadsheet to solve an equation that has a non-integer solution. How can you use the "Difference" column to find the two integer values the solution is between?

Activity 3: Mobiles with Algebra

Equipment   4 manila folders or cardboard sheets
2 plastic drinking straws
Sewing needle and string
Scissors
Tape
Centimeter ruler

Problem Statement

A mobile is a sculpture made with shapes suspended from levers. The levers are balanced about pivot points, or fulcrums, so that the mobile rotates in a current of air.

A lever in a mobile is balanced the same way two children of different weights balance a seesaw.

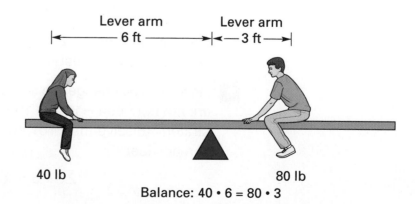

Balance: 40 • 6 = 80 • 3

The distance a child sits from the pivot point is called the lever arm. The seesaw balances when the product of the child's weight and the lever arm on one side equals the product of the child's weight and the lever arm on the other side.

Suppose the children are suspended from the seesaw on swings. In this case, the lever arms are the distances from the points where the swings are attached to the pivot point. As before, the product of each child's weight and lever arm must be equal for the seesaw to balance.

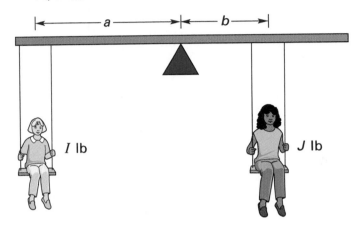

Balance: $I \cdot a = J \cdot b$

You will construct a two-level mobile using the formula above to locate the positions of the pivot points where the mobile is balanced.

Procedure

a Cut eight to ten identical shapes from the cardboard or manila folders. You can cut triangles, rectangles, or any other shape between 5 and 15 centimeters on a side. Make sure all the shapes are the same size.

b Use the needle to insert a 15- to 20-centimeter length of string in a drinking straw near each end of the straw. Tie the strings so they do not pull through the straw.

c Since the shapes are the same size and shape, they have the same weights. Assign each shape a "weight" of 1. Group the shapes in three stacks. Let I, J, and K represent the number of shapes in the stacks. I, J, and K can be any integers greater than zero as long as $I + J + K$ equals the total number of shapes.

Stack the *I* shapes in a group and tape them together. Repeat for the *J* shapes. Repeat for the *K* shapes. Label each group with the "weight" of the group.

d Tape the group of *I* shapes to one of the strings attached to the straw. Tape the group of *J* shapes to the other string.

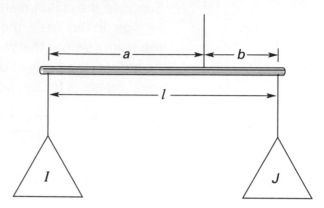

e The straw will balance, or hang horizontally from a third string inserted in the straw at a pivot point as shown in the diagram. To locate this point, the products of the weights and the lever arms must be equal. The distances *a* and *b* are related by the following formula.

$$Ia = Jb$$

Measure the distance *l* between the strings to the nearest tenth centimeter. Since $l = a + b$, what property allows you to conclude that $b = l - a$? Substitute $(l - a)$ for *b* in the formula:

$$Ia = J(l - a)$$

Substitute into the formula your values for *l*, *I*, and *J*. Solve for *a*. Substitute the value for *a* into the formula $Ia = Jb$ and find *b*.

f Locate the pivot point by measuring the distance *b* from the point of attachment for *J*. Insert a 15- to 30-centimeter length of string at the pivot point with the sewing needle. Do not remove the sewing needle—you will need it in Step **g**. Tie the string to the straw and see if the mobile balances. You may need to make a small (less than 1 millimeter) adjustment to the position of the string.

g Insert the string from Step **f** into the second straw near the end. Tie the string to the straw.

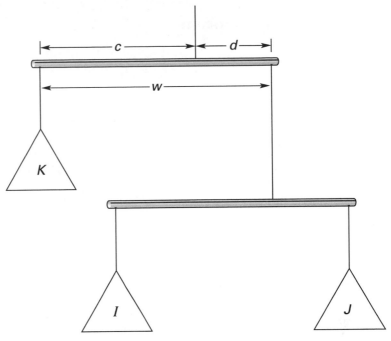

h Use the sewing needle to attach a string near the other end of the second straw. Tape the group of *K* shapes to this string. The straw has a weight of *K* at one end. What is the weight at the other end? You can neglect the weight of the first straw because it is very small compared to the weights of the shapes.

i To locate the pivot point for the second straw, the products of the weights and lever arms must be equal. Measure *w*. Use the same procedure as in Step **e** to calculate the distances *c* and *d* for the pivot point of the second straw.

j Insert a string with the sewing needle at the pivot point for the second straw. Does the mobile balance?

Discussion Questions

The formula, $Ia = Jb$, describes the relationship between the length of the lever arms *a* and *b*, and the respective weights *I* and *J*, for each side of a seesaw.

1. Draw a diagram to show how you can balance a 100-pound weight with a 10-pound weight.

2. List three pairs of values for *a* and *b* that would work.

Communicate

1. Explain how to use the Subtraction Property of Equality to solve an addition equation.

2. Explain how to use the Multiplication Property of Equality to solve a division equation.

3. Which two inverse operations would you use to solve $-2x - 5 = 7$? Which operation would you use first?

4. How is the Distributive Property used to combine like terms?

5. Why are the units of measure important when you solve a formula?

Skills

Solve each equation.

6. $q + 12.1 = 4.5$

7. $\dfrac{x}{5} = -6$

8. $-5 = d - 13$

9. $-14 = 3.5m$

10. $2a + 6 = 20$

11. $-5c - 3 = 12$

12. $-6 = 4 + \dfrac{x}{6}$

13. $\dfrac{k}{5} + 3 = 0$

14. $4(m + 3) = -8$

15. $6s - 7s = -5$

16. $7x - 6 = 12x + 29$

17. $5(t + 3) = -(t - 3)$

18. $3(y + 2) = 3y - 1$

19. $2b + 3 = 2(b + 1.5)$

Applications

Define a variable, write an equation, and solve.

20. Tennis rackets are on sale for $49. With sales tax, a racket costs $53. How much is the sales tax on the rackets?

21. Roberto earns $456 each week. If Roberto works 38 hours each week, how much does he earn per hour?

22. A plumber charges $55 for a service call plus $38 per hour. If you receive a bill for $150, how many hours did the plumber work at your home?

23. The sum of three consecutive integers is 144. What are the integers?

24. Two assembly teams produce the same number of computer keyboards per hour. One team works 8 hours and the other team works 6 hours. Together, the teams produce 280 keyboards. How many keyboards does each team produce?

25. You can calculate the area A of a rectangle with the formula $A = lw$, where l is the length and w is the width. Solve for w. What is the width of a rectangle that has an area of 10.5 square centimeters and a length of 6 centimeters?

Math Lab

26. The weight of water in a beaker is w. The weight of the water and the weight of the beaker combined is t. The weight of the beaker is b. Write a subtraction equation showing the relationship between w, t, and b. Solve the equation for t.

27. You are using a spreadsheet to solve an equation with variables on both sides of the equation. You have listed values

	A	B	C	D
1	**x**			**Diff**
2	−5			10
3	−4			5
4	−3			0
5	−2			−5
6	−1			−10
7	0			−15
8	1			−20

for x in column A and the difference between the right and left sides of the equation in column D. What is the solution of the equation?

28. How far must a 90-pound child sit from the pivot of a seesaw to balance a 60-pound child who sits 6 feet from the pivot?

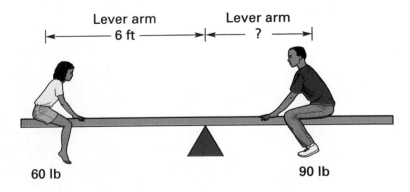

Lever arm
— 6 ft —

Lever arm
— ? —

60 lb   90 lb

CHAPTER 5

WHY SHOULD I LEARN THIS?

Sometimes quantities are represented by fractions, instead of integers or decimals. In these cases, you need to use different rules for adding, subtracting, multiplying, and dividing. Do you know what quantities fractions represent in music?

Contents: Rational Numbers

RATIONAL NUMBERS

LEARN HOW TO...

1. Write equivalent fractions.
2. Write fractions as decimals.
3. Compare rational numbers using inequalities.
4. Add, subtract, multiply, and divide rational numbers.
5. Solve inequalities using the Addition, Subtraction, and Multiplication Properties of Inequality.

In this chapter, you will study a set of numbers used everyday, the set of *rational numbers*. A rational number can be written as a *ratio* of two integers $\frac{a}{b}$ (where $b \neq 0$.) A *fraction* is a ratio that describes a part of a whole. For example, you can use a fraction to:

- record test results
- divide a pizza or a sandwich
- measure the length of a line segment with a ruler

If you answer 4 out of 5 test questions correctly, your teacher may record your score with the fraction $\frac{4}{5}$. This fraction compares the number of correct answers to the total number of questions. If a pizza is cut into 8 equal pieces and you get 3 of the pieces, your share of the pizza is the fraction $\frac{3}{8}$. If the length of a line segment on a drawing is $3\frac{7}{16}$ inches, the fraction $\frac{7}{16}$ describes where the endpoint of the segment lies between 3 and 4 inches.

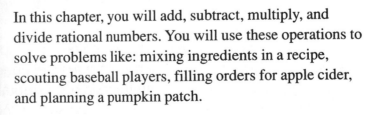

In this chapter, you will add, subtract, multiply, and divide rational numbers. You will use these operations to solve problems like: mixing ingredients in a recipe, scouting baseball players, filling orders for apple cider, and planning a pumpkin patch.

LESSON 5.1 EQUIVALENT FRACTIONS

OBJECTIVES
➤ Write equivalent fractions.
➤ Write fractions in simplest form.

Taylor and three of his classmates share a pizza. If the pizza is divided equally, what *fraction* of the pizza will Taylor get?

A **fraction** describes a part of a whole or a member of a group.

Fraction
A fraction is a number that can be written in the form $\frac{a}{b}$, where a and b are whole numbers, and $b \neq 0$.

Since Taylor gets 1 out of 4 pieces, his fraction of the pizza is $\frac{1}{4}$.

$$\frac{\text{Taylor's part}}{\text{Total number of equal parts}} = \frac{1}{4} \begin{array}{l} \rightarrow \text{ Numerator} \\ \rightarrow \text{ Denominator} \end{array}$$

You can represent fractions with a fraction bar. This fraction bar represents $\frac{5}{6}$, because 5 of the 6 equal parts are shaded.

ACTIVITY 1   Writing Equivalent Fractions

1 What fraction is represented by the fraction bar shown?

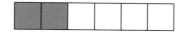

2 Separate the fraction bar as shown. How many of the 3 equal parts are shaded? What fraction does the shaded part represent?

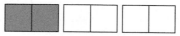

3 What is the relationship between $\frac{2}{6}$ and $\frac{1}{3}$? The fractions $\frac{2}{6}$ and $\frac{1}{3}$ are *equivalent* because they represent the same part of the fraction bar. **Equivalent fractions** are equal. They represent the same amount. Thus, $\frac{2}{6} = \frac{1}{3}$.

ONGOING ASSESSMENT

Taylor's pizza is sliced into eight equal pieces. How many pieces should each of the four students get?

$\frac{1}{4} = \frac{?}{8}$

1 Draw four "blank" fraction bars similar to the one shown below.

2 From top to bottom, draw fraction bars to represent $\frac{1}{2}, \frac{2}{4}, \frac{3}{6}$, and $\frac{4}{8}$. Are all four fractions equivalent? Explain.

3 Study the pattern in the sequence of equivalent fractions.

$$\frac{1}{2}, \frac{2}{4}, \frac{3}{6}, \frac{4}{8}, \ldots$$

What equivalent fraction would be next in the sequence? Explain how to write equivalent fractions by multiplication.

4 You can also write equivalent fractions using division. Start with $\frac{6}{12}$. Divide the numerator and denominator by 2, 3, and 6. Complete the following equations.

$$\frac{6 \div 2}{12 \div 2} = \frac{?}{?} \qquad \frac{6 \div 3}{12 \div 3} = \frac{?}{?} \qquad \frac{6 \div 6}{12 \div 6} = \frac{?}{?}$$

In Activity 2, you wrote equivalent fractions by multiplying or dividing the numerator and denominator by the same nonzero number.

Equivalent Fractions

If a, b, and n are whole numbers with $b \neq 0$ and $n \neq 0$, then

$$\frac{a}{b} = \frac{a \cdot n}{b \cdot n} \quad \text{and} \quad \frac{a}{b} = \frac{a \div n}{b \div n}$$

EXAMPLE 1 Finding Equivalent Fractions by Multiplying

Find two fractions equivalent to $\frac{2}{3}$.

SOLUTION

Multiply the numerator and denominator by the same nonzero number. First multiply by 2, then multiply by 3.

$$\frac{2}{3} = \frac{2 \cdot 2}{3 \cdot 2} = \frac{4}{6} \qquad \frac{2}{3} = \frac{2 \cdot 3}{3 \cdot 3} = \frac{6}{9}$$

The fractions $\frac{4}{6}$ and $\frac{6}{9}$ are equivalent to $\frac{2}{3}$.

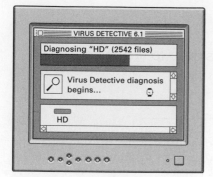

EXAMPLE 2 Finding Equivalent Fractions by Dividing

Ernesto finds that an antivirus program can detect a new type of virus in 18 out of 24 infected computers. If he runs the program on 12 infected computers, how many times should he expect the program to detect the virus? on 8 computers? on 4 computers?

SOLUTION

Find three fractions equivalent to $\frac{18}{24}$ with denominators of 12, 8 and 4.

Divide the numerator and denominator of $\frac{18}{24}$ by the same nonzero number. To find numbers to use as divisors, find the **common factors** of 18 and 24. A factor of 18 is any whole number that divides into 18 with no remainder.

Factors of 18: 1, **2**, **3**, **6**, 9, and 18.

Factors of 24: 1, **2**, **3**, 4, **6**, 8, 12, and 24.

The common factors of 18 and 24 are 1, 2, 3, and 6. Divide the numerator and denominator by 2, 3, and 6 to find equivalent fractions.

$$\frac{18}{24} = \frac{18 \div 2}{24 \div 2} = \frac{9}{12} \qquad \frac{18}{24} = \frac{18 \div 3}{24 \div 3} = \frac{6}{8} \qquad \frac{18}{24} = \frac{18 \div 6}{24 \div 6} = \frac{3}{4}$$

Three fractions equivalent to $\frac{18}{24}$ are $\frac{9}{12}$, $\frac{6}{8}$, and $\frac{3}{4}$.

Ernesto should expect the program to detect the virus in 9 out of 12, 6 out of 8, and 3 out of 4 computers.

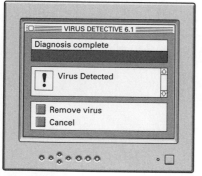

A fraction is in **simplest form** if 1 is the only factor common to both the numerator and denominator. To write a fraction in simplest form, divide the numerator and denominator by the *greatest common factor*. The **greatest common factor** of two numbers is the greatest integer that is a factor of both numbers. In Example 2, the greatest common factor of 18 and 24 is 6. In simplest form, $\frac{18}{24}$ is written as $\frac{3}{4}$.

EXAMPLE 3 Writing a Fraction in Simplest Form

Write $\frac{16}{36}$ in simplest form.

SOLUTION

Factors of 16: 1, 2, **4**, 8, 16.

Factors of 36: 1, 2, 3, **4**, 6, 9, 12, 18, 36.

The greatest common factor is 4. Divide the numerator and denominator by 4.

$$\frac{16}{36} = \frac{16 \div 4}{36 \div 4} = \frac{4}{9}$$

ONGOING ASSESSMENT

a. Find the common factors of 16 and 40. What is the greatest common factor?

b. Find three fractions equivalent to $\frac{16}{40}$.

c. Write $\frac{16}{40}$ in simplest form.

LESSON ASSESSMENT

Think and Discuss

1 Take a poll to find what fraction of your class plays a musical instrument. What two quantities must you know to write the fraction?

2 How can you tell if two fractions are equivalent?

3 Explain how to use common factors to write a fraction in simplest form. How do you know if the fraction is in simplest form?

4 Which fraction is greater, $\frac{3}{7}$ or $\frac{4}{7}$? Explain your reasoning.

Practice and Apply

Use a fraction to name the shaded part in Exercises 5–7.

5.

6.

7.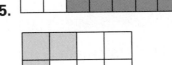

Which fraction is equivalent to the given fraction?

8. $\frac{5}{8}$ **a.** $\frac{15}{16}$ **b.** $\frac{20}{32}$ **c.** $\frac{11}{24}$ **d.** $\frac{50}{88}$

9. $\frac{10}{35}$ **a.** $\frac{1}{3}$ **b.** $\frac{2}{5}$ **c.** $\frac{2}{7}$ **d.** $\frac{15}{70}$

10. $\frac{10}{12}$ **a.** $\frac{5}{9}$ **b.** $\frac{10}{18}$ **c.** $\frac{15}{18}$ **d.** $\frac{20}{22}$

11. What are the common factors of 12 and 18? What is the greatest common factor of 12 and 18?

12. What are the common factors of 14 and 28? What is the greatest common factor of 14 and 28?

13. What are the common factors of 26 and 36? What is the greatest common factor of 26 and 36?

Write each answer in simplest form.

14. Katrina answered 40 out of 50 questions on a test correctly. What fraction of the questions were answered correctly?

15. Nicole hit safely 16 out of 48 times she batted. What fraction of her times at bat did Nicole hit safely?

16. In one week, Raymond and Andrew mowed 30 lawns. If Raymond mowed 18 of the lawns, what fraction of the lawns did he mow?

17. A bookcase contains 12 mysteries, 14 biographies, and 14 nonfiction books. What fraction of the books are mysteries?

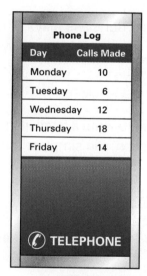

Phone Log	
Day	**Calls Made**
Monday	10
Tuesday	6
Wednesday	12
Thursday	18
Friday	14

Use the table shown at the left to complete Exercises 18–21. Write each fraction in simplest form.

18. What fraction of the calls were made on Monday?

19. What fraction of the calls were made on Friday?

20. What fraction of the calls were made on Monday and Friday combined?

21. What fraction of the calls were made before Thursday?

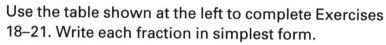

Mixed Review

Tell if the statement is *true* or *false*.

22. $0.88 < 0.088$

23. $-6 < -3$

24. 256.9847 rounded to the nearest hundredth is 257.

25. $5(4 + 9) = (4 + 9)5$ is an example of the Distributive Property.

Solve each equation.

26. $3a + 9 = 27$

27. $-5a - 7 = 18$

28. $4(n + 2) + 4n = -16$

29. $6n + 5 = 8n - 11$

LESSON 5.2 FRACTIONS AND DECIMALS

OBJECTIVES

➤ Write the decimal equivalent of a fraction.
➤ Write a repeating decimal as a fraction.

Breanne is assembling a bookshelf from a kit. The kit contains wood screws of three lengths. The instructions list the lengths as decimals.

0.625 inch   0.75 inch   0.875 inch

Breanne measures the lengths of the screws in fractions of an inch with a carpenter's tape.

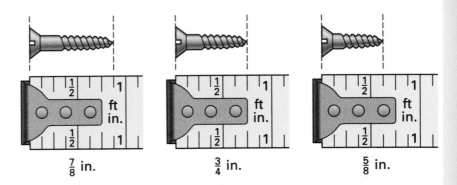

$\frac{7}{8}$ in. $\frac{3}{4}$ in. $\frac{5}{8}$ in.

Breanne can match the decimal values to the fractions by converting each measure from a fraction to a decimal.

EXAMPLE 1 Writing Decimal Equivalents

Write each fraction as a decimal.

a. $\frac{7}{8}$ **b.** $\frac{3}{4}$ **c.** $\frac{5}{8}$

SOLUTION

Divide each numerator by the denominator. Use pencil and paper or a calculator.

a. $\frac{7}{8} = 8\overline{)7.000}$
$$\begin{array}{r} 0.875 \\ \underline{6\,4} \\ 60 \\ \underline{56} \\ 40 \\ \underline{40} \\ 0 \end{array}$$

b. $\frac{3}{4} = 4\overline{)3.00}$
$$\begin{array}{r} 0.75 \\ \underline{2\,8} \\ 20 \\ \underline{20} \\ 0 \end{array}$$

c. $\frac{5}{8} = 8\overline{)5.000}$
$$\begin{array}{r} 0.625 \\ \underline{4\,8} \\ 20 \\ \underline{16} \\ 40 \\ \underline{40} \\ 0 \end{array}$$

7 ÷ 8 = 0.875   3 ÷ 4 = 0.75   5 ÷ 8 = 0.625

a. $\frac{7}{8} = 0.875$ **b.** $\frac{3}{4} = 0.75$ **c.** $\frac{5}{8} = 0.625$

In Example 1, each division has a remainder of zero. These decimals are called **terminating decimals**. Sometimes when you write a fraction as a decimal, the division results in a remainder with a repeating pattern of nonzero remainders. These decimals are called **repeating decimals**.

EXAMPLE 2 Writing Repeating Decimals

Write $\frac{1}{11}$ as a decimal.

SOLUTION

Divide the numerator by the denominator. Use pencil and paper or a calculator.

$$\frac{1}{11} = 11 \overline{)\begin{array}{l} 0.0909 \\ 1.0000 \end{array}}$$
$$\begin{array}{r} 99 \\ \hline 100 \\ 99 \\ \hline 1 \end{array}$$

1 ÷ 11 = 0.09090909

The pattern of digits 09 repeats itself. Draw a bar over these digits to show they continue with the same pattern.

$$\frac{1}{11} = 0.\overline{09}$$

ONGOING ASSESSMENT

Write each fraction as a decimal.

a. $\frac{7}{25}$ b. $\frac{7}{9}$

c. $\frac{9}{16}$ d. $\frac{3}{11}$

ACTIVITY 1   Writing a Terminating Decimal as a Fraction

Breanne's bookshelf kit has wooden dowels with diameters of 0.25 inch. How can Breanne find the fraction that is equivalent to 0.25? Since 0.25 is a terminating decimal, she can write 0.25 as a fraction.

$$0.25 = \frac{25}{100}$$

1 Why does Breanne use 100 as the denominator?

2 What is the greatest common factor of 25 and 100?

3 Write 0.25 as a fraction in simplest form.

You can use the same procedure to write a negative decimal as a fraction.

$$-0.6 = -\frac{6}{10} = -\frac{6 \div 2}{10 \div 2} = -\frac{3}{5}$$

There are three ways to write a negative fraction:

$$-\frac{3}{5} = \frac{-3}{5} = \frac{3}{-5}$$

ACTIVITY 2 **Writing a Repeating Decimal as a Fraction**

Write the repeating decimal $0.\overline{36}$ as a fraction. Start with $n = 0.3636 \ldots$ and use algebra to solve for n as a fraction in simplest form. Give a reason for each step. Steps 1 and 2 are completed for you.

Step		Reason
1.	$n = 0.3636 \ldots$	Given
2.	$100n = 36.363636 \ldots$	Multiplication Property of Equality; Multiply by 100 since two digits repeat
3.	$100n - n = (36.3636 \ldots)$ $- (0.3636 \ldots)$	?
4.	$99n = 36$	?
5.	$n = \frac{36}{99}$	?
6.	$n = \frac{4}{11}$	?

7. Check the solution by writing $\frac{4}{11}$ as a decimal.

ONGOING ASSESSMENT

Write each decimal as a fraction in simplest form.

a. 0.005 **b.** -0.25

c. $0.\overline{5}$ **d.** $-0.\overline{63}$

Critical Thinking In Activity 2, you found $\frac{4}{11} = 0.\overline{36}$. Why is the bar over both digits and not just over the 6?

CULTURAL CONNECTION

You can use fractions as measures of distance (go a quarter mile down the road and turn right), or volume (add a half-liter of oil), or area (paint two-thirds of the canvas as a landscape). Musicians use fractions as measures of time—the time created by a rhythmic pattern.

Music is composed of short tones and long tones. These are written as notes. The length of a note is measured by counting the time the note is held. A whole note is a very long tone; a half note is half as long; and a quarter note is one-fourth as long as a whole note.

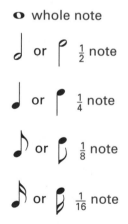

○ whole note

♩ or ꞁ $\frac{1}{2}$ note

♩ or ꞁ $\frac{1}{4}$ note

♪ or ꞁ $\frac{1}{8}$ note

♪ or ꞁ $\frac{1}{16}$ note

The combinations of notes into patterns is called rhythm. Rhythm is indicated in a piece of music by the time signature, which tells how many beats are in each measure, or grouping of notes.

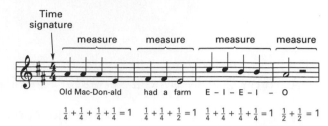

Old Mac-Don-ald   had a farm   E – I – E – I – O

$\frac{1}{4}+\frac{1}{4}+\frac{1}{4}+\frac{1}{4}=1$ $\frac{1}{4}+\frac{1}{4}+\frac{1}{2}=1$ $\frac{1}{4}+\frac{1}{4}+\frac{1}{4}+\frac{1}{4}=1$ $\frac{1}{2}+\frac{1}{2}=1$

There are two numbers in each time signature. In the time signature for "Old McDonald," the 4 at the top means that there are four beats to each measure. The 4 at the bottom means that each quarter note gets one beat. The symbol at the end of the last measure is called a *rest*. How many beats does this rest get?

This old man   he played one   he played nick-nack   on my drum

$\frac{1}{8}+\frac{1}{8}+\frac{1}{4}=\underline{?}$ $\frac{1}{8}+\frac{1}{8}+\frac{1}{4}=\underline{?}$ $\frac{1}{8}+\frac{1}{8}+\frac{1}{8}+\frac{1}{8}=\underline{?}$ $\frac{1}{8}+\frac{1}{8}+\frac{1}{4}=\underline{?}$

1. What is the time signature of this familiar nursery song? How does it compare with the time signature of "Old MacDonald"?

2. Find the music for another song by looking in a songbook or pieces of sheet music. Identify and explain the time signature.

LESSON ASSESSMENT

1. How do you find the decimal equivalent of a fraction?

2. What is the difference between a terminating decimal and a repeating decimal?

3. Explain how to write a terminating decimal as a fraction.

4. Explain how to write a repeating decimal as a fraction.

Practice and Apply

Write each fraction as a decimal.

5. $\frac{4}{5}$ **6.** $\frac{5}{6}$ **7.** $-\frac{1}{8}$

8. $\frac{7}{25}$ **9.** $-\frac{3}{20}$ **10.** $\frac{7}{15}$

11. $-\frac{7}{40}$ **12.** $\frac{7}{9}$ **13.** $-\frac{9}{16}$

Write each decimal as a fraction in simplest form.

14. 0.05   **15.** −0.625   **16.** 0.0125

17. −0.25   **18.** $0.\overline{15}$ **19.** $-0.\overline{3}$

Write each answer as a fraction in simplest form and as a decimal.

20. Shani made 11 out of 20 first serves in play. What is Shani's first-serve accuracy?

21. In the school election, 1200 students voted. Roberta received 800 votes. What part of the vote did Roberta receive?

22. Antwan has saved $75 for a new bike that costs $225. What fraction of the bike's cost has Antwan saved?

23. It is 340 miles from Kensington to Port City. Mr. Fonamarin has already driven 85 miles. What part of the distance has Mr. Fonamarin driven?

24. The high school soccer team has won 12 games and lost 8 games. What fraction of the total games played has the team won?

A ninth-grade class has 320 students. Two hundred eight of the students ride a bus to school.

25. What fraction of the ninth graders ride a school bus?

26. What fraction of the ninth graders use other forms of transportation?

Deshaun, Miliani, and Heath share a pizza. Deshaun ate $\frac{1}{4}$ of the pizza. Miliani ate $\frac{1}{4}$ of the pizza. Heath ate $\frac{1}{8}$ of the pizza.

27. How many pieces of pizza did each person eat?

28. Write a decimal equivalent for the fraction of pizza that is left.

Mixed Review

Use the double bar-graph to complete Exercises 29–32.

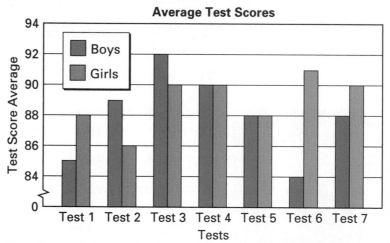

29. On which tests did the boys score higher than the girls?

30. On which tests did the girls outscore the boys by at least two points?

31. What is the median score for the boys? What is the median score for the girls?

32. What is the mean score for the boys? What is the mean score for the girls?

Let a = −5, b = 8, c = 22, and d = 3. Find the value of each expression.

33. $a - c + d$ **34.** $ab - cd$

35. $c(b - a)$ **36.** $\dfrac{b - c}{a + d}$

LESSON 5.3 RATIONAL NUMBERS AND INEQUALITIES

- Order rational numbers and decimals according to value.
- Graph solutions of inequalities on a number line.

Garrett works as an apprentice service technician in an auto repair shop. At the end of each workday, Garrett cleans all the tools. Sockets are stored in order, from smallest to largest. In what order should Garrett store the following sockets?

$\frac{1}{4}$ in. $\frac{3}{8}$ in. $\frac{5}{16}$ in. $\frac{9}{32}$ in.

Fractions such as $\frac{3}{8}$ are called *rational numbers*.

Rational Number

A rational number is any number that can be written in the form $\frac{a}{b}$, where a and b are integers and $b \neq 0$.

Since $0.375 = \frac{3}{8}$, 0.375 is also a rational number.

Garrett can use several methods to order the rational numbers that represent the four socket sizes.

ACTIVITY 1   Ordering with Fraction Bars

The fraction bars shown represent four fractions.

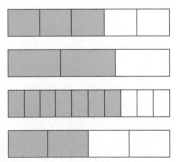

1 Write the fraction represented by each bar.

2 Which fraction bar has the greatest part of the bar shaded? Which has the least part of the bar shaded?

3 Write the four fractions in order from least to greatest.

EXAMPLE 1 Ordering with Common Denominators

a. Compare $\frac{3}{8}$ and $\frac{5}{8}$.   **b.** Compare $\frac{5}{6}$ and $\frac{3}{4}$.

SOLUTION

a. The fractions $\frac{3}{8}$ and $\frac{5}{8}$ have **common denominators**. These fractions represent 3 parts and 5 parts of the same whole amount of 8 parts. Since $3 < 5$,

$$\frac{3}{8} < \frac{5}{8} \qquad \text{and} \qquad \frac{5}{8} > \frac{3}{8}$$

b. The fractions $\frac{5}{6}$ and $\frac{3}{4}$ do not have common denominators. To compare these fractions, first use a common *multiple* of the denominators to write equivalent fractions. A **multiple** of a number results when you multiply that number by a nonzero whole number.

Multiples of 6: 6 **12** 18 24 30 36

Multiples of 4: 4 8 **12** 16 20 24

The **least common denominator** (LCD) of two fractions is the least common multiple of their denominators. The least common multiple of 6 and 4 is 12. Thus, 12 is the LCD of $\frac{5}{6}$ and $\frac{3}{4}$. Write equivalent fractions with the LCD.

$$\frac{5}{6} = \frac{5 \cdot 2}{6 \cdot 2} = \frac{10}{12} \qquad \frac{3}{4} = \frac{3 \cdot 3}{4 \cdot 3} = \frac{9}{12}$$

Since $10 > 9$, $\frac{10}{12} > \frac{9}{12}$ and $\frac{5}{6} > \frac{3}{4}$.

Critical Thinking Repeat Example 1, part **b** using 24 as the common multiple. How can you find a common multiple of any two nonzero numbers a and b without listing the multiples? If a and b are the denominators of two fractions, is ab a common denominator? Is ab always the LCD? Explain.

ONGOING ASSESSMENT

Use common denominators to order the fractions on Garrett's sockets from least to greatest.

Garrett can also find the decimal equivalents of the fractions.

Garrett needs to store the four socket sizes listed in the table.

Socket Size		Decimal Equivalent
$\frac{3}{4}$ in.	=	? in.
$\frac{7}{8}$ in.	=	? in.
$\frac{13}{16}$ in.	=	? in.
$\frac{25}{32}$ in.	=	? in.

1 Use a calculator to find the decimal equivalent of each fraction.

2 Use place value or a number line to order the decimals from least to greatest.

3 Complete the following combined inequality with the fractions from the table.

$$\underline{?} < \underline{?} < \underline{?} < \underline{?}$$

You can also use decimals and a number line to order negative rational numbers.

EXAMPLE 2 Ordering Negative Rational Numbers

Order the following temperatures from least to greatest.

$$0°C, \quad \frac{2}{3}°C, \quad -0.85°C, \quad -\frac{1}{5}°C$$

SOLUTION

First write each fraction as a decimal.

$$\frac{2}{3} = 0.\overline{6} \quad -\frac{1}{5} = -0.2$$

Graph the decimals on a number line.

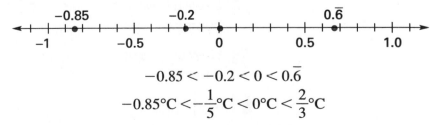

$$-0.85 < -0.2 < 0 < 0.\overline{6}$$
$$-0.85°C < -\frac{1}{5}°C < 0°C < \frac{2}{3}°C$$

In Example 2, you found that $-0.2 < 0$. Write three other decimals less than 0. How many numbers are there less than or equal to 0? You cannot list the entire set, but you can describe the set with a variable, x, and the inequality $x \le 0$.

Let x be a variable for temperature in degrees Centigrade. A **solution** of the inequality $x \le 0°C$ is any value of the variable that makes the inequality *true*. You can graph the solution on a number line.

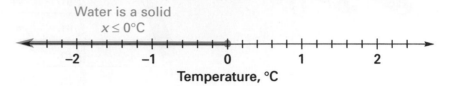

The closed circle shows that 0°C is a solution. This graph shows all the values of Centigrade temperature for which water will be frozen.

You can also graph the solution of $x > 0°C$.

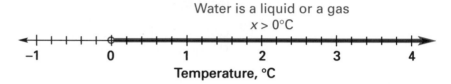

The open circle shows that 0°C is not a solution. This graph shows all the values of Centigrade temperature for which water will be a liquid or a gas.

LESSON ASSESSMENT

Think and Discuss

1. Explain how to compare two fractions with common denominators.

2. Write an algorithm for finding the least common denominator of two fractions.

3. Explain how to compare two fractions that do not have common denominators.

4. How do you use a calculator to find the decimal equivalent of a fraction?

5. Explain how to graph the solution of an inequality.

Use > or < to compare each pair of numbers.

6. $\dfrac{3}{4}$ _?_ $\dfrac{2}{3}$

7. $-\dfrac{7}{8}$ _?_ $-\dfrac{10}{12}$

8. $\dfrac{5}{8}$ _?_ 0.6

Use a combined inequality to order each set of numbers from least to greatest.

9. $\dfrac{3}{8}$, 0.4, $\dfrac{4}{9}$

10. $-\dfrac{2}{3}$, -0.58, $-\dfrac{3}{4}$

11. $\dfrac{1}{3}$, $-\dfrac{1}{2}$, $-\dfrac{1}{5}$, $\dfrac{1}{4}$

12. $-\dfrac{2}{3}$, -0.65, $-\dfrac{3}{8}$, -0.35

Graph the solution of each inequality on a number line.

13. $r \geq -1$ **14.** $t < 0.9$ **15.** $2 \leq x$ **16.** $-3 > y$

Compare fractions and decimals to answer Exercises 17–20.

17. In one bushel, 0.85 of the apples were used for pies. Is this more or less than $\dfrac{7}{8}$ of the apples in the bushel?

18. A produce scale shows the weight of a bunch of carrots as 0.48 pound. Does the bunch of carrots weigh more or less than $\dfrac{1}{2}$ pound?

19. Cassandra walked $\dfrac{2}{3}$ mile. Walt walked 0.7 mile. Who walked the greater distance?

20. Danny ate $\dfrac{3}{4}$ of his submarine sandwich. Tynesha ate $\dfrac{5}{8}$ of her submarine sandwich. Who ate more of their sandwich?

21. When fly-fishing, Jorge releases any fish he catches that is less than 6 inches long. On a number line, show the lengths of fish Jorge will keep.

Tell if the statement is *true* or *false*.

22. The product of five negative integers is a negative integer.

23. The sum of two negative integers is equal to the absolute value of the sum of the two integers.

24. The opposite of the sum of two integers is always positive.

25. The product of two integers is negative. One of the integers must be positive.

26. If a and b are integers, and $a > b$, then $|a| > |b|$.

Solve each equation.

27. $5m + 8 = -27$

28. $4(r - 3) = -12$

29. $3.8x = 5.2x + 11.2$

30. $7(d + 2) = 4d - 1$

Cumulative Problem Solving

Taylor and three of his classmates share a pizza. The pizza is cut into 10 equal pieces when it is delivered.

31. Each student will eat $\frac{1}{4}$ of the pizza. Taylor tries to write an equivalent fraction.

$$\frac{1}{4} = \frac{?}{10}$$

On the right side of this equation, the numerator will not be a whole number. Thus, you can solve the equation, but the right-hand side is not a fraction. How many pieces out of ten should each student get?

32. Write an equivalent fraction with denominator 20.

33. Explain how the group can evenly divide the pizza.

After taxes are deducted, Tyrone's monthly take-home pay is $1960. His average monthly expenses are shown.

		Amount (dollars)
◯	Housing	750
	Food	300
	Auto	350
	Utilities	120
	Miscellaneous	300

34. Write each expense as a fraction of Tyrone's take-home pay. Write each fraction as a decimal rounded to the nearest hundredth.

35. Order the five expenses from the least to the greatest fraction of Tyrone's take-home pay.

36. After expenses, how much does Tyrone have left each month for savings? Write this amount as a fraction of his take-home pay. Write the fraction as a decimal.

Josephina coaches a girls softball team. She calculates each player's batting average using the following fraction.

$$\frac{\text{Number of hits}}{\text{Number of times at bat}}$$

	A	B	C	D
1	Player	Hits	Times at Bat	Batting Average
2	Kyla	10	25	
3	Cheryl	14	33	
4	Kerri	31	60	
5	LaTasha	19	39	
6	Laura	9	23	
7	Ashley	9	26	
8	Adriel	17	36	
9	Shawna	32	58	
10	Crystal	34	55	

37. Calculate the batting averages of the players listed on the spreadsheet. Write each average as a decimal rounded to the nearest thousandth.

38. Josephina arranges the batting order from the highest batting average to the lowest. What should be the batting order for the players listed on the spreadsheet?

Gene restores old cars and sells them for a profit. He paid $2300 for one car. The cost of restoration was $4200. He needs to set a price for the car.

39. Gene wants to sell the car for at least the amount he has invested in it. Write an inequality for this amount. Graph the inequality on a number line like the one following.

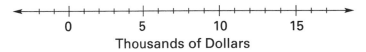

Thousands of Dollars

40. Gene researches prices of the same car model and year. The highest price he finds for a car in mint condition is $12,000. He wants to set his price lower than this amount. Write an inequality for this price, and graph it on the same number line.

41. The region where the graphs overlap defines Gene's price range. Highlight this region on the number line. Write the price as a combined inequality of the form:

$$\underline{\ ?\ } \leq x < \underline{\ ?\ }$$

LESSON 5.4 ADDING AND SUBTRACTING RATIONAL NUMBERS

OBJECTIVES

- ➡ Convert between improper fractions and mixed numbers.
- ➡ Add and subtract rational numbers.
- ➡ Solve equations containing rational numbers

Jiro is making bread from the recipe shown. He does not have rye flour, so he substitutes bread flour. How many cups of bread flour should Jiro use altogether?

Numbers such as $4\frac{2}{3}$ and $2\frac{1}{4}$ are called *mixed numbers*. A **mixed number** shows the sum of a whole number and a fraction. You can use fraction bars to represent the mixed number $2\frac{1}{4}$.

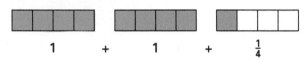

$$1 \quad + \quad 1 \quad + \quad \frac{1}{4}$$

Each square in the fraction bars above represents one-fourth. How many fourths are shaded in all? The fraction bars show that $2\frac{1}{4} = \frac{9}{4}$. The fraction $\frac{9}{4}$ is called an *improper fraction*. An **improper fraction** has a numerator greater than or equal to its denominator.

♥ ♥ ♥ ♥ ♥ ♥ ♥ ♥ ♥ ♥ ♥ ♥ ♥ ♥ ♥ ♥ ♥

$4\frac{2}{3}$ cups bread flour   1 cup warm water

$2\frac{1}{4}$ cups rye flour*   1 cup warm milk

1 pkg dry yeast   2 T melted butter

1 T salt   3 T molasses

*Bread flour may be substituted

♥ ♥ ♥ ♥ ♥ ♥ ♥ ♥ ♥ ♥ ♥ ♥ ♥ ♥ ♥ ♥ ♥

EXAMPLE 1   Writing Improper Fractions as Mixed Numbers

Write $\frac{20}{6}$ as a mixed number.

SOLUTION

Divide the numerator by the denominator. Write the remainder as a fraction with the same denominator. If necessary, simplify the fraction.

$$\frac{20}{6} = 6\overline{)20} \;\; \begin{array}{c} 3 \\ \underline{18} \\ 2 \end{array} = 3\frac{2}{6} = 3\frac{1}{3}$$

ONGOING ASSESSMENT

Write the following improper fractions as mixed numbers.

a. $\frac{19}{4}$ b. $-\frac{25}{8}$

c. $\frac{21}{9}$ d. $-\frac{106}{3}$

ACTIVITY   **Adding and Subtracting Fractions with Common Denominators**

1 Make a fraction bar with five equal parts.

2 Shade $\frac{2}{5}$ of the fraction bar.

3 Shade an additional $\frac{1}{5}$ of the fraction bar.

4 How much of the fraction bar is shaded now? Complete the following equation.

$$\frac{2}{5} + \frac{1}{5} = \underline{\ ?\ }$$

5 The fractions $\frac{2}{5}$ and $\frac{1}{5}$ have a common denominator. Complete the following: To add fractions with common denominators, add the _____?_____ and keep the same _____?_____.

6 Subtracting a number is the same as adding its opposite. Complete the following equation.

$$\frac{3}{5} - \frac{1}{5} = \frac{3}{5} + \left(-\frac{1}{5}\right)$$
$$= \frac{3}{5} + \frac{-1}{5}$$
$$= \frac{3-1}{5}$$
$$= \underline{\ ?\ }$$

The Activity demonstrates the following rule.

> **Adding and Subtracting Fractions with Common Denominators**
>
> If a, b, and c are whole numbers and $c \neq 0$,
>
> $$\frac{a}{c} + \frac{b}{c} = \frac{a+b}{c} \qquad \text{and} \qquad \frac{a}{c} - \frac{b}{c} = \frac{a-b}{c}$$

How can you add or subtract two fractions that do not have the same denominators? You can rewrite them as equivalent fractions with common denominators. Then add or subtract.

EXAMPLE 2 Subtracting Fractions with Different Denominators

A school's basketball arena can seat $\frac{2}{3}$ of the school's students. If $\frac{7}{8}$ of the school's students want to attend the championship game, what fraction of the students will not get seats?

SOLUTION

The fraction of students without seats is the difference between $\frac{7}{8}$ and $\frac{2}{3}$.

$$\frac{7}{8} - \frac{2}{3} = \frac{7 \cdot 3}{8 \cdot 3} - \frac{2 \cdot 8}{3 \cdot 8} \qquad \text{The LCD is 24}$$

$$= \frac{21}{24} - \frac{16}{24} = \frac{21 - 16}{24}$$

$$= \frac{5}{24}$$

The fraction of students who will not get seats is $\frac{5}{24}$.

ONGOING ASSESSMENT

Solve each equation.

a. $\frac{3}{7} + \frac{1}{7} = x$ **b.** $\frac{1}{7} - \frac{3}{7} = y$ **c.** $\frac{1}{2} + x = \frac{2}{5}$ **d.** $y - \frac{7}{4} = \frac{5}{6}$

EXAMPLE 3 Writing Mixed Numbers as Improper Fractions

Write $5\frac{3}{4}$ as an improper fraction.

SOLUTION

Use addition: $5\frac{3}{4} = 5 + \frac{3}{4}$

$$= \frac{5}{1} + \frac{3}{4} \qquad\qquad 5 = \frac{5}{1}$$

$$= \frac{5 \cdot 4}{1 \cdot 4} + \frac{3}{4} \qquad \text{The LCD is 4}$$

$$= \frac{20}{4} + \frac{3}{4} = \frac{23}{4}$$

Critical Thinking   Explain why the following shortcut gives the same result as the steps listed in Example 3.

$$5\frac{3}{4} = 5 \underset{\otimes}{\overset{\oplus}{\underbrace{\frac{3}{4}}}} = \frac{(5 \cdot 4) + 3}{4} = \frac{23}{4}$$

You can also use your calculator if it has an $\boxed{a\frac{b}{c}}$ key.

EXAMPLE 4 Adding Mixed Numbers

At the beginning of this lesson, Jiro is making bread. How many cups of bread flour does he need?

SOLUTION

$$4\frac{2}{3} + 2\frac{1}{4} = (4 + 2) + \left(\frac{2}{3} + \frac{1}{4}\right)$$

$$= (4 + 2) + \left(\frac{8}{12} + \frac{3}{12}\right) \qquad \text{The LCD is 12}$$

$$= 6 + \frac{11}{12} = 6\frac{11}{12}$$

Jiro needs $6\frac{11}{12}$ cups of bread flour.

With your calculator, 4 [a%c] 2 [a%c] 3 [+] 2 [a%c] 1 [a%c] 4 [=] $6\frac{11}{12}$

EXAMPLE 5 Solving Rational Number Equations

Solve the equation $x + 3\frac{2}{3} = 5\frac{3}{4}$.

SOLUTION

$$x + 3\frac{2}{3} = 5\frac{3}{4} \qquad \text{Given}$$

$$x = 5\frac{3}{4} - 3\frac{2}{3} \qquad \text{Subtraction Property of Equality}$$

$$= \frac{23}{4} - \frac{11}{3} \qquad \text{Rewrite as improper fractions}$$

$$= \frac{69}{12} - \frac{44}{12} \qquad \text{The LCD is 12}$$

$$= \frac{25}{12} \qquad \text{Simplify}$$

$$= 2\frac{1}{12} \qquad \text{Rewrite as a mixed number}$$

With your calculator, 5 [a%c] 3 [a%c] 4 [−] 3 [a%c] 2 [a%c] 3 [=] $2\frac{1}{12}$

You can use estimation to see if your answer is reasonable when you add or subtract rational numbers. In Example 5, $5\frac{3}{4}$ rounds to 6 and $3\frac{2}{3}$ rounds to 4. Thus, the answer should be close to 2. Is it?

ONGOING ASSESSMENT

Solve $p + 2\frac{1}{4} = 3\frac{5}{8}$. Use estimation to check if the answer is reasonable.

PROBLEM SOLVING

USING THE FOUR-STEP PLAN

Latoya is a professional seamstress who is making a blouse. She has selected material for the blouse from a bolt that has $4\frac{3}{8}$ yards of cloth. The blouse will require $1\frac{1}{4}$ yards. After Latoya cuts the cloth for the blouse, the material remaining on the bolt is called a *remnant*. She wants to use the remnant to make a combination of the garments shown in the table to sell in her shop. She does not want to make more than one of any garment.

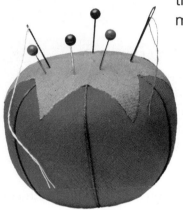

	Material Required (yards)
Vest	$\frac{7}{8}$
Shorts	$1\frac{1}{8}$
Skirt	$1\frac{7}{8}$
Casual dress	$2\frac{7}{8}$
Long dress	$3\frac{1}{2}$

Determine which garment or combination of garments Latoya can make from the remnant. Which garment or combination of garments would result in the least waste?

Step 1: Understand the Problem

If necessary, read the problem several times.

What is the goal of the problem?

What information is needed? What information is given?

Step 2: Develop a Plan

Problem-solving strategy: Write inequalities. The total amount of material used for the additional garments cannot be more than the remnant.

List each garment or combination of garments possible.

Step 3: Carry Out the Plan

How many inequalities can you write?

Step 4: Check the Results

Does your solution answer the problem stated?

LESSON ASSESSMENT

Think and Discuss

1 How do you write a mixed number as an improper fraction?

2 Explain how to add and subtract fractions with common denominators.

3 Write an algorithm for finding the sum or difference of two fractions with unlike denominators.

Practice and Apply

4. Write the voltage measurement as a mixed number, an improper fraction, and a decimal.

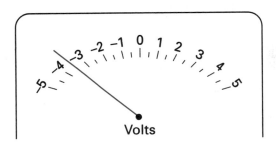

Volts

Write each improper fraction as a mixed number with the fraction written in simplest form.

5. $\dfrac{11}{5}$ **6.** $-\dfrac{21}{6}$ **7.** $\dfrac{54}{12}$ **8.** $\dfrac{84}{8}$

Write each mixed number as an improper fraction.

9. $-5\dfrac{2}{3}$ **10.** $7\dfrac{5}{8}$ **11.** $12\dfrac{4}{5}$ **12.** $-10\dfrac{7}{12}$

Let $a = \dfrac{1}{12}$, $b = \dfrac{3}{12}$, and $c = \dfrac{7}{12}$. Evaluate each expression.

13. $a + b$ **14.** $b + c$ **15.** $b - c$ **16.** $a + c - b$

Solve each equation.

17. $\dfrac{3}{4} = x - \dfrac{9}{10}$ **18.** $-\dfrac{1}{6} - y = \dfrac{3}{4}$

19. $\dfrac{1}{3} - \dfrac{7}{12} = z - \dfrac{5}{8}$ **20.** $n + 7\dfrac{1}{4} = 3\dfrac{2}{3}$

21. $m - 9\dfrac{3}{5} = -4\dfrac{7}{10}$ **22.** $-11\dfrac{5}{8} = s + 2\dfrac{1}{2}$

For Exercises 23–28, define a variable, write an equation, and solve.

23. Tangela removed a $\frac{3}{4}$-inch piece of tape from a dispenser. There are $2\frac{9}{16}$ inches of tape remaining on the dispenser. How long was the original strip of tape before Tangela removed the piece?

24. To paint his living room, Carlos used $4\frac{1}{3}$ gallons of white paint and $2\frac{1}{2}$ gallons of green paint. How many total gallons of paint did Carlos use?

25. The length of a rectangular picture frame is $\frac{2}{3}$ yard. The width is $\frac{3}{4}$ yard. What is the perimeter of the picture frame?

26. Chan recommends that his clients sell their shares of Glomar Industries when the price is $40 per share. The price of a share is $30\frac{3}{8}$. How much can the share price increase before Chan recommends a sell?

27. A recipe calls for a mixture of cereal and trail mix. Jill used a total of $6\frac{1}{6}$ cups of the cereal and trail mix. She used $3\frac{1}{2}$ cups of cereal. Did she use more or less cereal than trail mix? How much more or less?

28. Elena needs $28\frac{3}{4}$ square yards of carpeting to recarpet her living room and $32\frac{1}{2}$ square yards for her family room. Elena ordered 65 square yards of carpet. How much extra carpet did she order?

Mixed Review

Estimate each sum or difference. Use a calculator to find the exact answer.

29. $35.087 + 59.95$ **30.** $34,934 - 15,375 + 19,827$

Use the four-step problem-solving plan to solve each of the following.

31. You have a 3-gallon can and a 7-gallon can. There are no markings on either can. How can you use only these two cans to get 5 gallons of water?

32. At 12 o'clock, the hour and minute hand are together on a clock. How many times will the hands be together during the next 12 hours?

LESSON 5.5 MULTIPLYING RATIONAL NUMBERS

OBJECTIVES

➤ **Multiply rational numbers to solve problems.**

Fernando scouts high school pitchers and catchers for the State University baseball team. His goal is to scout 80 players for next year's class. Fernando wants $\frac{3}{4}$ of the players to be pitchers. He also wants $\frac{1}{2}$ of these pitchers to be left handed. How many left-handed pitchers should Fernando scout?

The fraction of the players who should be left-handed pitchers is $\frac{1}{2}$ of $\frac{3}{4}$. You can model this fraction with a grid.

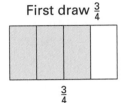

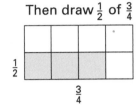

$\frac{1}{2}$ of $\frac{3}{4} = \frac{3}{8}$

The shaded area in the figure is a rectangle with width $\frac{1}{2}$ and length $\frac{3}{4}$. The area of this rectangle is the product (width) · (length). Thus,

$$\frac{1}{2} \text{ of } \frac{3}{4} = \frac{1}{2} \cdot \frac{3}{4} = \frac{3}{8}$$

ACTIVITY 1 — Multiplying Fractions

1 Match the grid models at the left with the following products of fractions. Complete each equation.

a.

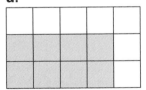

$$\frac{1}{2} \cdot \frac{5}{6} = \underline{\ ?\ } \qquad \frac{2}{3} \cdot \frac{4}{5} = \underline{\ ?\ } \qquad \frac{1}{3} \cdot \frac{1}{3} = \underline{\ ?\ }$$

b.

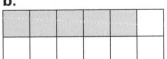

2 For each equation in Step 1, compare the product of the numerators on the left side with the numerator of the product. Compare the product of the denominators on the left side with the denominator of the product.

3 Write an algorithm for finding the product of two fractions without using a grid model.

c.

4 Compare your algorithm to the rule for multiplying rational numbers on the next page.

Multiplying Rational Numbers

If a, b, c, and d are whole numbers with $b \neq 0$ and $d \neq 0$, then

$$\frac{a}{b} \cdot \frac{c}{d} = \frac{a \cdot c}{b \cdot d}$$

EXAMPLE 1 Multiplying Rational Numbers

How many of the 80 players scouted by Fernando should be left-handed pitchers?

SOLUTION

A total of $\frac{3}{8}$ of the players scouted should be left-handed pitchers. You need to find $\frac{3}{8}$ of 80 or $\frac{3}{8} \cdot 80$.

$$\frac{3}{8} \cdot 80 = \frac{3}{8} \cdot \frac{80}{1}$$

$$= \frac{3 \cdot 80}{8 \cdot 1} = \frac{240}{8} = 30$$

Fernando should scout 30 left-handed pitchers.

ONGOING ASSESSMENT

Timothy had $16. He spent $\frac{3}{4}$ of his money for theater tickets. How much did he spend for the tickets?

ACTIVITY 2   **Multiplying by a Unit Fraction**

1 Use the rule for multiplying rational numbers to find each of the following.

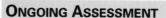

a. $\frac{1}{3}$ of 2   **b.** $\frac{1}{5}$ of 4   **c.** $\frac{1}{2}$ of 3

2 If n and x are any two numbers with $n \neq 0$, what is $\frac{1}{n}$ of x?

In Activity 2, you discovered a rule for multiplying by a fraction when its numerator is 1. This fraction is called a **unit fraction**.

Multiplying by a Unit Fraction

For any two numbers, a and b, $b \neq 0$,

$$\frac{1}{b} \cdot a = \frac{a}{b}$$

If the numerator and denominator have common factors, you can simplify before multiplying. One way to simplify is to divide the numerator and denominator of each fraction by the same number. This process is sometimes called *cancellation*.

EXAMPLE 2 Cancellation

Out of every 12 fire fighters responding to a train derailment, 5 are exposed to a caustic chemical. If 4 out of 9 people exposed to this chemical require hospitalization, what fraction of the fire fighters responding to the derailment will require hospitalization?

SOLUTION

Find the product $\dfrac{5}{12} \cdot \dfrac{4}{9}$.

$$\dfrac{5}{12} \cdot \dfrac{4}{9} = \dfrac{5}{\cancel{4} \cdot 3} \cdot \dfrac{\overset{1}{\cancel{4}}}{9} \qquad \text{Cancellation: Divide the numerator}$$
$$\qquad\qquad\qquad \text{and denominator by 4}$$

$$= \dfrac{5 \cdot 1}{3 \cdot 9}$$

$$= \dfrac{5}{27}$$

EXAMPLE 3 Multiplying Rational Numbers

Find the product $-3\dfrac{3}{5} \cdot 1\dfrac{1}{4}$.

SOLUTION

$$-3\dfrac{3}{5} \cdot 1\dfrac{1}{4} = -\dfrac{18}{5} \cdot \dfrac{5}{4} \qquad \text{Rewrite the mixed numbers as improper fractions}$$

$$= -\dfrac{\overset{9}{\cancel{18}}}{\underset{1}{\cancel{5}}} \cdot \dfrac{\overset{1}{\cancel{5}}}{\underset{2}{\cancel{4}}} \qquad \text{Cancellation: Divide the numerator and denominator by 2 and by 5}$$

$$= -\dfrac{9}{2} = -4\dfrac{1}{2} \qquad \text{Simplify}$$

ONGOING ASSESSMENT

Find each product.

a. $1\dfrac{5}{8} \cdot \dfrac{2}{7}$ b. $-2\dfrac{1}{3} \cdot 3\dfrac{2}{5}$ c. $\left(-\dfrac{4}{5}\right)\left(-4\dfrac{1}{2}\right)$

Critical Thinking How can you use estimation to make sure your answers to the Ongoing Assessment are reasonable?

LESSON ASSESSMENT

Think and Discuss

1 Explain how to find $\frac{2}{3}$ of $\frac{5}{9}$.

2 Explain how to multiply two mixed numbers.

3 Two methods of finding the product of rational numbers follow. Do both methods result in the same answer? Explain.

$$\frac{2}{5} \cdot 15 \cdot \frac{7}{8} = \frac{\overset{1}{\cancel{2}}}{\cancel{5}} \cdot \frac{\overset{3}{\cancel{15}}}{1} \cdot \frac{7}{\underset{4}{\cancel{8}}}$$
$$= \underline{?}$$

$$\frac{2}{5} \cdot 15 \cdot \frac{7}{8} = \frac{2}{5} \cdot \frac{15}{1} \cdot \frac{7}{8}$$
$$= \frac{2 \cdot 15 \cdot 7}{5 \cdot 8}$$
$$= \underline{?}$$

Practice and Apply

Write each product in simplest form.

4. $\frac{5}{8} \cdot \frac{2}{3}$

5. $\frac{3}{4} \cdot -\frac{8}{9}$

6. $-\frac{4}{15} \cdot \frac{3}{8} \cdot -\frac{5}{6}$

7. $\frac{2}{3} \cdot 20$

8. $-1\frac{1}{2} \cdot 2\frac{1}{2}$

9. $3\frac{3}{5} \cdot \frac{2}{3}$

10. $-4\frac{2}{3} \cdot -3\frac{3}{4}$

11. $-16 \cdot \frac{3}{4}$

12. $6\frac{2}{3} \cdot \$20$

13. Evaluate $a(b + c)$ when $a = 5\frac{1}{5}$, $b = 1\frac{1}{2}$, and $c = 3\frac{7}{10}$.

14. Evaluate $ab + ac$ when $a = -1\frac{1}{3}$, $b = 2\frac{1}{4}$, and $c = -1\frac{7}{8}$.

15. Stock in Super Computer Inc. is selling for $\$10\frac{3}{8}$ per share. What is the cost of 24 shares?

16. It will take Dalia 9 hours to wallpaper her bedroom. How many hours will it take Dalia to complete $\frac{3}{4}$ of the job?

17. Guillermo bought contact lenses for $270. He paid $\frac{1}{3}$ of the cost as a down payment and paid the rest in five equal monthly payments. How much was the down payment? How much was each monthly payment?

18. Damon took $\frac{2}{3}$ of his savings out of the bank. He spent $\frac{3}{5}$ of this amount on tuition. What part of his savings did Damon spend on the tuition?

19. On May 11, 1997, Susie Maroney became the first woman to swim across the Florida Straits, from Cuba to the U.S. She swam an average of $7\frac{1}{3}$ kilometers per hour. How far did she swim if she completed the crossing in $24\frac{1}{2}$ hours?

20. The area of a rectangle is the product of its length and width. Find the area in square feet of a rectangular flower garden that measures $6\frac{2}{3}$ feet by $5\frac{1}{4}$ feet.

Mixed Review

Solve each equation.

21. $3 - x = 1$

22. $15 + y = 8$

23. $2a + 4 = 12$

24. $6b - 12 = 6$

25. $3(w - 1) = 15$

26. $6g - 3g = 9$

27. $4d - 8 - d = 1$

28. $-c + 4c = 27$

This graph shows the monthly sales of new cars for one employee from December to June.

29. In which month was the most cars sold?

30. How many cars were sold in April?

31. In which months were more than 5 cars sold?

32. How many more cars were sold in June than in January?

33. What is the median of the car sales?

34. What is the mode of the car sales?

35. What is the mean of the car sales?

LESSON 5.6 DIVIDING RATIONAL NUMBERS

OBJECTIVES
- Use reciprocals to divide rational numbers.
- Solve equations containing fractions.

Marcia's Apple Orchard sells fresh-pressed apple cider in $\frac{1}{2}$-gallon containers. A customer orders 3 gallons of cider. To determine how many $\frac{1}{2}$-gallon containers are needed to fill this order, Marcia divides 3 gallons by $\frac{1}{2}$ gallon per container.

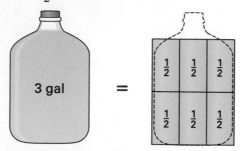

Marcia needs six $\frac{1}{2}$-gallon containers. She gets the same result if she multiplies $3 \cdot 2$.

$$3 \div \frac{1}{2} = 3 \cdot 2 = 6$$

The numbers 2 and $\frac{1}{2}$ have a special relationship. Their product is 1. Two numbers are *reciprocals* if their product is 1. The **reciprocal** of any nonzero number a is $\frac{1}{a}$. For any rational number $\frac{a}{b}$ with $a \neq 0$ and $b \neq 0$, the reciprocal is $\frac{b}{a}$. The relationship between two reciprocals is called the **Reciprocal Property**.

> **Reciprocal Property**
> If a and b are nonzero whole numbers, the reciprocal of $\frac{a}{b}$ is $\frac{b}{a}$ and
> $$\frac{a}{b} \cdot \frac{b}{a} = 1$$

ONGOING ASSESSMENT

Find the reciprocal of each of the following.

a. $\frac{1}{5}$ b. $-\frac{2}{5}$ c. $\frac{8}{3}$ d. $-\frac{7}{2}$

1 Copy the table below.

Gallons Needed	Gallons per Container	Division Equation	Multiplication Equation	Containers Needed
3	$\frac{1}{2}$	$3 \div \frac{1}{2} = 6$	$3 \cdot 2 = 6$	6
3	$\frac{1}{3}$	?	?	?
6	$\frac{3}{4}$	?	?	?
$\frac{8}{3}$	$\frac{2}{3}$	?	?	?

The first row of the table shows:

- the number of gallons needed

- the number of gallons per container

- Marcia's division equation

- an equivalent multiplication equation

- the number of containers needed for an order of 3 gallons of cider with $\frac{1}{2}$ gallon per container.

2 For each row, draw a diagram similar to the one shown at the beginning of the lesson to show the containers needed.

3 Complete the remaining rows of the table for the given number of gallons needed and gallons per container.

4 Replace the ? to make the following statement *true*.

$$\text{If } 7 \div \frac{1}{a} = 35, \text{ then } 7 \cdot \underline{?} = 35$$

In the activity, you discovered that dividing by a rational number is the same as multiplying by its reciprocal.

Dividing Rational Numbers

If a, b, c, and d are whole numbers and neither b, c, nor d is equal to zero, then

$$\frac{a}{b} \div \frac{c}{d} = \frac{a}{b} \cdot \frac{d}{c}$$

EXAMPLE 1 Dividing Rational Numbers

Find the quotients.

a. $\left(-\dfrac{3}{5}\right) \div \left(-\dfrac{4}{3}\right)$ **b.** $\dfrac{9}{2} \div 8$

SOLUTION

a. $\left(-\dfrac{3}{5}\right) \div \left(-\dfrac{4}{3}\right) = \left(-\dfrac{3}{5}\right) \cdot \left(-\dfrac{3}{4}\right)$ The reciprocal of $-\dfrac{4}{3}$ is $-\dfrac{3}{4}$

$$= \dfrac{-3 \cdot (-3)}{5 \cdot 4}$$

$$= \dfrac{9}{20}$$

b. $\dfrac{9}{2} \div 8 = \dfrac{9}{2} \div \dfrac{8}{1}$ Rewrite 8 as $\dfrac{8}{1}$

$$= \dfrac{9}{2} \cdot \dfrac{1}{8}$$ The reciprocal of $\dfrac{8}{1}$ is $\dfrac{1}{8}$

$$= \dfrac{9}{16}$$

EXAMPLE 2 Dividing Mixed Numbers

To pour a concrete foundation, the construction foreman needs to order $9\dfrac{1}{3}$ cubic yards of concrete. A truck can deliver $3\dfrac{1}{2}$ cubic yards of concrete in each load. How many truck loads of concrete must the foreman order?

SOLUTION

To find the number of loads needed, divide $9\dfrac{1}{3}$ by $3\dfrac{1}{2}$.

$$9\dfrac{1}{3} \div 3\dfrac{1}{2} = \dfrac{28}{3} \div \dfrac{7}{2}$$ Rewrite the mixed numbers as improper fractions

$$= \dfrac{\overset{4}{\cancel{28}}}{3} \cdot \dfrac{2}{\underset{1}{\cancel{7}}}$$ The reciprocal of $\dfrac{7}{2}$ is $\dfrac{2}{7}$

$$= \dfrac{4}{3} \cdot \dfrac{2}{1}$$

$$= \dfrac{8}{3} = 2\dfrac{2}{3}$$

The foreman needs to order $2\dfrac{2}{3}$ truck loads. If the foreman cannot order a fraction of a load, 3 full loads should be ordered.

Recall that you can solve a multiplication equation by dividing both sides by a number to undo the multiplication. Dividing by a number is the same as multiplying by its reciprocal.

EXAMPLE 3 Solving Multiplication Equations

Solve the equation $-\frac{3}{5}x = \frac{7}{10}$.

SOLUTION

Multiply each side of the equation by the reciprocal of $-\frac{3}{5}$.

$$-\frac{5}{3} \cdot -\frac{3}{5}x = -\frac{5}{3} \cdot \frac{7}{10} \qquad \text{Multiplication Property of Equality}$$

$$1 \cdot x = -\frac{\overset{1}{\cancel{5}}}{3} \cdot \frac{7}{\underset{2}{\cancel{10}}} \qquad \text{Reciprocal Property}$$

$$x = -\frac{7}{6} \text{ or } -1\frac{1}{6}$$

Check: $-\frac{\overset{1}{\cancel{3}}}{5} \cdot -\frac{7}{\underset{2}{\cancel{6}}} = \frac{-1 \cdot -7}{5 \cdot 2} = \frac{7}{10}$ ✓

The solution is $-1\frac{1}{6}$.

LESSON ASSESSMENT

Think and Discuss

1 Explain how to find the reciprocal of a rational number. Which rational numbers are their own reciprocals? Which rational number does not have a reciprocal?

2 Someone makes the following statement:

Instead of dividing rational numbers, I can use an inverse operation and get the same answer.

Is the statement *true*? Explain your reasoning.

3 Explain how you can divide a positive whole number (the dividend) by a number and get a quotient greater than the dividend.

4 List the steps required to solve the equation $x \div \frac{a}{b} = \frac{c}{d}$ for x. Give a reason for each step.

Find the reciprocal of each number.

5. $-\dfrac{7}{8}$ **6.** $-2\dfrac{2}{9}$ **7.** -1 **8.** $\dfrac{1}{r}, r \neq 0$

Find each quotient. Simplify the answer.

9. $-\dfrac{2}{3} \div \left(-\dfrac{3}{4}\right)$ **10.** $64 \div \left(-5\dfrac{1}{3}\right)$

11. $-2\dfrac{2}{5} \div 18$ **12.** $-2\dfrac{1}{2} \div 3\dfrac{1}{3}$

13. $8\dfrac{4}{5} \div \left(-7\dfrac{1}{3}\right)$ **14.** $-1\dfrac{7}{8} \div \left(-2\dfrac{1}{4}\right)$

Solve each equation.

15. $\dfrac{2}{3}f = -24$ **16.** $5\dfrac{3}{5} = -\dfrac{8}{7}p$

17. $6\dfrac{2}{5} = t \div \left(-3\dfrac{1}{8}\right)$ **18.** $-2\dfrac{1}{2}b = 3\dfrac{1}{8}$

19. $\dfrac{3}{4}q - \dfrac{1}{2} = \dfrac{5}{6}$ **20** $2\dfrac{1}{4}y + 1\dfrac{1}{2} = 1\dfrac{2}{3}y$

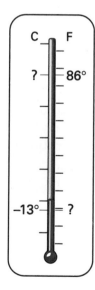

For Exercises 21–23, define a variable, write a multiplication equation, and solve.

21. The wall of an office is $58\dfrac{1}{2}$ feet long. Nine identical tables are aligned end-to-end along the length of the wall. How long is each table?

22. Alaina has $6\dfrac{2}{3}$ yards of ribbon to wrap gifts. How many gifts can Alaina wrap if she uses $1\dfrac{1}{3}$ yards of ribbon for each gift?

23. In an eighth grade class, $\dfrac{3}{8}$ of the students participate in athletics. If 132 eighth graders are in athletics, how many students are in the class?

The formula for changing Celsius degrees to Fahrenheit degrees is $F = \dfrac{9}{5}C + 32$.

24. Change $-13°C$ to Fahrenheit.

25. Change $86°F$ to Celsius.

26. Nathan is filling his new swimming pool for the first time. He has used 9600 gallons of water and the pool is $\dfrac{3}{4}$ full. How many gallons of water will Nathan's pool hold when it is full?

Tell whether each of the following is *true* or *false.*

27. The sum of two integers must be greater than either integer.

28. If the product of three integers is negative, one of the integers must be negative.

29. The opposite of an integer must be less than or equal to zero.

30. You can add the same negative integer to each side of an equation and the equation will stay balanced.

Solve each equation.

31. $5x - 9 = 2x + 3$

32. $-48 = 3(2x - 4)$

Cumulative Problem Solving

Written music uses fractions to describe the time value of a note within a measure.

The time signature of a piece of music tells the number of beats in one measure and the kind of note that gets one beat. For example, in music written in $\frac{4}{4}$ time,

o whole note

♩ or ♩ $\frac{1}{2}$ note

♩ or ♩ $\frac{1}{4}$ note

♪ or ♪ $\frac{1}{8}$ note

♪ or ♪ $\frac{1}{16}$ note

$$\frac{4}{4} \begin{array}{l} \rightarrow \\ \rightarrow \end{array} \underline{\begin{array}{c} \text{4 beats to a measure} \\ \text{a quarter note gets one beat} \end{array}}$$

The total value of the notes in each measure equals one.

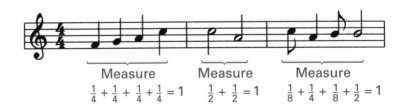

Measure   Measure   Measure

$\frac{1}{4} + \frac{1}{4} + \frac{1}{4} + \frac{1}{4} = 1$ $\frac{1}{2} + \frac{1}{2} = 1$ $\frac{1}{8} + \frac{1}{4} + \frac{1}{8} + \frac{1}{2} = 1$

Each of the following pieces of music is written in $\frac{4}{4}$ time. Name a single note that completes each measure.

33.   **34.**

35.   **36.**

To lift an object, the thrust required from a rocket motor is greater than the object's weight. A lunar lander weighs 3300 pounds on earth. The lander's weight on the moon is approximately $\frac{1}{6}$ its weight on earth.

37. Write an inequality for the thrust required from a rocket motor to lift the lander from the surface of the moon.

Antonio is the executor of Mrs. Tran's estate. He must determine how to divide the estate among the heirs. In accordance with Mrs. Tran's will, $\frac{1}{4}$ of the estate goes to her church, and $\frac{1}{8}$ goes to a charity. The remainder of the estate is to be divided so that $\frac{1}{2}$ goes to relatives in her family and $\frac{1}{2}$ goes to relatives in her husband's family. There are 5 people named in her family and 7 people named in her husband's family.

38. What total fraction of Mrs. Tran's estate should Antonio give to her church and charity?

39. After deducting for church and charity, what fraction of the estate remains for relatives?

40. What fraction of Mrs. Tran's estate should Antonio send to each of her named relatives?

41. What fraction of Mrs. Tran's estate should Antonio send to each of her husband's named relatives?

Elaine orders bricks for a construction project. She needs to determine how many bricks to order for a wall that measures 31 feet 6 inches by 10 feet $\frac{3}{4}$ inch.

A row of bricks is called a *course.* Each brick in a course is $7\frac{7}{8}$ inches in length and $2\frac{5}{8}$ inches high, including the mortar joints.

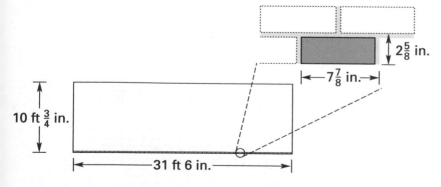

42. Convert 31 ft 6 in. to inches. How many bricks are in one course?

43. Convert 10 ft $\frac{3}{4}$ in. to inches. How many courses are required?

44. How many bricks should Elaine order for the wall?

LESSON 5.7 SOLVING INEQUALITIES WITH ADDITION AND SUBTRACTION

OBJECTIVES

➤ Solve inequalities using addition and subtraction properties.

For a Future Farmers of America project, Trevor plants a field of corn and pumpkins. He wants to plant pumpkins on $\frac{1}{2}$ acre. The total field can be no larger than $1\frac{1}{3}$ acres. What is the largest area Trevor can plant for the corn field?

Let x represent the area of the corn field. The sum of the areas of the corn field and the pumpkin patch must be *less than or equal to* $1\frac{1}{3}$ acres. Trevor needs to solve the **inequality**

$$x + \frac{1}{2} \leq 1\frac{1}{3}$$

ACTIVITY

The Addition and Subtraction Properties of Inequality

1 Draw a number line from −10 to 10. Plot 2, 4, and 8.

2 Start with the inequality $8 > 4$.

a. Add 2 to both sides of the inequality. Plot the new points on the number line. Is the new inequality *true*?

b. Subtract 4 from both sides of the original inequality. Plot the new points. Is the new inequality *true*?

c. Choose three numbers a, b, and c, so that $a > b$. Replace the ? with an inequality sign.

$$\text{If } a > b, \text{ then } a + c \underline{\ ?\ } b + c.$$

3 Start with the inequality $2 < 4$.

a. Add 2 to both sides of the inequality. Plot the new points on the number line. Is the new inequality *true*?

b. Subtract 4 from both sides of the original inequality in Step 3. Plot the points. Is the new inequality *true*?

c. Choose three numbers a, b, and c, so that $a < b$. Replace the ? with an inequality sign.

$$\text{If } a < b, \text{ then } a + c \underline{\ ?\ } b + c.$$

The Activity demonstrates two important properties of inequalities. You can add any number to both sides of an inequality and the resulting inequality is *true*.

Addition Property of Inequality

For any numbers a, b, and c,

$$\text{If } a \leq b, \text{ then } a + c \leq b + c.$$

$$\text{If } a \geq b, \text{ then } a + c \geq b + c.$$

You can subtract any number from both sides of an inequality and the resulting inequality is *true*.

Subtraction Property of Inequality

For any numbers, a, b, and c,

$$\text{If } a \leq b, \text{ then } a - c \leq b - c.$$

$$\text{If } a \geq b, \text{ then } a - c \geq b - c.$$

You can use these Addition and Subtraction Properties to solve inequalities in the same way you solved addition and subtraction equations. The inequality is **solved** when the variable is isolated on one side.

EXAMPLE 1 Using the Subtraction Property of Inequality

Solve and graph Trevor's inequality $x + \frac{1}{2} \leq 1\frac{1}{3}$.

SOLUTION

Isolate the variable on one side of the inequality.

$x + \dfrac{1}{2} \leq 1\dfrac{1}{3}$	Given
$x + \dfrac{1}{2} - \dfrac{1}{2} \leq 1\dfrac{1}{3} - \dfrac{1}{2}$	Subtraction Property of Inequality
$x \leq \dfrac{4}{3} - \dfrac{1}{2}$	Rewrite the mixed number as an improper fraction
$x \leq \dfrac{8}{6} - \dfrac{3}{6}$	The LCD is 6
$x \leq \dfrac{5}{6}$	Simplify

Trevor can plant no more than $\frac{5}{6}$ acre of corn. The graph of this solution is

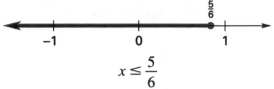

$$x \le \frac{5}{6}$$

Critical Thinking Why is the following graph the actual solution of Trevor's problem?

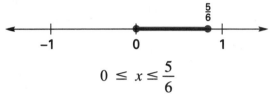

$$0 \le x \le \frac{5}{6}$$

Closed circles mean $\frac{5}{6}$ and 0 are part of the solution.

EXAMPLE 2 Using the Addition Property of Inequality

Solve and graph the inequality $a - 4\frac{2}{5} > -1\frac{4}{5}$.

SOLUTION

$$a - 4\frac{2}{5} > -1\frac{4}{5}$$

$$a - 4\frac{2}{5} + 4\frac{2}{5} > -1\frac{4}{5} + 4\frac{2}{5} \qquad \text{Addition Property of Inequality}$$

$$a > -\frac{9}{5} + \frac{22}{5}$$

$$a > \frac{13}{5} \text{ or } 2\frac{3}{5}$$

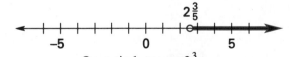

Open circle means $2\frac{3}{5}$ is not part of the solution.

ONGOING ASSESSMENT

Solve and graph each inequality.

a. $x + 1\frac{1}{4} < 3\frac{1}{2}$ **b.** $x - 4\frac{2}{3} \ge -1\frac{4}{5}$ **c.** $m + \frac{2}{3} \le 3\frac{1}{4}$

LESSON ASSESSMENT

1 How are solutions of equations and solutions of inequalities different?

2 How are the graphs of inequalities containing the symbols $<$ and $\leq$ different?

3 Explain how to solve the inequality $x - a < b$ for x. How would you graph the solution of this inequality?

4 Write the letter A, B, C, or D for the inequality symbol you would use for each of the following conditions.

a. "... is no more than ..."   **A.** $<$

b. "... is at least ..."   **B.** $\leq$

c. "... is fewer than ..."   **C.** $>$

d. "... has at most ..."   **D.** $\geq$

e. "... has more than ..."

f. "... is no less than ..."

Practice and Apply

Solve each inequality. Graph the solution on a number line.

5. $c + 7 < -11$ **6.** $r - 6 > -10$

7. $11.5 \geq z + 1.5$ **8.** $-1.25 < p - 7.25$

9. $t + \dfrac{7}{8} > \dfrac{1}{4}$ **10.** $2\dfrac{1}{2} \geq g - 3\dfrac{1}{4}$

11. $m - 5\dfrac{2}{3} \leq -8\dfrac{1}{4}$ **12.** $-8\dfrac{1}{6} + x < 3\dfrac{3}{4}$

For Exercises 13–20, define a variable, write an inequality, and solve.

13. After Rashidi paid $38.50 for a watch, he had less than $5.50 left. How much did Rashidi have before he bought the watch?

14. To compete in the power lifting meet, Lee can weigh at most $114\dfrac{1}{4}$ pounds. She weighs $109\dfrac{1}{2}$ pounds. How much weight can Lee gain and still compete in the meet?

15. If Bill makes over $400 in interest from his savings bonds, he will have to file an income tax return. He has already made $381 in interest this year. How much more interest can Bill make this year without having to file an income tax return?

16. It is at least $4\frac{1}{3}$ miles from Nick's house to Tarik's house. After walking $2\frac{1}{5}$ miles, how much farther does Nick have to walk to reach Tarik's house?

17. Roland deposited $23.50 in his checking account. He now has less than $75 in the account. How much did Roland have before he made the deposit?

18. After selling 28 copies of a CD, The Music Palace had more than 48 copies left. How many copies did The Music Palace have before selling the 28 CDs?

19. At birth, Beverly weighed $\frac{3}{4}$ of a pound more than her twin, Lauren. If Lauren weighed less than $5\frac{1}{2}$ pounds, how much did Beverly weigh?

20. Breckenridge needs at least $19\frac{1}{8}$ inches of snow in February to hold a downhill ski race. On February 21, the recorded snowfall for the month is $14\frac{3}{4}$ inches. How many inches of snow are needed for the rest of February to hold the race?

Mixed Review

Round each number to the nearest ten thousand.
21. 826,395   **22.** 37,409,856   **23.** 30,589

Round each number to the nearest thousandth.
24. 0.40356   **25.** 19.1842   **26.** 3.00078

Write the number that is one more than
27. 999,999   **28.** 59.3   **29.** −756.5

Tyronn received test scores of 96, 92, 94, 90, and 94.
30. What is the range of the test scores?

31. What is the median of the test scores?

32. What is the mean of the test scores?

33. What is the mode of the test scores?

LESSON 5.8 SOLVING INEQUALITIES WITH MULTIPLICATION AND DIVISION

OBJECTIVES

➤ Solve inequalities using multiplication and division properties.
➤ Use inequalities to find maximum and minimum amounts.

In Lesson 5.7, you solved inequalities by adding or subtracting the same numbers on both sides of the inequality signs. You can also multiply or divide both sides of an inequality by the same number. But, if the number you multiply or divide by is negative, you must reverse the inequality sign.

ACTIVITY The Multiplication Property of Inequality

1 Draw a number line from −10 to 10.

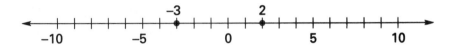

2 Start with the inequality −3 < 2.

a. Multiply both sides of the inequality by 3. Plot the new points on the number line. Is the new inequality *true*?

b. Multiply both sides of the original inequality by $\frac{1}{2}$. Plot the new points. Is the new inequality *true*?

c. Choose two numbers a and b, so that a < b. Let c be any *positive* number. Replace the ? with an inequality sign.

If a < b and c > 0, then ac __?__ bc.

3 Start again with the inequality −3 < 2.

a. Multiply both sides of the inequality by −3. Plot the new points on the number line. What must you do to the inequality sign to make the new inequality *true*?

b. Multiply both sides of the inequality by $-\frac{1}{2}$. Plot the new points. What must you do to the inequality sign to make the new inequality *true*?

c. Choose two numbers a and b, so that a < b. Let c be any *negative* number. Replace the ? with an inequality sign.

If a < b and c < 0, then ac __?__ bc.

The Activity demonstrates the **Multiplication Property of Inequality**. This property states that you can multiply both sides of an inequality by a *positive* number *without* changing the inequality sign. But, if you multiply both sides by a *negative* number, you must *reverse* the inequality sign.

Multiplication Property of Inequality
For any numbers *a*, *b*, and *c*,

If $a \leq b$ and $c > 0$, then $ac \leq bc$.

If $a \leq b$ and $c < 0$, then $ac \geq bc$.

Since dividing is the same as multiplying by a reciprocal, you must also reverse the inequality sign when you divide both sides by a negative number.

EXAMPLE 1 Using the Multiplication Property of Inequality

Solve the inequality $-\frac{2}{3}n < 6$. Graph the solution on a number line.

SOLUTION

Multiply each side of the inequality by the reciprocal of $-\frac{2}{3}$. Since the reciprocal is $-\frac{3}{2}$, the inequality sign must be reversed.

$$-\frac{2}{3}n < 6$$

$$-\frac{3}{2} \cdot \left(-\frac{2}{3}n\right) > -\frac{3}{2} \cdot 6 \qquad \text{Multiplication Property of Inequality } (c < 0)$$

$$1 \cdot n > -\frac{3}{2} \cdot 6$$

$$n > -9$$

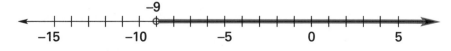

ONGOING ASSESSMENT

Solve each inequality. Graph the solution on a number line.

a. $-\frac{2}{5}r \leq 30$ **b.** $\frac{m}{2.5} \leq -3.6$ **c.** $5t + 3 > 12$

EXAMPLE 2 Finding a Maximum

Jina has $20 to spend on cosmetics. She has already spent $6. She wants to buy 4 lipsticks. What is the maximum amount Jina can spend on each lipstick if all four are the same price?

SOLUTION

Let x represent the cost of each lipstick.

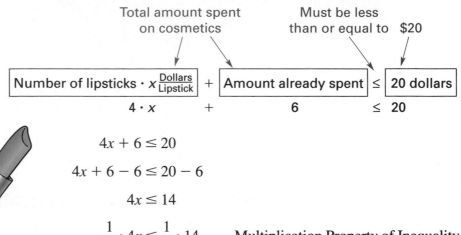

$$4x + 6 \leq 20$$

$$4x + 6 - 6 \leq 20 - 6$$

$$4x \leq 14$$

$$\frac{1}{4} \cdot 4x \leq \frac{1}{4} \cdot 14 \qquad \text{Multiplication Property of Inequality}$$

$$x \leq 3\frac{1}{2}$$

The maximum amount Jina can spend on each lipstick is $3.50.

LESSON ASSESSMENT

Think and Discuss

1 What is the most important difference between the Multiplication Property of Inequality and the Multiplication Property of Equality?

2 Explain why you do not need to have a Division Property of Inequality.

3 How do you know when the graph of an inequality has a closed circle or an open circle?

4 How do you know when an equality or an inequality is solved?

Solve each inequality. Graph the solution on a number line.

5. $\frac{3}{4}p < -6$ **6.** $-7d \geq 6$ **7.** $-2 \leq \frac{1}{2}y$

Solve each inequality.

8. $5a + 6 > 30$ **9.** $\frac{5}{8}z - 4 < -29$

10. $-\frac{2}{3}k - 7 \geq 33$ **11.** $36 \leq -1\frac{1}{5}b + 6$

12. $2\frac{3}{5}c - \frac{1}{2} > \frac{3}{10}$ **13.** $-1\frac{1}{8}q + 4\frac{1}{3} \leq 2\frac{5}{6}$

For Exercises 14–20, define a variable, write an inequality, and solve.

14. When the fuel tanks of an airliner are $\frac{3}{8}$ full, they contain at least 6300 gallons. How much fuel can the airliner hold when the tanks are full?

15. A department store is having a sale in which all items are at most $\frac{2}{3}$ the original price. If Natine buys perfume for $33.66, what is the lowest possible original price of the perfume?

16. On average, 1 out of 15 people who visit Margo's Florist shop place an order for roses. Last year, there were no more than 200 orders for roses. How many people visited Margo's Florist shop last year?

17. Riko is ordering a submarine sandwich for 6 people. Each person will eat the same size section of the sandwich. The section size should be at least 4 inches. What is the length of the smallest sandwich Riko should order?

4 in.

18. Randy earns a salary of $150 per week plus a commission of $\frac{1}{10}$ of his sales for the week. How much does Randy need to sell for his salary plus commission to be at least $214?

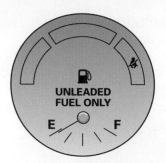

UNLEADED FUEL ONLY

E   F

19. Tanya earns $7.50 per hour working after school. She wants to buy skis that cost $160. If Tanya has saved $75, what is the fewest number of hours she must work until she can buy the skis?

20. Aryeh has driven 180 miles at an average speed of 65 miles per hour. He wants to stop for gas before driving a total of 450 miles. If he continues at this speed, how many more hours can Aryeh drive before stopping for gas?

Mixed Review

Round each number to the place value that is underlined.
21. 78.4$\underline{8}$32   **22.** 259,$\underline{9}$73   **23.** 18.$\underline{3}$5

Evaluate each expression when $a = 7$, $b = 4$, and $c = -3$.

24. $ac + b$ **25.** $cb - ca$ **26.** $\dfrac{3a}{b - c}$

Solve each equation.
27. $7r + 9 = -2r$ **28.** $5(w - 4) - 3w = w$

Solve each problem using the four-step problem-solving plan.
29. Rolondo is painting the outside of his house. He has calculated the area to be painted for each of the four sides of the house:

    595 square feet   900 square feet

    825 square feet   495 square feet

Each gallon of paint covers 225 square feet. How many gallons must Rolondo buy to paint his house?

30. Cans are stacked in a store as shown. If the pattern continues, how many cans will be in a stack of 15 rows?

Row 1 ⟶
Row 2 ⟶
Row 3 ⟶
Row 4 ⟶

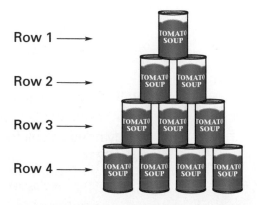

The semester grade in a math class is determined by the average of six tests. Conner's scores on the first five tests are 81, 86, 87, 89, and 92.

31. Let t represent Conner's score on the sixth test. Write an expression for the average of Conner's six tests.

32. Write and solve an inequality to find the score Conner must make on the sixth test to have an average of at least 90.

33. Write and solve an inequality to find the score Conner must make on the sixth test to have an average of at least 80.

34. Conner's semester average was 88. What did he make on the sixth test?

Phil is buying paint. Using an area formula, he has calculated that the surface area of the walls he will paint is 1575 square feet. He wants to buy enough paint to apply two coats to the walls. One gallon of the paint will cover at least 400 square feet. The costs of the paint in different size containers are shown in the table.

Container	Cost
5-gal bucket	$50
1-gal can	$12
1-quart can	$4.50

35. How many square feet will Phil paint if he applies two coats?

36. Let g represent the number of gallons of paint needed. Write an expression for the number of square feet covered by g gallons.

37. Write and solve an inequality to find the number of gallons Phil needs to buy.

38. If he wants to spend the least amount for the paint, what combination of containers should Phil buy? There are 4 quarts in one gallon.

Marie is buying fruit and bagels for a morning staff meeting. She wants to spend no more than $20. She spends $8 on fruit. Bagels cost $0.45 each. She needs to determine how many bagels she can buy.

39. Let n represent the number of bagels. Write an expression for the total amount Marie will spend on fruit and bagels.

40. Write and solve an inequality for the number of bagels Marie can buy if she spends no more than $20.

41. Should you round the solution up or down to the nearest whole number? Explain.

Madze gets an average of 650 milligrams (mg) of calcium per day in her diet. She wants to increase this amount to at least 1200 milligrams per day. The calcium content of several food items is shown in the table.

Serving Size	mg of Calcium
almonds, 1 oz	75
broccoli, $\frac{1}{2}$ c	47
chocolate milk, fat-free, 8 oz	246
hard-boiled egg	25
ice cream, 1 c	176
mozzarella, 1 oz	207
yogurt, chocolate, 6 oz	150
yogurt, fruit-flavor, 8 oz	345

42. Let c represent the number of milligrams of calcium Madze adds to her diet. Write and solve an inequality for c if Madze attains her goal.

43. Madze selects two food servings from the table to add to her diet. List all the possible combinations of selections that will increase her calcium intake to at least 1200 milligrams per day.

MATH LAB

Equipment   40 pennies, washers, or other small
uniform objects

Problem Statement

Objects arranged in rows and columns form an **array**. You
can find the number of objects in an array by multiplying the
number of rows and the number of columns.

3 rows $3 \cdot 5 = 15$
There are 15 pennies in the array.

5 columns

In this lab, you will assemble arrays to find the factors of
whole numbers.

Procedure

a You can make three arrays with 12 objects.

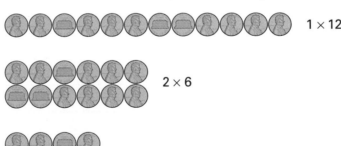

1×12

2×6

3×4

These three arrays show that the factors of 12 are 1, 2, 3, 4,
6, and 12. A factor of 12 is any whole number that divides
into 12 with no remainder.

Assemble as many arrays as possible with 18 objects. How
many arrays can you make? What are the factors of 18?

b Make a data table like the following one.

Assemble all possible arrays for each number listed in the table. Complete the table by listing the factors of each number.

Number	Factors
12	1, 2, 3, 4, 6, 12
18	
23	
26	
28	
35	
36	
37	
38	
39	
40	

c A **composite number** is a whole number that has more than two factors. A **prime number** is a whole number greater than 1 that has exactly two factors, 1 and itself.

Which of the numbers listed in the table are prime? How many arrays can you assemble for a prime number?

d Copy the following table.

Numbers	Common Factors	GCF
12 and 18		
12 and 36		
18 and 28		
23 and 35		
28 and 40		

Write the common factors of each pair of numbers listed in the table. Write the greatest common factor (GCF) of each pair of numbers.

Discussion Questions

1. What are the prime numbers between 1 and 40?

2. The prime factorization of 12 is 2 · 2 · 3 since each factor is a prime number. What is the prime factorization of 24? What is the GCF of 12 and 24? Describe how you can use the prime factorization of two numbers to find the GCF.

Equipment   Centimeter ruler
Yellow highlighter pen
Blue highlighter pen

Problem Statement

You will model multiplication of fractions using overlapping rectangles.

Procedure

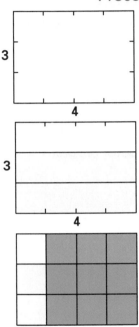

a Draw a rectangle 3 centimeters (cm) wide by 4 cm long. Draw tic marks at 1-cm intervals along each side.

b Connect the tic marks on the 3-cm sides with horizontal line segments. You have divided the large rectangle into three smaller rectangles measuring 1 cm by 4 cm. What fraction of the large rectangle is represented by each small rectangle?

c Highlight $\frac{2}{3}$ of the large rectangle with yellow.

d Connect the tic marks on the 4-cm sides with vertical line segments. You have created four rectangles measuring 1 cm by 3 cm. What fraction of the large rectangle is represented by each 1 cm × 3 cm rectangle?

e Highlight $\frac{3}{4}$ of the large rectangle with blue.

f You have divided the large rectangle into squares measuring 1 centimeter on each side. How many squares are there? The squares highlighted both yellow and blue are green. How many green squares are there? What fraction of the total number of squares are green? This fraction represents $\frac{2}{3}$ of $\frac{3}{4}$, or $\frac{2}{3} \cdot \frac{3}{4}$.

g Draw rectangles and highlight appropriate fractions to model the products listed in the table. Copy and complete the table.

Rectangle Dimensions	Model	Fraction Represented by Green Squares
2 cm by 3 cm	$\frac{1}{2} \cdot \frac{2}{3}$	
2 cm by 4 cm	$\frac{1}{2} \cdot \frac{3}{4}$	
3 cm by 5 cm	$\frac{1}{3} \cdot \frac{4}{5}$	

h For each model in the table, find the product of the numerators and the product of the denominators of the fractions being multiplied. Compare these products to the numerator and denominator of the fraction of green squares. Write a rule for multiplying two fractions.

Discussion Questions

1. Use your rule from Step **h** to multiply the following fractions.

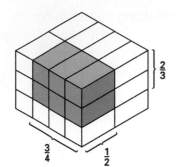

a. $\dfrac{1}{8} \cdot \dfrac{3}{11}$ b. $\dfrac{4}{7} \cdot \dfrac{2}{5}$ c. $\dfrac{5}{3} \cdot \dfrac{3}{2}$

2. Write the product modeled by the three-dimensional figure shown. What is the product?

Activity 3: Solving Inequalities with a Spreadsheet

Equipment   Spreadsheet computer program

Problem Statement

You will use a spreadsheet to solve inequalities by comparing the left and right sides.

Procedure

Follow Steps **a–d** to solve the following inequality.

$$3x \leq 9$$

a In row 1 of the spreadsheet, enter labels for the variable x and the expression for the left side of the inequality.

	A	B	C
1	*x*	3*x*	
2	−10	−30	
3	−9	−27	
4	−8	−24	
5	−7	−21	

= 3*A2

b In the column labeled x, list values from −10 to 10.

c Enter the formula for the expression on the left side of the inequality in cell B2. Copy the formula down the B column to cell B22.

d Print the spreadsheet. Circle the value of x that makes the left side of the inequality equal to the right side. Is this value of x a solution to the inequality? Circle the other values of x that make the inequality *true*. Write the original inequality on the spreadsheet. Write an inequality for the solution.

e Change the label and formulas in the spreadsheet for the following inequality.

$$-5x < 30$$

Repeat Step **d** to solve the inequality.

f Change the label and formulas and add a third column for the following inequality.

$$2x - 3 \leq -3x + 7$$

Repeat Step **d** to solve the inequality.

= 2*A2 – 3

	A	B	C
1	**x**	**2x – 3**	**–3x + 7**
2	–10	–23	37
3	–9	–21	34
4	–8	–19	31

= –3*A2 + 7

g Use the spreadsheet to find the solution of the following inequality.

$$x - 5 > 3x + 1$$

Discussion Questions

1. You are using a spreadsheet to solve the inequality $4x > 8$. You find that the value $x = 2$ makes the left side equal to the right side, but 2 is not a solution because the inequality is *greater than*. The next value of x in the spreadsheet that is a solution is 3. Why is it incorrect to conclude that the solution is $x \geq 3$?

2. Solve the four inequalities in this lab algebraically. Compare your solutions to those you found with the spreadsheet. For which inequalities do you reverse the inequality sign? Why must you reverse the inequality sign in these cases?

CHAPTER 5   ASSESSMENT

Communicate

1. Explain how to write a fraction in simplest form.

2. How do you find the least common denominator of two fractions?

3. List the steps required in writing an improper fraction as a mixed number.

4. Explain how to multiply two fractions. Explain how to divide two fractions.

5. When solving an inequality, when must you reverse the inequality sign?

Skills

Write each fraction in simplest form.

6. $\dfrac{16}{24}$

7. $-\dfrac{21}{35}$

Write each fraction as a decimal.

8. $-\dfrac{3}{5}$

9. $\dfrac{1}{9}$

Use $<$ or $>$ to compare each pair of rational numbers.

10. $\dfrac{5}{6} \ \underline{?} \ \dfrac{7}{8}$

11. $-\dfrac{3}{4} \ \underline{?} \ -\dfrac{8}{12}$

12. Write $-\dfrac{8}{3}$ as a mixed number

13. Write $11\dfrac{5}{6}$ as an improper fraction

Solve each equation.

14. $x - \dfrac{2}{3} = \dfrac{1}{6}$

15. $-2\dfrac{1}{4}y = -5\dfrac{2}{5}$

16. $\dfrac{2}{3}v - \dfrac{1}{2} = \dfrac{5}{6}$

17. $3\dfrac{1}{3}c + 4 = 1\dfrac{1}{4}$

18. Solve the inequality $-1\dfrac{2}{3}q \geq 1\dfrac{1}{4}$. Graph the solution on a number line.

Applications

Define a variable, write an equation or inequality, and solve.
19. Patrick uses $23\dfrac{1}{3}$ inches of ribbon to make a bow. How many bows can he make with 280 inches of ribbon?

20. Lauren's bowling average is $\frac{3}{4}$ of Paula's bowling average. Their combined average is 315. What are Lauren's and Paula's averages?

21. Damont is installing a baseboard along a wall that is $78\frac{1}{4}$ inches long. He installs one piece that measures $52\frac{3}{8}$ inches. What length should Damont cut the second piece so the baseboard covers the length of the wall?

22. Natalie has $40 for transportation, a card, and a gift. She needs $12.50 for transportation and $3 for a card. What is the maximum amount she can pay for the gift?

23. Together, Rashad and Victor collected more than 25 pounds of aluminum. Rashad collected $1\frac{1}{2}$ times the number of pounds collected by Victor. How many pounds of aluminum did Victor collect?

Math Lab

24. Write the factors of 15 and 24. What are the common factors? What is the greatest common factor?

25. Write the multiplication expression modeled by the overlapping rectangles. What is the product?

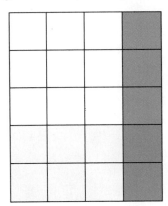

26. Use the values in the spreadsheet to write the solution to $3y - 1 \geq 2y + 4$.

	A	B	C
1	*y*	**3y − 1**	**2y + 4**
2	3	8	10
3	4	11	12
4	5	14	14
5	6	17	16
6	7	20	18
7	8	23	20

CHAPTER 6

WHY SHOULD I LEARN THIS?

When problems involve equal ratios, or equal rates, you use proportions. Artists often paint canvases from smaller, proportional drawings. The canvas and drawing have equal ratios of length to width.

RATIO, PROPORTION, AND PROBABILITY

LEARN HOW TO...

1. Solve problems using ratios and proportions.
2. Find the number of possible outcomes and the theoretical probability of an event.
3. Find the probabilities of independent and dependent events.
4. Use experimental probability and simulation to find the probabilities of events.

In this chapter, you will use ratios to solve many different types of problems including proportions, rates, and probability.

An artist makes a drawing with length 15 inches and width 10 inches. The ratio of the drawing's length to width is $\frac{15}{10}$. If the artist wants to make a painting with dimensions proportional to the drawing, he needs to use a length to width ratio that is equal, for example $\frac{75}{50}$.

You will learn to use proportional reasoning with rates and unit rates to solve problems involving selling price, gas mileage, computer speeds, and running logs.

Probability is also a ratio. You will learn how to calculate and apply theoretical probability, and how to use an experiment to estimate probability. You can also simulate experiments. Finally, you will see how to use probability and sampling from a large population to make predictions.

LESSON 6.1 RATIO AND PROPORTION

OBJECTIVES

➤ Write ratios and proportions.
➤ Determine if two ratios form a proportion.

Amanda makes fruit punch by mixing water with concentrate. In the directions, the *ratio* of water to concentrate is 3 to 1. A **ratio** is a comparison of two quantities by division. For example, the ratio for the fruit punch can be written as

$$3 \text{ to } 1 \qquad 3 : 1 \qquad \frac{3}{1}$$

ACTIVITY 1   Writing a Ratio

For this grid, you can write the ratio of red squares to the total number of squares as

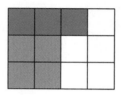

Red to Total	3 to 12
Red : Total	3 : 12
$\dfrac{\text{Red}}{\text{Total}}$	$\dfrac{3}{12}$

Since this ratio describes a part of a whole, the ratio is also a fraction.

1   Replace the ? by writing ratios for each comparison.

    a. $\dfrac{\text{Red}}{\text{Total}} = \dfrac{3}{12}$ **b.** $\dfrac{\text{Total}}{\text{Red}} = \underline{\ ?\ }$

    c. $\dfrac{\text{Blue}}{\text{Total}} = \underline{\ ?\ }$ **d.** $\dfrac{\text{Total}}{\text{Blue}} = \underline{\ ?\ }$

    e. $\dfrac{\text{Blue}}{\text{Red}} = \underline{\ ?\ }$ **f.** $\dfrac{\text{Red}}{\text{Blue}} = \underline{\ ?\ }$

2   Which of the ratios can be written as a whole number?

Equal ratios represent the same comparison. You can write equal ratios by multiplying or dividing the numerator and denominator by the same nonzero number.

In Activity 1, you wrote the ratio $\dfrac{Blue}{Red} = \dfrac{4}{3}$. You can multiply the numerator and denominator by 2 to get an equal ratio.

$$\frac{Blue}{Red} = \frac{4 \cdot 2}{3 \cdot 2} = \frac{8}{6}$$

The ratios $\dfrac{4}{3}$ and $\dfrac{8}{6}$ are equal. An equation that states two ratios are equal is called a **proportion**. You can write a proportion in three ways.

$$4 \text{ is to } 3 \text{ as } 8 \text{ is to } 6$$

$$4 : 3 :: 8 : 6$$

$$\frac{4}{3} = \frac{8}{6}$$

ACTIVITY 2   **Equal Ratios**

Start with the ratios $\dfrac{6}{9}$ and $\dfrac{8}{12}$.

1 Write each ratio in simplest form. Is the following proportion *true*?

$$\frac{6}{9} = \frac{8}{12}$$

Explain your answer.

2 The expressions $6 \cdot 12$ and $9 \cdot 8$ are called **cross products**. Are the cross products equal?

$$\frac{6}{9} \bowtie \frac{8}{12}$$

$$6 \cdot 12 \overset{?}{=} 9 \cdot 8$$

3 How can you use cross products to determine if two ratios are equal?

> **Cross-Products Property**
>
> If $\dfrac{a}{b} = \dfrac{c}{d}$, $b \neq 0$, $d \neq 0$, then $ad = bc$.

Amanda's fruit punch will have 3 cans of water per can of concentrate. Which of the following ratios for $\frac{\text{Water}}{\text{Concentrate}}$ should Amanda use to make 20 cans of punch?

a. $\frac{12}{8}$ **b.** $\frac{12}{4}$ **c.** $\frac{15}{5}$

SOLUTION

The $\frac{\text{Water}}{\text{Concentrate}}$ must be in the ratio $\frac{3}{1}$. The total amount of water plus concentrate must be 20 cans. Write a proportion and use the Cross-Products Property.

a. $\frac{3}{1} \overset{?}{=} \frac{12}{8}, 3 \cdot 8 \neq 12 \cdot 1$ The ratio $\frac{12}{8}$ does not form a proportion.

b. $\frac{3}{1} \overset{?}{=} \frac{12}{4}, 3 \cdot 4 = 12 \cdot 1$ The ratio forms a proportion, but the total amount of water plus concentrate is 16 cans.

c. $\frac{3}{1} \overset{?}{=} \frac{15}{5}, 3 \cdot 5 = 15 \cdot 1$ The ratio forms a proportion, and the total amount of water plus concentrate is 20 cans.

Amanda should use 15 cans of water and 5 cans of concentrate.

ONGOING ASSESSMENT

Which of the following proportions are *true*?

a. $\frac{6}{8} \overset{?}{=} \frac{9}{12}$ **b.** $\frac{5}{8} \overset{?}{=} \frac{10}{15}$ **c.** $\frac{4.5}{5} \overset{?}{=} \frac{90}{100}$

LESSON ASSESSMENT

Think and Discuss

1 How can you write the gas mileage of a car as a ratio? Explain the comparison made by this ratio.

2 Explain how to use multiplication and division to write ratios equal to $\frac{a}{b}$.

3 Write an algorithm for using the Cross-Products Property to determine if two ratios are equal.

Express each of the following as a ratio in simplest form.

4. $6 out of $18 is deducted for expenses.

5. 8 out of 10 doctors read the report.

6. The score included 38 putts in 18 holes of golf.

7. The school has 36 girls on 2 lacrosse teams.

Write each ratio in simplest form. Are the ratios for each exercise *all equal* or *not all equal*?

8. $\dfrac{3}{4}, \dfrac{6}{8}, \dfrac{15}{24}$

9. $\dfrac{2}{3}, \dfrac{8}{12}, \dfrac{14}{21}$

10. $\dfrac{5}{3}, \dfrac{15}{9}, \dfrac{25}{15}$

11. $\dfrac{7}{2}, \dfrac{28}{6}, \dfrac{35}{10}$

Use the Cross-Products Property to determine if the proportion is *true* or *false*. Write *yes* or *no*.

12. $\dfrac{8}{12} = \dfrac{15}{20}$

13. $\dfrac{2.1}{2.4} = \dfrac{14}{16}$

14. $\dfrac{6}{14} = \dfrac{15}{36}$

15. $\dfrac{72}{16} = \dfrac{63}{14}$

16. $\dfrac{56}{44} = \dfrac{4}{3.2}$

17. $\dfrac{30}{78} = \dfrac{10}{26}$

18. $-\dfrac{9}{2} = -\dfrac{36}{8}$

19. $-\dfrac{5}{1} = \dfrac{15}{3}$

20. $\dfrac{3x}{2} = \dfrac{21x}{14}$

To make a certain color of paint, Karl mixes 6 quarts of Eggshell, 2 quarts of Sea Foam, and 2 quarts of Desert Sand.

21. What is the ratio of Desert Sand to Eggshell?

22. What is the ratio of Sea Foam to the total amount of paint?

In a water polo tournament, Lareef scored on 12 out of 15 shots. Rahmen scored on 16 out of 20 shots.

23. Write a ratio for the number of shots scored to the number of shots attempted by each player.

24. Are the ratios equal? Explain how you found your answer.

A store gives you a free can of dog food for every 5 cans you buy. The table shows values for numbers of cans bought and numbers of free cans.

Cans Bought	5	15	x
Cans Free	1	y	5

25. What is the value of x?

26. What is the value of y?

The ratio of girls to boys in a class is $\frac{5}{8}$.

27. Write three possible combinations for the number of girls and the number of boys in the class. Write your answer as ordered pairs.

(number of girls, number of boys)

28. If 5 girls and 5 boys are added to the class, is the ratio of girls to boys still 5 to 8? Explain your answer.

Solve for the variable.

29. $\dfrac{3}{8} = \dfrac{x}{64}$

30. $\dfrac{y}{18} = \dfrac{4}{3}$

31. $-\dfrac{7}{4} = \dfrac{z}{28}$

32. $\dfrac{1}{a} = \dfrac{5}{25}$

33. $-\dfrac{16}{8} = \dfrac{8}{b}$

34. $\dfrac{9}{c} = -\dfrac{3}{12}$

Mixed Review

Evaluate each expression.

35. $234.95 + 146.7 + 28.086$

36. $\$123,045 - \$85,461$

37. $8 \cdot (3 - 5) \div 4$

38. $4 + 4 - 4 \cdot 4 \div 4$

39. $(-18)(-6)(1.2)$

40. $4\dfrac{1}{5} \div \left(-\dfrac{3}{10}\right)$

Solve each equation or inequality.

41. $5r + 9 = 24$

42. $7m - 3 > 4m + 12$

43. $-1\dfrac{1}{2}f \le -15$

44. $\dfrac{3}{4}c - \dfrac{1}{2} = \dfrac{5}{6}$

LESSON 6.2 DIMENSIONAL ANALYSIS

OBJECTIVES
- Find unit rates.
- Use conversion factors to convert units.

In Lesson 4.6, you used the distance formula $D = rt$. D is the distance traveled while moving at a rate (or speed) r during a period of time t. If you solve the distance formula for r, rate is a ratio.

$$r = \frac{D}{t}$$

In general, a **rate** is a ratio that compares two unlike quantities. For example, if a truck travels 100 miles in 2 hours, the rate is

$$r = \frac{D}{t} = \frac{100 \text{ miles}}{2 \text{ hours}}$$

A **unit rate** is a comparison to one unit. To write a unit rate, find an equivalent ratio with 1 as the denominator. You can use equal ratios to find unit rates. For the example above,

$$\frac{\text{Miles}}{\text{Hours}} \begin{array}{c} \rightarrow \\ \rightarrow \end{array} \frac{100}{2} = \frac{50}{1}$$

The unit rate is 50 miles for each hour traveled. You can write 50 miles per hour *or* 50 mi/h *or* $50\frac{\text{mi}}{\text{h}}$. The word *per* is often used in place of *for each*. You can abbreviate *per* with the / symbol.

ACTIVITY — Finding Unit Rates

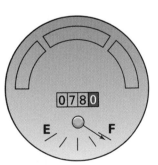

Write unit rates for each of the following. The first one is done as an example.

1 Sale price: 5 cans for \$2

$$\frac{5 \text{ cans}}{2 \text{ dollars}} = \frac{2.5 \text{ cans}}{1 \text{ dollar}} = 2.5 \text{ cans/dollar}$$

2 Gas mileage: 78 miles using 3 gallons of gas

$$\frac{78 \text{ miles}}{3 \text{ gallons}} = \frac{? \text{ miles}}{1 \text{ gallon}} = \underline{} \text{ mi/gal}$$

3 Starting wage: \$326 for 40 hours

$$\frac{326 \text{ dollars}}{40 \text{ hours}} = \frac{? \text{ dollars}}{1 \text{ hour}} = \$ \underline{} \text{/h}$$

4 Weight of oranges: 5 oranges weigh 0.75 kilograms

$$\frac{5 \text{ oranges}}{0.75 \text{ kg}} = \frac{?}{?} = \underline{} \text{ oranges/kg}$$

In the 1996 Summer Olympic Games, a world record of 19.32 seconds was set in the 200-meter dash. A world record of 9.84 seconds was set in the 100-meter dash. Did the runner of the 200-meter dash or the runner of the 100-meter dash run the fastest average speed?

When solving problems, you often need to change or convert the units of measurement of a quantity. To convert units of measurement, multiply by a *conversion factor*.

A **conversion factor** is a ratio in which the numerator equals the denominator, but in different units. This ratio is equal to 1.

For example, a length of 12 inches equals a length of 1 foot. Thus,

$$12 \text{ in.} = 1 \text{ ft} \qquad \text{and} \qquad \frac{12 \text{ in.}}{1 \text{ ft}} = 1$$

EXAMPLE 1 Using Conversion Factors

Use the following conversion factors.

$$\frac{5280 \text{ ft}}{1 \text{ mi}} \qquad \frac{60 \text{ min}}{1 \text{ h}} \qquad \frac{24 \text{ h}}{1 \text{ day}} \qquad \frac{1 \text{ week}}{7 \text{ day}}$$

a. Convert 1.75 miles to feet.

b. Convert 6800 feet to miles.

c. Convert 1 week to minutes.

SOLUTION

a. $1.75 \text{ mi} = \dfrac{1.75 \text{ mi}}{1} \cdot \dfrac{5280 \text{ ft}}{1 \text{ mi}} = 9240 \text{ ft}$

b. Since $\dfrac{5280 \text{ ft}}{1 \text{ mi}} = 1$, its reciprocal $\dfrac{1 \text{ mi}}{5280 \text{ ft}} = 1$.

$6800 \text{ ft} = \dfrac{6800 \text{ ft}}{1} \cdot \dfrac{1 \text{ mi}}{5280 \text{ ft}} = \text{about } 1.288 \text{ mi}$

c. $1 \text{ week} = \dfrac{1 \text{ week}}{1} \cdot \dfrac{7 \text{ day}}{1 \text{ week}} \cdot \dfrac{24 \text{ h}}{1 \text{ day}} \cdot \dfrac{60 \text{ min}}{1 \text{ h}} = 10,080 \text{ min}$

Use the conversion factors in Example 1.

a. Convert 18,480 feet to miles.

b. Convert 100,000 minutes to weeks.

Critical Thinking Use the following equalities to write ratios that can be used as conversion factors. Write two ratios from each equality. Why is each ratio equal to 1?

2.54 cm = 1 in.   1 kg = 2.205 lb   1.467 ft/s = 1 mi/h

EXAMPLE 2 Converting Units

Ichiro has taken a summer job that pays $7.50 per hour. At this rate, how much money will Ichiro earn working 8 hours per day, 5 days per week, for 6 weeks?

SOLUTION

Since Ichiro works 6 weeks, find the unit rate in dollars per week.

$$\frac{7.50 \text{ dollars}}{1 \text{ h}} \cdot \frac{8 \text{ h}}{1 \text{ day}} \cdot \frac{5 \text{ days}}{1 \text{ week}} = \frac{300 \text{ dollars}}{1 \text{ week}}$$

$$\text{Earnings} = \text{Rate} \cdot \text{Time}$$

$$= \frac{300 \text{ dollars}}{1 \text{ week}} \cdot 6 \text{ weeks}$$

$$= 1800 \text{ dollars}$$

Ichiro will earn $1800 in 6 weeks.

LESSON ASSESSMENT

Think and Discuss

1 How do you write a ratio as a unit rate?

2 Explain why you can use the reciprocal of any conversion factor as a conversion factor.

3 How do you know whether to use a given conversion factor or its reciprocal?

Practice and Apply

Write a unit rate for each of the following.

4. 14 boxes of files cost $33.60.

5. 54 ounces has a volume of 20 cubic centimeters.

6. 10 gallons is equivalent to 37.7 liters.

7. Walking 29.3 feet in 20 seconds.

Express each of the following as a unit rate. Use the unit rate to answer each question.

8. Jamie descended 8 flights of stairs in 2 minutes. At this rate, how many flights can he descend in 3 minutes?

9. Stephanie caught 12 fish in 3 hours. At this rate, how long will it take her to catch 20 fish?

10. Rashad's modem downloaded a 390-kilobyte file in 32 seconds. At this rate, how large a file can the modem download in 10 minutes?

11. Melinda planted 86 tulip bulbs in 40 minutes. At this rate, how long will it take her to plant 64 more bulbs?

In Exercises 12–15, set up a proportion. Use the Cross-Product Property to see if the rates are equal. Answer *yes* or *no*.

12. Yolanda bought 5 ears of corn for $1. Sandra bought 15 ears of corn for $3.

13. Tonika skied 10 kilometers in 35 minutes. Hakeem skied 15 kilometers in 51 minutes.

14. Colin earned $297.50 for working 35 hours. Sean earned $323 for working 38 hours.

15. Robot A makes 150 welds on 5 cars. Robot B makes 256 welds on 8 cars.

For Exercises 16–26, use the following conversion factors.

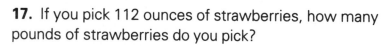

$$\frac{16\ oz}{1\ lb} \qquad \frac{1\ gal}{4\ qt} \qquad \frac{12\ in.}{1\ ft} \qquad \frac{3\ ft}{1\ yd} \qquad \frac{1\ h}{60\ min}$$

$$\frac{1\ qt}{2\ pt} \quad \frac{2.54\ cm}{1\ in.} \quad \frac{24\ h}{1\ day} \quad \frac{1\ kg}{2.2\ lb} \quad \frac{5280\ ft}{1\ mi} \quad \frac{0.62\ mi}{1\ km} \quad \frac{100\ cm}{1\ m}$$

16. At a blood drive, 26 pints of blood were collected. How many quarts were collected? How many gallons were collected?

17. If you pick 112 ounces of strawberries, how many pounds of strawberries do you pick?

18. A shot put weighs 4 kilograms. How many pounds does the shot put weigh?

19. A spool contains 200 yards of thread. How many feet of thread are on the spool?

20. If your heart beats 68 times a minute, how many times does it beat in one day?

21. During one month, Shareka uses her cellular phone for $3\frac{1}{2}$ hours. If the service charge is $0.45 per minute, how much will Shareka be charged this month?

22. Teresa won the state long jump competition with a jump of 17 feet 9 inches. How many inches did Teresa jump? How many meters?

23. Jeffrey reads 220 words per minute. He is reading a book that averages 400 words on a page. How long will it take Jeffrey to read 50 pages of the book?

24. A race car's gas mileage is 2.5 miles per gallon. How many kilometers can the car race on 40 gallons of fuel?

25. A car is traveling at 55 miles per hour. How many feet per second is the car traveling?

26. How many feet does the car travel in 10 seconds?

Mixed Review

The temperature drops 8 degrees from −15°F.
27. Write an expression that models the change in temperature.

28. Find the new temperature.

Marisa's stock gained $1\frac{3}{8}$ points, lost $\frac{3}{4}$ point, and then gained $\frac{1}{2}$ point. For stocks, 1 point equals $1.
29. Write an expression that models the change in value for Marisa's stock.

30. Find the overall gain or loss of value for Marisa's stock.

Carlos buys hamburger meat for his restaurant in 2-pound and 5-pound packages. This week Carlos bought 51 packages of meat, $\frac{1}{3}$ of which are 2-pound packages.
31. Carlos paid a total of $55.25 for the 2-pound packages. What is the cost of each 2-pound package?

32. He paid a total of $255 for the 5-pound packages. What is the cost of each 5-pound package?

33. What is the average cost per pound Carlos pays for the 2-pound and 5-pound packages?

LESSON 6.3 USING PROPORTIONS

Kyla is making oatmeal cookies for a school bake sale. The recipe uses $\frac{1}{2}$ cup of raisins to make 4 dozen cookies. How many cups of raisins will Kyla need to make 10 dozen cookies?

To find the answer, you can use the four-step problem-solving plan.

Step 1 Understand the Problem

The ratio of cups of raisins in 10 dozen cookies should equal the ratio called for in the recipe.

Step 2 Develop a Plan

Use a proportion. Write two ratios for the information given. In one ratio, let x be the unknown number of cups of raisins for 10 dozen cookies. Write a proportion by equating the ratios. Solve the proportion.

Step 3 Carry Out the Plan

$$\begin{array}{ccc} \text{Cups of raisins per} & & \text{Cups of raisins per} \\ \text{dozen cookies in the recipe} & = & \text{dozen cookies in 10 dozen} \end{array}$$

$$\begin{array}{l} \text{Cups of raisins} \quad \longrightarrow \\ \text{Dozens of cookies} \quad \longrightarrow \end{array} \quad \dfrac{\frac{1}{2}}{4} = \dfrac{x}{10}$$

Use the Cross-Products Property to solve for x.

$$\dfrac{\frac{1}{2}}{4} = \dfrac{x}{10}$$

$$4x = 5$$

$$x = \frac{5}{4} \quad \text{or} \quad 1\frac{1}{4}$$

Step 4 Check the Solution

Substitute the value of x into the original proportion.

$$\dfrac{\frac{1}{2}}{4} = \dfrac{\frac{5}{4}}{10}$$

$$\frac{1}{2} \cdot 10 = \frac{5}{4} \cdot 4 \quad \text{or} \quad 5 = 5 \checkmark$$

Kyla needs $1\frac{1}{4}$ cups of raisins for 10 dozen cookies.

When you write a proportion, make sure the corresponding quantities in each ratio are in the same position.

1 For similar rectangles, the ratios of width to length are equal. The rectangles are similar. Choose the correct ratio for finding the length x.

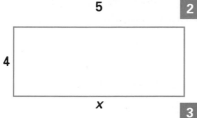

$$\frac{\text{Width}}{\text{Length}} \longrightarrow \frac{2}{5} = \underline{\ ?\ } \qquad \frac{4}{x} \ \text{or} \ \frac{x}{4}$$

2 Apples are on sale for $0.90/pound. Choose the correct ratio for calculating the number of pounds you can buy for $3.15.

$$\frac{\text{Dollars}}{\text{Lb}} \longrightarrow \frac{0.90}{1} = \underline{\ ?\ } \qquad \frac{y}{3.15} \ \text{or} \ \frac{3.15}{y}$$

3 Carmen jogs 3.2 kilometers in 25 minutes. Choose the correct ratio for calculating the number of kilometers Carmen will jog in 45 minutes.

$$\frac{\text{km}}{\text{min}} \longrightarrow \frac{3.2}{25} = \underline{\ ?\ } \qquad \frac{z}{45} \ \text{or} \ \frac{45}{z}$$

4 Explain how you chose the correct ratio for each proportion.

EXAMPLE   Solving a Proportion

Mario is installing tile using solid-color and two-color diagonal tiles. The basic pattern contains 16 diagonal tiles and 48 solid tiles. This pattern repeats around the perimeter of the room. If Mario needs 12 boxes of solid tiles for the job, how many boxes of diagonal tiles will he need?

SOLUTION

Let n represent the number of boxes of diagonal tiles. Mario can write two different proportions to solve this problem.

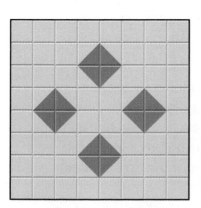

16 diagonal tiles

48 solid tiles

Method A	Method B
$\dfrac{\text{Diagonal tiles} \longrightarrow}{\text{Solid tiles} \longrightarrow} \dfrac{16}{48} = \dfrac{n}{12}$	$\dfrac{\text{Solid tiles} \longrightarrow}{\text{Diagonal tiles} \longrightarrow} \dfrac{48}{16} = \dfrac{12}{n}$
$48n = 16 \cdot 12$	$16 \cdot 12 = 48n$
$48n = 192$	$192 = 48n$
$n = 4$	$4 = n$

Mario needs 4 boxes of diagonal tiles.

USING THE FOUR-STEP PLAN

Javon is creating a spreadsheet to calculate amounts of ingredients for recipes for his catering business. A page of his spreadsheet shows the ingredients for a recipe for pesto sauce that Javon serves with pasta. The basic recipe serves 6. Javon wants to calculate the amounts of ingredients needed to serve 40. Complete the spreadsheet.

	A	B	C	D	E	F	G	H
1		Basic	Recipe			Catering	Requirements	
2	Amount Needed	Units	Ingredient	Servings	Servings	Amount Needed	Units	Ingredient
3	3/4	pound	fresh basil	6	40		pound	fresh basil
4	1/2	cup	pine nuts				cup	pine nuts
5	1/2	cup	olive oil				cup	olive oil
6	1/4	cup	lemon juice				cup	lemon juice
7	2	cloves	garlic				cloves	garlic

Step 1 Understand the Problem
What labels are used in the spreadsheet? What values in the spreadsheet will change for more or fewer guests? What values will stay the same?

Step 2 Develop a Plan
Use proportions.

$$\frac{\text{Amount needed} \rightarrow}{\text{Number of servings} \rightarrow} \frac{?}{?} = \frac{?}{?}$$

Step 3 Carry Out the Plan
Create the spreadsheet. Enter functions to calculate the amounts needed. Fractions can be displayed in some spreadsheet programs. For example, you can highlight the cells and open the *Format Cells* dialog box. Select the *Number* tab and select *Fraction*. Print the spreadsheet.

Step 4 Check the Results
Are the amounts reasonable? Change one number in the spreadsheet to calculate the recipe amounts needed to serve 2 people. What happens if you change the number of guests to 6?

LESSON ASSESSMENT

1 The units of a ratio are $\frac{km}{h}$. To write a proportion using this ratio, what units will you use for the numerator and denominator in the second ratio?

2 Explain how to write a proportion to solve the following problem.

You can buy 6 bananas for $1.50. How many bananas can you buy for $4.50?

3 How can you write a different proportion for Exercise 2 that will give the same result?

Practice and Apply

Solve each proportion.

4. $\dfrac{3}{5} = \dfrac{d}{45}$

5. $\dfrac{n}{16} = \dfrac{15}{24}$

6. $-\dfrac{12}{t} = \dfrac{11}{44}$

7. $\dfrac{6}{4.5} = \dfrac{20}{m}$

8. $-\dfrac{2.4}{c} = \dfrac{5.6}{35}$

9. $\dfrac{27}{63} = \dfrac{s}{56}$

10. $\dfrac{3x}{25} = -\dfrac{18}{50}$

11. $\dfrac{12}{42} = \dfrac{10}{7a}$

12. $\dfrac{65}{10x} = \dfrac{13}{6}$

13. $\dfrac{x-1}{5} = -1$

14. $\dfrac{1}{7} = \dfrac{3}{y+4}$

15. $\dfrac{5}{6} = \dfrac{x+2}{x-3}$

16. $\dfrac{g-1}{2} = \dfrac{2-g}{3}$

17. $\dfrac{3(h-2)}{2h} = 1$

18. $\dfrac{1}{h-8} = -3$

In Exercises 19–30, define a variable, write a proportion, and solve.

19. Will paid $12 for 16 cans of soda. How much will he pay for 48 cans?

20. A satellite downloads 4 photographs for every 10 times it passes overhead. How many photographs will it download in 25 passes?

21. A house painter used 120 gallons of paint to paint 4 houses. How many houses can she paint with 180 gallons of paint?

22. A recipe calls for $\frac{3}{4}$ teaspoon of butter for every 2 cups of milk. If you increase the recipe to use 3 cups of milk, how many teaspoons of butter are needed?

23. A survey finds that 2 out of 5 students study at least 2 hours per day. If 100 students are surveyed, how many study at least 2 hours per day?

24. Tanisha can swim 20 laps in 40 minutes. At this rate, how many laps can she swim in 1 hour?

25. The ratio of an object's weight on Earth to its weight on Mars is about 8 to 3. The Mars Pathfinder Lander weighed 792 pounds on Earth. What is its weight on Mars?

26. Mr. Williams gets 16.5 miles to each gallon of diesel fuel. How many gallons will he need to travel 231 miles?

27. If one family uses an average of 400 gallons of water per day, how many families will a supply of 6840 gallons serve for a day?

28. The ratio of girls to boys in a soccer league is $\frac{2}{3}$. If there are 150 players in the league, how many are girls?

29. A chain is made from alternating brass and gold wire. The ratio of the brass to gold pieces is 4 to 1. One chain is 20 centimeters long. How many centimeters of the chain are gold?

30. On a map, 1 inch represents 62 miles. If the distance on the map from St. Louis to Chicago is 4.25 inches, what is the actual distance between the two cities?

Hooke's law states that the distance a spring stretches varies directly with the force exerted on the spring.

31. An 8-pound weight stretches a spring 3 inches. How far will a 12-pound weight stretch the spring?

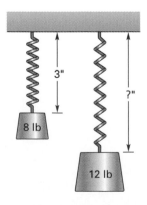

32. A 6-kilogram weight stretches a spring 4 centimeters. What weight is needed to stretch the spring 2 centimeters?

Use the box-and-whisker plot to answer Exercises 33–36.

33. Find the median.   **34.** Find Q_1.

35. Find Q_3.   **36.** Find the range.

37. Use the data below to construct a stem-and-leaf plot.

70 76 90 82 70 70 55 68 65 76 82 80

Solve each equation.

38. $2x + 8 = 5x - 4$ **39.** $-4(y + 3) = 9$

40. $\frac{1}{2}d - \frac{2}{3} = 1$ **41.** $-7.5 = 4.8x - 2.1(x + 1)$

42. $3d + 9 = 4(d - 1)$ **43.** $f(4 - 5) = 3(f + 8)$

Cumulative Problem Solving

The record for the fastest completion of the Indianapolis 500 race was set in 2 hours, 41 minutes, and 18 seconds. It takes 200 laps around the track to complete the 500-mile race.

44. Convert the driver's time to seconds. Write the seconds per lap as a unit rate.

45. Write the miles per lap as a unit rate.

46. What was the driver's average speed in miles per hour?

Tabia is a chemical technician in a plant that prepares eye drops and contact lens solutions. She is preparing a solution of salt and water that is, by weight, 10% salt. This means 100 pounds of the solution contains 10 pounds of salt.

47. What is the ratio of salt to water in the solution?

48. How much salt should Tabia use for 400 pounds of solution?

49. How much water should she use for 400 pounds of solution?

The service manual for adjusting a truck's headlight alignment states that the drop in the light beam should be no greater than 2 inches for each 25 feet the beam shines in front of the truck. The centers of the headlights are 32 inches above the ground.

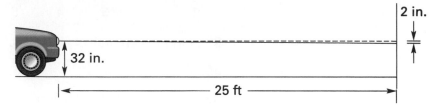

50. Write a ratio comparing the maximum drop in the beam to the distance in front of the truck as stated in the service manual.

51. Suppose the beam of the truck's headlights is adjusted to this ratio. How many feet in front of the truck would the headlight beams strike the ground?

Ivan's car has a fuel tank with a capacity of 18 gallons. Yesterday he drove 347 miles from Portland to Spokane. He started with a full tank in Portland, added 3.9 gallons in Biggs, and filled the tank in Spokane with 9.2 gallons.

52. How many gallons of gas did Ivan use yesterday?

53. Write the gas mileage for Ivan's car as a unit rate.

54. Today Ivan will drive 446 miles from Spokane to Calgary. Can he complete the trip without stopping for gas?

A newspaper photographer is taking pictures of a memorial that is 4 feet 6 inches wide and 17 feet tall. Her copy editor has space for a photograph that is 4 inches wide.

55. What is the ratio of the memorial's width to its height?

56. The photographer wants the picture to have the same ratio of width to height as the memorial. What height should she use for her photograph to fit the available space?

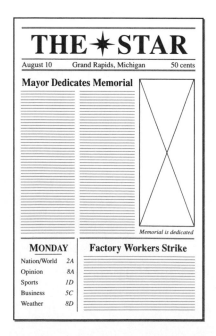

LESSON 6.4 PROBABILITY

OBJECTIVES
- - - - - - - - -
➤ Calculate theoretical probability.

A number cube has six faces numbered 1 through 6. When a number cube is rolled, the number that appears face up is called the **outcome** of the roll.

There are six possible outcomes when rolling a number cube. Each outcome is equally likely to occur.

ACTIVITY

Rolling a Number Cube

1 Make a table like the following one.

	Outcome						Total Number of Rolls
	1	2	3	4	5	6	
Your data							20
Class data							

2 Roll a number cube 20 times. Record the number of times 1, 2, 3, 4, 5, and 6 occur as an outcome.

3 Combine your data with the rest of the class.

4 An **event** is any specific outcome, or group of outcomes. Rolling a 2 is an example of an event. How many times did this event occur for the class's data?

5 For each of the outcomes, write a ratio that compares the number of times the outcome occurred to the total number of rolls. Each ratio is the *experimental probability* of the outcome. What is the class's experimental probability of rolling a 2?

6 What is the sum of the six ratios you wrote in Step 5? Why must this sum equal 1?

The probability of rolling a 2 in the Activity is called experimental probability because it is based on actual data. You will learn more about experimental probability in Lesson 6.7.

You can also calculate the **theoretical probability** of rolling a 2. This probability is a ratio comparing the number of ways to roll a 2 to the total number of possible outcomes. In this example, rolling a 2 is called a *favorable outcome*. The probability of rolling a 2 is written $P(2)$.

Since rolling a 2 is one of six possible outcomes,

$$P(2) = \frac{1}{6} = \frac{\text{Number of favorable outcomes}}{\text{Total number of possible outcomes}}$$

Probability

If all outcomes are equally likely, the probability of an event E is

$$P(E) = \frac{\text{Number of favorable outcomes}}{\text{Total number of possible outcomes}}$$

EXAMPLE Probabilities Using a Spinner

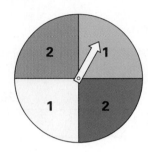

When you spin the spinner, the arrow may stop on any one of the four sectors. Find each probability.

a. $P(\text{blue})$ **b.** $P(1)$ **c.** $P(2 \text{ or green})$ **d.** $P(3)$

SOLUTION

The four sectors are the same size. Thus, all are equally likely.

a. One sector is blue. There is one favorable outcome for landing on blue.

$$P(\text{blue}) = \frac{1}{4}$$

b. Two sectors are labeled 1. There are two favorable outcomes for landing on 1.

$$P(1) = \frac{2}{4} = \frac{1}{2}$$

c. Three sectors are 2 or green. There are three favorable outcomes.

$$P(2 \text{ or green}) = \frac{3}{4}$$

d. There are no sectors labeled 3. There are no favorable outcomes. The probability of an impossible event is 0.

$$P(3) = \frac{0}{4} = 0$$

Critical Thinking Suppose you know the probabilities of possible events before an experiment. An event with higher probability is more likely to occur than an event with lower probability.

If someone spins the spinner in the Example, which of the following events is more likely: landing on red or landing on 1? Why?

ONGOING ASSESSMENT

Use the spinner from the Example to find the following probabilities.

a. $P(\text{yellow})$ **b.** $P(2)$

c. $P(\text{not green})$ **d.** $P(1 \text{ or } 2)$

Critical Thinking Which probability in the Ongoing Assessment represents an event that is certain to occur? What is the probability of a certain event?

LESSON ASSESSMENT

Think and Discuss

1 How are experimental and theoretical probabilities different?

2 Explain how to find the theoretical probability of an event.

3 Draw a spinner that has one large sector and three small sectors. Explain why the ratio for theoretical probability cannot be used for this spinner.

4 The probability of an event is 0.25. What is the probability that the event will not happen? Explain your reasoning.

Practice and Apply

Four boxed lunches for a picnic contain an orange, apple, pear, or banana.

5. If you select a box at random, what is the probability that it contains an apple?

6. What is the probability that it contains an orange or a banana?

Suppose you buy a raffle ticket for a season pass to an amusement park. A total of 2643 tickets were sold. The winner is determined by a single, random draw.

7. What is the probability that you will win the pass?

8. If you buy two tickets, what is your probability?

The cards shown are placed in a box. One card is randomly drawn from the box. Find each probability.

9. P(yellow) **10.** $P(a)$

11. P(vowel) **12.** $P(e$ or consonant$)$

13. $P(d, o,$ or $g)$ **14.** P(yellow or purple)

The numbered tickets shown are placed in a hat. One ticket is randomly drawn from the hat. Find each probability.

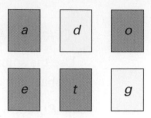

15. P(factor of 6) **16.** P(divisible by 4)

17. $P(\geq 3)$ **18.** P(between 2 and 7)

A group of dog owners participate in a survey. The bar graph shows the number of people from the group who own the breeds of dogs shown. A prize will be given to one of the owners selected at random. Find the probability that the winner will own one of the following.

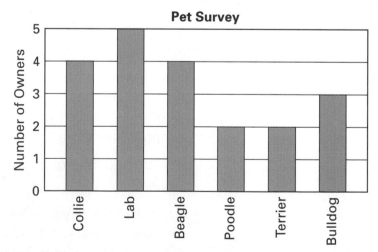

19. a beagle **20.** a bulldog

21. a collie or terrier **22.** not a lab

Next year, three teachers will teach Algebra 1. Mr. Gauss will teach 3 classes, Ms. Hypatia will teach 5 classes, and Mr. Newton will teach 4 classes. All Algebra 1 classes will have the same number of students. If students are randomly assigned to classes, what is the probability that your teacher will be the following?

23. Mr. Gauss   **24.** Ms. Hypatia

25. Mr. Gauss or Ms. Hypatia   **26.** Mr. Newton

A bag of chocolate candies contains green, red, brown, and yellow candies.

27. In one bag, $\frac{1}{6}$ of the candies are green, $\frac{1}{4}$ are red, $\frac{1}{2}$ are brown, and $\frac{1}{12}$ are yellow. If someone takes a candy from the bag without looking, what color is it most likely to be? Explain your answer.

28. Another bag contains 32 candies. If the probability of randomly selecting a green candy is $\frac{3}{8}$, how many green candies are in the bag?

29. A third bag contains 36 candies, and there are an equal number of each color. What is the probability of randomly selecting a brown candy?

Mixed Review

Name the property illustrated below.

30. $\frac{5}{7} \cdot 1\frac{2}{5} = 1$ **31.** $9 + (5 + 6) = (5 + 6) + 9$

Simplify.

32. $6a + 8b - 7a$ **33.** $-2(m - n) + m - 3n$

34. $-\frac{2}{3}c - \frac{1}{4}c$ **35.** $2\frac{3}{5}r + 3.6r$

36. The tax on a pair of shoes is 0.08 times the price of the shoes. If the total cost is $48.60, what is the price of the shoes?

37. A 10-milliliter pipette for a chemistry lab has a tolerance of ±0.06 milliliter. This means the actual capacity of the pipette is no less than 9.94 millileters and no more than 10.06 milliliters. Write a combined inequality that describes the actual capacity of the pipette. Graph the inequality on a number line.

LESSON 6.5 SAMPLE SPACE

OBJECTIVES
- Create tree diagrams to determine a sample space.
- Use the counting principle to find the number of possible outcomes.

To find the probability of an event, you need to know the total number of possible outcomes. The set of all possible outcomes is called the **sample space**.

In Lesson 6.4, you performed an experiment with a number cube. When you roll a number cube, the sample space is the set of six possible outcomes: {1, 2, 3, 4, 5, 6}.

When you toss a coin, there are two possible outcomes. The sample space is heads or tails: {H, T}. What is the sample space if you toss a coin several times? How can you determine the total number of possible outcomes?

EXAMPLE 1 Sample Space with Coin Tosses

A coin is tossed three times. Find the sample space. Then find each of the following probabilities.

a. P(three heads)   **b.** P(exactly two tails)

SOLUTION

You can construct a **tree diagram** to find the sample space.

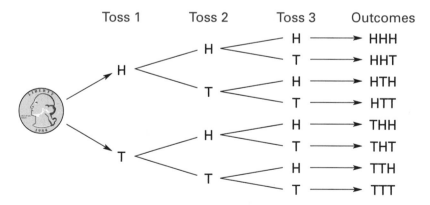

The sample space is the set of 8 possible outcomes.

a. There is one outcome with three heads: HHH.

$$P(\text{three heads}) = \frac{1}{8}$$

b. There are three outcomes with exactly two tails: HTT, THT, TTH.

$$P(\text{exactly two tails}) = \frac{3}{8}$$

A coin is tossed four times. Find the sample space. Then find each of the following probabilities.

a. P(four tails)

b. P(exactly two heads)

c. P(three or more heads)

ACTIVITY   **Counting Possibilities**

Suppose you pack the following clothes for a weekend trip.

Pants: jeans   **Shirts:** red   **Shoes:** trainers
           shorts   blue   sandals
                             plaid

How many different pants-shirt-shoes outfits can you create from these 7 articles of clothing?

1 Construct a tree diagram for the possible outcomes. The top branch is shown as an example.

Pants   Shirts   Shoes
                              trainers
            red
jeans   sandals

2 What is the total number of possible outcomes?

3 Compare your answer to the number found by multiplying the number of choices for each article of clothing.

   Pants   ·   **Shirts**   ·   **Shoes**
   2 choices   ·   3 choices   ·   2 choices
        $2 \cdot 3 \cdot 2 = $ ___?___

4 The choices of clothing have three stages: pants, shirts, and shoes. Suppose another event has three stages, and there are m choices for the first stage, n choices for the second stage, and p choices for the third stage. How can you find the number of possible outcomes for the event?

5 Test your answer to Step 4. Calculate the number of possible outcomes of tossing a coin three times. Does your answer agree with the results of Example 1?

In the Activity you used the **Counting Principle**.

> **Counting Principle**
>
> To find the number of possible outcomes for an event that has different stages, multiply the number of choices in each stage of the event.

EXAMPLE 2 Using the Counting Principle

Mika prints tickets for a ballet recital that will run four days. There will be two performances each day. There are five different prices of tickets for each performance. How many combinations of days, performances, and prices of tickets must Mika print?

SOLUTION

Use the Counting Principle. There are three stages.

Days of performances		Performances per day		Prices for each performance
4	·	2	·	5

$$4 \cdot 2 \cdot 5 = 40$$

Mika must print tickets for 40 combinations of days, performances, and prices.

LESSON ASSESSMENT

Think and Discuss

1. Explain how to use a tree diagram to find a sample space.

2. Write an algorithm for using the Counting Principle to find the possible outcomes in an event that has several stages.

Practice and Apply

Suppose you toss a coin and then roll a number cube.

3. Use a tree diagram to find the sample space.

4. How many outcomes are in the sample space?

5. Find P(head, 3).

6. Find P(head, even number).

7. Find P(tail, number less than or equal to 4).

For Exercises 8–13, suppose you have a set of red tickets numbered from 1 to 4 in one box and a set of green tickets numbered from 1 to 4 in another box. You randomly select one red ticket and one green ticket from the boxes.

8. Construct a sample space for the outcomes.

9. How many outcomes are in the sample space?

10. Find P(red 4 and green 1).

11. Find P(red 2 and green 5).

12. Find P(red odd number and green even number).

13. Find P(red number greater than 0 and green number less than or equal to 4).

14. Suppose you make a sandwich with one meat and one bread. How many different ways can you make the sandwich if you have 4 types of meat and 3 types of bread?

15. You have 2 kinds of wrapping paper, 5 colors of ribbon, and 2 sizes of bows. How many different combinations can you use for wrapping a package?

16. There are 4 ways to drive from Dallas to Austin. There are 3 ways to drive from Austin to Houston. How many different ways can you drive from Dallas to Houston if you stop in Austin on the way?

17. You roll 3 different number cubes. How many outcomes are in the sample space?

18. There are 30 different ways to order a pizza. You can order by crusts, toppings, and sizes. You can order 2 different crusts and 5 different toppings. How many different sizes can you order?

19. A license plate has 6 positions for letters and numbers. The first two positions must be letters. The last four positions must be nonzero whole numbers. How many different license plates can be produced using this combination of letters and numbers?

Answer each statement with *true* or *false*.

20. 56.975 rounded to the nearest hundredth is 56.98.

21. If the difference between two integers is negative, at least one of the integers must be negative.

22. The sum of two integers is always larger than either integer.

23. Dividing by a number is the same as multiplying by the reciprocal of the number.

24. If $81 = 3(x - 8)$, then $x = 35$.

25. If $a \geq 0$, then $-a \geq 0$.

Let $c = -1\frac{2}{3}$, $m = 3\frac{3}{4}$, and $r = 2\frac{5}{6}$. Evaluate each of the following.

26. cm

27. $m + r$

28. $\dfrac{c - m}{r}$

29. $m(c + r)$

Cumulative Problem Solving

To open a combination lock, you must enter the correct combination of three integers in order. The integers are greater than or equal to zero, and less than or equal to 40.

30. How many possible combinations are there for a lock?

31. What is the probability that someone can enter the correct combination in one try by selecting three numbers at random?

32. Suppose a bank needs a high-security lock that has a probability less than one in one million that someone can open it in one try. Will the lock described in Exercises 30–31 work? If not, describe a lock that would work. You can change the number and range of possible integers.

A new school is considering uniforms for students and teachers. The uniforms include red, white, or blue shirts with navy or khaki pants.

33. How many different outfits can students wear using these colors for shirts and pants?

34. Suppose navy and khaki shorts are added to the uniforms. How many different combinations of outfits are possible?

35. Suppose girls may wear navy or khaki skirts, pants, or shorts. How many different combinations of outfits are possible for girls?

You are planning an experiment to test the response of bacteria cultures to environmental changes. In the experiment, you will measure the effects of pH, temperature, and light on the bacteria. The table lists the different levels you will test for each factor.

Factor	Level
pH	6.6, 6.8, 7.0, 7.2, 7.4, 7.6
Temperature (°C)	65, 70, 75, 80, 85
Light	no light, low light, intense light

36. If you need one bacteria culture for each combination of levels listed in the table, how many cultures will you need to prepare?

37. If each combination of levels must be tested ten times, how many cultures will you need?

Kameko is the Quality Control Manager of a packaging company that produces cardboard boxes. In a production run of 1000 boxes, Kameko finds 6 boxes that are not cut correctly, 10 boxes with misaligned printing, and 12 boxes with smeared printing. None of the boxes has more than one defect.

38. What is the probability of randomly selecting a box from the production line with smeared printing?

39. What is the probability of selecting a box with a defect?

40. How many boxes with defects should Kameko expect in a production run of 7500 boxes?

LESSON 6.6 INDEPENDENT AND DEPENDENT EVENTS

OBJECTIVES

➤ Identify independent and dependent events.
➤ Calculate the probability of independent and dependent events.

Brian has 2 black socks and 2 white socks in his dresser drawer. He wants to wear a pair of white socks. Suppose Brian randomly picks two socks from the drawer.

Compare the following two ways Brian can pick his socks.

Case 1	Case 2
Brian picks a sock. He puts it back. He picks a second sock.	Brian picks a sock. He does not put it back. He picks a second sock.

What is the probability of picking a white sock on the first draw? On the second draw?

The probabilities of the events in the two cases are not the same. In **Case 1**, the second draw is not affected by what happened in the first draw. This is an example of *independent events*. Two events are **independent** if the outcome of the first event does not affect the second event.

In **Case 2**, the probability for the second draw is affected by the first draw. There are only three socks in the drawer for the second draw. This is an example of *dependent events*. Two events are **dependent** if the outcome of the first event affects the second event.

EXAMPLE 1 Independent Events

Suppose you toss a coin and roll a 6-sided number cube. What is the probability that the coin lands heads up *and* the number cube shows an odd number?

SOLUTION

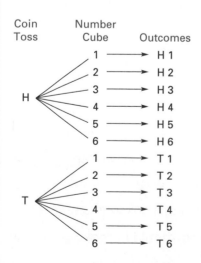

The outcome of the number cube is not affected by the coin toss. Thus, the events are independent. Construct a tree diagram to find the sample space.

There are 12 possible outcomes. The three favorable outcomes are H1, H3, and H5. Thus,

$$P(\text{H and odd}) = \frac{3}{12} = \frac{1}{4}$$

1 What is P(H) when tossing a coin?

2 What is P(odd) when rolling a number cube?

3 What is P(H) · P(odd)?

4 Compare P(H) · P(odd) to P(H and odd) from Example 1.

5 Use the following two methods to calculate P(T and less than 3).

> **Method 1** Use the sample space from Example 1.

> **Method 2** Multiply the probabilities of the two independent events.

6 How can you find the probability of two independent events if you know the probability of each event?

In the Activity, you discovered a formula to find the probability of two independent events.

> **Probability of Independent Events**
> Let A and B be independent events.
>
> $$P(A \text{ and } B) = P(A) \cdot P(B)$$

EXAMPLE 2 Probability of Independent Events

A bag contains 9 jelly beans. There are 2 yellow, 4 green, and 3 red. You draw one jelly bean, replace it and draw again. What is the probability that the first jelly bean is yellow and the second is red?

SOLUTION

Since you replace the first jelly bean, the second draw is not affected by the first. The events are independent.

$$P(\text{yellow and red}) = P(\text{yellow}) \cdot P(\text{red})$$

$$= \frac{2}{\overset{}{\underset{3}{9}}} \cdot \frac{\overset{1}{\cancel{3}}}{9} = \frac{2}{27}$$

The probability of drawing a yellow jelly bean, replacing it, and then drawing a red jelly bean is $\frac{2}{27}$.

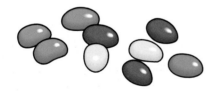

In Example 2, what is the probability of drawing a red jelly bean, replacing it, and drawing a green jelly bean?

If you do not replace the first jelly bean, the probability of the second draw is affected. These two draws are dependent events. Let A and B represent two dependent events, with B following A. The probability of B given that A has occurred is written $P(B \mid A)$.

Probability of Dependent Events

If A and B are dependent events, and B follows A, then

$$P(A \text{ and } B) = P(A) \cdot P(B \mid A)$$

EXAMPLE 3 Probability of Dependent Events

The bag from Example 2 contains 2 yellow, 4 green, and 3 red jelly beans. Suppose you draw two jelly beans without replacement. What is the probability of drawing a yellow, then a red?

SOLUTION

The events are dependent.

$$P(\text{yellow and red}) = P(\text{yellow}) \cdot P(\text{red} \mid \text{yellow})$$

$$= \frac{\overset{1}{\cancel{2}}}{\underset{3}{\cancel{9}}} \cdot \frac{\overset{1}{\cancel{3}}}{\underset{4}{\cancel{8}}} \quad \leftarrow \text{After one jelly bean has been removed, only 8 are left}$$

The probability of drawing a yellow, then a red jelly bean is $\frac{1}{12}$.

Critical Thinking Convert the probabilities in Example 2 and Example 3 to decimals. Which event is more likely? Explain why.

Using the same bag from Examples 2 and 3, what is the probability of drawing both yellow jelly beans with replacement? Explain why *without replacement* means the events are dependent.

LESSON ASSESSMENT

1 Give examples of independent events and dependent events. Explain why the events are independent or dependent.

2 How do you find the probability of independent events?

3 How do you find the probability of dependent events?

Practice and Apply

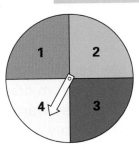

Use the spinner shown and a number cube to complete Exercises 4–7. Find $P(A$ and $B)$.

4. A: Spin 3.
   B: Roll 5.

5. A: Spin an even number.
   B: Roll an odd number.

6. A: Spin a number less than 4.
   B: Roll a number greater than 4.

7. A: Spin a factor of 6.
   B: Roll a number less than or equal to 4.

A cube has 3 blue faces, 2 yellow faces, and 1 red face. Find the probability each of the following faces appear when the cube is rolled.

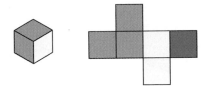

8. One roll: yellow

9. One roll: not blue

10. Two rolls: blue, then red

11. Two rolls: two yellows

12. Three rolls: red, then blue, then yellow

13. Three rolls: all blue

A coin bank contains 5 pennies, 3 nickels, and 4 quarters. A coin is drawn randomly and then replaced. A second coin is drawn. Find the probability of the following events.

14. The first coin is a penny and the second coin is a quarter.

15. The first coin is a nickel and the second coin is a quarter.

16. The first coin is a penny and the second coin is not a quarter.

Two letters are chosen at random without replacement from the word ALPHABET. Find the probability of the following events.

17. The first letter is a vowel and the second letter is a consonant.

18. Both letters are the same.

There are 6 boys and 4 girls in a contest. Winning tickets for three prizes will be awarded by a random drawing. Find the probability that the prizes will be awarded in the following order if each person can win only one prize.

19. girl, girl, boy

20. girl, girl, girl

21. boy, boy, boy

22. girl, not girl, not boy

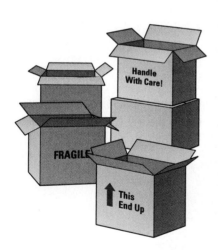

While packing for a move, your toothbrush is accidentally packed in a moving box. The toothbrush is in one of five boxes in your room.

23. What is the probability that the toothbrush is not in the first box you open?

24. What is the probability that the toothbrush is not in the first two boxes you open?

25. What is the probability that the toothbrush is not in the first four boxes you open?

Mixed Review

$$1.6 \quad 3.7 \quad 5.8 \quad 2.4 \quad 4.5$$

Use the data above to find:

26. the mean   **27.** the median   **28.** the mode

Find the value of $3a - 2b$ when

29. $a = -4$ and $b = -1$.   **30.** $a = -2$ and $b = 5$.

Find the value of $-\frac{2}{3}m + n$ when

31. $m = -6$ and $n = 2$.   **32.** $m = -\frac{1}{2}$ and $n = 1\frac{3}{4}$.

LESSON 6.7 EXPERIMENTAL PROBABILITY AND SIMULATION

OBJECTIVES

➤ Calculate experimental probability.
➤ Use a simulation to calculate probability.
➤ Calculate the odds in favor of an event.

After basketball practice, each player shoots at least 20 free throws, but they must continue until they make 5 in a row. Janet's results for her first 20 free throws are shown in the table. What is Janet's probability of making a free throw?

Free-Throw Outcomes									
M	M	M	M	X	X	M	M	X	M
M	X	M	M	M	X	X	M	M	M

M = Made   X = Missed

When Janet shoots free throws, the possible outcomes are not equally likely. Thus, you cannot use theoretical probability. Instead, you calculate the **experimental probability** based on the collection of data.

Experimental Probability

The experimental probability of an event E is

$$P(E) = \frac{\text{Number of favorable outcomes}}{\text{Total number of trials}}$$

EXAMPLE 1 Free-Throw Probability

Calculate the probability of Janet making a free throw.

SOLUTION

From the data in the table, Janet made 14 out of 20 free throws.

$$P(\text{making a free throw}) = \frac{\text{Number of free throws made}}{\text{Total number of free throws attempted}}$$

Janet's probability of making a free throw is $\frac{14}{20}$ or $\frac{7}{10}$.

Critical Thinking What is Janet's probability of missing a free throw? Why is the following a *true* statement?

$$P(\text{making a free throw}) + P(\text{missing a free throw}) = 1$$

Sometimes it is very difficult or even impossible to calculate the probability of an event. In this case, you can perform an experiment to estimate the probability or you can **simulate** the experiment. For example, you can use a sequence of **random numbers** to simulate Janet's free throws.

Random numbers can be generated by calculators or computer spreadsheets. There are also tables of random numbers printed in many textbooks.

ACTIVITY 1   Simulating Free Throws

1 Use a calculator, spreadsheet program, or table to generate a sequence of 20 random numbers between 1 and 10. Write the numbers in the order they are generated in a table similar to the one shown.

Simulated Free Throws					
	1	2	3	...	20
Random number	7	3	9	...	...
M = Made X = Missed	M	M	X	...	...

2 The list simulates Janet's 20 free throws. She has a 7 out of 10 chance of *making* each free throw. Label each number in the random sequence that is less than or equal to 7 as a free throw *made* (M). Label each number greater than 7 as a free throw *missed* (X).

3 Your list simulates one trial of 20 free throws attempted. Does your trial include at least five free throws made in a row? If so, you have simulated a favorable outcome.

4 Combine your trial with those from the rest of the class. How many favorable outcomes are there? How many trials are there?

5 Use the class's data to estimate Janet's probability of making 5 free throws in a row when she attempts 20.

The T-Shirt Company prints logos on shirts. Each batch of shirts printed contains 3 small, 4 medium, and 2 large sizes. A quality inspector selects two shirts from each batch for inspection. If the shirts are selected at random, what is the probability that both shirts are the same size? With the simulation in Activity 2, you can estimate this probability.

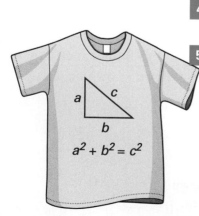

$a^2 + b^2 = c^2$

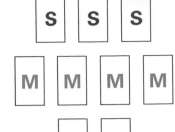

To perform this simulation, you will need 9 index cards. Mark 3 cards S, 4 cards M, and 2 cards L. The index cards simulate shirts printed in each batch.

1 Put the 9 cards face down and mix them thoroughly.

2 Turn 2 cards over. Record the sizes.

3 Repeat the simulation 10 times.

4 A favorable outcome is when both shirts selected are the same size. How many favorable outcomes occurred in your 10 trials?

5 Combine your data with those from the rest of the class. How many favorable outcomes were simulated? How many trials were simulated?

6 Calculate the experimental probability that two shirts the same size will be chosen for an inspection.

ONGOING ASSESSMENT

Design a simulation using coin tosses to find the experimental probability that exactly 2 children in a family with 3 children will be girls.

An event can have both *favorable outcomes* and *unfavorable outcomes*. The **odds in favor** of an event are given by a ratio.

$$\text{Odds in favor of an event} = \frac{\text{Number of favorable outcomes}}{\text{Number of unfavorable outcomes}}$$

EXAMPLE 2 Free-Throw Odds

Calculate the odds of Janet making a free throw in one attempt.

SOLUTION

From the data at the beginning of the lesson, Janet made 14 out of 20 free throws. Therefore, she misses 6 out of 20.

$$\text{Odds in favor} = \frac{14}{6} = \frac{7}{3}$$

Janet's odds of making a free throw are 7 to 3.

ONGOING ASSESSMENT

In Activity 2, what are the odds of randomly selecting a small T-shirt?

CULTURAL CONNECTION

In this chapter, you have used the tools of *probability* to try to *predict* the outcome of random experiments. By contrast, in *statistics*, you observe the outcome and try to *infer* information about the experiment.

James Bernoulli, a Swiss mathematician who lived from 1654 to 1705, wrote one of the earliest books on probability and statistics, *Ars Conjectandi* ("The Art of Making Conjectures"). A *conjecture* is a guess, or prediction, of the outcome of an experiment or the basic principles of an experiment.

Bernoulli explained many principles of probability and statistics with *ball and urn experiments*. For example, suppose an urn contains 75 red balls and 25 blue balls. A trial consists of randomly drawing a ball from the urn and then replacing it. What is the probability of drawing a blue ball in a trial?

Now suppose the urn contains an unknown number of red and blue balls. You repeat the trial 100 times. You draw blue 47 times and red 53 times. Make a conjecture about the fraction of balls in the urn that are red.

Today, pollsters use sampling and statistics to find out what people think about candidates for office, TV shows, and toothpaste. Polling is an outgrowth of Bernoulli's ideas: You can predict preferences of an entire population from a random sample drawn from that population.

LESSON ASSESSMENT

Think and Discuss

1. Is it possible to perform an experiment several times and get different experimental probabilities for the same event? Explain your answer.

2. Explain how to set up an experiment to find the probability that when 2 coins are tossed, both will land heads up.

3. When would you use a simulation to find the probability of an event?

4. How can you use random numbers in a simulation?

5. Kim's Florist takes orders for flowers on its web site. In one week, the web site was visited 2660 times and received 52 orders for flowers. Estimate the probability that someone visiting the web site will place an order.

6. Aiko is a pitcher on a softball team. In the first three innings of a game, she throws 48 pitches. Eighteen of the pitches were strikes. What is the experimental probability that Aiko will throw a strike on the first pitch of the fourth inning?

7. A quality control technician at a Delmar Batteries manufacturing plant tests 125 car batteries and finds 2 were not charged. Estimate the probability that a Delmar battery shipped from this plant will not be charged.

8. A public health screening of 1350 teenagers revealed that 15 had high blood pressure. What is the experimental probability that a teenager will have high blood pressure?

There are 3 true-false questions on a test.

9. Design a coin-toss simulation to find the experimental probability that a student will get all 3 questions correct by guessing.

10. Repeat the simulation 10 times and record the results.

11. From your simulation, what is the experimental probability that a student will guess all 3 questions correctly?

12. Compare your experimental probability to the theoretical probability.

Two coins are tossed at the same time. Use the data in the table to estimate the probability of each event.

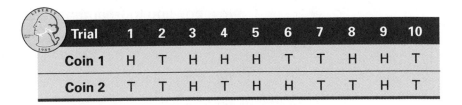

Trial	1	2	3	4	5	6	7	8	9	10
Coin 1	H	T	H	H	H	T	T	H	H	T
Coin 2	T	T	H	T	H	H	T	T	H	T

13. Coin 1 is heads.   **14.** Both coins are heads.

15. Both coins are tails.   **16.** Both coins are the same.

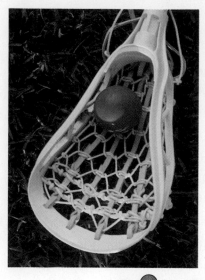

Kirstin is a lacrosse player who scores on 2 out of 5 shots at the goal.

17. Describe a random-number simulation to estimate the probability that Kirstin will score on her next 2 shots.

18. Perform your simulation 10 times and record your results.

19. From your simulation, what is the experimental probability that Kirsten will score on her next 2 shots?

20. Compare your experimental probability to the theoretical probability.

The types of books checked out of the library during one day are shown in the following table.

Mystery	Biography	Nonfiction	Science Fiction	Hobbies	Science
14	12	26	24	7	3

PUBLIC LIBRARY

Use the data to find the experimental probability that a book checked out is:

21. a biography.

22. a mystery or a science fiction book.

23. a science book.

24. not a nonfiction book.

Mixed Review

Use the four-step problem-solving plan to solve Exercise 25.

25. A marching band has 72 members. One of the marches calls for a rectangular formation with at least 6 band members in each row and in each column. What are the possible arrangements of rows and columns for the rectangular formation?

In a bowling tournament, Lashandra had the following scores:

110   124   117   125   120   124

26. What is the range?

27. What is the mean?

28. What is the median?

29. What is the mode?

LESSON 6.8 SAMPLING

➤ Use a sample population to make prediction about a larger population.
➤ Determine if a sample is biased.

Pollsters use experimental probability to determine people's preferences. For example, the winning candidate in an election can be predicted before all votes are counted.

A small subset of the total voting population is interviewed after they vote. This subset is called a **sample.** If each person in the population has an equal chance of being chosen, the sample is called a **random sample.** If a large enough sample is tested, the probabilities for the sample can be applied to the larger population.

EXAMPLE Making a Prediction

In a city's election for mayor, the votes of a random sample of 550 people were recorded. The results are shown in the table. Approximately 175,000 people are expected to vote in the election. Predict the number of votes Ms. Rivera will receive.

Candidate	Votes
Ms. Rivera	231
Mr. Winston	208
Mr. Gordon	111

SOLUTION

Find the experimental probability someone in the sample votes for Ms. Rivera.

$$P(\text{Rivera}) = \frac{231}{550} = 0.42$$

To predict the number of votes Ms. Rivera will receive, multiply this probability by the total number of votes.

$P(\text{Rivera})$	$\cdot$	Total number of votes	$=$	Predicted number of votes for Rivera
0.42	$\cdot$	175,000	$=$	73,500

Ms. Rivera should receive approximately 73,500 votes.

ONGOING ASSESSMENT

Predict the number of votes Mr. Gordon will receive in the Example.

Good surveys do not use *biased samples*. Biased samples can result from using a subset that is not large enough to represent the population. For example, would you accurately predict the average height of professional athletes if you surveyed only professional basketball players?

Biased samples can also result from using unfair questions. Biased questions sometimes make assumptions about the population or make one answer seem better than another.

ONGOING ASSESSMENT

Explain why each of the following is a biased question.

1. Do you want to go to the 5:00 or 7:30 movie?

2. Do you prefer a standard car wash or the Super-Deluxe Treatment?

LESSON ASSESSMENT

Think and Discuss

1 How can you use experimental probability and a random sample to predict the outcome of an election?

2 Explain how you can make sure a random sample is selected if you want to estimate the number of cat owners in your school.

Practice and Apply

3. When 60 students were polled, 24 said they would attend the football homecoming game. About how many of the school's 1640 students will attend the game?

4. A random sample showed that 329 out of 620 citizens favored construction of a new municipal building. Estimate the number of the 54,600 citizens of the city expected to favor the construction.

5. An advertising agency surveys TV viewers to determine the number of people that remember the agency's ads. A poll of 845 viewers shows that 63 remember an ad for eyeglasses. If there were approximately 1.9 million viewers of the ad, about how many people would remember the ad?

Tell whether or not it is appropriate to use a poll to determine the following.

6. the number of words per minute you can read

7. the amount of sales of a new ice cream flavor

8. the number of hours per week ninth graders spend on homework

9. the winning number on a raffle ticket

An Internet service company polls a random sample of 242 customers to determine the number of hours per day spent on the Internet. The results are shown in the table. The company has 5450 customers.

Number of Hours	Number of Customers
Less than 1	53
1 – 2	72
2 – 3	60
3 – 4	32
More than 4	25

Find the probability that a person polled spends the following range of hours on the Internet.

10. less than 1   **11.** 1 to 2   **12.** 2 to 3

13. 3 to 4   **14.** more than 4

Predict how many of the 5450 customers spend each range of hours on the Internet.

15. less than 1   **16.** 1 to 2   **17.** 2 to 3

18. 3 to 4   **19.** more than 4

20. Display the results on a chart. How many hours do most customers spend on the Internet?

Mixed Review

Give the value of the underlined digit.

21. 1<u>7</u>,245,650   **22.** 416,00<u>8</u>,915   **23.** 235.86<u>0</u>41

24. Round 34,074,628 to the nearest hundred thousand.

25. Round 0.006748 to the nearest ten-thousandth.

For Exercises 26–27, write a rule for finding the next number in the sequence. Then find the next three numbers.

26. 7.25   8.5   9.75   11

27. 4   2   1   0.5

Solve each equation.

28. $6(x + 3) = 27$ **29.** $\frac{3}{4}x + 1\frac{1}{2} = -4\frac{1}{2}$

Cumulative Problem Solving

Alban has made a pencil drawing 24 inches long and 18 inches wide. He wants to make a stone carving from the drawing. He has a platform 4 feet wide and 12 feet long. He wants the carving to be as large as possible within the limits of the size of the platform. He also wants the carving to have the same ratio of length to width as the drawing.

30. What length of platform should Alban cut for his carving?

31. If Alban allows 3 inches around the perimeter of the platform for border, what length of platform should he cut?

Gail and Consuela are among 5 students in their class with perfect attendance for the school year. The school awards a prize to each of the 5 students. The prizes are 3 movie tickets with refreshments and two $10 gift certificates. The prizes are written on 5 slips of paper and dropped into a jar. Each of the 5 students draws for an award without replacement. Gail and Consuela are best friends and want to go to a movie together.

32. Are the drawings dependent or independent events?

33. Gail draws first. What is the probability she will draw a movie ticket?

34. Consuela draws second. If Gail drew a movie ticket, what is the probability Consuela will also draw a movie ticket?

35. What is the probability Gail and Consuela will both draw movie tickets?

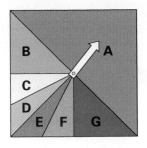

Everyone in a class of 25 students makes a spinner like the one shown. Each student spins 10 times and records the result as a letter A through G. When the data for the class are combined, the results are shown in the table.

Result	Number of Spins
A	119
B	32
C	12
D	14
E	19
F	16
G	38

Find the following experimental probabilities.

36. $P(A)$ **37.** $P(B \text{ or } G)$ **38.** $P(C, D, E, \text{ or } F)$

39. How many times would you expect the spinner to land on A if you spin 1000 times? Explain your answer.

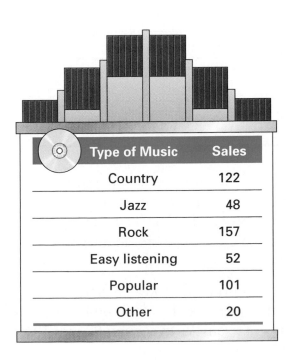

Type of Music	Sales
Country	122
Jazz	48
Rock	157
Easy listening	52
Popular	101
Other	20

Heath is the store manager of Music-Mania. He keeps the statistics of the types of music his customers buy. The results of the latest 500 sales are shown in the table.

Heath uses experimental probability to predict future sales and needed inventory for each type of music.

40. For each music type listed, calculate the probability that a future sale will be that type.

41. Music-Mania averages 28,000 sales per year. How many sales of each type of music should Heath expect?

MATH LAB

Equipment   Measuring tape
Centimeter ruler

Problem Statement

In this Activity, you will use ratios and proportions to make scale drawings of a classroom floor and one wall. Your drawings will show the locations of objects in the room.

Procedure

Record all measurements in feet and inches.

a   Measure the length and width of a classroom. Record the measurements in a table similar to the one shown.

	Actual Measurement ft and in.	decimal ft	Drawing Measurement cm
Classroom length			
Classroom width			
Desk-top length			
Desk-top width			
Distance from corner of desk to 1st wall			
Distance from corner of desk to 2nd wall			

b   Select a desk or table to include in your drawing. Measure the length and width of the top of the desk. Measure the horizontal distance from one corner of the desk to each of the two nearest walls. Record the measurements in the table.

c   Convert each measurement from feet and inches to decimal feet by dividing the number of inches by 12. Round to the nearest hundredth foot. For example, to convert 27 feet 10 inches, use $27\frac{10}{12}$ feet = 27.83 feet.

d Use the ratio 1 centimeter to 2 feet as the scale factor for your drawings.

$$\text{Scale factor} = \frac{1 \text{ cm}}{2 \text{ ft}} \quad \begin{matrix} \leftarrow \\ \leftarrow \end{matrix} \quad \frac{\text{Length on the drawing}}{\text{Actual length}}$$

Write a proportion to find the drawing measurement for each measurement in the table. Solve the proportions and record the values for the drawing measurements.

e Make a scale drawing of your classroom floor. Draw the desk- or table-top in the correct location.

f Perform the necessary measurements to make a scale drawing of one wall of the classroom. Include in your measurements the length and height of the wall and at least one object on the wall, such as a window, door, or chalkboard. Prepare a data table to record your measurements and calculations.

Discussion Questions

1. Explain why the ratio $\frac{1 \text{ cm}}{2 \text{ ft}}$ is not a conversion factor.

2. How could you change the scale factor to make your scale drawing twice as large?

Activity 2: Probabilities with Number Cubes

Equipment   Three number cubes

Problem Statement

You will compare theoretical probabilities and experimental probabilities for rolling matching numbers on number cubes.

Procedure

For this Activity, write all values for probabilities as decimals rounded to the nearest thousandth.

Two Number Cubes

a When you roll two number cubes, each cube can land with a number 1 through 6 face up. Construct a tree diagram to find the sample space for rolling two number cubes. How many possible outcomes are in the sample space?

b Use the Counting Principle to calculate the number of possible outcomes of rolling two number cubes. Compare your answer to the result from Step **a**.

c For this Activity, a favorable outcome is rolling the same number on both cubes. How many favorable outcomes are there? What is the theoretical probability of rolling the same number on both cubes? Record the value in a table similar to the one shown.

	2 Number Cubes Group Data	Class Data	3 Number Cubes Group Data	Class Data
Theoretical Probability P_T				
Number of Trials				
Number of Favorable Outcomes				
Experimental Probability P_E				
$\lvert P_T - P_E \rvert$				

d Have each member of the group roll two number cubes 10 times. Each roll is a trial. Record the number of trials and favorable outcomes for the group.

e The experimental probability of an event E is

$$P(E) = \frac{\text{Number of favorable outcomes}}{\text{Total number of trials}}$$

What is your group's experimental probability of rolling matching numbers on the number cubes? Record this value in the table.

f Combine your data with those of the rest of the class. How many trials were there for the whole class? What is the total number of favorable outcomes for the class? What is the experimental probability for the class data? Record these values in the table.

g Calculate the difference between your group's experimental probability and the theoretical probability. Calculate the difference between the class's experimental probability and the theoretical probability. Which has the smallest absolute value?

Three Number Cubes

h How many possible outcomes are there for rolling three number cubes? Calculate the theoretical probability of rolling three matching numbers on the cubes.

i Repeat Steps **d–g** for three number cubes.

Discussion Questions

1. Would you expect your group's or the class's experimental probability to be closest to the theoretical probability for rolling matching numbers?

2. How does increasing the number of trials affect the relationship between the experimental probability and the theoretical probability?

Activity 3: Birthday Simulations

Equipment Spreadsheet computer program

Problem Statement

What is the probability that someone chosen at random will have your birthday? For example, suppose your birthday is October 2. The probability that the other person's birthday is also October 2 is

$$P(\text{same birthday}) = \frac{\text{Number of favorable outcomes}}{\text{Total number of possible outcomes}}$$

$$= \frac{1}{365} \approx 0.0027$$

Suppose you compare the birthdays of everyone in a group of people. What is the probability of finding two people in the group with the same birthday? This probability is more difficult to calculate theoretically. You will find experimental probabilities using your group, the class, and random birth dates generated with a spreadsheet.

Procedure

Experimental Probability for a Small Group

a As a first trial, record the birthdays of each member of your group. If two people in the group have the same birthday, this trial represents a favorable outcome.

b Follow the instructions below to generate 20 more simulated trials. The spreadsheet function RANDBETWEEN(**a, b**) generates a random number greater than or equal to **a** and less than or equal to **b**. If your spreadsheet program does not have RANDBETWEEN, your teacher will supply the correct function name to use as a replacement.

In cell A1, enter the function RANDBETWEEN(1, 365). If someone in the group has a birthday on February 29, use 366 for the upper limit. The program inserts a random number representing a day of the year for someone's birthday.

Copy the function down the A-column filling the number of rows corresponding to the number of people in your lab group. The example shown uses a group size of 5. Make sure all lab groups use the same group size. The data will be combined.

= RANDBETWEEN (1,365)

	A	B	C
1	216	323	94
2	104	263	283
3	5	86	228
4	99	185	135
5	211	21	310
6			
7	198	161	237
8	110	113	284
9	239	282	36
10	18	306	283
11	43	7	247
12			

Copy the column across to create 9 more columns.

Copy the 10 columns, and paste them below the first 10. Skip one row for separation, as shown in the example.

c Print the spreadsheet. You now have 21 trials, including the data from Step **a**. A matching pair of birthdays within a trial represents a favorable outcome. How many favorable outcomes are there? Calculate the experimental probability for these trials, and write the result as a decimal. Record your group's data in a table similar to the one shown.

	Group Size	Number of Favorable Outcomes	Number of Trials	Experimental Probability
Group data	5		21	
Class data	5			
Group data	25		11	
Class data	25			

d Combine your data with the other groups in the class. Calculate the experimental probability using all the trials generated by the class, and record the result as a decimal in the table.

Experimental Probability for the Class

e Write your group's birthdays on the board. If two people in the class have the same birthday, your class represents a favorable outcome for the first trial.

f Start a new spreadsheet. Use RANDBETWEEN(1, 365) to generate random birth dates for a group size equal to the number of students in your class. Copy and paste the column to create 10 trials on the spreadsheet.

g Print the spreadsheet. You now have 11 trials, including the data from Step **e.** How many favorable outcomes are there? Calculate and record the experimental probability for these trials.

h Combine your data with the other groups in the class. Calculate the experimental probability using all the trials generated by the class. Do not count the class data more than once.

Discussion Questions

Theoretical Probability of Two Matching Birthdays in a Group

Group Size	Probability
4	0.016
5	0.027
6	0.040
23	0.51
25	0.57
27	0.63
30	0.70

The table at left shows the theoretical probabilities of 2 matching birthdays in a group. Compare your experimental probabilities to the theoretical.

1. Are the experimental probabilities you calculated for your group data or class data closest to the theoretical probabilities? Why is one set of data more accurate than the other?

2. Suppose you generate 1000 trials for a group size of 30. About how many trials will contain matching birthdays?

3. What group size is required for you to be certain of finding two people with the same birthday?

CHAPTER 6   ASSESSMENT

Communicate

1. Explain how to solve the proportion $\frac{a}{b} = \frac{c}{d}$ for a.

2. Write three examples of unit rates.

3. Describe how to find the probability of an event.

4. How is the Counting Principle used to find the number of possible outcomes for an event?

5. Explain the difference between an independent and a dependent event.

Skills

Each of the 25 students in Ms. Santiago's homeroom takes a foreign language class: 12 take Spanish, 8 take French, and 5 take German. Write ratios for the following.

6. students taking German to students taking French

7. students taking Spanish to students not taking Spanish

Solve each proportion.

8. $\frac{8}{10} = \frac{x}{25}$

9. $\frac{1.8}{x} = \frac{2.4}{64}$

10. $\frac{4y}{7} = -\frac{32}{28}$

11. $\frac{5}{2} = \frac{y + 8}{y - 4}$

12. Write a unit rate for the following.

   Gas price: $15.60 for 12 gallons

13. Write a conversion factor and change 2.5 hours to minutes.

Applications

In Exercises 14–15, define a variable, write a proportion, and solve.

14. A plane flies 1680 miles in 4 hours. How far will the plane fly in 9 hours at the same speed?

15. Seven collector pins cost $59.50. How much will you pay for 22 pins?

A penny is tossed and a number cube is rolled.

16. Use a tree diagram to find the sample space.

17. What is the probability that tails will appear on the penny and a number greater than 2 will appear on the cube?

18. A soccer team has 4 styles of jerseys and 2 styles of shorts. How many different combinations of uniforms can the team wear?

A bag contains 5 red marbles, 7 black marbles, and 3 blue marbles.

19. One marble is drawn and replaced. Another marble is drawn. What is the probability that the first marble is red and the second marble is blue?

20. Suppose one marble is drawn and not replaced. Then a second marble is drawn. What is the probability that both marbles are black?

21. Suppose that, on average, Janet makes 6 out of 10 free throws. Describe how you can use random numbers to simulate Janet's free-throw attempts.

22. In one game, Janet attempts 8 free throws. How can you use simulation to find the experimental probability that Janet will make 3 free throws in a row in this game?

Math Lab

23. You measure the width of a classroom as 24 feet 6 inches. How long would you draw this width on a scale drawing if you use the scale factor $\frac{1\text{ cm}}{2\text{ ft}}$? Record your answer to the nearest tenth centimeter.

24. A class finds that the experimental probability for rolling matching numbers on two number cubes is 0.21. How much greater is this value than the theoretical probability of rolling matching numbers on two number cubes?

25. A spreadsheet is used to generate random numbers from 1 to 365 to represent birthdays for a group of 23 people. Of 60 trials, 28 include a pair of matching numbers. Using this data, what is the experimental probability that in a group of 23 people, two will have the same birthday?

CHAPTER 7

WHY SHOULD I LEARN THIS?

A percent (%) is a ratio that compares a number to 100. If you own stock that increases 8% in value, how would you calculate the dollar amount of the increase?

PERCENT

LEARN HOW TO...

1. Write fractions and decimals as percents.
2. Write percents as fractions and decimals.
3. Estimate a percent of a number.
4. Solve problems using percent and percent change.
5. Calculate simple and compound interest for savings and loans.

You have used ratios to solve problems involving proportions, rates, and probability. In this chapter, you will study a ratio called percent. Percents are used to give information in many areas people deal with everyday—on TV, in shopping malls, and in magazines and newspapers. For example, in a newspaper, percents are used

- on the front page: Budget increase 15%

- on the sports page: 30% of 3-point attempts made

- on the business page: Market up 8.5%

- on the weather page: 30% chance of rain

- and in advertisements: 20%-off sale

In this chapter, you will see how fractions, decimals, and percents are related. You will also use estimating skills to find a percent of a number. This skill is important when you work with money.

You will also learn how to write and solve percent problems using proportions and equations. This will help you solve problems involving population increase and decrease, tax increase and decrease, commission, discount and sale price, and simple and compound interest.

LESSON 7.1 FRACTIONS, DECIMALS, AND PERCENTS

OBJECTIVES
- - - - - - - -
➤ Write fractions and decimals as percents.
➤ Write percents as fractions and decimals.

In Chapter 6, you used ratios to represent probabilities. For example, the probability that heads will appear when a coin is tossed is $\frac{1}{2}$. This probability can also be expressed as a decimal or a *percent*. **Percent** means *per 100*. So 50 percent means the ratio $\frac{50}{100}$. The symbol for percent is %.

> **Percent**
>
> A percent is a ratio that compares a number to 100.

If the denominator of a fraction is not 100, you can write it as a percent with an equivalent ratio. Multiply the numerator and denominator by a number that gives 100 for the denominator. For example,

$$\frac{1}{2} = \frac{1 \cdot 50}{2 \cdot 50}$$

$$= \frac{50}{100}$$

$$= 50\%$$

Notice that the numerator and denominator are multiplied by 50, since $2 \cdot 50 = 100$. When changing a fraction to a percent, you must make the denominator equal 100. You can write the probability of tossing heads on a coin in any of the following ways.

$$\frac{1}{2} \qquad 50 \text{ out of } 100$$

$$50 \text{ per } 100 \qquad 50\%$$

EXAMPLE 1 Writing a Fraction as a Percent

Raymond needs a legal document delivered tomorrow to a client in St. Louis. His office has used two delivery companies in the past.

Overnight Inc. has delivered 19 out of 25 letters the next day. Aero-Express has delivered 28 out of 32 letters the next day.

Which delivery company should Raymond choose if he wants to use the one with the highest percent of next-day deliveries?

Write a fraction for each next-day delivery company. Write each fraction as a percent.

a. For Overnight Inc., write $\frac{19}{25}$ as a percent.

$$\frac{19}{25} = \frac{19 \cdot 4}{25 \cdot 4} = \frac{76}{100} = 76\%$$

b. For Aero-Express, write $\frac{28}{32}$ as a percent.

Since the denominator of $\frac{28}{32}$ is not a factor of 100, use your calculator to divide.

$$28 \boxed{\div} \ 32 \boxed{=} \ 0.875$$

Convert 0.875 to a percent.

$$0.875 = \frac{0.875 \cdot 100}{1 \cdot 100} = \frac{87.5}{100} = 87.5\%$$

Since 87.5% > 76%, Raymond should use Aero-Express.

You can see from Example 1, that to write 0.875 as a percent, move the decimal point two places to the right and add the % symbol.

$$0.875 = 87.5\%$$

You can also write a percent as a decimal. Move the decimal point two places to the left and drop the % symbol.

$$76\% = 0.76$$

EXAMPLE 2 Rewriting Decimals and Percents

Write each decimal as a percent.   **a.** 0.06   **b.** 1.2

Write each percent as a decimal.   **c.** 17%   **d.** 0.8%

SOLUTION

a. $0.06 = 006. \% = 6\%$

b. $1.2 \ = 120. \% = 120\%$

c. $17\% = \ .17 \ = 0.17$

d. $0.8\% = \ .008 \ = 0.008$

Write each decimal as a percent.   **a.** 0.033   **b.** 2.15

Write each percent as a decimal.   **c.** 110%   **d.** $11\frac{1}{2}\%$

Critical Thinking   When you write the following percents as decimals, what is the place value of the underlined digit?

a. 2<u>5</u>0%   **b.** 2<u>5</u>%   **c.** 2.<u>5</u>%   **d.** 0.2<u>5</u>%

EXAMPLE 3 Percent as a Fraction of the Total

An achievement test has multiple-choice questions. If you answer 62 questions correctly and 18 incorrectly, what percent of the questions did you get correct?

SOLUTION

Find the fraction of correct answers. Convert to percent.

$$\frac{\text{Correct answers} \rightarrow}{\text{Total questions} \rightarrow} \frac{62}{62 + 18} = \frac{62}{80} = 0.775 \text{ or } 77.5\%$$

You answered 77.5% of the questions correctly.

ONGOING ASSESSMENT

In Example 3, what percent of the questions did you answer incorrectly? Explain the sum of the two percents.

ACTIVITY   **Percent-to-Fraction Algorithms**

1 Use the algorithm below to write 45% as a fraction in simplest form.

• Write the percent as a ratio with the denominator 100.

• Reduce the ratio to simplest form.

2 Use the algorithm to write the following as fractions in simplest form.

a. 60%   **b.** 150%   **c.** 2.5%

Critical Thinking   Write an algorithm for converting 0.165 to a fraction in simplest form.

CULTURAL CONNECTION

A percent is the ratio of a number to 100. The number 100 is convenient for the denominator because we use the base-ten or decimal number system. The decimal system probably originated from people counting with their fingers.

The ancient Mayans of Central America counted with their fingers and toes. They developed a very sophisticated number system based on 20 (a *vigesimal* system). The Mayans used the value of zero at a time when most of the world's civilizations had no

concept of zero. Mayan numbers are written in hieroglyphs. They use only three symbols: a dot—worth 1 unit, a bar—worth 5 units, and the zero—symbolized by a shell.

In the decimal system, there are 10 digits (0–9). In the vigesimal system, there are 20 digits (0–19). In the vigesimal system, numbers in higher place values increase by multiples of 20 instead of 10. Compare the two ways of representing the numbers 43 and 1538.

In the decimal system:

$$43 = 10 \cdot 4 + 3 = 40 + 3$$

$$1538 = (10 \cdot 10 \cdot 10)1 + (10 \cdot 10)5 + 10 \cdot 3 + 8$$
$$= 1000 + 500 + 30 + 8$$

In Mayan symbols, the digits are written vertically:

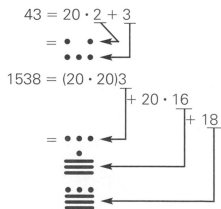

Use multiples of 10 and 20 to represent the following numbers in the decimal and vigesimal systems. Write each number using Mayan symbols.

a. 67   **b.** 573   **c.** 2095   **d.** 12,419

LESSON ASSESSMENT

Think and Discuss

1 What is a *percent*?

2 How do you write a fraction as a percent?

3 How do you write a decimal as a percent?

4 How do you write a percent as a decimal?

5 *Cent* means 100, and *mil* means 1000. What is the meaning of *permil*? Explain how to write $\frac{1}{2}$ as a *permil*.

Practice and Apply

Write each fraction as a percent.

6. $\frac{1}{5}$ **7.** $\frac{7}{20}$ **8.** $\frac{13}{10}$

Write each fraction as a percent rounded to the nearest tenth of a percent.

9. $\frac{5}{6}$ **10.** $\frac{7}{12}$ **11.** $\frac{7}{15}$

12. $\frac{9}{6}$ **13.** $\frac{21}{24}$ **14.** $1\frac{2}{3}$

Write each percent as a fraction in simplest form.

15. 16%   **16.** 75%   **17.** 60%

18. 125%   **19.** $16\frac{2}{3}$%   **20.** 550%

21. 0.5%   **22.** 15%   **23.** 100%

24. An opinion poll shows that 3 out of every 5 people prefer to shop downtown. What percent of the people polled prefer to shop downtown?

25. In the Nimitz High School band, 8 of the 12 percussionists play drums. What percent of the percussionists play drums?

26. A weather forecaster predicts a 40% chance of rain. Write the chance of rain as a fraction.

27. The probability of tossing 5 on a number cube is $\frac{1}{6}$. Write this probability as a percent.

28. A manufacturing plant produces cordless phones. The quality control inspector rejects phones for defects at a rate

of 0.0012 rejects per phone manufactured. What percent of the plant's phones are rejected?

29. Of Tai's income, 28% is deducted for federal income tax. What fraction of her income is deducted?

30. A vitamin supplement contains 125% of the recommended daily allowance of vitamin C. Write this percent as a decimal.

A school auditorium has 240 seats. One evening, 180 adults and 60 children attended a school play.

31. What percent of the seats were filled with adults?

32. What percent of the seats were filled with children?

Historically, 45% of graduating seniors from East High School have entered college and 3% have entered military service.

33. Predict the fraction of this year's graduating class that will enter college.

34. Predict the fraction that will not enter college or the military.

Marcie and Dreanna are making new dresses for the dolls at Children's Hospital. The hospital has 28 dolls.

35. If Marcie makes 16 dresses and Dreanna makes 18 dresses, what percent of the dolls will have new dresses?

36. What does it mean when a percent is greater than one hundred?

Mixed Review

Solve each equation.

37. $-6s + 15 = 27$ **38.** $8r - 5 = 9 - 6r$

Solve and graph each inequality on a number line.

39. $35 \leq 4m + 11$ **40.** $18 - 2n > 26$

Tell which fraction is larger.

41. A. $\dfrac{3}{10}$ B. $\dfrac{2}{5}$ C. $\dfrac{7}{20}$ D. $\dfrac{1}{4}$

42. A. $\dfrac{11}{30}$ B. $\dfrac{1}{3}$ C. $\dfrac{4}{15}$ D. $\dfrac{3}{10}$

43. A. $\dfrac{3}{7}$ B. $\dfrac{5}{12}$ C. $\dfrac{5}{9}$ D. $\dfrac{3}{10}$

LESSON 7.2 FINDING A PERCENT OF A NUMBER

OBJECTIVES
➤ **Find the percent of a number.**
➤ **Use percents to Interpret circle graphs.**

Brent works for the U.S. Park Service during the summer. He will earn $650 per month. His employer deducts 15% from his paycheck for income tax. How much will be deducted each month from Brent's paycheck?

To find the amount deducted, Brent must find a percent of a number. He can write 15% as the ratio of 15 to 100. Then he can write a proportion by equating this ratio to a fraction written as *part* of a *whole*.

$$15\% = \frac{15}{100} = \frac{\text{Part}}{\text{Whole}}$$

The amount deducted is a part of his whole earnings. Thus, the part is unknown while the whole is given. Let x represent the unknown part.

$$\frac{15}{100} = \frac{\text{Part}}{\text{Whole}}$$

$$\frac{15}{100} = \frac{x}{650}$$

$$100x = 15 \cdot 650$$

$$100x = 9750$$

$$x = 97.50$$

Brent will have $97.50 deducted each month for income tax.

ACTIVITY A Percent Equation

Start with the proportion for Brent's income tax deduction.

$$\frac{15}{100} = \frac{\text{Part}}{\text{Whole}}$$

1 Write the left side of the equation as a decimal. When you write a percent as a decimal, the result is called a **decimal percent.**

2 Treat the words *part* and *whole* as variables. Multiply both sides of the equation by the whole. Simplify the right side of the equation.

3 Substitute x for the part and 650 for the whole. Solve for x.

4 Did you get the same result using the proportions?

5 Write a multiplication equation you can use to solve a percent problem.

In the Activity, you derived the following multiplication equation.

$$\text{decimal percent} \cdot \text{whole} = \text{part}$$

EXAMPLE 1 Using Proportions and Equations

What is 12% of 250?

SOLUTION

The percent and whole are given. You need to find the part. Let x equal the unknown part.

Method 1	**Method 2**
Use a proportion.	Use the multiplication equation.
$\dfrac{12}{100} = \dfrac{\text{part}}{\text{whole}}$	$\text{decimal percent} \cdot \text{whole} = \text{part}$
$\dfrac{12}{100} = \dfrac{x}{250}$	$0.12 \cdot 250 = x$
$100x = 3000$	$(0.12)(250) = x$
$x = 30$	$x = 30$

12% of 250 is 30.

EXAMPLE 2 Percents Greater than 100

125% of 60 is what number?

SOLUTION

Use a proportion. Let x be the unknown part.

$$\frac{125}{100} = \frac{\text{Part}}{\text{Whole}}$$

$$\frac{125}{100} = \frac{x}{60}$$

$$100x = 7500$$

$$x = 75$$

125% of 60 is 75.

EXAMPLE 3 Finding the Percent of a Number

Specialty Metal Works makes brazing solder that contains 48% zinc and 52% other metal. How many pounds of zinc are needed for a 500-pound batch of solder?

SOLUTION

Use the four-step problem-solving strategy.

Step 1 Understand the Problem

You are given the percent (48% zinc) and the whole (500 pounds of solder). You need to find the part (pounds of zinc).

Step 2 Develop a Plan

Use a proportion or the multiplication equation.

Step 3 Carry Out the Plan

Let x represent the unknown number of pounds of zinc. Substitute the known values into the multiplication equation.

$$\text{decimal percent} \cdot \text{whole} = \text{part}$$
$$0.48 \cdot 500 = x$$
$$240 = x$$

The batch of solder needs 240 pounds of zinc.

Step 4 Check the Results

Repeat Step 3 using a proportion. Did you get the same result?

Critical Thinking   How many pounds of other metal are needed?

A **circle graph,** sometimes called a **pie chart,** compares percents. In a circle graph, the circle represents the whole, or total amount. The sections of the circle represent the parts.

The sections, or *pieces of the pie,* are drawn in proportion to the size of the parts they represent. A part that is 25% of the whole is shown as a section that is 25% of the circle.

EXAMPLE 4 Using a Circle Graph

Use the circle graph to determine how many students prefer each snack.

Favorite Snacks
(120 students surveyed)

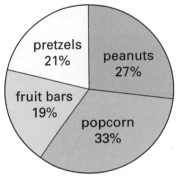

SOLUTION

A total of 120 students were surveyed. Use the multiplication equation to find the number of students who prefer each snack.

decimal percent · whole = part

Pretzels: 21% of 120 $= 0.21 \cdot 120 = 25.2 \approx 25$ students

Peanuts: 27% of 120 $= 0.27 \cdot 120 = 32.4 \approx 32$ students

Popcorn: 33% of 120 $= 0.33 \cdot 120 = 39.6 \approx 40$ students

Fruit bars: 19% of 120 $= 0.19 \cdot 120 = 22.8 \approx 23$ students

You can check your results by adding the numbers of students preferring each snack. The total should be 120.

ONGOING ASSESSMENT

In Example 4, what percent of the students surveyed prefer fruit bars or popcorn? How many students prefer fruit bars or popcorn?

LESSON ASSESSMENT

1 How can you find a percent of a number using a proportion?

2 How can you find a percent of a number using a multiplication equation?

3 Suppose you are finding 150% of a number.

$$150\% \cdot \text{whole} = \text{part}$$

Which is greater, the whole or the part? Explain.

4 What is the total percent in a circle graph? What would the graph look like if the total percent was less than this?

Practice and Apply

Use a proportion or a multiplication equation to find the following.

5. Find 30% of 200.

6. 25% of 120 is what number?

7. What is 12.5% of 8.4?

8. What number is 7.5% of 96?

9. Find 240% of 25.

10. What is $83\frac{1}{3}\%$ of $660?

11. What is 3% of 215?

12. Find 19.2% of 2345.

13. What number is 56% of 106?

14. 115% of 88 is what number?

15. The enrollment at Booker T. Washington High School is 3800. If 35% of the students are freshmen, how many students are in the freshman class?

16. Suppose the sales tax is 8% in your city. What is the total tax on your purchase if you buy a shirt for $25 and a jacket for $85?

17. Tammy receives a 4.5% commission on each car she sells. How much commission does Tammy receive on a car she sells for $12,500?

18. Mario cuts a granite slab for a custom cabinet top. It will take Mario's saw 40 minutes to cut through the slab with a used blade. If he replaces the blade with a new one, it will take 65% of the time. How long will it take Mario to cut the slab using the new blade?

Winton Jeweler's has 250 pieces of jewelry in inventory. The inventory percents by jewelry types are shown in the table.

Winton Jeweler's Inventory By Percent	
Earrings (pairs)	28%
Rings	26%
Bracelets	20%
Watches	12%
Pins	8%
Necklaces	6%

19. How many rings are in the inventory?

20. How many watches are in the inventory?

Grades Earned on Final Test

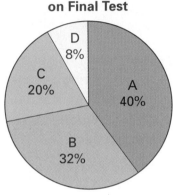

This circle graph shows the grades earned by 140 students on a final test.

21. How many students earned an A?

22. How many more students earned a B than earned a C?

In January, The Shirt Shop sold 240 shirts and in February, they sold 320. These circle graphs show the percent of shirts sold by size.

Shirt Shop Sales

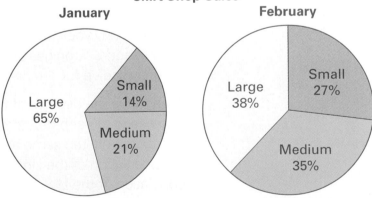

23. How many large shirts were sold in January?

24. How many medium shirts were sold in February?

25. How many more small shirts were sold in February than in January?

Find each quotient to the nearest thousandth.

26. $3.45 \div 12$ **27.** $1.93 \div 8.7$ **28.** $367 \div 26$

Evaluate each expression when $s = -1\frac{1}{2}$, $t = 3\frac{1}{3}$, and $u = -5\frac{1}{4}$.

29. $s + t - u$ **30.** $(s)(t)(u)$ **31.** $(t + u) \div s$

Eight tickets numbered from 1 to 8 are placed in a box. One ticket is removed and then replaced. A second ticket is removed. What is the probability that

32. the first number is 3 and the second number is 4?

33. the first number is even and the second number is less than 5?

34. both numbers are 8?

Cumulative Problem Solving

Bao and his brother Luoc are starting a lawn-care business. Bao buys a lawn mower for $260. Luoc buys a string trimmer for $105 and an edger for $135. After they pay for gas and oil, they will divide the money they earn for the first week in proportion to the amount each spent for equipment.

35. What fraction of the equipment costs did Bao pay? What fraction did Luoc pay?

36. What percent of their earnings will Bao receive? What percent will Luoc receive?

37. The first week, they cut 14 lawns and are paid $280. They spend $25 on gas and oil. How much should each brother receive for the first week?

Jeanette is the director of the Crestview Hospital blood bank. She needs to keep the percent of each blood type in the bank approximately the same as the percent of that blood type in the population of the United States. Approximately 6% of the population of the U.S. has A-negative blood. The Crestview Hospital blood bank has 210 pints of blood, 18 of which are type A-negative.

38. What percent of the hospital's blood supply is A-negative?

39. Should Jeanette order more pints of A-negative blood? Explain your answer.

Randall is the quality control manager at a plant that manufactures halogen light bulbs. On a typical 8-hour shift, an assembly machine can produce 1300 light bulbs. If the machine is operating correctly, it will produce only 0.5% of the bulbs with defects. If the percent of defects goes above 0.5%, Randall takes the machine off-line for maintenance and repair.

40. The plant extends a shift to 10 hours to fill a rush order. During the 10-hour shift, a machine produces 1650 light bulbs, 5 of which are rejected for defects. Should Randall take this machine off-line? Explain your reasoning.

41. What percent of the light bulbs produced by the machine during the 10-hour shift are accepted?

Margarita is a sales representative for a wholesale supplier of furniture. She is paid a commission, or a percent of the sales price of the furniture she sells. She earns a 3% commission on the first $100,000 in sales, a 3.5% commission on the next $150,000, and a 4% commission on all sales over $250,000. This year, Margarita has sold $685,000 worth of furniture.

42. What is the amount of sales for which Margarita will earn a 3% commission? What is the amount for which she will earn 3.5%? What is the amount for which she will earn 4%?

43. Calculate the total commission Margarita will be paid this year.

To stay alive a bat must eat an amount approximately equal to 80% of its body weight every night.

44. If a bat weighs 7.5 grams, estimate the number of grams of food it eats every night.

45. Suppose mosquitoes in the bat's diet average 0.002 grams each. If the bat ate only mosquitoes, about how many must it eat every night?

LESSON 7.3 ESTIMATING PERCENTS

OBJECTIVES
- ➡ Use estimation when solving percent problems.

Celeste and three of her friends are eating at a restaurant. The bill for their meal is $48.60. Celeste wants to leave the server a tip of 15%. How much should Celeste leave for the tip?

EXAMPLE 1 Estimating a Tip

Use mental math to estimate 15% of $48.60.

SOLUTION

Use the Distributive Property.

$$15\% \text{ of } \$48.60 = (10\% + 5\%)(\$48.60)$$
$$= 10\%(\$48.60) + 5\%(\$48.60)$$

To find 10%, multiply by 0.1, or move the decimal point one place to the left.	To find 5%, calculate half of 10%.
$10\%(\$48.60) = \$4.86$	$5\%(\$48.60) \approx \frac{1}{2}(\$4.90)$
$\approx \$4.90$	$\approx \$2.45$

Thus, 15% of $48.60 ≈ $4.90 + $2.45 ≈ $7.35.

Celeste should leave a tip of about $7.35.

You can use mental math to estimate multiples of 10% and 1%. Remember, for 10% move the decimal one place to the left and for 1% move the decimal two places to the left.

ACTIVITY 1   Estimating with 1% or 10%

1 Use the following plans and algorithms to find the estimates.

a. Estimate 3.2% of 1286.

Plan: Round 3.2% to 3%. Use 3% = 3 · 1%.

Algorithm:

```
Find 1%     →   Round to the   →   Multiply
of 1286         nearest ten         by 3
```

b. Estimate 68% of 327.

Plan: Round 68% to 70%. Use 70% = 7 · 10%.

Algorithm:

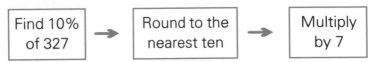

2 | Write a plan and an algorithm for estimating 1.9% of 432. Find the estimate.

Estimate the following percents using the methods in Example 1 and Activity 1.

a. 5.8% of 763   **b.** 42% of 42   **c.** 151% of 39

ACTIVITY 2   **Estimating Percents with Fraction Equivalents**

1 | Find 25% of 60.

2 | Write 25% as a fraction in simplest form. Multiply this fraction by 60. Compare this result to the value you found in Step 1.

3 | Repeat Steps 1 and 2 for 50% and 75%.

4 | Repeat Steps 1 and 2 for $33\frac{1}{3}$% and $66\frac{2}{3}$%.

5 | How can you use a fraction to find a percent of a number?

The table shows the percents and equivalent fractions used in Activity 2. You can use the fractions to estimate percents with compatible numbers.

$$25\% = 0.25 = \tfrac{1}{4}$$
$$33\tfrac{1}{3}\% = 0.\overline{3} = \tfrac{1}{3}$$
$$50\% = 0.5 = \tfrac{1}{2}$$
$$66\tfrac{2}{3}\% = 0.\overline{6} = \tfrac{2}{3}$$
$$75\% = 0.75 = \tfrac{3}{4}$$
$$100\% = 1$$

EXAMPLE 2 Using Estimation

Midview High School reserves 35% of its parking so that each senior has a space. There are 626 parking spaces. Estimate the number of spaces reserved for seniors.

SOLUTION

Use $33\frac{1}{3}\% = \frac{1}{3}$ as an estimate for 35%. Use 630 as an estimate of 626 (630 and 3 are compatible numbers since 630 is divisible by 3).

$$35\% \text{ of } 626 \approx 33\tfrac{1}{3}\% \text{ of } 630$$
$$\approx \tfrac{1}{3}(630)$$
$$\approx 210$$

About 210 spaces are reserved for seniors.

ONGOING ASSESSMENT

Estimate the following percents using equivalent fractions and compatible numbers.

a. 48% of 64.39   **b.** 77% of 164   **c.** 67.1% of 39.6

Critical Thinking What is the relationship between 25% and 12.5%? Use this relationship to find the fraction equivalent of 12.5%. What is 12.5% of 168?

LESSON ASSESSMENT

Think and Discuss

1 How might each of the following estimate percents in their jobs?

    a. magazine publisher

    b. building contractor

    c. computer programmer

2 Explain how to use mental math to estimate 15% of a number.

3 Explain how to use a multiple of 10% to estimate 62% of a number.

4 Explain how to use an equivalent fraction to estimate $66\frac{2}{3}\%$ of a number.

Estimate the amount of a 15% tip for the following restaurant bills.

5.

GUEST CHECK			
Server Bill	Table # 6	Guests 2	Date 6/1	922160
1	12" cheese pizza	9.99
2	tossed salad	1.95
3	tossed salad	1.95
4	iced tea	.77
5	soft drink	.95
6		
7		
8		
9		
10		
11		
12		
13		
14		
15		
16		
17		
18		
	Total	$15.61

6.

GUEST CHECK			
Server Asha	Table # 8	Guests 3	Date 6/1	922161
1	turkey sandwich	4.95
2	tossed salad	1.95
3	milk	.80
4	hamburger	5.95
5	french fries	1.95
6	fruit juice	.95
7	chicken salad	5.95
8	bagel	1.25
9	soft drink	.95
10		
11		
12		
13		
14		
15		
16		
17		
18		
	Total	$24.70

7.

GUEST CHECK			
Server Asha	Table # 14	Guests 4	Date 6/1	922163
1	ham sandwich	4.95
2	applesauce	1.25
3	milk	.80
4	tofu burger	4.95
5	vegetable soup	2.29
6	cole slaw	1.25
7	fruit juice	.95
8	tuna sandwich	4.95
9	onion rings	1.95
10	fruit juice	.95
11	turkey sandwich	4.95
12	vegetable soup	2.29
13	french fries	1.95
14	milk	.80
15	ice cream	1.95
16	sherbet	1.95
17	apple pie	2.25
18	ice cream	1.95
	Total	$42.38

In Exercises 8–11, use multiples of 1% and 10% to find each estimate.

8. Estimate 18% of 278.

9. Estimate 4.1% of 612.

10. Estimate 9.2% of 569.

11. Estimate 72% of 823.

In Exercises 12–17, use an equivalent fraction to find each estimate.

12. Estimate 27% of 354.

13. Estimate 97% of 216.

14. Estimate 68% of 958.

15. Estimate 53% of 2436.

16. Estimate 32% of 3450.

17. Estimate 74.5% of 2949.

In Exercises 18–21, write the equivalent percent for each fraction. Use these fractions to find each estimate in Exercises 22–25.

18. $\dfrac{1}{8} = \dfrac{1}{2} \cdot \dfrac{1}{4} = \dfrac{1}{2} \cdot 25\% = \underline{\ ?\ }\%$

19. $\dfrac{3}{8} = \underline{\ ?\ }\%$

20. $\dfrac{5}{8} = \underline{\ ?\ }\%$

21. $\dfrac{7}{8} = \underline{\ ?\ }\%$

22. Estimate 38% of 88.

23. Estimate 85% of 108.

24. Estimate 12% of 325.

25. Estimate 61% of 865.

26. In a recent survey of 1458 Internet subscribers, 62% used the service at least twice a week. About how many of the subscribers use the Internet service twice a week?

27. The Lin family income is $2650 per month. They budget 26% of their income for their mortgage payment. About how much money does the Lin family budget for their mortgage payment each month?

28. In one week, 88% of the 3264 people who took the state driver's license exam passed. About how many people passed the exam?

29. Rashunda's monthly earnings are $858.76. Her employer deducts 7.65% for Social Security. Estimate the amount of Rashunda's earnings that is deducted for Social Security.

30. A regional chain of grocery stores has 116 stores in a two-state region. About 74% of the stores have delicatessens. Estimate the number of stores in the region that have delicatessens.

31. A transportation department report shows that 3.9% of a city's paved roads need repair. If a city has 1026 miles of paved roads, estimate the number of miles of roads that need repair.

32. The winner of a recent election for mayor received 65% of the votes. If 6113 people voted in the election, estimate the number of votes received by the winner.

33. Three people order a meal costing a total of $32.38. How much should each person contribute toward the tip for the server if the tip is 15% of the cost?

Mixed Review

Solve each equation.

34. $2b - 3 = 9$

35. $7r - 8 = 2r + 12$

36. $3.6 = 2.4 + 0.2c$

37. $\frac{1}{5}(z - 3) = -4$

38. $\frac{d}{4.5} + 3.3 = 5.7$

39. $12\left(n + \frac{2}{3}\right) = -4$

LESSON 7.4 SOLVING PERCENT EQUATIONS

OBJECTIVES
- - - - - - - - - - - - - -
➤ Solve problems involving percent.

Danielle is a real estate agent. She earns a 3% commission on each house she sells. What is the total value of the houses Danielle must sell if she wants to earn $30,000 in commissions?

You can calculate the total amount of sales using a proportion or a multiplication equation.

EXAMPLE 1 Using a Proportion

3% of what dollar amount is $30,000?

SOLUTION

Danielle's $30,000 commission is part of the total sales. Let x represent the unknown total sales. Use a proportion.

$$3\% = \frac{3}{100} = \frac{\text{Part}}{\text{Whole}}$$

$$\frac{3}{100} = \frac{30,000}{x}$$

$$3x = 30,000 \cdot 100$$

$$3x = 3,000,000$$

$$x = 1,000,000$$

Danielle needs $1,000,000 in total sales to earn $30,000 in commissions.

ONGOING ASSESSMENT

a. Solve Example 1 using the following multiplication equation.

$$\text{decimal percent} \cdot \text{whole} = \text{part}$$

b. Use a proportion or multiplication equation to solve the following.

12 is 20% of what number?

c. Identify the part and the whole.

5% of x is y

d is 10% of c

Supply the missing reasons to find the following.

What percent of 25 is 4?

The part is 4 and the whole is 25. Let y be the unknown percent.

1.	decimal percent $\cdot$ whole = part		Given
2.	y $\cdot$ 25 = 4		_?_
3.	$25y = 4$		_?_
4.	$y = \dfrac{4}{25}$		_?_
5.	$y = 0.16$		_?_
6.	$y = 16\%$		_?_

ONGOING ASSESSMENT

a. Solve the problem in the Activity using a proportion. Why is the result equivalent?

b. Use a proportion or multiplication equation to solve the following.

30 is what percent of 20?

EXAMPLE 2 Finding Percent

On her last test, Marcia got the answers to 21 out of 28 questions correct. What percent of the questions did Marcia answer correctly?

SOLUTION

Use the multiplication equation. Let y represent the unknown percent of questions answered correctly. The number of correct answers is the part and the total number of questions is the whole.

$$\text{decimal percent} \cdot \text{whole} = \text{part}$$
$$y \cdot 28 = 21$$
$$y = \frac{21}{28}$$
$$y = 0.75 \text{ or } 75\%$$

Marcia answered 75% of the questions correctly.

You can now solve equations for the percent, part, or whole. For each of the following, write a multiplication equation or proportion and solve.

a. What is 25% of 90?

b. 45 is what percent of 135?

c. 45 is 24% of what number?

LESSON ASSESSMENT

Think and Discuss

For Exercises 1 and 2, use the following question.

15 is 50% of what number?

1 What is the *part*? What is the *whole*?

2 What mathematical symbol does the word *is* represent?

For Exercises 3 and 4, use the following question.

20 is what percent of 85?

3 Which number represents the *part*? Which number represents the *whole*?

4 What mathematical operation does the word *of* represent?

Practice and Apply

Solve Exercises 5–8 using a proportion.

5. 8 is what percent of 16?

6. What is 37.5% of 144?

7. 45% of what number is 48.6?

8. 9.6 is what percent of 67.2?

Solve Exercises 9–12 using a multiplication equation.

9. 12% of what number is 30?

10. What is 125% of 12.4?

11. 80 is what percent of 60?

12. 2.5% of what number is 75?

For Exercises 13–22, write an equation or proportion to model the problem and solve.

13. A city's sales tax rate is 8.5%. How much tax is added to the price of a coat that sells for $70?

14. Alisha answered 30 out of 40 problems correctly on her last test. What percent of the problems did Alisha answer correctly?

15. Rolondo left a 15% tip for the server at a restaurant. If he left $4.80, what was the cost of the meal?

16. Bill's monthly budget is $2500. He pays $600 for rent. What percent of his monthly budget does Bill pay for rent?

17. A fund-raising chart for a school band is shown below. The band has raised $4250. How much is the goal for the fund drive?

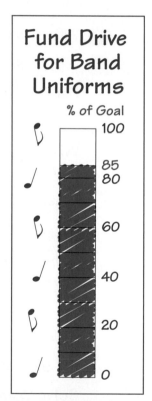

Fund Drive for Band Uniforms

% of Goal

100
85
80
60
40
20
0

18. A school store earns a commission of $112.50. If the store's rate of commission is $4\frac{1}{2}$%, what was the dollar amount of the store's sales? Fill in the blanks with the dollar amounts:

_____ is $4\frac{1}{2}$% of _____

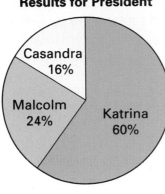

Student Council Election Results for President

Casandra 16%

Malcolm 24%

Katrina 60%

19. The results of the student council election are shown in the circle graph at left. If Katrina received 480 votes, how many students voted in the election?

20. In a science experiment, 225 seedlings were planted. After ten days, 25 seedlings died. What percent of the seedlings lived?

21. Paula needs to cut a metal pipe 120 centimeters long for a gas furnace. The pipe will fit the furnace if it is 0.3% shorter or longer than 120 centimeters. What are the maximum and minimum lengths Paula can cut the pipe?

22. In February it snowed 12 out of 28 days. On what percent of the days in February did it snow?

Mixed Review

Evaluate each of the following when $a = -\frac{2}{3}$, $b = 1\frac{1}{2}$, and $c = 2\frac{5}{6}$.

23. $a + b - c$ **24.** $ab - bc$ **25.** $(b + c)a$

Solve each equation.

26. $7m + 12.4 = 42.5$ **27.** $\frac{2}{3}s = 11 - \frac{1}{4}s$

28. Solve and graph the inequality $-3.2c - 1.6 \leq 8$ on a number line.

Use the four-step problem-solving plan to solve Exercises 29 and 30.

29. Colt has saved $1000 to repair or replace his 16-foot stock trailer. A new trailer costs $3200. The dealer will give Colt a $1500 trade-in allowance for his old trailer. The repairs needed for the old trailer and the costs are shown below.

New flooring	$127
Repair frame and hitch	$425
Replace two tires	$280

Should Colt buy a new trailer or repair the old one?

30. Odina's flight to Seattle departs at 3:15 P.M. It is a one-hour drive from her office to the airport. She plans to stop for 45 minutes to eat lunch on the way. She needs to arrive at the airport one hour before the departure time. What time should Odina leave her office for the airport?

Werner buys salvaged sheet metal to replace the roof of a hay barn. He needs 68 sheets. He wants to buy approximately 20% more than he needs to allow for damaged sheets that cannot be used.

31. Estimate the number of extra sheets Werner should buy to allow for damaged sheets.

32. What is the total number of sheets he should buy?

33. During installation, Werner finds that 75% of the sheets are usable. How many sheets are usable? Does Werner have enough usable sheet metal to replace the barn roof?

Cheri is presenting a proposal for a research project to the directors of the Marine Wildlife Institute. The total budget for the proposed project is $47,350. During her presentation, Cheri is asked, "What are the approximate equipment cost, personnel cost for researchers, and administrative cost?"

34. Cheri estimates that the equipment cost is 35% of the budget. How should she answer this part of the question?

35. Cheri estimates that the personnel cost for researchers is 60% of the budget. How should she answer this part of the question?

36. Cheri estimates that the administrative cost is 5% of the budget. How should she answer this part of the question?

A consumer research group tests claims made by manufacturers of business machines. One company claims that its copier will jam only 0.2 times per 1000 copies. The research group collects data from four offices that use this brand of copier. In one month, there were a total of 382,926 copies made and 129 paper jams recorded.

37. According to the manufacturer's claim, what percent of the copies will jam?

38. According to the data collected by the research group, what percent of the copies made by the four offices jammed?

39. Is the manufacturer's claim accurate for the copiers at these four offices? Explain.

Wilson is running against the incumbent for a seat on the Jacksburg city council. The newspaper reports that in the last city election, only 4.3% of the 123,500 eligible voters in Jacksburg voted. In the last election, the city council incumbent was re-elected by a margin of 64% to 36%.

40. Estimate the number of people who voted in the last election in Jacksburg.

41. About how many people voted for the incumbent in the last election? About how many voted for the challenger?

42. Suppose 5% of the eligible voters in Jacksburg vote in this election. What is the least number of votes Wilson can receive and still win the election?

Bakari is working part time to buy a car. He wants to earn enough to make a $270 monthly car payment. After federal, state, Social Security, and Medicare taxes are withheld, his net pay will be 78% of his gross pay.

43. What gross pay must Bakari earn per month to make his car payment?

44. Suppose Bakari wants to make his car payment and save $50 per month for college. What gross pay must he earn?

The instructions for a carpet cleaner tell you to mix one part shampoo concentrate with 11 parts water. The cleaner's reservoir holds 64 fluid ounces of shampoo-water mixture.

45. If you prepare a mixture with 1 fluid ounce of concentrate and 11 fluid ounces of water, what is the total number of fluid ounces in the mixture?

46. What percent of the mixture is concentrate?

47. How many fluid ounces of concentrate are needed to make a full reservoir of the cleaning mixture?

Charice is an estimator for a heating and air conditioning contractor. The bid price she submits for installing a system includes the cost of parts plus overhead. The overhead is 80% of the parts cost. She is working on a bid where the cost of the parts is $32,500.

48. What amount should Charice use as the overhead cost?

49. What is the total bid price Charice should submit?

LESSON 7.5 PERCENT CHANGE

OBJECTIVES
- ➤ Find percent increase and percent decrease.
- ➤ Use the complement of a percent to solve problems.

In the last lesson, you calculated percents using a proportion. For example, $x\%$ is

$$\frac{x}{100} = \frac{\text{Part}}{\text{Whole}}$$

When a quantity *changes* in value, you can also use a proportion to calculate the **percent change** in the quantity. The part is the amount of change and the whole is the original amount. If $y\%$ is a percent change, then

$$\frac{y}{100} = \frac{\text{Amount of change}}{\text{Original amount}}$$

ACTIVITY 1   Percent Increase and Decrease

1 Start with 10 coins. Remove 2 coins.

  a. What fraction of the coins did you remove? What is the percent equivalent to this fraction?

  b. Substitute the amount of change and original amount into a proportion and solve for the percent change. Compare the result to the percent calculated in **a.** Is this a percent increase or decrease?

2 Now start with 6 coins. Add 2 coins.

  a. What fraction of the original number of coins did you add? What is the percent equivalent to this fraction?

  b. Substitute the amount of change and original amount into a proportion and solve for the percent change. Compare the result to the percent calculated in **a.** Is this a percent increase or decrease?

Critical Thinking   If you start with 10 coins and remove 2, the change is a 20% decrease. If you then remove 2 more coins, is the change another 20% decrease?

You can also use a multiplication equation to calculate a percent change.

$$\text{decimal percent change} \cdot \text{original amount} = \text{amount of change}$$

EXAMPLE 1 Percent Increase

The manager of a tire store buys tires at wholesale prices and sells them at retail prices. To set a retail price, the manager adds an increase, or *mark up,* to the wholesale price. To stay competitive, the manager wants to keep this increase to less than 20%.

The wholesale price of a set of Captain Tires is $250. The manufacturer's suggested retail price (MSRP) is $310. Is the MSRP less than or greater than a 20% increase over wholesale?

SOLUTION

The amount of change is the difference between the retail and wholesale prices.

$$\text{amount of change} = \$310 - \$250 = \$60$$

Use the multiplication equation. Let r represent the unknown percent change.

$$\text{decimal percent change} \cdot \text{original amount} = \text{amount of change}$$

$$r \cdot 250 = 60$$
$$250r = 60$$
$$r = \frac{60}{250}$$
$$r = 0.24 \text{ or } 24\%$$

The MSRP is greater than a 20% increase over the wholesale price.

ONGOING ASSESSMENT

Metro Community College raises its tuition from $1320 per year to $1425 per year. What percent increase is the change in tuition?

Retail stores often reduce the regular prices of merchandise. A reduction in price is called a *discount.*

EXAMPLE 2 Percent Decrease

What is the sale price for the sunglasses advertised?

SOLUTION

Use the proportion.

$$\frac{35}{100} = \frac{\text{Amount of change}}{\text{Original amount}} \to \frac{\text{Discount}}{\text{Original price}}$$

Let d represent the unknown discount.

$$\frac{35}{100} = \frac{d}{24.95}$$

$$100d = 35(24.95)$$

$$d = 35 \boxed{\times} 24.95 \boxed{\div} 100 \boxed{=} 8.7325$$

To find the sale price, subtract the discount from the original price.

original price − discount = sale price

$24.95 − $8.73 = $16.22

The sale price of the sunglasses is $16.22.

When the sum of two percents is 100%, the percents are called **complements**. For example, the price of the sunglasses in Example 2 was reduced 35%. The complement of 35% is 65%.

Original Price $24.95
Marked Down 35%

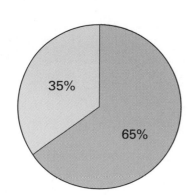

35%

65%

ACTIVITY 2 — The Complement of a Percent

SALE:
reduced 20%

Sale Price
$56.80

Medium wt.
Hiking boots
10D

When a price is reduced by a percent, you can find the reduced price by multiplying by the complement. Supply the reasons below to show why this works for the sunglasses.

1.	sale price = original price − discount	Given
2.	= 24.95 − (0.35)(24.95)	?
3.	= (24.95)(1 − 0.35)	?
4.	= (24.95)(0.65)	?
5.	= 16.2175 or $16.22	?

Critical Thinking   Suppose you are given the sale price and discount percent of a pair of hiking boots. Explain how to use the complement to find the original price of the boots.

USING THE FOUR-STEP PLAN

Number of Blouses	Original Retail Price
8	$12.99
5	$13.99
2	$15.99
7	$17.99
6	$19.99
3	$21.99

Jenelle is the manager of The Modern Woman clothing store in an outlet mall.

Jenelle wants to mark down the prices of 31 blouses for a sale. The original retail prices are shown in the table.

She wants to divide the blouses into two racks, and mark each rack with a single price.

Jenelle marks down every blouse at least 20%. But she will lose money if they are marked down more than 40%. Determine a single price Jenelle can put on each rack of blouses. Which blouses should go on each rack?

Step 1 Understand the Problem

What do you need to find? What conditions must a solution satisfy? Do you have enough information?

Step 2 Develop a Plan

Make a table. Use three columns to show the original retail, 20% discount, and 40% discount prices of the blouses.

There will be two racks: a low-price and a high-price rack. Divide the blouses in the table into two groups. Use the table to find a single price for each rack.

Step 3 Carry Out the Plan

You should find a range of prices that will work for each rack.

Let x and y be the prices for the racks. Write the solutions as compound inequalities.

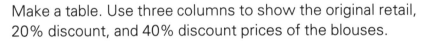

$$\underline{\ ?\ } < x \le \underline{\ ?\ } \qquad \text{and} \qquad \underline{\ ?\ } < y \le \underline{\ ?\ }$$

Step 4 Check the Results

Recommend a single price for each rack of blouses. Do the prices satisfy the conditions needed by Jenelle?

LESSON ASSESSMENT

Think and Discuss

1 Explain why a sales tax rate is an example of a percent increase.

2 What percent increase corresponds to doubling the price of an item? What percent corresponds to tripling the price?

3 Explain why a rate of discount is an example of a percent decrease.

4 The price of a share of stock fell from $20 to $10, or a decrease of 50%. The price then rose from $10 to $20, or an increase of 100%. Explain why the percents of change are different even though the amount of change is the same.

Practice and Apply

For Exercises 5–7, find the retail price when

5. the wholesale price is $25 and the markup rate is 20%.

6. the wholesale price is $84 and the markup rate is 12.5%.

7. the wholesale price is $36.90 and the markup rate is $33\frac{1}{3}$%.

For Exercises 8–10, find the sale price when

8. the original price is $25 and the discount rate is 20%.

9. the original price is $84 and the discount rate is 12.5%.

10. the original price is $36.90 and the discount rate is $33\frac{1}{3}$%.

For Exercises 11 and 12, find the original price when

11. the sale price is $90 and the discount rate is 20%.

12. the sale price is $161 and the discount rate is 15%.

Solve each problem. If necessary, round to the nearest tenth percent.

13. Last year, the total school enrollment was 840. This year the enrollment increased by 5%. How many students are enrolled this year?

14. Ms. Johnson's salary increased from $500 per week to $530 per week. What was the percent increase of Ms. Johnson's salary?

15. In January, Temon spent $80 on entertainment expenses. In February, he spent $70. What percent did Temon's entertainment expenses decrease?

16. The Lion's volleyball team won 4 fewer matches this year than it won last year. If this is a 20% decrease, how many matches did the Lions win last year?

17. An airline reduces its one-way fare from Los Angeles to New York from $525 to $450. What is the percent decrease in the airfare?

18. Over a 10-year period, the population of Weberville grew by 210 people to 2500 people. What is the percent increase of the population of Weberville?

19. Zachary bought a car for $12,000. The value of the car decreases by 15% the first year he owns it. How much is the car worth after Zachary owns the car one year?

20. Juanita's best discus throw at the final track meet of the season is 8.09 meters farther than her best throw at the first meet. This is an 18% improvement in distance. How long was Juanita's best throw at the first meet?

21. The price of a computer before the sales tax is added is $1650. The price after the sales tax is added is $1773.75. What is the sales tax rate?

22. The Andersons bought a house for $80,000. Five years later they sold the house for 6% more than they paid for it. By how much did the price of the Andersons' house increase?

In the 1968 Olympic Games in Mexico City, Bob Beamon set a world record with a long jump of 8.90 meters. The previous record was 8.35 meters.

23. What percent increase was Beamon's record?

24. Beamon's record was not beaten until Mike Powell jumped 8.95 meters in the 1991 Track and Field World Championships. What percent increase was Powell's record over Beamon's?

25. A transformer reduces voltage from a high-power electrical line to a house by 91%. The difference in voltage between the line and the house is 2180 volts. What is the voltage of the electrical line?

26. A vitamin supplement contains 125% of the recommended daily allowance (RDA) of vitamin C. If the RDA of vitamin C is 60 milligrams, how many milligrams of vitamin C does the supplement contain?

27. Before 6:00, the price for a movie at the Hi Lite Theater is $3.75. It costs $66\frac{2}{3}$% more to go to the same movie after 6:00. What is the price of the movie after 6:00?

28. In Laramie, the average high temperature in February is 48°F. In March, the average high temperature increases 14.6%. In April, the average high temperature increases 9.1% (from March). What is the total percent increase in high temperature in Laramie from February to April?

29. On May 1, a sporting goods store increases the price of swimsuits by 20%. On September 1, the store announces a 20%-off sale. How does the sale price of a swimsuit compare to the price before May 1?

Mixed Review

30. Evaluate $ab + c$ when $a = 2.2$, $b = 3.8$, and $c = -4.7$.

31. Evaluate $st - uv$ when $s = \frac{2}{3}$, $t = -\frac{1}{2}$, $u = -\frac{1}{4}$, and $v = \frac{1}{3}$.

Solve each equation.

32. $2.3m - 0.45 = 3$

33. $\frac{2d - 4}{5} = d + 1$

For Exercises 34–37, write a proportion and solve.
34. Six grapefruit cost $1.25. How much will 21 grapefruit cost?

35. Masika earns $11 for working 2 hours. How much will Masika earn if she works 9 hours?

A jar contains four pennies, three nickels, and five dimes.
36. You draw a coin at random. What is the probability that the coin is a penny or a dime?

37. You draw a coin, replace it and draw again. What is the probability that you draw a penny and then a nickel?

LESSON 7.6 SIMPLE AND COMPOUND INTEREST

OBJECTIVES
➤ Calculate simple interest.
➤ Calculate compound interest.

Sean is planning to attend college in 5 years. He has saved $1000 for his college expenses. Sean wants to put his savings in the bank to earn interest. The bank offers three savings plans.

First AmeriBank Savings Accounts
Choose one of our convenient plans:

Plan 1   Pays 6% simple interest annually.

Plan 2   Pays 6% interest compounded annually.

Plan 3   Pays 6% annual interest compounded quarterly.

To open your savings account, talk to any of our branch personnel.

Member FDIC   **1-800-555-1234**

Which plan should Sean choose if he wants his savings to earn the most interest over 5 years?

Simple Interest

The amount of money Sean starts with in the bank is called the **principal**. The money paid by the bank for the use of Sean's money is called **interest**. **Simple interest** is paid only on the original principal. Sean can calculate the amount of simple interest using a formula.

$$I = Prt$$

I is the interest earned, P is the principal, r is the percent interest paid per year (also called *interest rate*) written as a decimal percent, and t is the time in years.

ACTIVITY 1   Finding Simple Interest

1. What are P, r, and t if Sean uses Plan 1?

2. Calculate the simple interest Sean will earn with Plan 1.

3. The **balance** is the principal plus the interest earned. What is Sean's balance after 5 years if he chooses Plan 1?

What is the interest on $500 earning 6% simple interest for one year? What is the interest for one month? (Hint: t is in years. How many years is one month?)

Compound Interest

When the bank pays **compound interest**, it adds each interest payment to the balance. Then the bank uses the new balance as the principal to compute the next interest payment.

ACTIVITY 2   Interest Compounded Yearly

For Plan 2, the bank compounds interest at the end of each year.

= B2*0.06*1

	A	B	C	D
1	Year	Balance at Start of Year	Interest Paid	Balance at End of Year
2	1	1000	60	1060
3	2	1060	63.60	1123.60
4	3			
5	4			
6	5			

1. Create a spreadsheet similar to the one shown or use a calculator to complete the spreadsheet for 5 years. Years 1 and 2 are shown as examples.

2. What is Sean's balance after 5 years if he chooses Plan 2?

Critical Thinking   Explain why the balance at the end of each year (column D) equals 1.06 times the balance at the start of the year (column B).

ACTIVITY 3   Interest Compounded Quarterly

For Plan 3, the bank pays compound interest quarterly, or four times per year. Thus, t is $\frac{1}{4}$ year.

= C2*0.06*(1/4)

	A	B	C	D	E
1	Year	Quarter	Balance at Start of Quarter	Interest Paid	Balance at End of Quarter
2	1	1	1000	15	1015
3		2	1015		
4		3			
5		4			
6	2	1			
7		2			
8		3			
9		4			

1. Create a spreadsheet similar to the one shown, or use a calculator to complete the spreadsheet for 5 years. The first quarter of year 1 is shown as an example.

2. What is Sean's balance after 5 years if he chooses Plan 3?

Last month, the unpaid balance on your credit card bill was $360. This month, the credit card company charges you $5.40 interest for the unpaid balance.

What yearly rate of interest are you paying for unpaid balances?

SOLUTION

Convert 1 month to years.

$$t = \frac{1 \text{ month}}{1} \cdot \frac{1 \text{ year}}{12 \text{ months}} = \frac{1}{12} \text{ year}$$

Simple interest is charged for the month.

$$I = Prt$$

$$r = \frac{I}{Pt}$$

$$= \frac{5.40}{(360)\left(\dfrac{1}{12}\right)}$$

$$= \frac{5.40}{30}$$

$$= 0.18 \text{ or } 18\%$$

You are paying an 18% interest rate for unpaid balances.

LESSON ASSESSMENT

Think and Discuss

1 What is the difference between simple interest and compound interest?

2 How do you find simple interest when the time is given in months?

3 How do you find the rate of simple interest if you know the principal, the interest paid, and the time of a loan?

4 When you borrow money, you must repay the interest *plus* the principal. Let *A* be the amount you repay. Write a formula for *A* if you pay simple interest for a loan.

5. Trella invests $1250 for 9 months in a government savings bond. The bond pays simple interest at an annual rate of 5.5%. How much will Trella earn on her investment?

6. Norman bought a corporate bond for $5000. The bond pays $6\frac{3}{8}$% simple interest. How much interest will Norman's investment earn per year?

As a source of income, Sarena wants to purchase shares of a bond mutual fund. This type of fund combines money from many investors and buys government and corporate bonds. The fund pays the interest received from the bonds to owners of shares of the fund. The payments are called *dividends*. The annual percent interest paid to the fund owners is called the *yield* of the fund.

7. If Sarena buys shares worth $65,000 and the fund yields 5%, how much will Sarena receive each year in dividends?

8. If Sarena needs $4800 per year in dividends, how much will she need to invest if the fund yields 5%?

9. If Sarena needs $480 per month in dividends, what yield must the fund produce if Sarena invests $65,000?

Nakesha borrows $4000 from a bank to start a new business. She agrees to pay the bank $8\frac{1}{4}$% simple interest for 3 years. At the end of 3 years, she must repay the loan.

10. How much interest will Nakesha pay over the 3 years of the loan?

11. If she makes equal monthly interest payments, how much is each payment?

Prospectus

ABC Bond Mutual Fund
January 1, 2001

SMITH & CO. INC.

MEMBER NEW YORK STOCK EXCHANGE

CAMCORDERS

Joshua buys a $500 camcorder from a department store. He makes a $100 down payment and pays $75 per month for 6 months.

12. How much interest does Joshua pay with this payment plan?

13. What annual percent interest is charged?

You have $5000 to deposit in the National Savings and Loan. A savings account pays 5% interest compounded monthly. A certificate of deposit (CD) pays 6% simple interest.

14. How much would you have in the savings account at the end of one year?

15. How much would you have in the CD at the end of one year?

16. Would the savings account or the CD pay more interest in one year? How much more?

The State Bank Credit Card charges an annual interest rate of 12%.

17. What percent interest do you pay per month on an unpaid balance?

18. Suppose you have an unpaid balance of $1600, and you pay $200 per month plus the interest for the month, until the balance is paid off. How many months will it take to repay the balance?

	A	B	C	D
1	Month	Balance Owed	Interest	Payment
2	1	$1600	0	$200
3	2	$1400	$14	$214
4	3			
5	4			

19. How much total interest will you pay?

Use the box-and-whisker plot to complete Exercises 20–24.

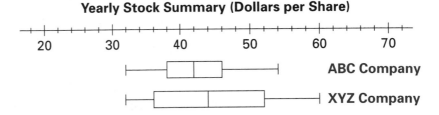

Yearly Stock Summary (Dollars per Share)

20. Find the median dollar per share for each company.

21. Find the first quartile for each company.

22. Find the third quartile for each company.

23. Find the lowest price per share for each company.

24. Find the highest price per share for each company.

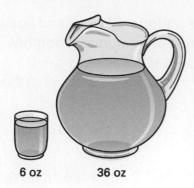

6 oz   36 oz

For Exercises 25–27, write and solve a proportion.

25. A 6-ounce glass of apple juice contains about 90 calories. How many calories are in 36 ounces of apple juice?

26. Natalie earns $96 for working 12 hours. How much will Natalie earn if she works 18 hours?

27. If you buy 12 oranges for $1.50, how much will it cost to buy 21 oranges?

A dime and a quarter are tossed. Answer the following questions.

28. What is the probability that the dime appears heads and the quarter appears tails?

29. What is the probability that both coins appear heads?

Cumulative Problem Solving

The Social Security system in the United States began paying monthly benefits to retirees in 1940. Today, the financial future of the system is a topic of national debate. One factor causing a financial strain on the system is the increase in life expectancy of Americans.

	U.S. Population (millions)		Percent of Population Surviving from Age 21 to Age 65	
Year	Male	Female	Male	Female
1940	66	66	53.9	60.6
1960	88	91	60.1	71.3
1980	110	117	67.8	80.9
2000 (est.)	134	140	75.4	86.8

30. Make a table to show the numbers of males and females surviving from age 21 to age 65 for the years shown.

31. What is the percent increase in the total population from 1940 to 2000?

32. What is the percent increase from 1940 to 2000 in the total population surviving from age 21 to age 65?

33. Explain why the percent increases from Exercises 31 and 32 illustrate a concern for the financial future of Social Security.

At the beginning of the Industrial Revolution, the atmospheric concentration of carbon dioxide (CO_2) was about 280 parts per million (ppm). By 1990, the concentration had increased to 353 parts per million.

In 1997, leaders of many industrialized nations met in Kyoto, Japan to reach an agreement on reducing atmospheric concentrations of CO_2. The goal set at the conference would limit the concentration of atmospheric CO_2 to 382 parts per million by the year 2010.

Parts per Million (ppm) of Atmospheric CO_2

Year	PPM
1790	280
1990	353
2010	382 (goal)

34. What was the percent increase in CO_2 concentration between 1790 and 1990?

35. If the goal of the Kyoto conference is met, what will be the percent increase in CO_2 concentration between 1990 and 2010?

36. If the goal of the conference is met, will the rate of increase of CO_2 concentration slow significantly? Explain.

Justin and Elaine are saving for the down payment on a house they will buy in October. Last January, they bought a 9-month $15,000 certificate of deposit (CD) that pays 5% annual interest compounded quarterly. The CD matures 9 months after it is purchased. At that time, Justin and Elaine will receive the principal plus interest earned.

37. In what month will the CD mature?

38. How much will Justin and Elaine receive at maturity?

Lucinda is working with a volunteer group renovating a children's playground in a park. The original playground measures 30 feet × 42 feet. The volunteer group is expanding the length and width by $\frac{1}{3}$. Lucinda needs to calculate the new total area so she can order pea gravel to cover the playground.

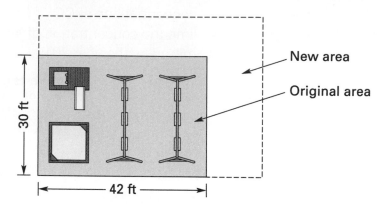

New area

Original area

30 ft

42 ft

39. By what percent is the group increasing the length and width of the playground?

40. The area of the playground is the length times the width. Calculate the area of the original playground. Calculate the area of the new playground. By what percent is the group increasing the area of the playground?

41. Explain why the percents from Exercises 39 and 40 are not equal.

Pulley A is turning at 90 revolutions per minute (rpm). It is being driven by Pulley B turning at 60 rpm. When the speed of Pulley B is reduced to 54 rpm, the speed of Pulley A is 81 rpm.

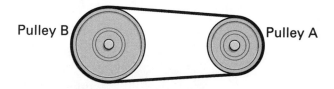

Pulley B

Pulley A

42. When the pulley speeds are reduced, what is the percent of decrease in the speed of Pulley B? Pulley A? How do the percents of decrease compare?

43. Based on your answers in Exercise 42, if the speed of Pulley B is increased to 80 rpm, what do you think the speed of Pulley A will be?

MATH LAB

Equipment Masking tape
Measuring tape
10 small washers

Problem Statement

You will toss washers into a marked area on the floor and count the number of washers landing in each section of the area. Then you will calculate the percent of the washers landing in each section. You will compare the experimental results to the theoretical probability of a washer landing in each section.

Procedure

a Use masking tape to mark an area with four sections on the floor as shown. Mark a toss line about 10 feet from the taped area.

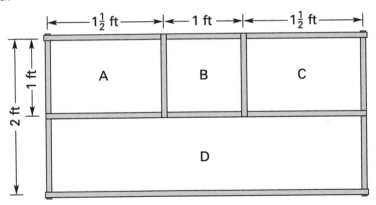

b Have one group member stand on the toss line and toss all 10 washers at once into the taped area. If washers land outside the taped area, toss those washers again. Repeat until all the washers are inside the taped area.

c Count the number of washers in each section. Record the count for each section for Trial 1 in a data table similar to the one on the next page.

d Repeat Step **b** for each group member. Record the number of washers in each section as Trial 2, Trial 3, and so on.

Number of Washers Landing in Each Section

Trial	Section A	Section B	Section C	Section D
1				
2				
3				
4				
5				
Group totals				
Class totals				
Percent of total number of washers				
Section area				
Percent of total area				

e Add the total number of washers landing in each of the four sections for the group. Combine your group's data with the rest of the class. Record the class totals.

f How many washers were tossed by the class? Find the fraction of the total that landed in each section. Calculate the percent of washers that landed in each section. Record these percents in the table.

g Calculate the number of square feet in each section using this formula.

$$\text{Area} = \text{length} \cdot \text{width}$$

Record these values in the table.

h What is the total area of the taped sections? Calculate the percent of the total area represented by each section. Record these values in the table.

Discussion Questions

1. If a washer is randomly tossed inside the taped area, what is the theoretical probability that it will land in Section A? Section B? Section C? Section D?

2. Compare the experimental results to the theoretical probabilities. Is the experimental distribution of the washers what you would expect? Explain.

Equipment   Three clear (glass or plastic) 250-mL beakers
200-mL graduated cylinder
Food coloring
Water

Problem Statement

Chemists, pharmacists, farmers, and gardeners combine water and concentrated solutions to form mixtures. In this Activity you will add a concentrated solution to clear water to form mixtures of food coloring and water. Your goal is to match the color of your mixture to the color of a sample solution prepared by your teacher.

You will then find the percent of the mixture that is concentrated solution and the percent that is clear water. You will compare your results to the percents used by your teacher to prepare the sample.

Procedure

Your teacher will give each group approximately 150 milliliters of concentrate.

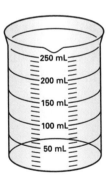
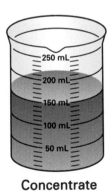
Concentrate
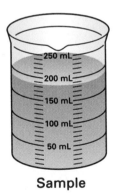
Sample

Your teacher will also give each group a sample solution that was prepared by mixing concentrate with water. Each sample will contain a different percent of concentrate.

a Measure 50 milliliters of clear water in the graduated cylinder. Pour the water into an empty beaker.

b Slowly add the concentrate to the water until the mixture in the beaker matches the color of the sample.

c Pour the mixture into the graduated cylinder.

d Measure the total volume of the mixture. Record the volume for Trial 1 in a data table similar to the following one.

		Volume	Percent
Trial 1	Mixture		100%
	Water	50 mL	
	Concentrate		
Trial 2	Mixture		100%
	Water	50 mL	
	Concentrate		
Trial 3	Mixture		100%
	Water	50 mL	
	Concentrate		

e Subtract the volume of the water from the mixture volume to find the volume of concentrate added. Record the volume of the concentrate for Trial 1.

f What percent of the mixture is water? What percent of the mixture is concentrate? Record the percents in the table.

g Repeat steps **a** through **f** for Trial 2.

h Calculate the average volumes of mixture and concentrate for Trials 1 and 2. Calculate the water and concentrate percents using averages.

Discussion Questions

1. Your teacher will provide the percents of concentrate and water used to prepare your group's sample solution. Compare your results to these percents. Explain any differences.

2. What is the sum of the percents for the water and the concentrate? Is this sum reasonable? Explain.

3. Suppose you are asked to prepare a 750-milliliter solution that matches the color of your group's sample solution. How many milliliters each of water and concentrate should you mix?

Activity 3: Paying Off a Credit Card Balance

Equipment Spreadsheet computer program

Problem Statement

You have used a credit card to pay for airline tickets that cost $1357. You have decided to pay for the tickets over several months. Your credit card company charges 18% annual interest on the unpaid balance. You will make no additional purchases with the credit card until the balance is paid off.

Part of each monthly payment is for the interest and part is for reducing the balance.

$$\text{monthly payment} = \frac{\text{amount of}}{\text{monthly interest}} + \frac{\text{amount applied}}{\text{to the balance}}$$

In this Activity you will calculate the number of months needed to pay off the balance and the amount paid for interest using three options.

Option I: Paying $100 per month

Option II: Paying $150 per month

Option III: Paying the minimum amount per month required to pay off the balance in 6 months

Procedure

Spreadsheet Setup

a Set up a spreadsheet with five column headings as follows.

	A	B	C	D	E	F
1	Month	Balance	Monthly Payment	Applied to Interest	Applied to Balance	
2						
3						
4						

The *Monthly Payment* is the amount sent to the credit card company.

Applied to Interest is the amount of the payment that pays the interest on the balance owed for that month.

Applied to Balance is the amount of the payment that reduces the balance owed.

Notice how you follow these logical steps as you use the spreadsheet to work through Options I, II, and III.

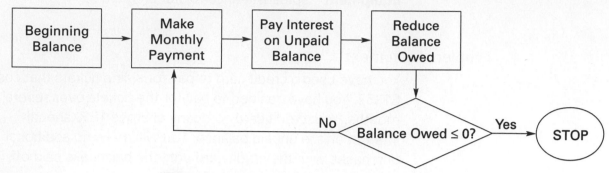

b Enter the months 1 through 20 in column A. Enter the beginning balance $1357.00 for month 1 in cell B2. You can format columns B–E to display currency or numbers with two decimal places. Highlight the columns (begin in row 2) and open the *Format Cells* menu and *Number* tab.

$$= B2 *0.18 * 1/12$$

$$= C2 - D2$$

	A	B	C	D	E	F
1	**Month**	**Balance**	**Monthly Payment**	**Applied to Interest**	**Applied to Balance**	
2	1	$1357.00				
3	2					
4	3					
5	4					

$$= B2 - E2$$

c In column D, enter the formula for simple interest $I = Prt$.

Why is $t = \frac{1}{12}$? Copy the formula down the column to month 20.

d The difference between the payment and interest is the amount the balance is reduced. In column E, subtract the amount applied to interest from the payment. Copy the formula down the column to month 20.

e In column B for the second month, calculate the new balance by subtracting the amount applied to the balance from the previous month's balance. Copy the formula down the column to month 20.

f Enter the label *Totals* in cell B23. To calculate the total amount of all payments, enter the formula =SUM(C2:C21) in cell C23. Copy the formula in cell D23 to calculate the total amount of interest paid.

Option I: Payments of $100 per month

g So far, you have not entered a monthly payment. What happens to the balance if you do not make a payment?

h Enter a $100 payment in column C. Copy the payment for all 20 months.

i In which month is the balance paid off? Delete all rows with a negative balance. In the last remaining row, add the balance to the interest for that month. Enter this total amount in the last row of column C. This is the last payment that is due.

j Use the information from the spreadsheet to complete the first row of a data table similar to the following one.

	Amount of Monthly Payment	Number of Monthly Payments	Total Amount of All Payments	Total Amount of Interest Paid
Option 1	$100			
Option 2	$150			
Option 3		6		

Option II: Payments of $150 per month

k Repeat steps **h–j** using a monthly payment of $150.

Option III: Pay-off in 6 Months

l Use trial and error to find the minimum monthly payments (to the nearest $10) needed to pay off the $1357 balance in 6 months. (Hint: Estimate the monthly payments needed to pay $1357 with no interest, and use this estimate as a starting point.)

Discussion Questions

1. Which payment option, $100 per month or $150 per month, requires you to pay the most interest? Explain why this should be expected.

2. You are considering two loan options to buy an automobile. One loan is for 60 months and the other is for 36 months. The interest rate is the same for each loan. What are the advantages and disadvantages of each loan?

CHAPTER 7   ASSESSMENT

Communicate

1. Explain why $\frac{x}{100} = x\%$.

2. List the steps you can follow to estimate $y\%$ of a number using a fraction.

3. How do you rewrite a percent proportion or multiplication equation to find percent change?

4. Explain the difference between simple interest and compound interest.

Skills

Write each fraction as a percent.

5. $\frac{3}{5}$ 　　　　　　　　**6.** $\frac{1}{6}$

Write each percent as a fraction in simplest form.

7. 45% 　　　　　　　　**8.** 64%

9. What percent of 38 is 19?

10. 42 is what percent of 112?

11. What is 0.5% of 2350?

Estimate each of the following.

12. 5% of 960 　　　　　　　　**13.** 19% of 62

Applications

14. A survey of 60 students was taken to find out which radio station they preferred. The data from the survey is shown in the circle graph. How many students prefer

a. WBAL? 　　b. KERK?

c. WELD? 　　d. WDCA?

e. KIND?

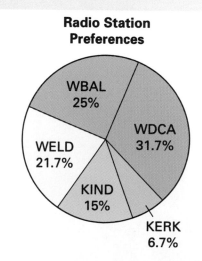

Radio Station Preferences

WBAL 25%

WDCA 31.7%

WELD 21.7%

KIND 15%

KERK 6.7%

15. The sales tax rate in Centerville is 8.5%. If Rhonda's total grocery bill is $45.57, how much sales tax did she pay?

16. A camera usually sells for $75. This week it is on sale for $50. What is the discount for the sale? What percent was the original price marked down?

17. Approximately 13% of the U.S. population is left-handed. How many left-handed students would you expect to find in a school with an enrollment of 420 students?

18. Nine years ago, a TV network ran an average of 7.4 minutes of advertising in its prime-time 30-minute programs. Since then, the network has increased its advertising time by 29%. By how many minutes has the network increased its advertising time?

19. The number of students taking college entrance exams at H. B. Gonzalez High School increased from 120 to 138 students. What is the percent increase?

20. A farmer plants cotton on 80% of his land. If he planted 336 acres of cotton, how many acres of land does the farmer have? How many acres can the farmer plant in other crops?

Math Labs

21. Your class tosses 300 washers into a taped area on the floor. Fifty-seven of the washers land in Section A. What percent of the washers land in the other sections?

22. Your group matches the color of a sample solution by mixing 100 milliliters of water with 120 milliliters of concentrate. What percent of the mixture is concentrate?

23. After making a payment on a credit card bill, Ashanti has a remaining balance of $1242. The credit card company charges interest at a rate of 18% per year. How much interest will Ashanti be charged next month for the balance?

First
AmeriBank

4660 7227 0412 8778

VALID THRU 04/02   CreditCard

ASHANTI MILLER

CHAPTER 8

WHY SHOULD I LEARN THIS?

The best way to locate positions on a plane is with a coordinate graph. For example, an archaeologist uses a coordinate graph to map locations of artifacts found at a dig site.

Contents: Graphing on the Coordinate Plane

GRAPHING ON THE COORDINATE PLANE

LEARN HOW TO...

1. Graph ordered pairs on a coordinate plane.
2. Find the slope of a line given two points on the line.
3. Use the slope-intercept form to graph linear equations and inequalities on a coordinate plane.
4. Solve a system of linear equations or a system of linear inequalities by graphing.
5. Use a function rule to evaluate and graph a function.

In previous chapters, you modeled problems using equations and inequalities with one variable. For example, the time t in hours needed to hike 6 miles at a rate of 3 miles per hour can be found by solving the following equation.

$$6 = 3t$$

You can write a more general equation using two variables. The time t in hours needed to hike D miles at the rate of 3 miles per hour can be found by solving the following equation.

$$D = 3t$$

Equations such as $D = 3t$ are called linear equations. In this chapter, you will use graphs of linear equations to solve problems involving rates. These problems include canoe rentals, floor coverings, and entrees at a banquet.

When a problem statement includes words like *at least* or *no more than,* you use inequalities to model the problem. You can also solve inequalities in two variables by graphing.

LESSON 8.1 COORDINATE GRAPHS

Maps are often divided into squares that form a grid. Each square is identified with a letter for the column and a number for the row. You can find a location on the map using the letter and number of the square that contains the location.

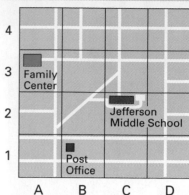

For example, Jefferson Middle School is located in square C2. The Family Center is in A3. In which square is the Post Office?

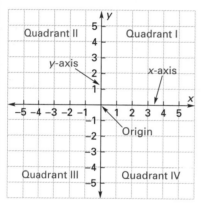

When graphing, you locate points on a grid of uniformly spaced horizontal and vertical lines. This grid is called a **coordinate plane.** A coordinate plane is formed by two perpendicular number lines called **axes.** The axes divide the plane into four **quadrants.**

The horizontal number line is the **x-axis.** The vertical number line is the **y-axis.** The point at which the two axes intersect is the **origin.**

On a map, a point can be anywhere in a square. But a point on the coordinate plane has a definite location that is named by an **ordered pair** (x, y). The first value in the ordered pair is the **x-coordinate** of the point. The second value is the **y-coordinate.**

ACTIVITY **Coordinates of Points**

Use the coordinate plane shown.

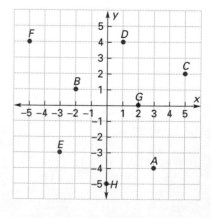

1 Find the coordinates of point A as follows.

Start at the origin. Move 3 units to the right along the x-axis, and then 4 units down. The coordinates of A are $(3, -4)$. Is the y-coordinate above or below the x-axis?

What is the sign of the y-coordinate of a point in Quadrant III or Quadrant IV?

2 Find the coordinates of point *B* as follows.

Start at the origin. Move 2 units to the left along the *x*-axis, and then 1 unit up. The coordinates of *B* are (−2, 1). Is the *x*-coordinate to the right or left of the *y*-axis?

What is the sign of the *x*-coordinate of a point in Quadrant II or Quadrant III?

3 Find the coordinates of *C* through *H*. Why is the *y*-coordinate of *G* zero? Why is the *x*-coordinate of *H* zero?

The Activity illustrates the basic properties of points in the coordinate plane.

- All points to the right of the *y*-axis have positive *x*-coordinates. All points to the left of the *y*-axis have negative *x*-coordinates.

- All points above the *x*-axis have positive *y*-coordinates. All points below the *x*-axis have negative *y*-coordinates.

- The horizontal distance a point lies from the *y*-axis measures the value of its *x*-coordinate. The vertical distance a point lies from the *x*-axis measures the value of its *y*-coordinate.

ONGOING ASSESSMENT

a. Tell which quadrant or axis contains each point in the Activity.

b. What is the ordered pair for the origin?

EXAMPLE Graphing Points on a Coordinate Plane

Graph each point on a coordinate plane.

a. $P(-1, 3)$ **b.** $Q(4, -2)$ **c.** $R(0, -4)$

SOLUTION

a. Start at the origin. Move 1 unit to the left along the *x*-axis. Then move 3 units up.

b. Start at the origin. Move 4 units to the right along the *x*-axis. Then move 2 units down.

c. Start at the origin. Move 0 units to the right. Then move 4 units down.

ONGOING ASSESSMENT

Graph each point on a coordinate plane.

a. $L(-3, -5)$ **b.** $M\left(2, -2\frac{1}{2}\right)$ **c.** $N(-4, 0)$

For centuries people have decorated walls and ceilings with murals. Murals are found on the walls of prehistoric caves, tomb chambers of ancient Egypt, and public and private buildings of ancient Greece and Rome. In the fourteenth century, artists painted murals in churches of southern Europe. In the 1600s through the 1800s, murals were painted mainly on secular buildings.

In the twentieth century, mural painting was revived by Mexican artists Diego Rivera, José Orozco, and David Siqueiros. Their murals, painted during the 1930s, illustrated social and political commentaries. In the United States the tradition of mural painting is continued by many artists. Los Angeles alone has more than 1500 murals.

To paint murals, many artists use a coordinate system to enlarge a small drawing to fit the larger area of the mural.

The artist lays one coordinate system over the drawing and a proportionally enlarged coordinate system over the wall to be painted.

Drawing

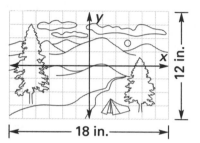

Mural wall

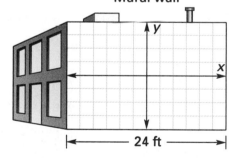

Suppose you want to reproduce a 18 in. × 12 in. drawing on a wall that is 24 feet wide.

1. How tall must the wall be if you want to reproduce the mural in the drawing's proportions?

2. The origin of the coordinate system is at the center of the drawing. How would you locate the origin if you want it to be at the center of the wall?

LESSON ASSESSMENT

1 How are ordered pairs used to locate points on a coordinate plane?

2 Name the ordered pairs for four points that are 3 units from the *y*-axis and 2 units from the *x*-axis.

3 A vertical line on a coordinate plane passes through $A(3, 1)$. Describe the *x*-coordinate of every point on the line.

4 A horizontal line on a coordinate plane passes through $A(3, 1)$. Describe the *y*-coordinate of every point on the line.

Practice and Apply

Give the coordinates of each point.

5. *A*   **6.** *B*

7. *C*   **8.** *D*

9. *E*   **10.** *F*

11. *G*   **12.** *H*

Which of the points in Exercises 5–12 are

13. in Quadrant I?   **14.** in Quadrant II?

15. in Quadrant III?   **16.** in Quadrant IV?

17. on the *x*-axis?   **18.** on the *y*-axis?

Graph each of the following points on the same coordinate plane.

19. $L(-3, 2)$ **20.** $M(0, -5)$ **21.** $N(1, -4)$

22. $P(-3, 0)$ **23.** $Q(-2, -1)$ **24.** $R(5, 2)$

25. Graph the points $A(2, 3)$, $B(4, 3)$, $C(2, 1)$, and $D(4, 1)$ on the same coordinate plane. Connect the points to make a square. What is the length of each side of the square?

26. Graph the points $S(-6, 1)$, $T(-6, 5)$, and $U(-1, 5)$ on the same coordinate plane. Graph and label point V to complete a rectangle. What is the length of each side of the rectangle?

Copy and complete the table showing the signs of the coordinate values in each quadrant and on each axis. Use $+$ if the coordinates are positive, $-$ if the coordinates are negative, and 0 if the coordinates are neither. The first quadrant is completed.

Signs of Coordinate Values

		x-coordinates	*y*-coordinates
	Quadrant I	+	+
27.	Quadrant II	?	?
28.	Quadrant III	?	?
29.	Quadrant IV	?	?
30.	*x*-axis	?	?
31.	*y*-axis	?	?

Round each number to the place value underlined.
32. 34,<u>5</u>68.09   **33.** 0.00<u>5</u>47

Name the property illustrated.
34. $23 + (38 + 17) = (23 + 38) + 17$

35. $(9 + 0) + 3 = 9 + 3$

Use the histogram to complete Exercises 36–38.
36. How many people participated in the run?

37. How many participants ran 25–32 laps?

38. How many more participants ran 17–24 laps than ran 9–16 laps?

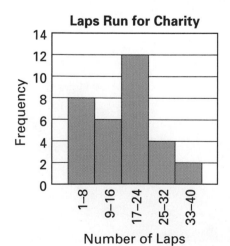

Laps Run for Charity

LESSON 8.2   GRAPHING LINEAR EQUATIONS

OBJECTIVES
- Solve and graph rate equations.
- Graph linear equations using tables.

Lindsay is competing in an orienteering event. In this event, Lindsay uses a map and compass to find locations in the woods called control sites. Lindsay must visit as many control sites as possible within three hours.

To calculate distances and times between control sites, Lindsay uses the rate formula $D = rt$. Lindsay's average hiking speed in orienteering events is 3 miles per hour. Thus, to find how many miles she can hike in the event, she uses the following equation.

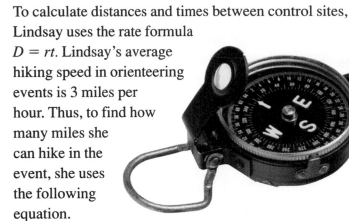

$$D = 3t$$

This is an **equation in two variables.** An ordered pair (t, D) that makes the equation *true* is a **solution of the equation.**

EXAMPLE 1   Solutions of the Rate Equation

How far does Lindsay hike after 0, 1, 2, and 3 hours?

SOLUTION

Find the solutions of the equation $D = 3t$ using 0, 1, 2, and 3 as values for t.

Make a table.

t	$D = 3t$	(t, D)
0	$3(0) = 0$	$(0, 0)$
1	$3(1) = 3$	$(1, 3)$
2	$3(2) = 6$	$(2, 6)$
3	$3(3) = 9$	$(3, 9)$

The table shows four solutions of $D = 3t$. However, this equation has an infinite number of solutions. You can show this by graphing the equation.

EXAMPLE 2 Graphing the Rate Equation

Graph the equation $D = 3t$.

SOLUTION

Graph the ordered pairs from the table in Example 1 on a coordinate plane. Connect the points with a straight line. Draw arrowheads to show that the line extends forever in both directions.

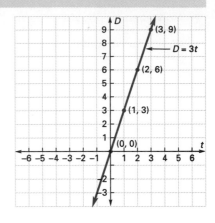

ACTIVITY **Solutions from the Graph**

1 From the graph in Example 2, estimate the miles hiked when $t = 1.5$ hours. Write an ordered pair for (t, D) and substitute the values into the equation $D = 3t$. Is this ordered pair a solution of the equation?

2 Use the graph to find t when $D = -3$. Write an ordered pair for (t, D) and substitute the values into the equation. Is this ordered pair a solution of the equation? Does this solution make sense? Explain.

3 Every point on the line graphed in Example 2 can be described by an ordered pair (t, D). What is the relationship between these ordered pairs and the equation $D = 3t$?

The graph of an equation in two variables consists of all points whose coordinates are solutions of the equation. The equation $D = 3t$ is a **linear equation** because its graph is a straight line on a coordinate plane.

EXAMPLE 3 Graphing a Linear Equation Using a Table

Graph the equation $y + 2x = 3$.

SOLUTION

1. Solve the equation for y.

$$y = -2x + 3$$

2. Make a table with columns for x, y, and (x, y).

3. Choose at least three reasonable values for x. For example, use -2, 0, and 2. Substitute these values for x into the equation and calculate the values for y. Complete the table.

4. Graph each ordered pair on a coordinate plane.

5. Connect the points with a line.

You can also draw the graph by entering the equation in a graphics calculator.

x	$y = -2x + 3$	(x, y)
-2	$-2(-2) + 3 = 7$	$(-2, 7)$
0	$-2(0) + 3 = 3$	$(0, 3)$
2	$-2(2) + 3 = -1$	$(2, -1)$

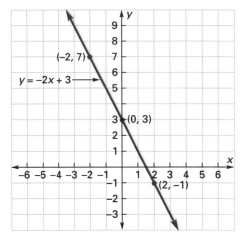

The following instructions might be different for your calculator, but the steps will be similar.

- To select the function graphing mode, press (MODE) and move the cursor to *Func*.

- Press (Y=) and enter $-2x + 3$.

- Now press (GRAPH). You should see the graph of $y = -2x + 3$ appear on the screen.

You can change the scale of the axes with the (WINDOW) key. This calculator screen uses the following settings.

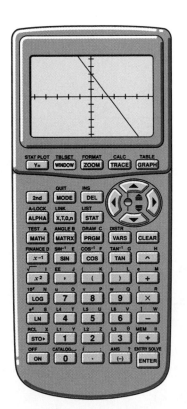

$$\text{Xmin} = -5 \qquad \text{Ymin} = -5$$

$$\text{Xmax} = 5 \qquad \text{Ymax} = 5$$

$$\text{Xscl} = 1 \qquad \text{Yscl} = 1$$

Critical Thinking Suppose you chose three other values for x to graph the equation in Example 3. Would the solution be the same line? Explain your answer.

ONGOING ASSESSMENT

Graph each equation on a coordinate plane.

a. $y + 2x = -1$ **b.** $y - 5x = 2$

LESSON ASSESSMENT

Think and Discuss

1 How do you write solutions of an equation with two variables, x and y?

2 Why is the equation $y = 2x + 1$ called a linear equation?

3 Write an algorithm for graphing a linear equation.

4 Every solution of the equation $y = 3x - 4$ is also a solution of $3y = 9x - 12$. How are the graphs of these equations related?

Practice and Apply

Name three solutions of each equation graphed.

5.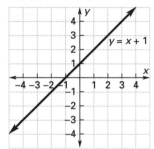

6.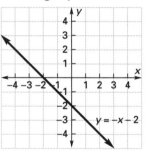

7.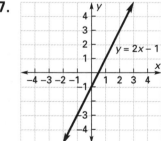

8.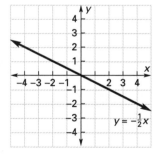

Graph each of the following equations. If you use a graphics calculator, make a sketch of the graph.

9. $y = 5x - 3$

10. $y = -3x + 4$

11. $y = -x$

12. $y = x + 5$

13. $2y = 4x - 2$

14. $\frac{1}{2}y = -2x - 1$

15. $y + 3x = -1$

16. $y - x = 4$

17. $3y + 6x = -15$

18. $2y - x = 4$

Neekesha is taking a test. She estimates that she can complete one test question every 2 minutes. Let x represent the number of test questions Neekesha completes. Let y represent the total number of minutes Neekesha spends on the test. Then $y = 2x$.

19. How long will it take Neekesha to complete the following?

a. 3 questions   **b.** 5 questions   **c.** 8 questions

20. Use the answers from Exercise 19 to write three ordered pairs that are solutions of $y = 2x$. Graph the equation.

Carmen and Ernesto own a T-shirt shop. They spend $45 for silk screening supplies and $4 for each T-shirt. Let x represent the number of T-shirts bought. Let y represent the total cost of the T-shirts and the supplies. Then $y = 4x + 45$.

21. Find the total cost for the following.

a. 0 T-shirts   **b.** 10 T-shirts   **c.** 20 T-shirts

22. Use the answers from Exercise 21 to graph the equation $y = 4x + 45$. (Adjust the scales on the axes to make sure you can fit all the values on the graph.)

The formula to convert degrees Celsius to degrees Fahrenheit is $F = \frac{9}{5}C + 32$.

23. Find the degrees Fahrenheit for the following temperatures.

a. 0°C   **b.** 50°C   **c.** 100°C

24. Use the answers from Exercise 23 to graph the equation $y = \frac{9}{5}x + 32$. (Adjust the scales on the axes to make sure you can fit all the values on the graph.)

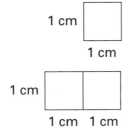
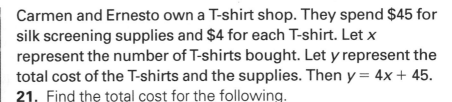

1 cm   1 cm

1 cm

1 cm   1 cm

The perimeter of a square is 4 centimeters. When two squares are placed end-to-end, the perimeter of the rectangle they form is 6 centimeters.

25. What is the perimeter of the rectangle formed by 3 of the squares placed end-to-end?

26. What is the perimeter of the rectangle formed by 4 of the squares placed end-to-end?

27. Write an equation that describes the perimeter P of the rectangle when there are n squares placed end-to-end.

28. Graph the equation.

29. Write $\dfrac{24}{60}$ in simplest form.

30. Find the product $-1\dfrac{3}{8} \cdot 1\dfrac{2}{3}$.

31. Find the quotient $-2\dfrac{1}{2} \div -3\dfrac{1}{3}$.

Solve each proportion.

32. $\dfrac{9}{16} = \dfrac{n}{24}$

33. $\dfrac{8}{r} = \dfrac{10}{8}$

34. $\dfrac{2.4}{6} = \dfrac{3.2}{d}$

35. $\dfrac{n}{0.6} = \dfrac{3}{1.8}$

36. Which of the following is equivalent to $\dfrac{x}{3} > 8$?

a. $x > \dfrac{8}{3}$

b. $x > 24$

c. $x < \dfrac{8}{3}$

d. $x < 24$

37. Find 15% of $220.

38. What percent of 12 is 4?

39. 20% of what number is 18?

40. What is 87.5% of $2400?

Cumulative Problem Solving

You are writing a computer program that controls movements of a robotic welder on an assembly line. The program uses a coordinate plane and ordered pairs to describe the location of nine weld spots.

41. The first four welds are at the corners of a rectangular piece of metal. The welds are at $A(2, 1)$, $B(2, -3)$, $C(-4, -3)$, and $D(-4, 1)$. Graph each point on a coordinate plane. Connect the points to form a rectangle. Label each point and its coordinates.

42. The second four welds are at the midpoints of the sides of the rectangle. (The midpoint of a side is halfway between each corner.) Graph these points and label the coordinates.

43. The final weld is at the center of the rectangle. Graph this point and label its coordinates.

Adeolla is buying food for a spaghetti dinner fund-raiser. She needs to determine how much spaghetti is needed. The package instructions recommend 3.5 ounces of dry noodles per serving.

44. Let x represent the unknown number of servings, and let y represent the number of ounces of dry noodles needed. Write an equation Adeolla can use to calculate y for various values of x.

45. Make a table of values for x, y, and (x, y) for five values of x between 0 and 300.

46. Graph the ordered pairs in the table on a coordinate plane. (Adjust the scale on the axes to make sure you can fit all the values on the graph.)

47. How many ounces of dry noodles does Adeolla need for 175 servings?

Jasmine is an electronics technician who has received a shipment of parts from a supplier. She suspects some of the resistors in the shipment are defective.

Resistors are labeled with a design resistance. The actual resistance must be between a highest and lowest acceptable value, or the resistor is defective. These values for four resistors are shown in the table.

Labeled Resistance (ohms)	Highest Acceptable Resistance (ohms)	Lowest Acceptable Resistance (ohms)
100	105	95
200	210	190
500	525	475
1000	1050	950

48. Draw a coordinate plane on graph paper. Label the horizontal axis *Labeled Resistance (ohms)* and the vertical axis *Resistance (ohms)*.

49. From the data in the table, write four ordered pairs (labeled resistance, highest acceptable resistance). Graph each ordered pair on the coordinate plane and draw a line of best fit.

50. Write four ordered pairs (labeled resistance, lowest acceptable resistance). Graph each ordered pair and draw a line of best fit.

51. Jasmine measures the resistance of five resistors from the shipment. The labeled and measured values are shown in the following table. Use your graph to determine which of these five resistors are acceptable and which are defective.

Labeled Resistance (ohms)	Measured Resistance (ohms)
150	145
210	205
480	440
650	695
800	780

Cynthia is a driving instructor who wants to use a graph to show her students how the braking distance of a vehicle is related to its speed. She uses the data below.

Speed (mph)	Braking Distance (ft)
20	20
30	50
40	90
50	140
60	200

52. Write the speed and braking distance values as ordered pairs (speed, braking distance).

53. Draw a coordinate system on a sheet of graph paper. Label the horizontal axis *Speed (mph)* and the vertical axis *Braking Distance (ft)*. Graph the ordered pairs.

54. Does a linear equation describe the braking distances in the table? Explain your answer.

55. How can Cynthia use the graph to show the danger of excessive speed?

LESSON 8.3 SLOPE

OBJECTIVES

➡ Calculate the slope of a line given two points on the line.
➡ Find the slope of a line from its graph.

Robyn is a dental technician. Before patients see the dentist, she records their blood pressures and heart rates. To calculate heart rate, Robyn counts heartbeats. The number of beats counted at 5-second intervals is shown in the table. What should Robyn record for Mr. Thornton's heart rate in beats per second?

Mr. Thornton's Heartbeat Count

Number of Seconds	Number of Heartbeats
5	6
10	12
15	18

ACTIVITY   Finding the Rise to Run Ratio

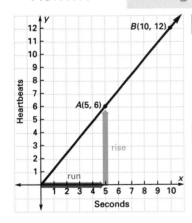

1 Draw a coordinate plane on graph paper. Label the horizontal axis *Seconds* and the vertical axis *Heartbeats.* Graph the three points from Mr. Thornton's heartbeat table. Label the points *A, B,* and *C.* Connect the points with a line. The first two points are shown as an example.

2 When you move from one point on the line to another—for example, from the origin to *A*—you move vertically and horizontally. The number of units moved vertically is called the **rise.** The number of units moved horizontally is called the **run.** Notice Mr. Thornton's heart rate is the ratio $\frac{\text{Rise}}{\text{Run}}$.

$$\text{Heart rate} = \frac{\text{Heartbeats}}{\text{Seconds}} = \frac{\text{Rise}}{\text{Run}}$$

What is Mr. Thornton's heart rate in beats per second?

3 What are the rise and run from the origin to *B*? Calculate the heart rate using the values.

4 What are the rise and run from *A* to *B*? Calculate the ratio $\frac{\text{Rise}}{\text{Run}}$.

5 Predict the ratio $\frac{\text{Rise}}{\text{Run}}$ between *B* and *C.* Calculate the ratio and compare it to your prediction.

The **slope** of a line is the ratio of the rise to the run. In the Activity, you discovered the slope of a line is the same between any two points on the line.

Slope of a Line
The slope m of a line is

$$m = \frac{\text{Rise}}{\text{Run}}$$

EXAMPLE Finding the Slope of a Line

Find the slope of the line containing $R(2, 3)$ and $T(5, 1)$.

SOLUTION

The rise of the line is the vertical change. You can find the vertical change by subtracting the y-coordinates. The run is the horizontal change. You can find the horizontal change by subtracting the x-coordinates. Make sure you subtract the x-coordinates in the same order that you subtracted the y-coordinates.

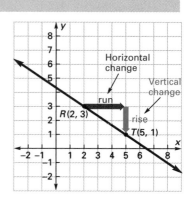

Vertical Change	Horizontal Change
Subtract the y-coordinate of R from the y-coordinate of T.	Subtract the x-coordinate of R from the x-coordinate of T.
rise = vertical change	run = horizontal change
$= 1 - 3$	$= 5 - 2$
$= -2$	$= 3$

$$m = \frac{\text{Rise}}{\text{Run}} = \frac{-2}{3}$$

The slope of the line containing R and T is $-\frac{2}{3}$.

Draw a coordinate plane and graph the line in the Example. Draw a *positive* rise and a *negative* run and calculate the slope of the line. Is the slope $-\frac{2}{3}$?

A line with a positive slope rises to the right. A line with a negative slope rises to the left.

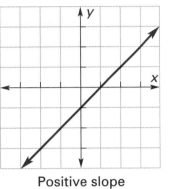

Positive slope   Negative slope

ONGOING ASSESSMENT

Which of the following lines have a positive slope and which have a negative slope?

a. 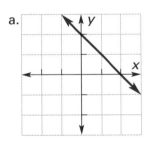   b.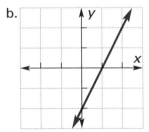

c. 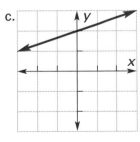   d.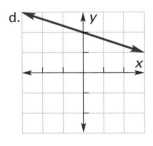

Critical Thinking   What is the slope of a horizontal line? What is the slope of a vertical line?

LESSON ASSESSMENT

Think and Discuss

1 Explain the difference between the rise and the run of a line.

2 How do you find the slope of a line if you know two points on the line?

3 Fill in the blanks with *increase* or *decrease* to describe how the coordinate values change for points on a line.

If the line has a positive slope, the *y*-values __?__ as the *x*-values increase.

If the line has a negative slope, the *y*-values __?__ as the *x*-values increase.

Practice and Apply

Find the slope of each line.

4.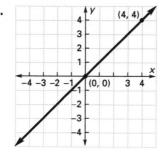

5.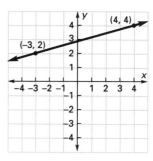

6.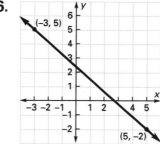

7.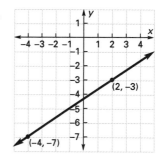

Find the slope of the line through each pair of points.

8. $(5, -2)$ and $(-4, 2)$

9. $(-8, 3)$ and $(0, 0)$

10. $(7, -3)$ and $(-5, -5)$

11. $(0, 0)$ and $(7, 3)$

12. $(2.5, 1.8)$ and $(3, 0.4)$

13. $\left(-9, \dfrac{1}{2}\right)$ and $\left(5, \dfrac{3}{4}\right)$

Suppose (*a, b*) and (*c, d*) are two points on a line.

14. Write a formula for finding the slope of the line through the two points.

15. Use the formula to find the slope of the line through (−1, 3) and (2, 9).

When a carpenter measures the length of a board, he can convert the measurement from feet to inches with the conversion factor $\frac{12 \text{ in.}}{1 \text{ ft.}}$. Let *x* represent the length of a board in feet. Let *y* represent the length in inches. Then *y* = 12*x*.

16. Pick three values for *x*. Make a table of values for *x, y,* and (*x, y*).

17. Draw a coordinate plane and graph the ordered pairs in the table. Connect the points with a line.

18. What is the slope of the line?

19. Compare the slope to the original equation *y* = 12*x*. What is the meaning of the slope of the line?

An airplane cruises at a speed of 8 $\frac{miles}{min}$. Let x represent the time in minutes. Let y represent the distance traveled by the airplane in miles. Then x is related to y by the rate equation $y = 8x$.

20. Pick three values for x. Make a table of values for x, y, and (x, y).

21. Draw a coordinate plane and graph the ordered pairs in the table. Connect the points with a line.

22. What is the slope of the line?

23. Compare the slope to the original equation $y = 8x$. What is the meaning of the slope of the line?

24. A straight line on a graph passes through the points (1, 5) and (2, −7). Find two other points that lie on the same line.

25. A straight line on a graph passes through the points (−2, 1) and (2, −1). Find two other points that lie on the same line.

Mixed Review

In a track meet, Sam threw the shot put $46\frac{1}{2}$ feet, and Roberto threw the shot put $49\frac{2}{3}$ feet.

26. What is the average of the two throws?

27. How much farther was Roberto's throw than Sam's?

Solve each equation.

28. $3\frac{1}{3}x = 2\frac{2}{5}$

29. $-4.4 = 8(x - 1.8)$

Graph each inequality on a number line.

30. $3x + 8 \leq -12$

31. $15 - 5x > 25$

Solve each percent equation.

32. $33\frac{1}{3}\%$ of what number is 25?

33. What percent of 48 is 96?

Simplify.

34. $\frac{1}{2} + \frac{3}{4} + \frac{8}{3}$

35. $\frac{3}{2} + \frac{5}{8} + \frac{7}{12}$

36. $5 - \frac{1}{3} - \frac{5}{4}$

37. $3 - \frac{1}{4} - \frac{5}{6}$

LESSON 8.4 SLOPE-INTERCEPT FORM

OBJECTIVES

- Write the slope-intercept form of an equation.
- Graph an equation in slope-intercept form.

To intercept a pass in football, a defensive player must run a path that crosses the path of the ball. Similarly, on a coordinate plane, when a line crosses the x- or y-axis, it intercepts the axis.

The x-coordinate of the point where a line crosses the x-axis is called the **x-intercept.** What is the x-intercept of this graphed line? What is the value of y at this point?

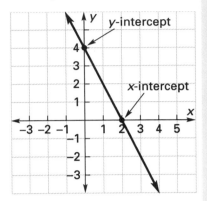

The y-coordinate of the point where a line crosses the y-axis is called the **y-intercept.** What is the y-intercept of this graphed line? What is the value of x at this point?

ACTIVITY

The Slope-Intercept Form of an Equation

1 Draw a coordinate plane on graph paper. Make a table of values for $y = 3x - 2$ and graph the line. What is the y-intercept of the line? What is the slope of the line?

2 On the same coordinate plane, graph the line $y = -2x + 4$. What is the y-intercept of the line? What is the slope?

3 Record the slopes and y-intercepts from Steps 1 and 2 in a table like the following one.

Equation	Slope	y-intercept
$y = 3x - 2$	?	?
$y = -2x + 4$	?	?

Notice that each equation contains its slope and y-intercept on the right side of the equal sign.

4 Both equations from Steps 1 and 2 are written in the form $y = mx + b$. What part of this equation form is the slope? What part is the y-intercept?

5 What are the slope and y-intercept of the equation $y = 4x + 1$? Check your answers by graphing the equation.

The equations in the Activity are written in **slope-intercept form.**

> ## Slope-Intercept Form of an Equation
> The slope-intercept form of a linear equation is
> $$y = mx + b$$
> where m is the slope and b is the y-intercept of the line.

EXAMPLE 1 Writing an Equation in Slope-Intercept Form

Find the slope, y-intercept, and x-intercept of the line whose equation is $2x + 3y = -6$.

SOLUTION

Write the equation in slope-intercept form by solving for y.

$$2x + 3y = -6$$

$$3y = -2x - 6 \qquad \text{Subtract } 2x \text{ from both sides}$$

$$y = -\frac{2}{3}x - 2 \qquad \text{Divide both sides by 3}$$

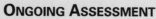

$$m = -\frac{2}{3} \qquad b = -2$$

To find the x-intercept, let $y = 0$. Solve for x.

$$2x + 3(0) = -6$$

$$2x = -6$$

$$x = -3$$

The slope is $-\dfrac{2}{3}$, the y-intercept is -2, and the x-intercept is -3.

ONGOING ASSESSMENT

Find the slope, y-intercept, and x-intercept of the line whose equation is $4x - 2y = 10$.

EXAMPLE 2 Graphing an Equation in Slope-Intercept Form

The bilge of a sailboat contains 12 gallons of water. A pump removes the water at a rate of 2 gallons per minute. How many minutes will it take to empty the bilge?

SOLUTION

Write an equation. Let *y* represent the number of gallons of water in the bilge. Let *x* represent the number of minutes the pump runs.

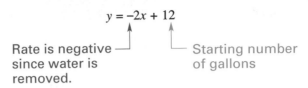

$$y = -2x + 12$$

Rate is negative since water is removed.

Starting number of gallons

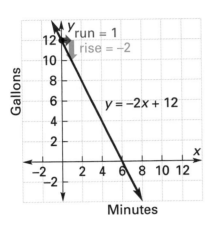

Gallons

Minutes

Graph the equation.

Step 1 There are 12 gallons when the pump starts at $x = 0$. Thus, the *y*-intercept is 12. Graph a point at (0, 12).

Step 2 The amount of water decreases by 2 gallons per minute. Thus, the slope is -2 or $-\frac{2}{1}$. Move 1 unit to the right of (0, 12) and then 2 units down. Plot a second point.

Step 3 Draw a line through the points. Label the graph.

Check your answer by substituting $y = 0$ into the equation $y = -2x + 12$ and solving for *x*.

The bilge is empty when $y = 0$. This is also the *x*-intercept, which is 6. It will take 6 minutes to empty the bilge.

Critical Thinking Explain the meaning of the slope in Example 2.

You can also use a graphics calculator to find the *x*-intercept of the equation graphed in Example 2.

• First graph $y = -2x + 12$.

• Press the TRACE key.

• Move the cursor with the ◄ and ► keys until the cursor is at the intersection of the line and the *x*-axis.

• The *x*- and *y*-coordinates for this point are displayed at the bottom of the screen.

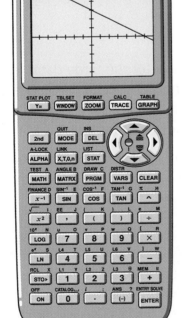

ONGOING ASSESSMENT

Use the slope-intercept form to graph each equation on the same coordinate plane.

a. $y = -\frac{1}{3}x - 2$ **b.** $-4x + 2y = 12$

Critical Thinking Describe how a line can have an *x*-intercept and a *y*-intercept at the same point.

USING THE FOUR-STEP PLAN

You are downloading four files from the Internet to your computer. One of the files is quite large, and you want to predict how long it will take to download.

You measure the time required to download the first three files. The file sizes and times are shown in the table. The file sizes are in units of kB, or kilobytes.

The size of the fourth file is 8.6 MB, or 8600 kB. How many minutes will it take to download this file?

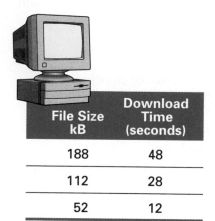

File Size kB	Download Time (seconds)
188	48
112	28
52	12

Step 1 Understand the Problem

What facts are you given? What do you need to find out? How can you use the given information? Is one set of data related to the other?

Step 2 Develop a Plan

Graph the data on a coordinate plane to show the relationship between time and file size. Use the relationship to predict the time for the 8.6 MB file.

Step 3 Carry Out the Plan

Define variables. Write ordered pairs for the three data points. Graph the ordered pairs on a coordinate plane. Draw a line of best fit. Write an equation for the line in slope-intercept form. What rate does the slope describe?

Substitute 8.6 MB into the equation and solve for the time. How many seconds will it take to download the 8.6 MB file? How many minutes?

Step 4 Check the Results

Does the line accurately describe the data? Choose a point on the graph that is not in your data table. Substitute the values into your equation. Do the values make the equation *true*? Is the calculated time for the 8.6 MB file reasonable?

LESSON ASSESSMENT

Think and Discuss

1 How do you find the slope and the y-intercept of the equation $5x - 2y = 10$?

2 How do you find the x-intercept of the equation in Exercise 1?

3 Write an algorithm for graphing a linear equation written in slope-intercept form.

Practice and Apply

Write the slope, y-intercept, and equation of the line graphed.

4.
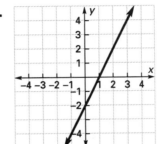

5.
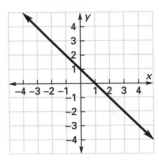

6.
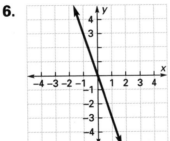

7.
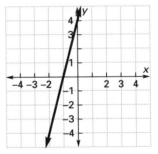

Find the slope, y-intercept, and x-intercept. Graph the equation. If you use a graphics calculator, make a sketch of the graph.

8. $y = 3x - 4$

9. $y = -2x + 3$

10. $y = -x$

11. $y = -\dfrac{2}{3}x + 1$

12. $y = -\dfrac{5}{4}x - 3$

13. $y = \dfrac{1}{3}x$

14. $2x + y = 4$

15. $3x = y - 2$

16. $5x - 4y = 20$

A supplier of animal feed to the Dale City Zoo has a temporary delivery problem. The zoo has a 680-pound supply of fish in storage to use for penguin food. The fish are fed to the penguins at a rate of 40 $\frac{lb}{day}$.

17. Let x represent the number of days without delivery of fish. Let y represent the number of pounds of fish in storage. Write an equation for the pounds of fish.

pounds of fish in storage	=	pounds of fish used in x days	+	pounds of fish initially

18. Graph the equation. What is the slope of the line? Is the slope positive or negative? What is the meaning of the slope?

19. What is the y-intercept of the line? What is the meaning of the y-intercept?

20. What is the x-intercept of the line? What is the meaning of the x-intercept?

Use graph paper or a graphics calculator to complete Exercises 21 and 22.

21. Graph each of the following linear equations on the same coordinate plane.

a. $y = \frac{1}{5}x$ **b.** $y = \frac{1}{2}x$

c. $y = x$ **d.** $y = 2x$

e. $y = 5x$

f. Describe the change in appearance of a line as the slope increases but the y-intercept stays the same.

22. Graph each of the following linear equations on the same coordinate plane.

a. $y = x - 5$ **b.** $y = x - 2$

c. $y = x$ **d.** $y = x + 2$

e. $y = x + 5$

f. Describe the change in appearance of a line as the y-intercept increases but the slope stays the same.

Paul wants to learn to windsurf. The cost for instruction is $10, and the rental cost for a sailboard is $5 per hour.

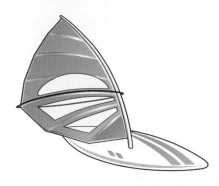

23. Let x represent the number of hours Paul rents a sailboard. Let y represent the total cost. Write an equation for the total cost.

total cost	=	sailboard rental cost for x hours	+	cost for instruction

24. Graph the equation. What is the slope of the line? What is the meaning of the slope?

25. What is the y-intercept of the line? What is the meaning of the y-intercept?

26. If Paul wants to windsurf four hours, what will be the total cost of instruction and sailboard rental?

Mixed Review

Replace each ? by $<$ or $>$.
27. 5.62 __?__ 5.616   **28.** 17,083 __?__ 17,803

Solve each equation.
29. $3x - 8 = 5x + 12$ **30.** $8.4 = 2.4(x + 1)$

Copy the following grid. Shade $\frac{5}{8}$ of the grid red. Shade another $\frac{1}{4}$ of the grid blue.

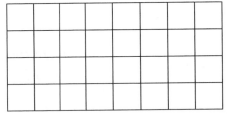

31. What part of the grid is not shaded?

32. What is the ratio of the red squares to the blue squares?

Louise and Melinda are flying a small airplane 645 miles from Detroit to Kansas City. Every half-hour during the flight they record their radar position to determine their distance from Detroit. The first three reports are listed in the table.

33. Write each time and distance as an ordered pair (t, D). Graph the ordered pairs on a coordinate plane. Draw a line of best fit.

34. Find the slope of the line. What rate does the slope represent? What is the rate?

35. Use the slope to find the approximate total time it will take Louise and Melinda to fly from Detroit to Kansas City.

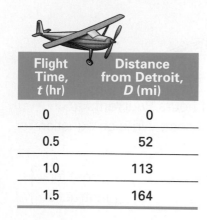

Flight Time, t (hr)	Distance from Detroit, D (mi)
0	0
0.5	52
1.0	113
1.5	164

A Forest Service water truck weighs 15,000 pounds when it is empty. Water weighs approximately 8.3 pounds per gallon.

36. Let x represent the number of gallons of water carried by the truck. Let y represent the total weight of the truck and water. Write an equation in slope-intercept form relating these variables.

37. The capacity of the water tank on the truck is 1500 gallons. What is the total weight of the truck and water?

38. The truck will be used to deliver water to fire fighters. But the truck must pass over a bridge whose maximum safe load is 25,000 pounds. What is the maximum number of gallons of water that should be loaded on the truck?

You are using a foot pump to inflate a bicycle tire. The pump has a gauge which you use to check the pressure in the tire. Before you begin, the tire is flat, and the gauge reads 0 pounds per square inch (psi). After 5 strokes on the foot pump, the gauge reads 11 psi; after 10 strokes, it reads 26 psi; and after 15 strokes, it reads 38 psi.

39. Write ordered pairs (x, y) for the data, where x represents the number of strokes and y represents the pressure reading in psi. Graph the ordered pairs on a coordinate plane. Draw a line of best fit.

40. Write an equation for the line in slope-intercept form.

41. About how many total pump strokes are needed to inflate the tire to a pressure of 55 psi?

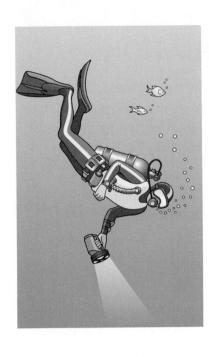

Scuba divers experience pressure that increases with their depth underwater. The following linear equation describes the relationship between the pressure y in pounds per square inch (psi) and the depth below the surface x in feet.

$$y = 0.43x + 14.7$$

42. What is the y-intercept of the line represented by this equation? What is the pressure at the water's surface? This is the normal atmospheric pressure experienced by a person at sea level.

43. What is the slope of the line? How much does the pressure change for each foot a scuba diver descends below the surface?

44. Find the pressure on a diver at depths of 10, 20, and 30 feet.

Overnight Delivery Company spends $1500 per year on maintenance for each of its trucks. The fuel cost for each truck is $0.108 per mile.

45. Define variables for the number of miles a truck is driven and the total cost to operate the truck for a year. Write an equation in slope-intercept form relating the variables.

46. On average, Overnight Delivery's trucks are driven 28,000 miles per year. Use the equation to find the average annual operation cost per truck.

47. How much does the company pay in operation costs if it has 12 trucks in its fleet?

Sound travels at about 1100 feet per second. You can use this speed to estimate your distance from a lightning flash by counting the seconds until you hear thunder.

48. Write an equation for the distance y you are from the lightning if you count x seconds between the flash and thunder.

49. The graph of all (x, y) ordered pairs that make the equation *true* is a line. What is the slope of the line in Exercise 48? What is the y-intercept?

50. How far away is the lightning if you count 3 seconds between the flash and thunder? How long will it take to hear thunder from lightning 2 miles away? (1 mile = 5280 feet)

LESSON 8.5 SYSTEMS OF EQUATIONS

OBJECTIVES
- ➡ Solve a system of equations by graphing.
- ➡ Use slope to determine if lines are parallel.

Melissa and Colin are comparing the prices of two canoe rental companies. River Runners charges $5 per hour for a canoe. The Happy Paddler charges an $8 fee plus $3 per hour. After how many hours of rental will the amount charged by each company be the same?

Let x represent the number of hours a canoe is rented. Let y represent the total cost of renting a canoe. The equations relating cost to hours for the rental companies follow.

River Runners: Total cost $= 5 \dfrac{\text{dollars}}{\text{hour}} \cdot x$ hours

$$y = 5x$$

Happy Paddler: Total cost $= 3 \dfrac{\text{dollars}}{\text{hour}} \cdot x$ hours $+ 8$ dollars

$$y = 3x + 8$$

Two or more equations with two or more variables form a **system of equations.** A solution of a system of equations in two variables is an ordered pair that makes both equations *true*.

EXAMPLE 1 Solving a System of Equations

Solve this system of equations by graphing. $y = 5x$
$$y = 3x + 8$$

SOLUTION

Create a table of values or use the slope-intercept form of an equation to graph both equations on the same coordinate plane.

Each equation has an infinite number of solutions. But the ordered pair (4, 20), where the lines intersect, is the only solution common to both equations.

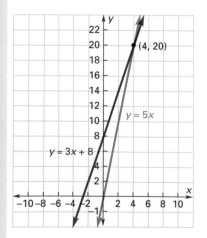

Check the solution by substituting the ordered pair into both equations.

$y = 5x$	$y = 3x + 8$
$20 = 5(4)$	$20 = 3(4) + 8$
$20 = 20$ ✓	$20 = 20$ ✓

If the canoe is rented for 4 hours, the cost from River Runners will be the same as the cost from Happy Paddlers.

Critical Thinking If the canoe is rented for less than 4 hours, which company charges less? If the canoe is rented for more than 4 hours, which company charges less?

EXAMPLE 2 Solving a System of Equations

Tali and Perry collect old movie posters. Together they have collected 18 posters. Tali has collected twice as many as Perry. Find the number of posters each person has collected.

SOLUTION

Use graph paper or a graphics calculator to solve a system of equations. Let p represent the number of posters collected by Perry. Let t represent the number of posters collected by Tali.

There are two conditions given in the problem. First, the total number of posters collected by Perry and Tali is 18. The equation that models this condition follows.

$$p + t = 18$$

Second, Tali has collected twice as many posters as Perry. The equation that models this condition follows.

$$t = 2p$$

Graph both equations on the same (p, t) coordinate plane.

The intersection of the two lines is (6, 12). Thus, Perry collected 6 posters and Tali collected 12 posters.

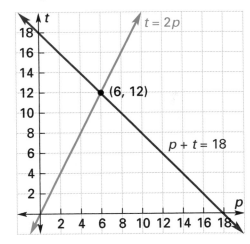

Check the solution.

$$p + t = 18$$
$$6 + 12 = 18 \quad \checkmark$$
$$t = 2p$$
$$12 = 2(6) \quad \checkmark$$

ONGOING ASSESSMENT

Solve this system of equations by graphing.

$$y = -3x + 4$$
$$y = 2x - 1$$

Not all systems of equations have a solution.

1 Graph $y = 2x + 1$ on graph paper or using a graphics calculator. What is the slope of the line? What is the y-intercept?

2 Graph $y = 2x - 3$ on the same coordinate plane. What is the slope of the line? What is the y-intercept?

3 At what points do the lines intersect? Is there a solution for this system of equations?

Two lines on a coordinate plane that have the same slope but different y-intercepts are *parallel*. In a plane, **parallel lines** do not intersect. If the graphs of the equations are parallel lines, the system of equations has no solution.

Ongoing Assessment

Tell which of the following systems of equations have no solution.

a. $2y = x + 1$ **b.** $x - \dfrac{1}{3}y = 2$ **c.** $x + y = 1$

      $y = 2x - 4$ $y = 3x - 2$ $x - y = 1$

LESSON ASSESSMENT

Think and Discuss

1 What is a system of equations?

2 An *intersection* is the set of elements common to two sets. How is this used in solving a system of equations?

3 Write an algorithm for finding the solution of a system of equations by graphing.

4 Draw three parallel lines on a coordinate plane. What is the relationship between the slopes of the lines? What is the relationship between the y-intercepts?

Tell which ordered pair is the solution of the system of equations.

5. $x + y = 7$ **a.** $(4, 4)$ **c.** $(-2, -5)$

    $x - y = 3$ **b.** $(-3, -4)$ **d.** $(5, 2)$

6. $2x + y = 9$ **a.** $(-1, 4)$ **c.** $(1, 4)$

    $3x - y = 11$ **b.** $(4, 1)$ **d.** $(4, -1)$

7. $2x + 3y = -7$ **a.** $(-2, -1)$ **c.** $(2, 1)$

    $5x - y = -9$ **b.** $(1, 2)$ **d.** $(-1, -2)$

8. $4x + 2y = -4$ **a.** $(0, 0.5)$ **c.** $(0.5, -3)$

    $x - \frac{1}{3}y = 1.5$ **b.** $(-0.5, 3)$ **d.** $(0, -0.5)$

Solve each system of equations by graphing. If you use a graphics calculator, make a sketch of the graphs.

9. $y = 2x + 6$ **10.** $y = 3x + 1$ **11.** $y = 4x - 2$

    $y = 3x + 4$ $y = -x - 3$ $y = -3x + 5$

12. $2x + y = 9$ **13.** $x + y = 10$ **14.** $3x + y = 6$

    $y = \frac{1}{2}x - 1$ $x - y = 4$ $x + y = 2$

Mrs. Vanderpool is redecorating her family room. She needs to replace the flooring for an area of 300 square feet (sq ft), part with tile and part with carpet. The tile costs \$1 per sq ft, and the carpet costs \$2 per sq ft. Mrs. Vanderpool spends \$500 for all the flooring materials. Let t represent the number of square feet of tile needed, and let c represent the number of square feet of carpet needed.

15. Write an equation for the square feet of flooring needed.

sq ft of tile needed	+	sq ft of carpet needed	=	total sq ft of flooring needed

16. Write an equation for the total cost of flooring.

cost of t sq ft of tile	+	cost of c sq ft of carpet	=	total cost of flooring

17. Solve the system of equations by graphing. How many square feet of each type of flooring should Mrs. Vanderpool buy for her family room?

Helena is catering a banquet for 250 people. Each person will be served a chicken dish that costs $5 each or a beef dish that costs $7 each. Helena has a budget of $1500.

Let *c* represent the number of chicken dishes Helena will serve, and let *b* represent the number of beef dishes.

18. Write an equation for the total number of dishes Helena will serve at the banquet.

| number of chicken dishes | + | number of beef dishes | = | total number of dishes |

19. Write an equation for the total cost of the two dishes.

| cost of *c* chicken dishes | + | cost of *b* beef dishes | = | total cost of food |

20. Solve the system of equations by graphing. How many dishes of each type will Helena serve?

The length of a poster is 60 centimeters longer than its width. The perimeter of the poster is 360 centimeters.
21. Define variables for the length and width of the poster.

22. Write an equation relating the length and width. Write an equation for the perimeter.

23. Solve the system by graphing.

24. What are the dimensions of the poster?

Mixed Review

25. Which is greater?

　　　a. $(-85) + 55$　　or　　**b.** $85 + (-55)$

26. Which is less?

　　　a. $|-129 - 212|$　　or　　**b.** $|-129| - |212|$

Graph each inequality on a number line.
27. $3x - 7 \geq -40$　　　　　　**28.** $9 - 2x > 19$

A box contains 3 nickels, 5 dimes, and 4 quarters.
29. One coin is removed. What is the probability that it will be a quarter?

30. Two coins are removed without replacement. What is the probability that both will be quarters?

LESSON 8.6 GRAPHING LINEAR INEQUALITIES

OBJECTIVES

➤ Determine if an ordered pair is a solution to a linear inequality.
➤ Graph a linear inequality.

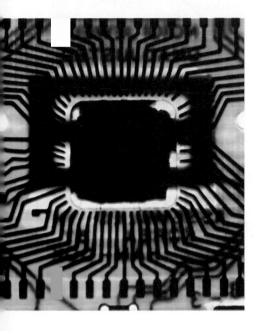

Shanice is supervising the installation of new network control cards in an office's computers. Team A can install 4 cards per hour, and Team B can install 2 cards per hour. In one day, Shanice's teams must install more than 16 cards. How many hours should each team work to meet this installation goal?

Since Shanice needs *more than* 16 cards installed, she can model the problem with a **linear inequality** with two variables. Let x represent the number of hours Team A works, and let y represent the number of hours Team B works.

number of cards installed by Team A	+	number of cards installed by Team B	>	must be more than 16
$4x$	+	$2y$		> 16

$$4x + 2y > 16$$

How can Shanice find solutions of this inequality? The **solutions of an inequality** are ordered pairs that makes the inequality *true*.

EXAMPLE 1 Solutions of Linear Inequalities

Tell whether each ordered pair is a solution of $2x - 3y \leq 1$.

a. $(-3, 2)$ **b.** $(-4, -5)$ **c.** $(2, 1)$

SOLUTION

Substitute each ordered pair in the inequality to determine if it makes a *true* statement.

a.	**b.**	**c.**
$2x - 3y \leq 1$	$2x - 3y \leq 1$	$2x - 3y \leq 1$
$2(-3) - 3(2) \leq 1$	$2(-4) - 3(-5) \leq 1$	$2(2) - 3(1) \leq 1$
$-6 - 6 \leq 1$	$-8 + 15 \leq 1$	$4 - 3 \leq 1$
$-12 \leq 1$	$7 \leq 1$	$1 \leq 1$
True. $(-3, 2)$ is a solution.	*False.* $(-4, -5)$ is not a solution.	*True.* $(2, 1)$ is a solution.

ONGOING ASSESSMENT

Is $(1, 4)$ a solution of $y \geq 5x - 1$?

Solutions on a Coordinate Plane

Use the following steps to display the solutions of $y \geq x + 2$ on a coordinate plane.

1 Draw a coordinate plane on graph paper. Graph the equation $y = x + 2$.

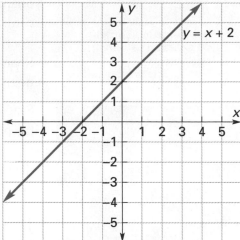

2 Choose a point on the line and substitute the ordered pair into the inequality. Does this ordered pair make the inequality *true*?

3 Choose 3 points above the line and substitute the ordered pairs into the inequality. Do these ordered pairs make the inequality *true*?

4 Choose 3 points below the line and substitute the ordered pairs into the inequality. Do these ordered pairs make the inequality *true*?

5 Shade the region above or below the line that contains points that make the inequality *true*.

The Activity leads to the following summary for graphing solutions to inequalities on a coordinate plane.

- A linear inequality divides the coordinate plane into two regions separated by a line called the **boundary.** The equation of the boundary is obtained by replacing the inequality sign with an equal sign.

- If the inequality is $<$ or $>$, the boundary line does not contain solutions. Draw the boundary as a dashed line.

- If the inequality is $\leq$ or $\geq$, the boundary line contains solutions. Draw the boundary as a solid line.

- If one point in a region is a solution to the inequality, all the points in that region are solutions. Shade this region.

- If one point in a region is not a solution to the inequality, no points in that region are solutions. Do not shade this region.

EXAMPLE 2 Graphing a Linear Inequality

Graph Shanice's inequality $4x + 2y > 16$.

SOLUTION

Solve the inequality for y.

$$4x + 2y > 16$$

$$2y > -4x + 16$$

$$y > -2x + 8$$

To find the boundary, write the inequality as an equation. Since the inequality is $>$, draw a dashed line for the graph of $y = -2x + 8$.

Choose $(0, 0)$ as a test point to find the region of the graph that contains the solutions. Substitute $(0, 0)$ into the inequality.

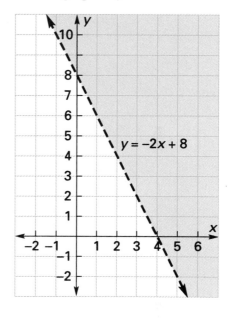

$$y > -2x + 8$$

$$0 > -2(0) + 8$$

$$0 > 0 + 8$$

$$0 > 8$$

This is *false*. Therefore, $(0, 0)$ is not in the region that contains the solutions. Shade above the boundary.

Check the graph by substituting a point from the shaded region into the inequality. The ordered pair for this point should make the inequality *true*.

ONGOING ASSESSMENT

Graph each inequality.

  a. $y \le 2x - 1$

  b. $y > 4x + 2$

  c. $2x + y \ge 6$

Critical Thinking   Suppose an inequality is written in slope-intercept form. How can you use the inequality symbol to determine the shaded region of the graph?

LESSON ASSESSMENT

1 When you graph an inequality, you graph an equation first. What equation do you graph?

2 How can you determine if the boundary line of a linear inequality should be drawn dashed or solid?

3 Explain how to determine which region to shade when you graph a linear inequality.

Practice and Apply

Write the inequality graphed.

4.

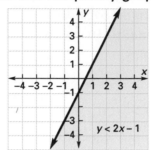

$y < 2x - 1$

5.

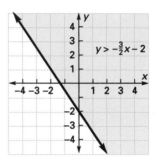

$y > -\frac{3}{2}x - 2$

6.

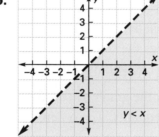

$y < x$

7.

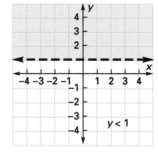

$y < 1$

For Exercises 8–10, tell whether each ordered pair is a solution of the inequality.

8. $y < 2x + 5$ **a.** (2, 9)   **b.** (6, 0)   **c.** (0, 0)

9. $y \geq -3x + 2$ **a.** (4, −9)   **b.** (−2, 8)   **c.** (0, 0)

10. $2x - 4y \leq 8$ **a.** (1, −2)   **b.** (−1, 2)   **c.** (0, 0)

Graph each inequality.

11. $y > 3x + 4$ **12.** $y \leq -\frac{1}{2}x + 3$ **13.** $y \geq -x - 2$

14. $y - 3x < -2$ **15.** $2x - 3y < 12$ **16.** $4x + 2y \leq -10$

Gordon sells fresh herbs to restaurants. He sells basil for $10 per pound and thyme for $5 per pound. His expenses for growing these herbs total $150 per month. If Gordon wants the sales income to at least meet expenses, how many pounds of each herb must he sell?

Let *b* represent the number of pounds of basil sold, and *t* represent the number of pounds of thyme sold.

17. Write an inequality that shows the sales income at least meets expenses.

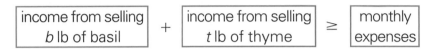

18. Graph the linear inequality.

19. The linear inequality has solutions in three quadrants. Which quadrant contains solutions that make sense? Explain your answer.

20. Write five ordered pairs that describe numbers of pounds of each herb that Gordon can sell and meet or exceed expenses.

Susan owns a small business that makes computer cables. She makes 6-foot cables and 4-foot cables. She buys cable material on spools that each contain 100 feet. What combinations of 6-foot and 4-foot lengths can Susan get from a spool?

Let *x* represent the number of 6-foot cables Susan makes from one spool, and let *y* represent the number of 4-foot cables.

21. Write an inequality showing that the total length of cable used does not exceed 100 feet.

$$\boxed{\begin{array}{c}\text{length of cable used to}\\ \text{make } x \text{ 6-ft cables}\end{array}} + \boxed{\begin{array}{c}\text{length of cable used to}\\ \text{make } y \text{ 4-ft cables}\end{array}} \leq \boxed{\begin{array}{c}\text{total length}\\ \text{on a spool}\end{array}}$$

22. Graph the linear inequality.

23. The linear inequality has solutions in all four quadrants. Which quadrant contains solutions that make sense? Explain your answer.

24. Write five ordered pairs that describe numbers of cables of each length that Susan can make from one spool.

In Exercises 25–27, use the inequalities $y > 2x - 1$ and $y < -x + 3$.

25. Graph both inequalities on the same coordinate plane.

26. Choose a test point from the region where the solutions overlap. Substitute the coordinates of the test point into each inequality. Does the ordered pair make both inequalities *true*?

27. Describe the region that contains the solutions of both inequalities.

In Exercises 25–27, you graphed the solution of a system of linear inequalities. Graph the solution of the following systems.

28. $y > 3x + 2$

$y \geq -2x - 4$

29. $y \leq 3x - 1$

$y \leq -2x + 3$

30. $y \geq 2x$

$y < -x + 4$

31. $y < 4$

$y < -3x + 4$

Mixed Review

Give the value of each underlined digit.

32. 6<u>4</u>,128.48   **33.** 889,356.1<u>23</u>   **34.** 5,<u>3</u>91,065.8

Round each number to the (a) nearest hundred and (b) nearest hundredth.

35. 457.095   **36.** 9845.302   **37.** 34,581.9638

Use the four-step problem-solving plan to solve the following problem.

38. Ruiz collects promotional toys given away by a restaurant chain. The table shows the number of toys he collects the first four weeks of the promotion.

Week	Number of Toys Collected
1	10
2	15
3	21
4	28

If Ruiz continues in this sequence, how many promotional toys will he have at the end of the sixth week?

Lesson 8.7 Functions

Objectives

➤ Use domain and range to determine if a relation is a function.

➤ Evaluate a function at a given value.

The table and graph show the distance D in kilometers that a test car moves while traveling at a speed of 200 kilometers per hour for a time of t hours.

t	$D = 200t$
0	$200(0) = 0$
1	$200(1) = 200$
2	$200(2) = 400$
3	$200(3) = 600$

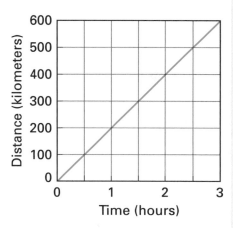

An equation, a table, and a graph are three ways to represent a *relation*. A **relation** is a set of ordered pairs. The set of ordered pairs for (t, D) in the table can be written

$$\{(0, 0), (1, 200), (2, 400), (3, 600)\}$$

For an ordered pair, such as (1, 200), 1 is called the first component and 200 is called the second component. The set of all first components of a relation is called its **domain.** The set of all second components is called its **range.**

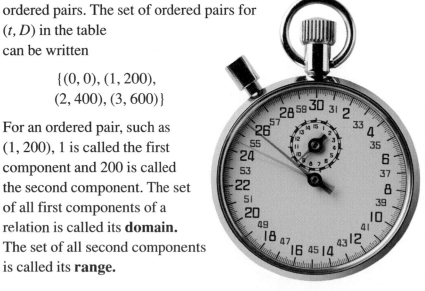

EXAMPLE 1 Finding the Domain and Range

Find the domain and range for each relation.

a. $\{(0, -2), (1, -1), (2, 0)\}$

b.

x	y
18	−6
12	−4
6	−2
0	0

c.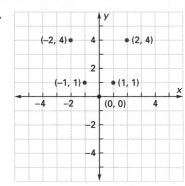

d.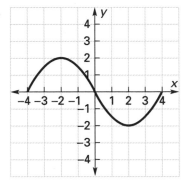

SOLUTION

a. Domain: $\{0, 1, 2\}$ Range: $\{-2, -1, 0\}$

b. Domain: $\{18, 12, 6, 0\}$ Range: $\{-6, -4, -2, 0\}$

c. Domain: $\{-2, -1, 0, 1, 2\}$ Range: $\{0, 1, 4\}$

d. There is a point on the curve for every value of x from -4 to $+4$, and for every value of y from -2 to $+2$.

Domain: $\{-4 \leq x \leq 4\}$ Range: $\{-2 \leq y \leq 2\}$

ONGOING ASSESSMENT

Find the domain and range for the relation shown in the graph.

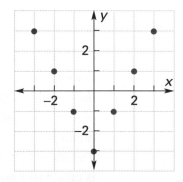

In the test car example, the relation between distance and time is a **function.** Each relation in Example 1 is also a function.

> ## Function
> A function is a relation in which each element of the domain is paired with exactly one element of the range.

EXAMPLE 2 Determining a Function

Tell whether each of the following relations is a function.

a. $\{(1, 7), (4, 22), (7, 37)\}$

b.

x	y
−1	3
0	3
1	0
1	2

c.

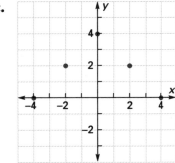

SOLUTION

a. Function. Each element of the domain is paired with exactly one element from the range.

b. Not a function. 1 is paired with both 0 and 2.

c. Function. Each element of the domain is paired with exactly one element from the range. Notice that, in a function, one element of the range can be paired with two elements of the domain. For example, $y = 0$ is paired with $x = -4$ and $x = 4$.

You can use a pencil test to determine if the graph of a relation is a function.

1 Which of the following relations is a function?

$$A = \{(-2, 2), (0, 0), (2, 2), (-1, 1)\}$$

$$B = \{(2, -2), (0, 3), (-1, 1), (0, 2)\}$$

2 Graph each of the relations on a separate coordinate plane.

3 Place a pencil parallel to the y-axis on the graph of the relation A. Keep your pencil in a vertical position and move it to the right and left. Does the pencil ever intersect two points of the relation at the same time? If so, then one element of the domain is paired with two elements of the range.

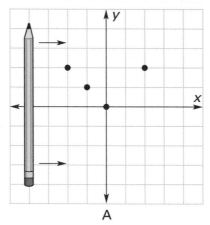

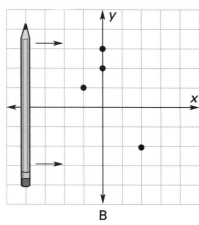

A   B

4 Repeat Step 3 for the graph of the relation B. Does your pencil intersect two points of this relation at the same time?

5 How can you use the pencil test to determine if the graph of a relation is the graph of a function?

ONGOING ASSESSMENT

Use the pencil test to determine if each relation is a function.

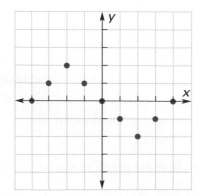

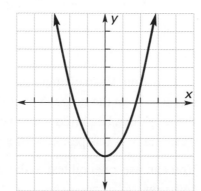

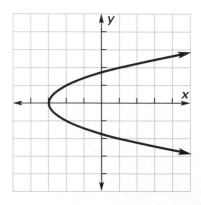

Critical Thinking: Are the graphs of all linear equations functions? Explain your answer.

In mathematics, you can often describe a function by a **function rule.** In the test car example, in t hours the car travels $200t$ kilometers. There are three ways to write this relation as a function rule.

In words:	t is paired with $200t$
In arrow notation:	$t \rightarrow 200t$
In function notation:	$f(t) = 200t$

The function notation is read

  "*f of t equals* $200t$"   or   "*the value of f at t is* $200t$"

Function notation is shorthand for showing the pairing between values in the domain and range.

Instead of writing *when* $t = 2, D = 400$, you can write $f(2) = 400$.

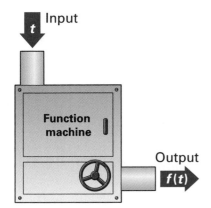

Input
t

Function machine

Output
$f(t)$

A function machine models the way a function pairs t and $f(t)$.

Input x	Output $f(x)$
–2	$f(-2) = 2(-2) - 3 = -7$
0	$f(0) = 2(0) - 3 = -3$
5	$f(5) = 2(5) - 3 = 7$

EXAMPLE 3 Evaluating a Function

a. Find $f(-2), f(0)$, and $f(5)$ for the function $f(x) = 2x - 3$.

b. Graph the function.

SOLUTION

a. A value of x is an **input** for the function. The corresponding value of $f(x)$ is an **output.** Make an input/output table.

$$f(x) = 2x - 3$$

b. To graph the function, let the variable y represent the output $f(x)$. Graph the equation $y = 2x - 3$.

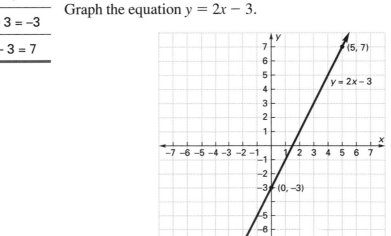

a. Make an input/output table for the function $f(x) = -3x + 2$ with the domain $\{-2, -1, 0, 1, 2\}$. Graph the function.

b. How can you tell that the graph represents a function?

LESSON ASSESSMENT

Think and Discuss

1 Name three ways you can represent a relation.

2 When is a relation also a function?

3 When you draw the graph of the function $f(x) = 3x$, what variable do you use to represent the domain? How do you find the range?

4 What is an input/output table?

Practice and Apply

Identify the domain and range of each relation.

5. $\{(0, 0), (1, 1), (2, 8), (3, 2)\}$

6.

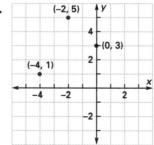

7.

x	y
3	-1
3	0
3	1

8.

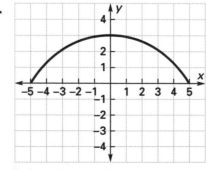

For Exercises 9–16, determine if the relation is a function.

9. {(−1, 0), (0, 0), (1, 0), (2, 0)}

10. {(0, 0), (1, 1), (−1, 1), (2, 4), (−2, 4)}

11.

x	y
−5	0
0	1
0	2
5	3

12.

x	y
0	−5
1	0
2	0
3	5

13.

14.
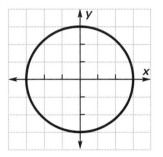

15.
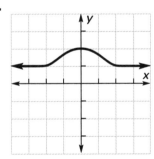

16.
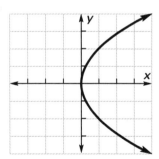

For Exercises 17–20, make an input/output table for each function with the given domain. Graph each function.

17. $f(x) = -4x + 4$ for {−2, 0, 2}

18. $f(x) = 2x - 1.5$ for {0, 0.5, 1}

19. $f(x) = \frac{2}{3}x + 4$ for {−1, 0, 3}

20. $f(x) = 3x - 2$ for $\left\{ -\frac{2}{3}, -\frac{1}{3} \right\}$

21. Graph $f(x) = 5x + 2$ for $-1 \le x \le 1$. What is the range?

22. Graph $f(x) = -x + 4$ for $0 \le x \le 12$. What is the range?

Find an equation that defines each function in Exercises 23–26. For each function, find $f(6)$.

23.

Input x	Output $f(x)$
0	–3
1	–2
2	–1
3	0
4	1

24.

Input x	Output $f(x)$
–4	1
–3	2
–2	3
–1	4
0	5

25.

Input x	Output $f(x)$
–2	–6
0	0
2	6
4	12

26.

Input x	Output $f(x)$
7	–14
8	–16
9	–18
10	–20

In a sailing contest, a boat's time and distance from the starting buoy are recorded on a graph.

27. Copy the graph on graph paper.

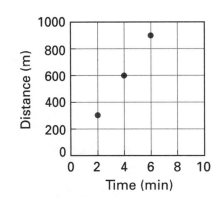

28. Draw a line through the points plotted to show the (time, distance) relation.

29. The relation shown on your graph is a function. Write a rule for the function in the form $f(t) = \underline{\ ?\ }$, where the input is time (in minutes) and the output is distance (in meters).

30. Use your rule to calculate the distance traveled by the sailboat in 15 minutes.

The function $f(x) = \frac{9}{5}x + 32$ can be used to convert degrees
Celsius to degrees Fahrenheit. The input x to the function is the temperature in degrees Celsius and the output $f(x)$ is the temperature in degrees Fahrenheit.

31. Make an input/output table to show the following.

    a. $f(-10)$

    b. $f(0)$

    c. $f(10)$

32. Graph the function.

33. Does the graph represent a function? How can you tell?

Mixed Review

Use the Order of Operations to simplify each expression.

34. $50 + 12 \div 3 \cdot 8$

35. $18.5 \cdot 2.5 - 10.5 \div 5$

Evaluate each expression when $m = -\frac{2}{3}$ and $n = \frac{1}{2}$.

36. $mn + n$

37. $\frac{3}{4}(n - m)$

Solve each equation.

38. $0.3c + 3.5 = c - 4.3$

39. $-\frac{3}{5}d = \frac{1}{3}d - 7$

There are 14 red marbles, 12 blue marbles, and 24 yellow marbles in a box. Find each ratio.

40. red marbles to blue marbles

41. blue marbles to yellow marbles

42. yellow marbles to total marbles

43. Slips of paper numbered from 1 to 40 are placed in a box. One slip of paper is removed from the box. What is the probability that the number on the slip is a multiple of 4?

44. A shirt that originally sells for $38.40 is on sale for 20% off. What is the sale price of the shirt?

Cumulative Problem Solving

Hector is buying flowers for three planters in his yard. He wants to buy a mixture of pansies and marigolds. In one planter, Hector wants to plant 15 pansies. In the other two planters, he wants half pansies and half marigolds. He concludes that the total number of pansies will be 15 more than the total number of marigolds. Hector has a budget for 75 flowers in all.

Let p represent the number of pansies, and let m represent the number of marigolds Hector needs to buy.

45. Write an equation for the total number of flowers.

46. Write a second equation showing that the number of pansies is 15 more than the number of marigolds.

47. Graph the system of equations on the same coordinate plane.

48. How many pansies and how many marigolds should Hector buy?

Craig is a geneticist studying the growth patterns of pine trees. He needs to collect cones from healthy trees of a certain age and height to use in his research. To select healthy trees, Craig uses the inequality

$$y > 0.2x + 1$$

where x is the age of a tree in years, and y is the height of the tree in meters.

49. Graph the inequality on a coordinate plane.

50. Craig wants to collect cones from healthy trees that are between 10 and 12 years old. Use the graph to find three different heights of trees from which Craig should collect cones.

Samantha is ordering live bass and catfish to stock a pond. She wants a 10 to 1 ratio of bass to catfish. She can buy a total of 550 fish.

Let x represent the number of bass Samantha orders, and let y represent the number of catfish.

51. Write an equation for the total number of fish ordered.

52. Write a proportion using the two ratios of bass to catfish. Simplify the proportion, and write a second equation relating x and y.

53. Graph the system of equations from Exercises 51 and 52 on a coordinate plane.

54. How many bass and how many catfish should Samantha order?

The band playing for the school prom will be paid $250 plus $2 per ticket sold. The maximum number of prom tickets that can be sold is 550.

55. Let x represent the number of tickets sold. Write a function rule $f(x)$ for the total amount the band is paid.

56. Describe the domain of the function. Describe the range.

57. How much will the band be paid if 461 tickets are sold?

MATH LAB

Equipment   Centimeter ruler
Cloth metric measuring tape
Meterstick
5 different cylindrical containers, such as:
   small juice can
   soup can
   1-lb coffee can
   3-lb coffee can
   5-gal bucket
Graph paper

Problem Statement

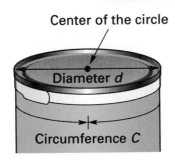

Center of the circle

Diameter *d*

Circumference *C*

$$C = \pi d$$
$$\pi = \frac{C}{d}$$

The *diameter* of a circle is the distance across the circle through the center. The *circumference* is the distance around the circle.

The ratio of a circle's circumference to its diameter is equal to a constant called *pi*. The symbol for *pi* is the Greek letter π. The value of π is approximately 3.14.

In this Activity, you will measure the circumferences and diameters of several circles, and graph the measurements. The graph and formula will be used to predict the diameter and circumference of other circles.

Procedure

a Measure the diameter *d* (to the nearest tenth centimeter) of the juice can, soup can, and 3-lb coffee can. Record the measurements in a table similar to the one shown.

Container	Diameter *d* (cm)	Circumference *C* (cm)	(*d, C*)	$\frac{C}{d}$
Juice can				
Soup can				
3-lb coffee can				

b Measure the circumference *C* (to the nearest tenth centimeter) of each can in Step **a** with the cloth measuring tape. Record the measurements in the table.

c Record ordered pairs (d, C) for each can in the table.

d Draw a coordinate plane on graph paper. Label the vertical axis C and the horizontal axis d. Use a scale for the C-axis so the axis extends to 150 centimeters. Use a scale for the d-axis so the axis extends to 50 centimeters.

e Graph the ordered pairs (d, C). Draw a line of best fit. Make sure the line passes through the origin.

f From the measurements in the table, calculate values of $\frac{C}{d}$ for the three cans. Record these values to the nearest hundredth in the table.

g Measure the diameter of the 1-lb coffee can. Estimate the circumference of the can from the graph. Calculate the circumference using the formula $C = \pi d$. Measure the circumference. Record the values in a table.

Container	Measured Diameter	Estimated Circumference	Calculated Circumference	Measured Circumference
1-lb coffee can				

h Measure the circumference of the 5-gal bucket. Estimate the diameter of the bucket from the graph. Calculate the diameter using the formula $C = \pi d$. Measure the diameter.

Container	Measured Circumference	Estimated Diameter	Calculated Diameter	Measured Diameter
5-gal bucket				

Discussion Questions

1. Compare the following. Explain any differences.

   - The calculated values of $\frac{C}{d}$ should approximate π. Compare the calculated values to the value your calculator displays for π.

   - Compare the estimated and calculated values of the circumference of the 1-lb coffee can to the measured value.

   - Compare the estimated and calculated values of the diameter of the 5-gal bucket to the measured value.

2. Is the relationship between the diameter and the circumference of a circle linear? Explain.

Equipment   Spring (with a spring constant
                  between 3 and 10 N/m)
                  Support assembly
                  Mass hanger with 50-g, 100-g, and
                  200-g slotted masses
                  Meterstick
                  Graph paper

Problem Statement

You will measure the distances several masses stretch a
spring, and then graph the relationship between distance and
mass. The relationship will be written as an equation in
slope-intercept form. You will use the graph and equation to
predict the distances other masses will stretch the spring.
Then you will compare your predictions to measured values.

Procedure

a Attach the spring and mass hanger to the support assembly.
Adjust the height so the bottom edge of the hanger is above
the table top when it is empty and below the table top when
150 g are placed on the hanger.

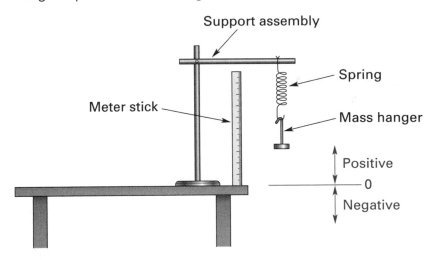

b You will measure distances between the table top and
bottom edge of the hanger, and record the values in a table
similar to the one on the next page. Record a positive value if
the distance is above the table top, and a negative value if the
distance is below the table top.

Slotted Mass x (g)	Distance Above (+) or Below (–) Tabletop y (cm)	(x, y)
0		
50		
100		
200		

c Measure and record the distances (to the nearest tenth centimeter) when each of the following masses are placed on the hanger.

0 g, 50 g, 100 g, 200 g

d Let x represent the mass and let y represent the distance. Record ordered pairs (x, y) for each slotted mass.

e Draw a coordinate plane on graph paper. Graph the ordered pairs. Draw a line of best fit.

f Find the slope and y-intercept of the line. Write an equation of the line in slope-intercept form. Record your values in a table like the one below.

Slope	y–intercept	Equation

g From your graph, estimate the distance above or below the table top for 150 g on the hanger. Estimate the distance for 250 g. Calculate the distances with the slope-intercept form of the equation. Record the values in a table like the one below.

	Distances Above (+) or Below (–) Tabletop		
Slotted Mass (g)	Estimated (cm)	Calculated (cm)	Measured (cm)
150			
250			

h Place 150 g on the hanger, and measure the distance. Repeat for 250 g. Record the values in the table.

Discussion Questions

1. Compare the estimated, calculated, and measured distances for the 150-g mass. Repeat for the 250-g mass. Explain any differences.

2. Does the line that you graphed in Step **e** continue forever? Explain your answer.

Activity 3: Break-Even Point with a Spreadsheet

Equipment   Spreadsheet computer program

Problem Statement

Kaleigh is starting a business selling hats with her school's logo. She needs to determine how many hats she must sell to break even. The break-even point is when her sales income equals her total cost.

Kaleigh has an initial, fixed cost to start the business (for stencils, inventory, advertising, display equipment, and so on). To maintain a constant inventory, she buys replacement hats from a wholesale company. For example, suppose Kaleigh's fixed cost is $210 and she pays $8.95 per hat. Let x represent the number of hats sold and let y represent her total cost.

$$\boxed{\text{total cost}} = \boxed{\text{fixed cost}} + \boxed{\text{cost for } x \text{ hats}}$$
$$y \quad = \quad 210 \quad + \quad 8.95 \cdot x$$

Suppose Kaleigh sells hats for $13.95 each. Her total income for selling x hats is $13.95 \cdot x$. In slope-intercept form,

total cost $= 8.95x + 210$

total income $= 13.95x$

These equations form a system of linear equations. The break-even point is the solution of the system of equations.

In this Activity, you will use a spreadsheet to calculate total cost and income for selling 0 to 50 hats. You will determine the number of hat sales required to break even for several different values of fixed cost, cost per hat, and sales price.

Procedure

a Enter labels as shown in a spreadsheet below.

	A	B	C	D
1	Cost per Hat	Fixed Cost	Selling Price	
2				
3				
4	Hats Sold	Total Cost	Income	Profit
5				
6				
7				
8				

b In the second row, enter $8.95 for the cost per hat, $210 for the fixed cost, and $13.95 for the selling price.

c Beginning in cell A5, enter the numbers 0 through 50 down the column. These numbers represent the number of hats sold. (Hint: You can enter 0 in cell A5 and "=A5+1" in cell A6. Then copy cell A6 down to cell A55.)

	A	B	C	D
1	Cost per Hat	Fixed Cost	Selling Price	
2	$8.95	$210.00	$13.95	
3				
4	Hats Sold	Total Cost	Income	Profit
5	0	$210.00	$0.00	−$210.00
6	1	$218.95	$13.95	−$205.00
7	2	$227.90	$27.90	−$200.00
8	3	$236.85	$41.85	−$195.00

= A5*A2 + B2   = A5*C2

d In cell B5, enter a formula for calculating the total cost. Copy the formula down to row 55. (Hint: If you use the formula shown in the illustration, the values for the cost per hat and fixed cost do not change when you copy the formula.)

e In cell C5, enter a formula for calculating the income. Copy the formula down to row 55. The spreadsheet now displays values from the total cost and income equations.

f Kaleigh's profit is the income minus the total cost. Enter a formula to calculate the profit in cell D5. Copy the formula down to row 55.

g The break-even point is where the income equals total cost. What is the profit at this point? How many hats must Kaleigh sell to break even? Record the number in a table like the one shown.

h Change the data in the spreadsheet for the other costs and prices listed in the table. Calculate the break-even points for these data. To complete the last row of the table, use a trial and error strategy to find the selling price.

Cost per Hat	Fixed Cost	Selling Price	Number of Hats to Break Even
$8.95	$210	$13.95	?
$9.25	$160	$14.95	?
$7.50	$290	$15.95	?
$8.25	$175	$16.50	?
$8.25	$175	?	50

Discussion Questions

1. For some costs and prices in the table, the profit calculated by the spreadsheet did not equal zero for any number of hats sold. Explain how you should choose the number of hats sold to break even in these cases.

2. Explain how you could change the system of equations to find the selling price for a break-even point of 50 hats, instead of using trial and error.

CHAPTER 8   ASSESSMENT

1. How do you graph an ordered pair on a coordinate plane?

2. How do you find the slope of a line that is graphed on a coordinate plane?

3. What is the slope-intercept form of an equation? What part of the equation represents the slope? What part represents the y-intercept?

4. List the steps you can follow to find the solution of a system of equations by graphing.

Skills

5. Graph $A(-2, 4)$, $B(3, -5)$, and $C(-1, -1)$ on a coordinate plane. Name the quadrant that contains each point.

Graph each equation on a coordinate plane.

6. $y = 3x - 2$ **7.** $2x + y = -2$

Write each equation in slope-intercept form. Find the slope and y-intercept of each equation.

8. $2x + y = -2$ **9.** $9x + 2y = 8$

10. Solve this system by graphing. $x - y = -5$
$$-2x + y = 7$$

11. Which ordered pair is a solution of $x + 3y \le -2$?

    a. $(-1, 1)$ **b.** $(1, -1)$ **c.** $(0, 0)$

Let $f(x) = \frac{1}{2}x - 1$. Find each of the following values.

12. $f(0)$ **13.** $f(-2)$ **14.** $f(4)$

Applications

The Alpha Electric Company charges $50 for a service call plus $40 per hour on the job. The Beta Electric Company charges a flat rate of $45 per hour.

15. Define variables and write a system of equations that model the charges for each company.

16. Solve the system of equations by graphing. How many hours are required for a service call if both companies charge the same for their work?

The fee to join a skating club is $20. Monthly dues are $5. Let x represent the number of months you are a member of the club. Let y represent the total amount you pay to the club.

17. Write a linear equation to model the amount paid to the club for the initial fee plus monthly dues.

18. Graph the equation on a coordinate plane.

19. How much does it cost to belong to the club for the first 6 months?

Dalia's car has a fuel tank that holds 64 liters of gas. The car averages 12 kilometers per liter of gas consumed. Dalia starts with a full tank of gas and drives 600 kilometers on a trip.

20. A graph of the kilometers driven and liters of gas consumed is linear. What is the slope of the line?

21. Use the slope to find the number of liters of gas consumed in the 600-kilometer trip.

22. How many liters of gas are left at the end of the trip?

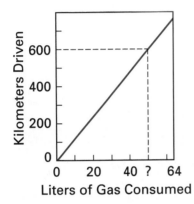

Kilometers Driven vs. Liters of Gas Consumed

Math Lab

23. The circumference C and diameter d of a circle are related by the linear equation $C = \pi d$. If you graph this equation, what is the slope? What is the diameter of a circle whose circumference is 12 centimeters?

24. A spring and mass hanger are suspended above a tabletop. When it is empty, the hanger is 45 centimeters above the table. When a 100-gram mass is placed in the hanger, it is 25 centimeters above the table. Write these two data points as ordered pairs (mass x, distance y). If you graph these points on a coordinate plane and connect them with a line, what is the y-intercept of the line? What is the slope? Write an equation of the line in slope-intercept form.

25. A part of a spreadsheet from a break-even analysis is shown. How many hats must be sold to break even?

4	Hats Sold	Total Cost	Total Income	Profit
39	34	$608	$596.70	–$11.30
40	35	$620	$614.25	–$5.75
41	36	$632	$631.80	–$0.20
42	37	$644	$649.35	$5.35

WHY SHOULD I LEARN THIS?

You can use the basic properties of geometry to solve problems involving points, lines, planes, angles, and polygons. How are polygons used in designing and constructing bridges?

Contents: Introduction to Geometry

INTRODUCTION TO GEOMETRY

LEARN HOW TO...

1. Understand how the figures of geometry are composed of the three basic figures: points, lines, and planes.
2. Solve problems using the perimeter and angle measures of triangles and other polygons.
3. Identify and solve problems using congruent polygons.
4. Perform geometric transformations using translations, reflections, or rotations.

In the last chapter, you studied algebraic relationships among variables in functions. In this chapter, you will study geometric relationships among points, lines, and planes. These are the basic figures of geometry.

More complicated figures are constructed from the basic figures. For example, segments and rays are constructed from lines. Angles are constructed from rays, and polygons are constructed from angles and segments. In this chapter, you will use segment lengths and angle measurements to investigate the properties of polygons.

Architects and engineers use polygons to design buildings, bridges, and airplanes. With a computer-aided design (CAD) program, the designer can quickly see effects of sliding, flipping, or turning polygons. These changes in position are called transformations.

LESSON 9.1 BASIC GEOMETRIC FIGURES

In the last chapter, you used ordered pairs to locate points on a coordinate plane. You used tables of ordered pairs and equations to draw straight lines on a coordinate plane. Points, lines, and planes are also important in geometry. They are the **basic figures** of geometry.

A **point** is a location in space.

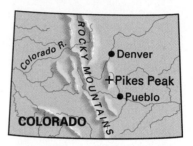

A point locates the nail's position when hanging a picture.

A crossmark + on a map locates the highest point on Pikes Peak.

Make a small pencil dot anywhere on a sheet of paper. Label the dot with the capital letter A. The dot represents point A.

The dot, the nail on the wall, and the + on the map are only representations of points. In geometry, points have no size. A point identifies an object's location, but not its size.

Draw a second dot on your paper to represent point B. Place a straightedge on the paper so that it touches both A and B. Draw a pencil mark on the paper along the straightedge through both points. Draw arrows at the ends to show that the mark extends beyond the points. The pencil mark represents a *line*.

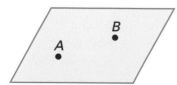

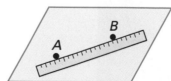

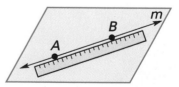

How many different ways are there of drawing a line through A and B?

In plane geometry, a **line** is a set of points that extends forever in opposite directions. Lines have no thickness or width. A line is named by two points on the line. There are four ways of naming the line containing A and B: line AB, line BA, $\overleftrightarrow{AB}$, or $\overleftrightarrow{BA}$. You can also name a line with a lowercase letter such as m.

The third basic figure of geometry is the *plane*. A **plane** is a flat surface that extends forever. You can represent planes with walls, floors, tabletops, and pieces of paper like the one containing $\overleftrightarrow{AB}$. Although these models cannot show it, planes extend forever, but they have no thickness. Use a capital letter to name a plane.

In geometry, the intersection of two figures is the set of points that both figures have in common.

If two lines intersect, they have exactly one point in common. The intersection of m and n is point A.

If two planes intersect, they have exactly one line in common. The intersection of P and Q is m.

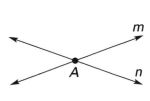

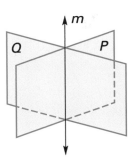

ACTIVITY

Naming Line Segments and Rays

1 Place your hand palm down on a piece of paper. Draw one point at the tip of your thumb, one at your index finger, and one at your little finger. Label the points Q, R, and S.

2 Using a straightedge, draw part of a line connecting Q and R. The figure you have drawn is called a **line segment** or **segment**. Points Q and R are the **endpoints** of the line segment. There are four ways to name the segment: segment QR, segment RQ, $\overline{QR}$, or $\overline{RQ}$.

3 How many other segments can you draw using Q, R, and S? Draw and name the segments.

4 Draw two other points on the paper. Label the points *B* and *C*.

5 Using a straightedge, draw part of a line that has an endpoint at *B*, passes through *C*, and extends forever in that direction. The figure you have drawn is a **ray**. There are two ways of naming the ray: ray *BC* or $\overrightarrow{BC}$. Notice the first letter in the name is the endpoint of the ray.

6 Draw point *A* not on $\overrightarrow{BC}$. Draw $\overrightarrow{AB}$ and $\overrightarrow{CA}$.

A straight road on a map models a line segment. A laser beam models a ray.

ONGOING ASSESSMENT

How are rays and line segments the same? How are they different?

Examine the drawing. $\overrightarrow{AB}$ and $\overrightarrow{AC}$ below share a common endpoint. The figure formed is called an **angle**. The common endpoint *A* is the **vertex** of the angle. The **sides** of the angle are $\overrightarrow{AB}$ and $\overrightarrow{AC}$.

The symbol $\angle$ is used to abbreviate *angle*. You can name this angle by writing any of the following: $\angle BAC$, $\angle CAB$, $\angle A$, or $\angle 1$.

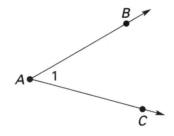

Notice the letter for the vertex is always in the center when three letters are used to name an angle.

EXAMPLE   Naming Geometric Figures

1. Name each line segment containing point *P*.

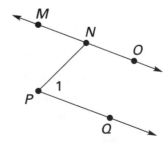

2. Name each ray containing endpoint *N*.

3. Give four different ways of naming the angle containing vertex *P*.

4. Points that lie on the same line are **collinear**. Name three collinear points.

SOLUTION

1. $\overline{NP}$ and $\overline{PQ}$

2. $\overrightarrow{NM}$ and $\overrightarrow{NO}$

3. $\angle NPQ$, $\angle QPN$, $\angle P$, and $\angle 1$

4. *M*, *N*, and *O* are collinear.

LESSON ASSESSMENT

Think and Discuss

1 Explain how each geometric figure is different than the model listed beside it.

Figure	**Model**
a. point	a star in the sky
b. line	a goal line on a football field
c. plane	a window glass
d. ray	a flashlight beam
e. angle	hands on a watch

2 Explain why you should not use $\angle A$ to name this figure.

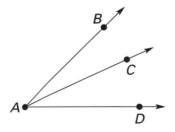

3 How many planes are represented by the floor, walls, and ceiling of your classroom?

4 Some of the planes in your classroom intersect to form lines. How many of these lines can you count? Describe the points where the lines intersect.

Name each geometric figure. Use symbols where possible.

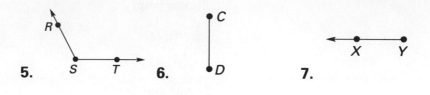

5.

6.

7.

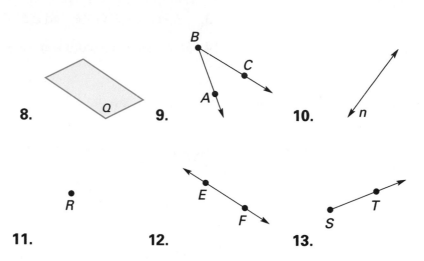

8.

9.

10.

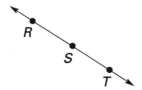

11.

12.

13.

Use this figure to answer Exercises 14–16.

14. Name the line in three different ways.

15. Name three line segments.

16. Name four rays.

17. How many different ways are there to name this angle? Write the names.

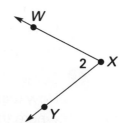

Make a sketch of each figure.

18. $\overleftrightarrow{AB}$ **19.** $\overrightarrow{QR}$ **20.** $\overline{XY}$ **21.** $\angle STU$

22. Line m and $\overline{IJ}$ intersecting at I.

23. Collinear points A, B, and C with C between A and B.

24. $\angle WXY$ and $\angle YXZ$ sharing a common side, $\overrightarrow{XY}$.

Draw figures for Exercises 25–27. Use the figures to answer each question.

25. What is the vertex of $\angle LMN$?

26. What are the sides of $\angle LMN$?

27. Points I, J, and K are collinear. Points H, J, and L are collinear. What is the intersection of $\overleftrightarrow{IK}$ and $\overleftrightarrow{HL}$?

Draw a figure for each of the following. If the figure cannot be drawn, write *impossible*.

28. Line AB with point C between A and B

29. Two different lines m and n passing through points P and Q

30. $\overrightarrow{XY}$ and $\overrightarrow{YX}$

31. $\angle AOB$ and $\overline{OB}$

32. Two noncollinear points

33. $\overleftrightarrow{AB}$, point P not on $\overleftrightarrow{AB}$ and $\overrightarrow{AP}$

34. A plane and a point not in that plane

Mixed Review

Write each fraction as a percent.

35. $\dfrac{3}{4}$ **36.** $\dfrac{1}{8}$ **37.** $2\dfrac{1}{2}$

Write each percent as a fraction in simplest form.

38. 0.125%   **39.** 4%   **40.** $16\dfrac{2}{3}$%

A number cube with numbers 1 through 6 is rolled two times.

41. What is the probability that the first number is even and the second number is prime?

42. What is the probability that neither of the two numbers is even?

LESSON 9.2 ANGLES

OBJECTIVES
- Measure angles.
- Draw angles of a specific measurement.
- Classify angles including supplementary and complementary.
- Construct a circle graph using angles measures.

You can model an angle with two pencils. Place the pencils with their erasers together. Think of each pencil as a ray that forms a side of the angle.

To change the shape of the angle, pivot one of the pencils around the vertex. How many different angles can you make?

Angles are measured as part of a circle. The circle is divided into 360 parts. Each part is one **degree**, written 1°.

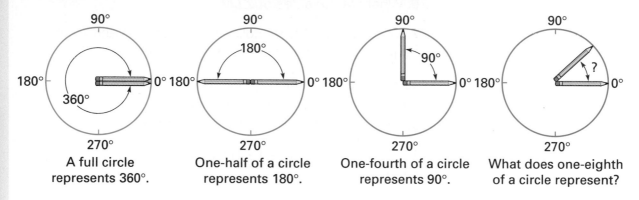

A full circle represents 360°.

One-half of a circle represents 180°.

One-fourth of a circle represents 90°.

What does one-eighth of a circle represent?

A **protractor** is a tool for measuring angles.

ACTIVITY 1   Measuring an Angle

Follow these steps to measure ∠CAB.

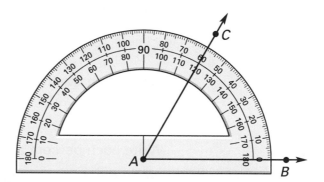

1   Place the midpoint mark of the protractor over vertex *A*.

2   Align $\overrightarrow{AB}$ with the 0° mark on the protractor. This example uses the outside scale.

3   The measure of ∠CAB is the number where $\overrightarrow{AC}$ crosses the scale of the protractor. What is the measure of ∠CAB?

You can write *The measure of ∠CAB is equal to 60 degrees* as
m∠CAB = 60°.

ONGOING ASSESSMENT

Find the measure of each angle.

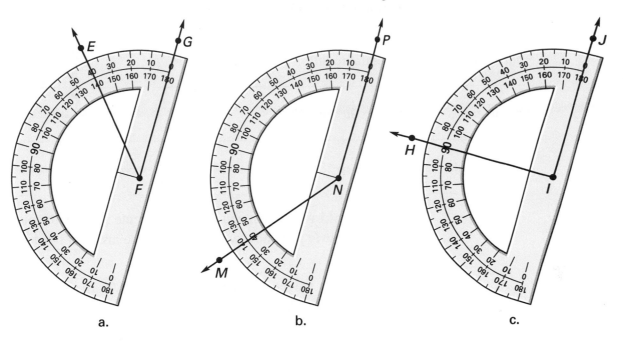

a.   b.   c.

EXAMPLE 1   Drawing an Angle

Draw an angle that measures 120°.

SOLUTION

Draw a ray. Label the ray $\overrightarrow{IJ}$. Place the midpoint of the protractor over the endpoint *I*. Align $\overrightarrow{IJ}$ with the 0°-mark on the outside scale. Make a point at 120°. Label the point *K*. Draw $\overrightarrow{IK}$.

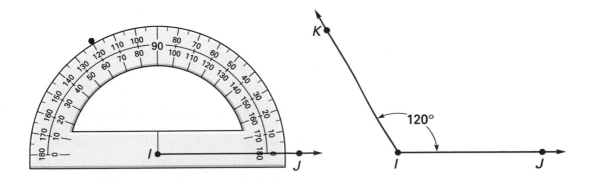

m∠KIJ = 120°

Angles are classified by the number of degrees they contain.

Classifying Angles

Name	Measure	Example	Application
acute angle	between 0° and 90°		
right angle	equal to 90°		
obtuse angle	between 90° and 180°		
straight angle	equal to 180°		

Critical Thinking When you measure an acute angle with your protractor, how do you know whether to read the inside or outside scale?

When the sum of the measures of two angles is 180°, the angles are **supplementary**. When the sum of the measures of two angles is 90°, the angles are **complementary**.

EXAMPLE 2 Supplementary and Complementary Angles

Which pairs of angles below are supplementary? Which are complementary?

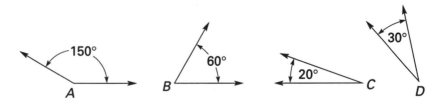

SOLUTION

Since m∠A + m∠D = 180°, ∠A and ∠D are supplementary.

Since m∠B + m∠D = 90°, ∠B and ∠D are complementary.

Two angles are **adjacent** if they share a common side, but do not overlap each other. In this drawing, ∠1 and ∠2 are adjacent.

ACTIVITY 2   Adjacent Supplementary Angles

1 Draw a line segment with endpoints *A* and *B*. Draw point *C* anywhere on $\overline{AB}$ between *A* and *B*. Draw point *D* not on $\overleftrightarrow{AB}$.

A   B

2 Draw $\overline{CD}$. Measure ∠*ACD* and ∠*DCB*. Write the measures on your drawing.

3 What is m∠*ACD* + m∠*DCB*? Explain why ∠*ACD* and ∠*DCB* are adjacent and supplementary. Classify ∠*ACB*.

ACTIVITY 3   Adjacent Complementary Angles

1 Using your protractor, draw a 90° angle. Label the angle ∠*EFG*. A 90° angle is also called a **right angle**. The symbol at the vertex in this figure shows that ∠*EFG* is a right angle. Draw a point *H* anywhere in the interior of ∠*EFG*.

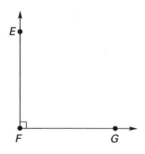

2 Draw $\overrightarrow{FH}$. Measure ∠*EFH* and ∠*HFG*. Write the measures on your drawing.

3 What is m∠*EFH* + m∠*HFG*? Are ∠*EFH* and ∠*HFG* adjacent? Are they complementary?

Use the results of Activity 2 and Activity 3 to complete the following.

Two adjacent supplementary angles form a(n) _____ *angle.*

Two adjacent complementary angles form a(n) _____ *angle.*

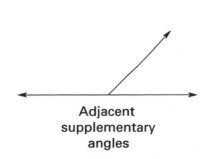

Adjacent
supplementary
angles

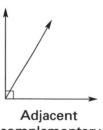

Adjacent
complementary
angles

EXAMPLE 3 Construct a Circle Graph

Construct a circle graph for the data in the table.

Favorite Subject Survey

Class	Favorite Subject
Math	25%
Science	10%
History	50%
English	15%

SOLUTION

A **central angle** has its vertex at the center of a circle. To find the measures of the central angles needed to construct the circle graph, multiply 360° by each of the percents in the table.

Favorite Subject Survey

Class	Favorite Subject	Angle Measure
Math	25%	25% of 360° = 90°
Science	10%	10% of 360° = 36°
History	50%	50% of 360° = 180°
English	15%	15% of 360° = 54°

Draw a circle with a compass. Mark the center of the circle. Use the center for the vertex of the four angles. Use the angle measures in the table and a protractor to complete the circle graph.

Favorite Subject Survey

LESSON ASSESSMENT

Think and Discuss

1 One definition of *degree* is a step or stage in a process. How is this similar to using degrees to measure angles?

2 A protractor has an inside scale and an outside scale. Use adjacent angles to explain why the sum of the numbers at each scale mark equals 180°.

3 Suppose two equal adjacent angles are supplementary. Describe these angles.

4 List the steps to construct a circle graph to show the percent of students in your class who buy lunch from the cafeteria.

Trace each angle on your paper. Find the measure of the angle. Then classify the angle.

5.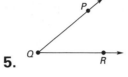

6.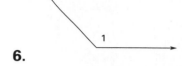

7.

8.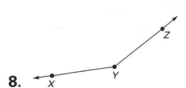

Use a protractor to draw each of the following angles.

9. m∠ABC = 45°   **10.** m∠XYZ = 70°

11. m∠JKL = 120°   **12.** m∠STU = 160°

Tell whether ∠1 and ∠2 are supplementary, complementary, or neither.

13. 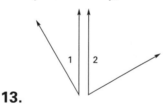   **14.**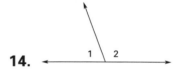

15. 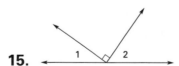   **16.**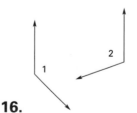

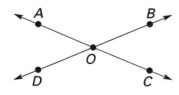

Use a straightedge and pencil to draw two intersecting lines. Label the intersection point *O*. Label *A, B, C,* and *D* clockwise as shown in this illustration. Use the drawing to complete Exercises 17–18.

17. What is m∠AOB + m∠BOC?

18. What is m∠AOB + m∠AOD?

19. What do you think is *true* about adjacent angles formed by intersecting lines?

Construct a circle graph to represent each set of data.

20. Weather conditions for the summer months:

> Sunny: 45%
> Cloudy: 20%
> Partly Cloudy: 35%

21. Preferred cafeteria meals of 80 students:

Pizza: 28   Hamburgers: 19   Spaghetti: 13
Fish: 12   Grilled Cheese: 8

22. Monthly sales for The Appliance Warehouse:

40 refrigerators   30 television sets
20 washers and dryers   10 dishwashers

23. Coverage of the Earth's surface:

> Pacific Ocean: 35%
> Atlantic Ocean: 17%
> Indian Ocean: 15%
> Arctic Ocean: 3%
> Other Water: 5%
> Land: 25%

Mixed Review

24. Write each italicized number in decimal form.

The *Cassini* spacecraft passed within *one hundred seventy-six* miles of Venus. *Cassini* should reach its goal—Jupiter—on July first, *two thousand four.* Cassini moves at *eighty-seven thousand* miles per hour and will travel *seven* years on its *two billion, two hundred million*-mile trip.

Evaluate each expression when $a = \frac{1}{3}$, $b = -\frac{3}{4}$, **and** $c = \frac{1}{6}$.

25. $a + b - c$

26. $ab + c$

27. $\dfrac{ab}{c}$

28. $a(b + c)$

Write a percent equation and solve.

29. 40 is what percent of 160?

30. 25% of what number is 136?

31. What is 37.5% of $680?

LESSON 9.3 TRIANGLES

OBJECTIVES

- Classify triangles.
- Find measurements of angles in a triangle.

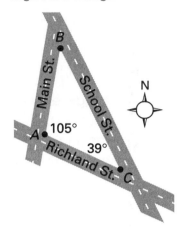

Aeisha is a surveyor taking measurements of a lot enclosed by three streets. The lot is in the shape of a *triangle*. **Triangle** means *three angles*.

Aeisha has measured two of the angles. How can she calculate the measure of the third angle without surveying?

A triangle is named by the vertices of its angles. The *triangle symbol, Δ*, is used to abbreviate *triangle*. The name of the triangle formed by the three streets can be written Δ*ABC*. What are two other names for Δ*ABC*?

In geometry, figures that have the same size and shape are called **congruent figures**. If two segments are congruent, they have the same length. If two angles are congruent, they have the same measure.

Triangles are often classified by the number of sides that are congruent. The tic marks on the sides of the triangles indicate the congruent sides.

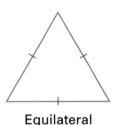

Equilateral
3 congruent sides

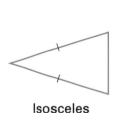

Isosceles
2 congruent sides

Scalene
No congruent sides

Triangles are also classified by their angles. Congruent angles are shown by the rounded marks on the angles.

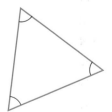

Equiangular
3 congruent angles

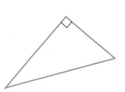

Right
1 angle measures 90°.

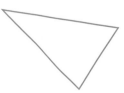

Acute
Each angle measures less than 90°.

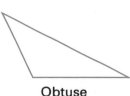

Obtuse
1 angle measures more than 90°.

1 Draw a right triangle, an acute triangle, and an obtuse triangle. Draw each triangle large enough to measure the angles with a protractor.

2 Trace one of the triangles onto a second piece of paper. Cut out the triangle along its sides. Cut or tear two corners from each triangle, and arrange them as shown.

3 The three angles are adjacent. What type of angle do they form? Compare your results with others in your class. Make a guess about the sum of the measures of the angles of a triangle. When you make a guess from observations, you are making a **conjecture**.

4 Measure the angles of each triangle in Step 1. Write the measure of each angle on the triangles.

5 Find the sum of the measures of the angles of each triangle. Compare your results with the rest of your class. Do the measurements confirm your conjecture?

Angle-Sum Property for Triangles
The sum of the measures of the angles in a triangle is 180°.

EXAMPLE 1 Finding a Third Angle Measure

How can Aeisha find m∠B without surveying?

SOLUTION

Use the Angle-Sum Property for Triangles.

$$m\angle A + m\angle B + m\angle C = 180°$$

$$105° + m\angle B + 39° = 180°$$

$$m\angle B + 144° = 180°$$

$$m\angle B = 36°$$

The measure of the angle formed by Main Street and School Street is 36°.

EXAMPLE 2 Angle Measures in a Right Triangle

You are building a concrete ramp. A wooden form is needed to hold the concrete in place as it dries. The form is in the shape of a right triangle. The ramp will make a 10° angle with the ground. What measure should you make the third angle?

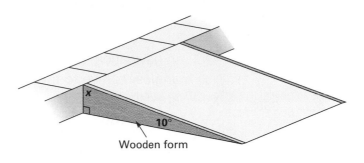

Wooden form

SOLUTION

Let x represent the measure of the unknown angle. Since the wooden form is a right triangle, one angle measures 90°.

$$x + 10° + 90° = 180°$$

$$x = 180° - 90° - 10°$$

$$x = 80°$$

The third angle of the form should measure 80°.

ONGOING ASSESSMENT

Find the measure of the unknown angle for each triangle.

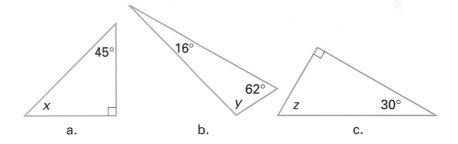

a.   b.   c.

Critical Thinking Is the following statement *true* for all right triangles? Explain your reasoning.

In a right triangle, the acute angles are complementary.

Use the statement to show how to solve Example 2 and Ongoing Assessment **a** and **c**.

PROBLEM SOLVING

USING THE FOUR-STEP PLAN

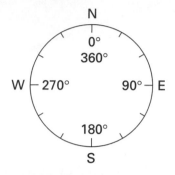

In navigation, a magnetic compass is used to measure angles relative to the magnetic North Pole. These angles are called *headings*. A heading of 0° or 360° is North, 90° is East, 180° is South, and 270° is West.

Two search-and-rescue teams can locate a downed airplane by measuring headings to an emergency radio beacon transmitted from the airplane.

On a coordinate grid, where x- and y-distances are measured in miles, Team A is at (1, 1) and Team B is at (4, 8). Team A measures the heading to the beacon as 40°. Team B measures the heading as 150°. What are the approximate coordinates of the downed airplane? Estimate the distance each team is from the airplane. Which team is closest to the airplane?

Step 1 Understand the Problem

How many lines can you draw through a point with a given heading? If two lines on a plane are not parallel, do they intersect? In how many points?

Step 2 Develop a Plan

Draw a diagram. Locate Team A and Team B on a coordinate plane. Draw the heading to the beacon from each team. What point represents the location of the downed airplane?

Step 3 Carry Out the Plan

Use a straightedge and protractor to draw the diagram on grid paper. Make sure the scale intervals on the axes are the same, so that the drawing will be a scale drawing. To measure the length of a segment on the scale drawing, set a compass width to the distance and measure the width on one of the axes.

Step 4 Check the Results

Are your answers reasonable?

LESSON ASSESSMENT

1 Can a triangle have two angles that are supplementary? Explain.

2 In an equiangular triangle, all three angles are congruent. What are the measures of each angle of an equiangular triangle?

3 Can an acute triangle have two angles that are complementary? Explain.

4 Explain why an obtuse triangle must have two acute angles.

Practice and Apply

Classify each triangle by its sides and angles.

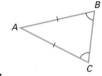

5.

6.

7.

8.

9.

10.

For Exercises 11–16, draw the triangle if possible. If it cannot be drawn, explain why not.

11. A right isosceles triangle   **12.** An obtuse isosceles triangle

13. An obtuse right triangle   **14.** An acute scalene triangle

15. An obtuse scalene triangle **16.** A right equilateral triangle

For Exercises 17–19, find m∠C.

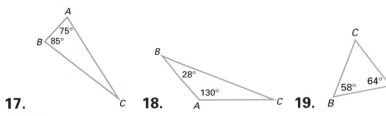

17.   **18.**   **19.**

For Exercises 20–22, find the values of *x*.

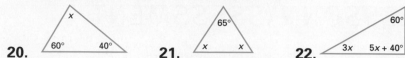

20.   **21.**   **22.**

23. In a certain right triangle, the acute angles are congruent. Find the measures of the congruent angles.

24. In a certain right triangle, the acute angle measures are in a 2:1 ratio. Find the measures of the acute angles.

Mixed Review

Solve each equation.

25. $3m + 8 = 7$ **26.** $-2r - 6 = -5$

27. $8 = \dfrac{2}{3}d + 4$ **28.** $-1\dfrac{1}{2}g - 8 = 7$

Solve and graph each inequality on a coordinate plane.

29. $5p - 3 > 12$ **30.** $-\dfrac{2}{3}x + 3 \le 27$

Tickets numbered 1 through 20 are placed in a box. One ticket is drawn. Find each probability.

31. The ticket number is odd.

32. The ticket number is a multiple of 4.

33. The ticket number is greater than 6.

34. The ticket number is less than or equal to 10.

Cumulative Problem Solving

The illustration at the left shows part of a football field. Suppose a kicker attempts field goals from *C* and *D*. To make a field goal, the football must be kicked between the goal posts, represented by *A* and *B*. The ball must also pass over the crossbar.

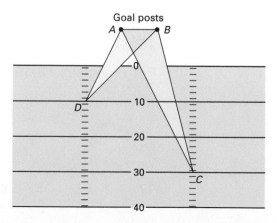

35. Trace ∠ADB and ∠ACB. What is m∠ADB? What is m∠ACB?

36. Explain why it is more difficult to make a field goal from point *C* than from point *D*.

You locate a point on a coordinate plane by giving its *x*- and *y*-coordinates. You locate a point on a globe by giving its latitude and longitude.

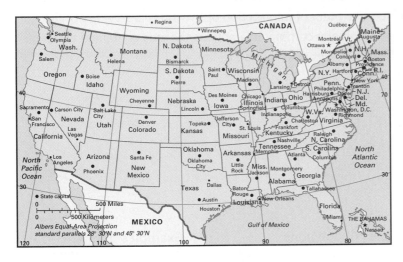

- Latitude lines run east and west. The equator is 0° latitude. When you give a point's latitude, you must specify whether it is north or south of the equator.

- Longitude lines run north and south. The 0° longitude line runs through Greenwich, England. When you give a point's longitude, you must specify whether it is east or west of Greenwich.

All points in the U.S. have north latitude and west longitude. For example, Columbus, OH is located at approximately 40° north latitude and 83° west longitude. This is abbreviated 40° N, 83° W.

37. What city is located at 30° N, 90° W?

38. Give the approximate latitude and longitude of Philadelphia.

39. An airplane's flight path runs approximately from 36° N, 106° W to 45° N, 101° W. What are the beginning and ending cities for the flight?

Emmett is an orthopedics technician adjusting crutches for a patient with a broken ankle. When the hand piece is properly adjusted, the patient's arm and elbow make an angle between 20° and 30°.

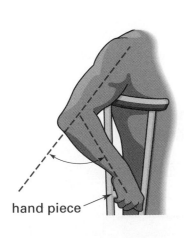

hand piece

40. Trace the angle made by the patient's arm and elbow in the illustration. What is the measure of the angle?

41. Is the hand piece properly adjusted? If not, should Emmett move the hand piece up or down?

LESSON 9.4 POLYGONS

OBJECTIVES
- - - - - - - - - - - - - -
➤ Classify polygons including regular polygons.
➤ Calculate the perimeter of a polygon.
➤ Find the measurements of the angles of a polygon.

Weather stripping

Logan is installing a window that has five sides. He needs to apply weather stripping around the outside of the window. The window has the shape of a **polygon**.

A polygon is formed by three or more consecutive segments called **sides**. Each side intersects exactly two other sides—one at each of its endpoints. The point of intersection of two sides is a **vertex** of the polygon. A polygon completely encloses the area contained within its sides. Thus, a polygon is a closed figure.

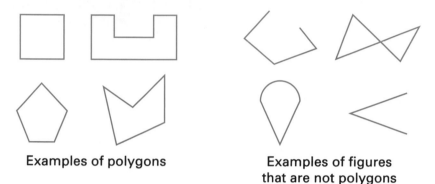

Examples of polygons   Examples of figures that are not polygons

Polygons are classified by the number of sides they contain. Several examples of polygons are shown.

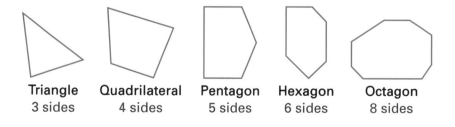

| Triangle | Quadrilateral | Pentagon | Hexagon | Octagon |
| 3 sides | 4 sides | 5 sides | 6 sides | 8 sides |

ONGOING ASSESSMENT

Study the prefixes in the table. Then draw a heptagon, nonagon, and decagon.

Prefix	Meaning
hept	7
non	9
dec	10

A polygon with all sides congruent and all angles congruent is called a **regular polygon**. To name a polygon, list its vertices in order. (*Vertices* is the plural of *vertex*.) Polygon *ABCDEF* is a regular hexagon.

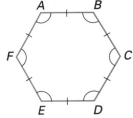

EXAMPLE 1 Perimeter

Logan's window is a pentagon. The dimensions are shown in the illustration. How many feet of weather stripping does Logan need?

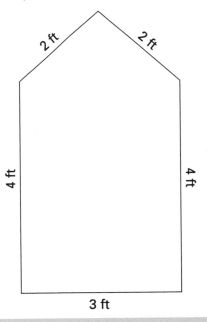

SOLUTION

Logan must find the *perimeter* of the window. The **perimeter** of a geometric figure is the distance around the figure. The perimeter of a polygon is the sum of the lengths of its sides.

$$\text{Perimeter} = 3 + 4 + 2 + 2 + 4$$

$$= 15$$

Logan needs 15 feet of weather stripping.

ONGOING ASSESSMENT

Find the perimeter of a regular hexagon with sides measuring 12 centimeters.

In the last lesson, you learned that the sum of the measures of the angles of a triangle is 180°. You can find the sum of the angles of any polygon by dividing the polygon into triangles.

1 A **diagonal** of a polygon is a line segment joining two nonconsecutive vertices. A diagonal of a quadrilateral is shown in this figure. How many triangles are formed by this diagonal and the sides of the quadrilateral? What is the sum of all the measures of the angles in these triangles?

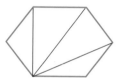

diagonal

2 A pentagon and hexagon are shown, with all possible diagonals drawn from one vertex. How many triangles are formed in the pentagon? How many are formed in the hexagon? What is the sum of the measures of the angles in all the triangles in the pentagon? What is the sum in the hexagon?

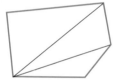

3 Copy the following table. Enter your answers from Step 2.

Polygon	Number of Sides	Number of Triangles	Sum of the Measures of the Angles
Triangle	3	1	1 • 180° = 180°
Quadrilateral	4	2	2 • 180° = 360°
Pentagon	5	?	?
Hexagon	6	?	?
n-gon	n	?	?

4 Observe the pattern in the table. How many triangles do you form in a polygon with n sides if you draw all possible diagonals from one vertex?

5 What is the sum of the measures of the angles in a polygon with n sides?

The Activity leads to the following property.

Angle-Sum Property for Polygons
The sum of the measures of the angles in a polygon with n sides is

$$(n - 2)(180°)$$

EXAMPLE 2 Finding the Measure of an Angle in a Polygon

Justine is drawing the plans for a mountain cabin. The cabin will have a floor in the shape of a regular 12-sided polygon. When Justine draws the floor, what measure should she use for each angle of the polygon?

SOLUTION

Since the floor has the shape of a regular polygon, each angle has the same measure. Let x represent this measure. Since there are 12 sides, there are 12 angles. The sum of the measures of the angles equals $12x$.

Use the Angle-Sum Property for Polygons. The number of sides n is 12.

$$12x = (n - 2)(180°)$$
$$12x = (12 - 2)(180°)$$
$$12x = 10(180°)$$
$$12x = 1800°$$
$$x = \frac{1800°}{12} = 150°$$

Each angle of the polygon should measure $150°$.

ONGOING ASSESSMENT

a. How many angles are in an octogon?

b. What is the sum of the measures of the angles in an octagon?

c. What is the measure of each angle in a regular octagon?

Critical Thinking The sum of the measures of the angles in a regular polygon is $2520°$. How many sides does the polygon have?

Geometrical shapes and patterns are commonly found in nature. In 1202, Leonardo Fibonacci, an Italian mathematician who was educated in North Africa, wrote about a natural pattern now called the Fibonacci sequence. The first eight numbers of this sequence are

1, 1, 2, 3, 5, 8, 13, 21, ...

In the Fibonacci sequence, each number (beginning with 2) is the sum of the two previous numbers. For example,

2 + 3 = 5,   3 + 5 = 8, ...

A few examples of this pattern in nature are:

- the number of petals and the arrangement of leaves around many plants

- the shape of a snail shell and some sea shells

- the arrangement of florets on cauliflower and broccoli

- the number of spirals found in pine cones, pineapples, and seed heads of many flowers

You can see the Fibonacci sequence geometrically by adding squares together. Start with a square with sides equal to 1. Add a square of the same size to form a rectangle. Continue adding squares with sides equal to the length of the rectangle. If you write the length of the sides of the squares in order as they are added, you get the Fibonacci sequence.

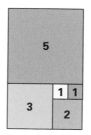

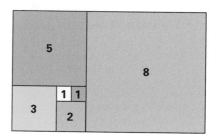

1. Draw the next two rectangles in the pattern. Label the squares with the lengths of their sides, as shown above.

2. Calculate the perimeters of the eight rectangles. Write the sequence represented by the perimeters.

3. How is the sequence of the perimeters like the Fibonacci sequence?

LESSON ASSESSMENT

Think and Discuss

1 What is the relationship between the number of sides, vertices, and angles for any polygon?

2 In baseball and softball, home plate is a pentagon. Explain why it is not a regular polygon.

3 How can you find the perimeter of a regular polygon with *n* sides?

4 Write an algorithm for finding the measure of each angle in a regular *n*-sided polygon.

Practice and Apply

Name each polygon and tell if it appears to be regular.

5.

6.

7.

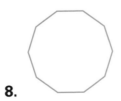

8.

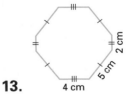

9.

10.

Find the perimeter of each polygon.

11. 1.5 m, 1.5 m, 2 m, 2 m, 3 m

12. $1\frac{1}{2}$ in.

13. 4 cm, 2 cm, 5 cm

14. The floor of a gazebo is in the shape of a regular octagon. Each side measures 9 feet. A gate 3 feet wide is placed on one side. A railing is placed around the rest of the gazebo. How long is the railing?

Find the sum of all the angles of a polygon with the following number of sides.

15. 8   **16.** 12   **17.** 15

What is the measure of each angle for the following regular polygons?

18. Nonagon   **19.** Heptagon   **20.** 20-gon

In Exercises 21–23, find the values of x.

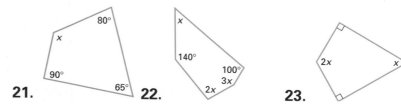

21.   **22.**   **23.**

In this figure, *ABCD* is a parallelogram and *EBFD* is a square. Find each of the following.

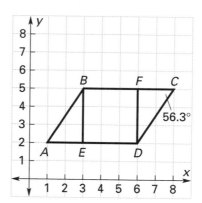

24. The length of $\overline{ED}$

25. m∠CFD

26. The length of $\overline{BC}$

27. m∠CDF

28. The perimeter of *BFDE*

Find the number of sides for each polygon if the sum of its angle measures are the following.

29. 1620°   **30.** 1260°   **31.** 3600°

Use this line graph to complete Exercises 32–35.

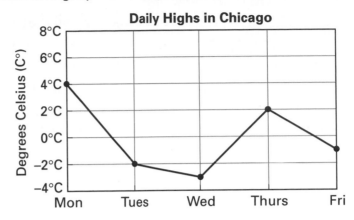

Daily Highs in Chicago

32. How much lower was the high temperature on Wednesday than on Monday?

33. How much higher was the high temperature on Thursday than on Tuesday?

34. On which day was the temperature the farthest from zero?

35. What was the average temperature for the five days?

Write and evaluate an equation for each situation.
36. The discount on a $175 dress is $35. What is the rate of discount as a percent?

37. Chuong borrowed $1500 for 8 months. The annual rate of interest on the loan is 8%. What is the total amount Chuong must repay for the loan?

For Exercises 38–43, evaluate each function when x is -2, 0, and 4.

38. $f(x) = 3x + 9$

39. $g(x) = 5(x - 3) - 2$

40. $h(x) = -\dfrac{3}{10}x + 1$

41. $f(x) = 9x(2 + x)$

42. $g(x) = \dfrac{-3x}{x - 1}$

43. $h(x) = 9 - \dfrac{x}{1 + x}$

LESSON 9.5 CONGRUENCE

Alyssa makes nylon kites. For one design, she sews triangular panels together. She makes many copies of these triangles from a pattern. How can Alyssa make sure all the triangles are the same size?

In Lesson 9.3, you used congruent figures—sides and angles— to classify different triangles. For example, isosceles $\triangle ABC$ has two congruent angles and two congruent sides.

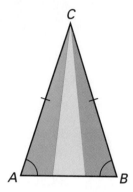

The symbol $\cong$ means *is congruent to*. Thus in $\triangle ABC$,

$$\angle A \cong \angle B \text{ and } \overline{AC} \cong \overline{BC}$$

EXAMPLE 1 Congruent Figures

Which segments are congruent? Which angles are congruent?

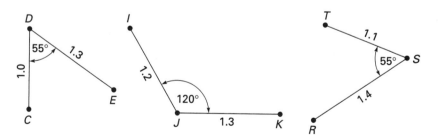

SOLUTION

$$\overline{DE} \cong \overline{JK} \text{ and } \angle D \cong \angle S$$

ACTIVITY 1   Vertical Angles

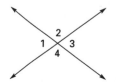

1 Using a straightedge, draw two intersecting lines on a piece of paper. Label the angles in a clockwise direction as shown in the drawing. The angle pair $\angle 1$ and $\angle 3$ are called **vertical angles**. The angle pair $\angle 2$ and $\angle 4$ are also vertical angles.

2 Measure ∠1 and ∠3. How are these angles related?

3 Measure ∠2 and ∠4. How are these angles related?

4 Compare your results with your classmates. What is the relationship between pairs of vertical angles?

> **Vertical Angles**
> The vertical angles formed by intersecting lines are congruent.

ACTIVITY 2   **Corresponding Parts**

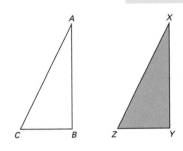

1 Trace △ABC on a piece of paper.

2 Slide the tracing over △XYZ. Is △XYZ ≅ △ABC? Explain.

3 ∠A corresponds to ∠X. Name the other pairs of **corresponding angles**.

4 $\overline{AB}$ corresponds to $\overline{XY}$. Name the other pairs of **corresponding sides**.

5 What is the relationship between corresponding angles of congruent triangles? What is the relationship between corresponding sides?

The corresponding angles and sides of two polygons are called *corresponding parts*.

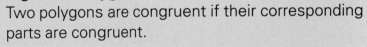

> **Congruent Polygons**
> Two polygons are congruent if their corresponding parts are congruent.

The quadrilaterals shown are congruent. The marks on the sides and angles indicate the congruent corresponding parts. For example, $\overline{RS}$ and $\overline{JK}$ both have 2 tic marks to show they are congruent corresponding parts. And ∠Q and ∠I both have 1 mark to show congruence. When you write a congruence statement, list the vertices in the same order as the corresponding angles.

ONGOING ASSESSMENT

Why is it incorrect to write *QRST* ≅ *IKJL*?

$QRST \cong IJKL$

EXAMPLE 2 Congruent Polygons

Which pairs of polygons are congruent?

a.

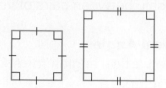

b.

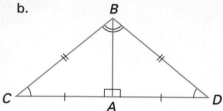

SOLUTION

a. These quadrilaterals are squares. Corresponding angles are congruent, but corresponding sides are not. The squares are not congruent.

b. The triangles share a common side, $\overline{AB}$. All corresponding sides and angles are congruent. $\triangle ABC \cong \triangle ABD$.

ONGOING ASSESSMENT

A **rectangle** is a quadrilateral with four right angles. Opposite sides of a rectangle are parallel and congruent.

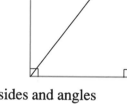

a. Alyssa cuts a rectangular piece of nylon along the diagonal to make two congruent triangles. Show the triangles are congruent by cutting a piece of notebook paper along its diagonal and overlaying the corresponding sides and angles of the triangles.

b. Draw a rectangle and its diagonal. Mark the corresponding parts of the congruent triangles.

Critical Thinking Are the triangles shown congruent? Explain your reasoning.

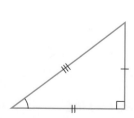

LESSON ASSESSMENT

Think and Discuss

1 Explain how you know the front cover and back cover of a book are congruent.

2 How do the legs of the ironing board form two pairs of congruent angles?

3 If two lines intersect to form a right angle, they are *perpendicular.* In the figure below, *m* is perpendicular to *n.* What are the measures of the other three angles? Explain your reasoning.

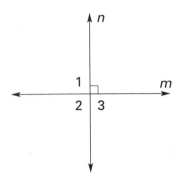

4 If $\triangle ABC \cong \triangle EFG$, which angle of $\triangle EFG$ is congruent to $\angle C$? Which side of $\triangle ABC$ is congruent to $\overline{EG}$? Explain your reasoning.

Practice and Apply

5. Which of the figures in the diagram appear to be congruent?

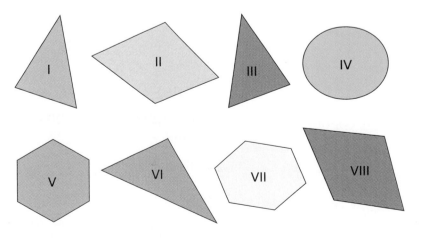

Use this figure to complete Exercises 6–10.

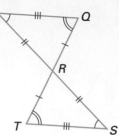

6. $\overline{QR} \cong$ ___?___

7. $\angle RTS \cong$ ___?___

8. $\angle TRS \cong$ ___?___

9. $\overline{RP} \cong$ ___?___

10. $\triangle$ ___?___ $\cong \triangle$ ___?___

11. $\triangle ABC \cong \triangle DEF$. Copy the diagram below and mark the corresponding parts.

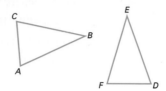

$\triangle MNO \cong \triangle CBA$. Write each angle measure or segment length.

12. $\angle B$ 13. $\overline{MN}$ 14. $\angle C$ 15. $\overline{NO}$

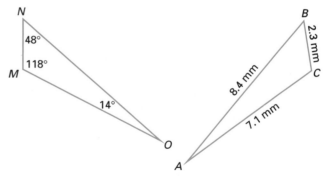

This roof truss has several congruent triangles. List the triangle congruent to each of the following.

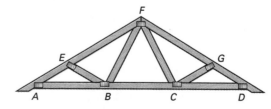

16. $\triangle ABE$ 17. $\triangle FGC$ 18. $\triangle ABF$

In this figure, m$\angle 1 = (80 + x)°$, and m$\angle 3 = (3x)°$.

19. Find x.

20. Find m$\angle 1$.

21. Find m$\angle 2$.

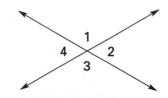

Use this illustration to answer Exercises 22–23.

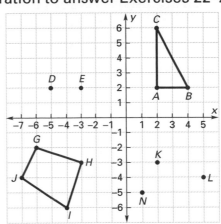

22. Give two possible sets of coordinates of point F so that $\triangle DEF \cong \triangle ABC$.

23. Give the coordinates of point M so that quadrilateral $GHIJ \cong$ quadrilateral $KLMN$.

Mixed Review

Replace the ? with $<$, $>$, or $=$ to make a *true* statement.

24. 76,408 __?__ 74,608

25. 4.708 __?__ 4.75

26. $\dfrac{2}{3}$ __?__ $\dfrac{13}{16}$

27. $2\dfrac{3}{8}$ __?__ 2.37

28. You have five ribbons of the following lengths in feet.

$$1\frac{3}{8} \qquad 2\frac{1}{4} \qquad 2\frac{5}{8} \qquad 3\frac{1}{8} \qquad 3\frac{1}{2}$$

List the ways you can combine three ribbons for a kite tail with total length between 6 and 8 feet.

29. A groundskeeper can line 10 feet of the boundary of a baseball field in 30 seconds. How long will it take the groundskeeper to line 400 feet of the boundary?

30. About 67% of your body weight is water. If you weigh 125 pounds, how much of your body weight is water?

31. If you deposit $800 in an account that draws simple interest at 5.5% per year, how much will you have in your account at the end of six months?

Draw a coordinate grid and plot each of the following points.

32. $(-3, 5)$ **33.** $(0, 2)$ **34.** $(4, 4)$ **35.** $(2.5, -1.5)$

Angela is an archeologist studying three stones from an ancient Mayan ruin. She conjectures that these stones fit together with others like them to complete a regular polygon shape.

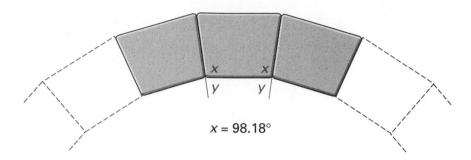

x = 98.18°

36. Angela measures the interior angles of each stone and finds that $x = 98.18°$. What is y?

37. If Angela's conjecture is *true,* what is the measure of each angle in the regular polygon?

38. How many stones are there in all if they complete a regular polygon?

Hernan is designing a hexagonal lighting fixture. The fixture will be made with six identical wooden slats. To construct the fixture, the edges along each slat must be cut at an angle, called a *bevel.*

39. What is the measure of each angle of a regular hexagon?

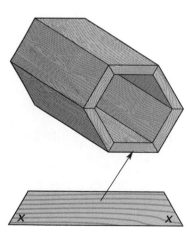

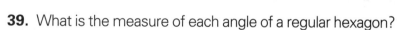

40. What is the measure of the bevel angle, *x,* for Hernan's design?

A subroutine in a computer-aided design program uses linear functions in the form $f(x) = mx + b$ to draw a polygon. The following set of functions are input to the subroutine.

$$s(x) = -2x - 6$$
$$g(x) = x - 4$$
$$h(x) = x + 6$$
$$t(x) = -2x + 6$$

41. Name the polygon drawn by the subroutine.

42. Is the polygon regular? Explain.

LESSON 9.6 TRANSLATIONS

OBJECTIVES

→ Identify a transformation as a reflection, rotation, or translation.
→ Make a translation according to a rule.
→ Given the equation of a line, write the equation of the image of the line when translated vertically.

Geometric patterns in architecture, art, fabric, wallpaper, and flooring are created by sliding, flipping, and turning figures. These movements are called **transformations**.

A transformation starts with an original figure and ends with a new figure in a new position. The new figure is the **image** of the original figure.

Original figure   Image

A **translation** is a slide from one location to another.

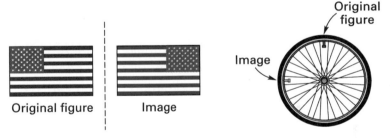

Original figure | Image

A **reflection** is a flip across a line.

A **rotation** is a turn around a point.

You can transform geometric figures on a coordinate plane.

EXAMPLE 1 Translating a Point

Translate point $A(1, 2)$ to the right 2 units and up 4 units. What are the coordinates of the image of A?

SOLUTION

Locate A on a coordinate plane. Use prime notation to identify the image. For example, point A' is read A *prime*. The image is $A'(3, 6)$. You can write the translation using an arrow:
$A(1, 2) \rightarrow A'(3, 6)$.

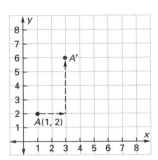

1 Draw a coordinate plane on graph paper. Draw △*ABC* with vertices at the coordinates shown.

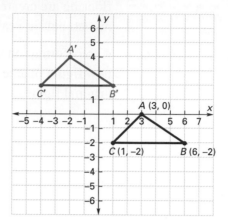

2 Trace △*ABC*. Cut out the tracing.

3 Place the tracing on the plane with its vertices at *A, B,* and *C*. In this position, the tracing represents △*ABC*. Slide the tracing so each vertex translates 5 units to the left and 4 units up. In this position, the tracing represents the image, △*A′B′C′*. What are the coordinates of the vertices of △*A′B′C′*?

4 In the translation △*ABC* → △*A′B′C′*, what is the change in the *x*-coordinate of each vertex? What is the change in the *y*-coordinate of each vertex?

5 In the translation △*ABC* → △*A′B′C′*, what is the change in the *x*-coordinate of all points on the triangle? What is the change in the *y*-coordinate of all points on the triangle?

6 Is △*ABC* ≅ △*A′B′C′*? A transformation that does not change the size or shape of a figure is called a **rigid motion**. Is a translation a rigid motion?

Activity 1 demonstrates how to translate a polygon on a coordinate plane. First, translate the vertices of the polygon. Then form the image of the polygon by connecting the vertices.

In a translation, every point on the polygon slides the same number of units. Thus, you can write a shorthand **translation rule** for finding the coordinates of the image. The rule for the translation in Activity 1 is

$$(x, y) \rightarrow (x - 5, y + 4)$$

EXAMPLE 2 Using a Translation Rule

A **parallelogram** is a quadrilateral whose opposite sides are parallel. The vertices of parallelogram WXYZ have the following coordinates.

$W(-3, 1)$ $X(1, 1)$ $Y(2, -1)$ $Z(-2, -1)$

A computer graphics program uses translation commands. How will the program display the image of WXYZ if the following translation rule is used by the program?

$$(x, y) \rightarrow (x + 4, y - 5)$$

SOLUTION

Make a table for the coordinates of the vertices.

$(x, y) \longrightarrow (x + 4, y - 5)$
$W(-3, 1) \longrightarrow W'(-3 + 4, 1 - 5) = W'(1, -4)$
$X(1, 1) \longrightarrow X'(1 + 4, 1 - 5) \ = X'(5, -4)$
$Y(2, -1) \longrightarrow Y'(2 + 4, -1 - 5) \ = Y'(6, -6)$
$Z(-2, -1) \longrightarrow Z'(-2 + 4, -1 - 5) = Z'(2, -6)$

Graph the vertices, and then connect them to form the image $W'X'Y'Z'$.

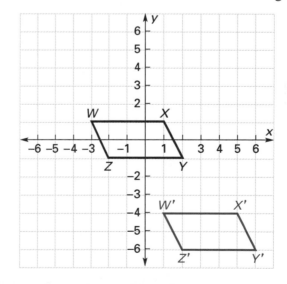

ONGOING ASSESSMENT

The vertices of the endpoints of $\overline{QR}$ are located at $Q(4,0)$ and $R(7, -3)$. Find the coordinates of the image $\overline{Q'R'}$ for the translation rule $(x, y) \rightarrow (x - 8, y + 2)$.

Critical Thinking Suppose you are given a translation rule and the coordinates of the image of a point. Explain how to find the coordinates of the original point. Find the coordinates of T if its image is $T'(3, -4)$ and the translation rule is the same as the Ongoing Assessment.

ACTIVITY 2   Translating a Line

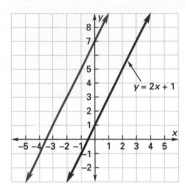

The graph of $y = 2x + 1$ and its image are shown on the coordinate plane. The image is a translation 6 units up.

1 What is the slope of $y = 2x + 1$? What is the slope of the image?

2 What is the y-intercept of $y = 2x + 1$? What is the y-intercept of the image?

3 Write the equation of the line that represents the image.

4 Compare the equation of the image to the equation of the original line. How are they the same? How are they different?

5 Suppose you are given the equation of a line and are told to translate the line w units along the y-axis. Explain how to find the equation of the image.

ONGOING ASSESSMENT

The graph of $y = -3x - 2$ is translated 3 units down. What is the equation of the image?

LESSON ASSESSMENT

Think and Discuss

1 One meaning of the word *translation* is the *process of changing*. What changes when a figure is translated?

2 On a certain map, north is *up* and west is *left*. What direction do you travel if you move 3 miles up and 2 miles to the right?

3 When a polygon is translated, is the image congruent to the original polygon? Explain.

4 An equation has a slope of -3 and a y-intercept of 5. Explain how to write the equation of the image of the line after a translation 4 units down.

For Exercises 5 and 6, use the translation $A(4, 1) \rightarrow A'(0, 8)$.

5. How far, and in which direction, has *A* moved?

6. Write the translation rule.

Match the rug design with the transformation used to create it. **A.** Translation **B.** Reflection **C.** Rotation

7. **8.** **9.**

For Exercises 10 and 11, let *Q* have coordinates (2, 5). Find the coordinates of the image *Q'* after each translation.

10. down 4 units   **11.** left 6 units, up 3 units

For Exercises 12 and 13, let point *P* have the coordinates $(-3, 7)$. **Find the image coordinates *P'* for each translation.**

12. $(x, y) \rightarrow (x - 5, y + 3)$ **13.** $(x, y) \rightarrow (x + 5, y - 3)$

14. Complete **a** and **b** on the same coordinate plane.

  a. Graph $\triangle ABC$, with vertices $A(2, 1)$, $B(-3, 0)$, and $C(0, -4)$.

  b. Graph the image and label the coordinates if the triangle is translated 3 units to the right and 6 units up.

15. Complete **a**, **b**, and **c** on the same coordinate plane.

  a. Graph rectangle *DEFG,* where the vertices are $D(4, 1)$, $E(4, 5)$, $F(7, 5)$, and $G(7, 1)$.

  b. Translate the rectangle so that the image of *G* is $G'(0, 0)$. Describe the translation.

  c. Label the coordinates of the image.

16. Graph $\triangle ABC$, with vertices $A(-1, 2)$, $B(2, 6)$, and $C(4, 3)$. Graph the image of the triangle for the translation rule $(x, y) \rightarrow (x + 2, y - 1)$.

17. Graph parallelogram *WXYZ* with vertices $W(-1, 3)$, $X(3, 3)$, $Y(4, 0)$, and $Z(0, 0)$. Graph the image of the parallelogram for the translation $(x, y) \rightarrow (x - 3, y - 2)$.

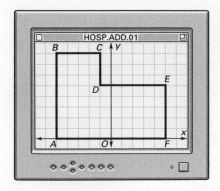

Fernando is an architect designing an addition to a hospital. The outline of the addition, polygon *ABCDEF*, is shown on a computer graphics terminal.

18. Classify the polygon.

19. Fernando needs to translate the polygon so that Point *A* is at the origin. What translation rule should he use?

20. Find the coordinates of each vertex of the image.

21. The line whose equation is $y = -3x + 2$ is moved up 4 units. What is the equation of the image?

22. The line whose equation is $y = \frac{2}{3}x - 1$ is the image of a line that has been moved down $2\frac{1}{2}$ units. What is the equation of the original line?

Mixed Review

Evaluate each expression.

23. $3c + 5d$ when $c = 2.8$ and $d = -1.3$

24. $\frac{3}{5}x - \frac{2}{3}y$ when $x = \frac{1}{3}$ and $y = \frac{3}{4}$

There are 24 boys and 18 girls in the debate club.

25. What is the ratio of boys to girls?

26. What is the ratio of girls to the total membership of the club?

Use conversion factors to convert each of the following.

27. 432 feet to yards

28. 12.5 pounds to ounces

29. 6.75 feet to inches

Solve each percent problem.

30. What is $12\frac{1}{2}\%$ of $148?

31. 15 is what percent of 10?

32. 40% of what number is 36?

33. At a 30%-off sale, Martin bought a radio-controlled airplane for $154. What was the original price of the airplane?

LESSON 9.7 REFLECTIONS

OBJECTIVES
➤ Locate the line of reflection.
➤ Graph a reflection in the coordinate plane.
➤ Identify lines of symmetry.

When you place a book in front of a mirror, you see a **reflection**. The image of the book appears to be located *behind* the mirror. The book and its image also appear to be the *same distance* from the mirror.

Looking from above, the mirror is represented by a line. This is called the **line of reflection**. Let A, B, C, and D represent the four corners of the book cover. A', B', C', and D' are the corresponding image points.

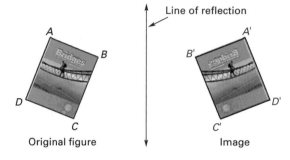

Original figure   Image

ACTIVITY 1   Properties of a Reflection

1 Fold a piece of graph paper along a diagonal and make a crease. Open the paper. The crease represents a line of reflection. Draw a rectangle on one side of the line. Label the rectangle *ABCD*.

2 Use your pencil point to make a small hole through each vertex of *ABCD*. Fold the paper along the line of reflection.

3 Mark the image points of the vertices through the holes. Open the paper. Draw the image of the rectangle by connecting the image points. Label the corresponding image points $A'B'C'D'$.

4 Using a straightedge, draw $\overline{AA'}$, $\overline{BB'}$, $\overline{CC'}$, and $\overline{DD'}$. Intersecting lines or segments that form 90° angles are **perpendicular**. Is each segment perpendicular to the line of reflection?

5 Measure the distance along $\overline{AA'}$ from A to the line of reflection, and the distance from A' to the line of reflection. Compare these distances. Repeat for the other three pairs of vertices.

In Activity 1, you discovered two Properties of a Reflection.

> **Properties of a Reflection**
> • The line of reflection is perpendicular to any segment connecting a point on the original figure to its corresponding image point.
>
> • The line of reflection is halfway between each point on the original figure and its corresponding image point.

EXAMPLE 1 Graphing the Reflection of a Point

Reflect $R(3, 4)$ over the line $y = 1$.

SOLUTION

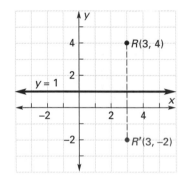

1. Graph $R(3, 4)$ on a coordinate plane.

2. Draw the line of reflection $y = 1$.

3. Draw a dashed line segment through R perpendicular to the line of reflection. From the first property of a reflection, the image of R lies on this dashed line.

4. From the second property of a reflection, R and its image are the same distance from the line of reflection. Thus R' is three units below the line $y = 1$.

You have shown $R(3, 4) \rightarrow R'(3, -2)$.

To graph the reflection of a polygon, reflect the vertices and then connect the image points.

EXAMPLE 2 Graphing the Reflection of a Triangle

The vertices of ΔRST are $R(3, 4)$, $S(4, 2)$, and $T(1, 1)$. What are the coordinates of the image of ΔRST after a reflection over the line $x = -1$?

SOLUTION

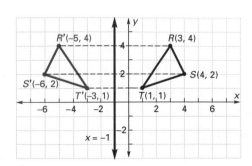

1. Graph ΔRST on a coordinate plane.

2. Draw the line of reflection $x = -1$.

3. Draw dashed line segments through each vertex perpendicular to the line of reflection.

4. Graph $R \rightarrow R'$. Since R is 4 units to the right of the line of reflection, the image R' is 4 units to the left of this line. Graph $S \rightarrow S'$ and $T \rightarrow T'$.

5. Connect R', S', and T'.

$\triangle RST \rightarrow \triangle R'S'T'$ where the coordinates of the vertices are $R'(-5, 4)$, $S'(-6, 2)$, and $T'(-3, 1)$.

ONGOING ASSESSMENT

A **trapezoid** is a quadrilateral with exactly one pair of parallel sides. Reflect trapezoid $ABCD$ at the left over the x-axis.

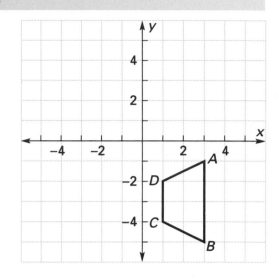

If you can reflect a figure over a line in such a way that every point on the image is also a point on the original figure, the line is a **line of symmetry**. Lines of symmetry do not have to be horizontal or vertical.

ACTIVITY 2   Lines of Symmetry

1 A square piece of paper $ABCD$ is folded along a line through its center and parallel to a side. When $ABCD$ is reflected over the fold line, is every point on the image also a point on the original figure? Is the fold a line of symmetry?

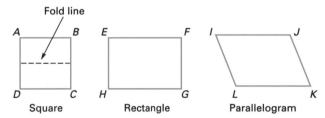

Square   Rectangle   Parallelogram

2 Identify three other lines of symmetry for square $ABCD$.

3 Identify all lines of symmetry for rectangle $EFGH$.

4 Identify all lines of symmetry for parallelogram $IJKL$.

Critical Thinking   In Activity 2, how can you conclude that $\overline{AD}$ is perpendicular to the fold line? How can you use a line of symmetry to conclude that the diagonals of a square are perpendicular?

LESSON ASSESSMENT

Think and Discuss

1 What is the line of reflection for $A(x, y) \rightarrow A'(-x, y)$? Explain your reasoning.

2 When a polygon is reflected over a line of reflection, is the image congruent to the original polygon?

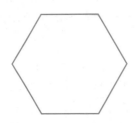

3 When you reflect a point over the x-axis or the y-axis, the absolute values of the coordinates do not change. How do the signs of the coordinates change when the point is reflected over the x-axis? How do they change when the point is reflected over the y-axis?

4 Trace the regular hexagon. How many lines of symmetry are there? Draw each one.

Practice and Apply

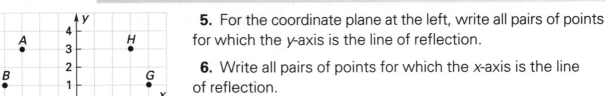

5. For the coordinate plane at the left, write all pairs of points for which the y-axis is the line of reflection.

6. Write all pairs of points for which the x-axis is the line of reflection.

Give the coordinates of the image point if each of the following is reflected over the x-axis. Graph the reflection on a coordinate plane.

7. $A(-4, 5)$ **8.** $B(-2, -3)$ **9.** $C(0, 3)$

Give the coordinates of the image point if each of the following is reflected over the y-axis. Graph the reflection on a coordinate plane.

10. $S(1, 6)$ **11.** $T(-4, 5)$ **12.** $U(-2, -1)$

For Exercises 13–16, use $\triangle PQR$ with vertices $P(-4, 5)$, $Q(-1, 2)$, and $R(-3, 1)$. Graph the image of $\triangle PQR$ for each of the following transformations. Label the coordinates of the vertices of each final image.

13. over the x-axis

14. over the line $x = 2$

15. over the line $y = -1$

16. $(x, y) \rightarrow (x + 2, y + 3)$

For Exercises 17–21, use the segment with endpoints
M(2, 3) and N(5, 2).

17. Graph $\overline{MN}$.

18. Graph the image of $\overline{MN}$ defined by the rule $(x, y) \rightarrow (x, -y)$.

19. Describe the change in coordinates of the original segment to its final image.

20. Graph the image of $\overline{MN}$ defined by the rule $(x, y) \rightarrow (x - 3, -y)$.

21. Describe the change in coordinates of the original segment to its final image.

For Exercises 22–24, use $E(-3, 4)$ and $F(4, -3)$.

22. Graph E, F, and the line $y = x$ on the same coordinate grid.

23. What is the relationship between the coordinates of E and F?

24. F is the image of E reflected over the line $y = x$. Write a rule that describes the reflection of a point over the line $y = x$ in the form $(x, y) \rightarrow (\underline{?}, \underline{?})$.

Mixed Review

For Exercises 25–28, define a variable, write an equation, and solve.

25. The school record for the high jump is 7 ft $1\frac{1}{2}$ in. At the state meet, Ken jumped 6 ft 9 in. How many inches was Ken's jump below the school record?

26. The marching band has 36 freshmen. This is 30% of the total membership. How many members are in the band?

27. The length of a rectangle is 9 feet more than its width. The perimeter of the rectangle is 42 feet. What is the width of the rectangle?

28. Roberto bought 4 tickets to a concert. He paid $158.40, which included taxes of $14.40. What was the cost of each ticket before the taxes?

Evaluate each function for the given values. Then graph the function.

29. $f(x) = \frac{2}{3}x + 4$ for $x = -3$, 0, and 6

30. $f(x) = -\frac{2}{3}x + 3$ for $x = 0$, $x = \frac{9}{2}$, and $x = 3$

LESSON 9.8 ROTATIONS

OBJECTIVES
- Rotate a geometric figure about a given point.
- Name the angle of rotation.

Point *P* on the Ferris wheel rotates in a circle as the wheel turns about a center point. When the point makes a complete rotation, it turns through 360° and returns to its original position. What is the position of point *P* if it makes a rotation of 90°?

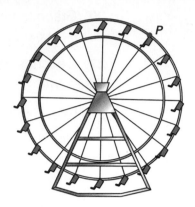

ACTIVITY 1   90° Rotations

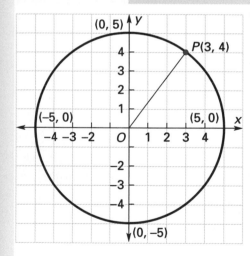

1 Draw an *xy*-coordinate plane on graph paper. Use a compass to draw a circle with radius 5 units and center *O* at the origin. Draw *P* at (3, 4). This point represents the original position of point *P* on the Ferris wheel. Draw $\overline{OP}$.

2 Use a protractor to draw a line perpendicular to $\overline{OP}$ through *O*. Label the point where this line intersects the circle in Quadrant II as *P'*. Draw $\overline{OP'}$.

3 *P'* is the image of *P* after a rotation of 90°. Find the images of *P* after rotations of 180° and 270°. Label these points *P''* and *P'''*. How many right angles have you drawn?

A **rotation** is a transformation that turns a figure about a fixed point. The Ferris wheel in Activity 1 is an example of a counterclockwise rotation about the origin. Unless otherwise stated, assume all rotations are in a counterclockwise direction.

EXAMPLE Rotating a Triangle

The vertices of a triangle are *A*(1, 3), *B*(4, 3), and *C*(4, 7). Draw the image of △*ABC* after each of the following rotations about the origin.

a. 90°   **b.** 180°   **c.** 270°

SOLUTION

First draw $\triangle ABC$ on an xy-coordinate plane.

a. Draw $\triangle ABC \rightarrow \triangle A'B'C'$.

To locate A', use a compass to draw a circle with its center at the origin O and a radius equal to the length of $\overline{OA}$. Draw a dashed line perpendicular to $\overline{OA}$ through the origin. A' is the point where this line intersects the circle in Quadrant II. Use a similar procedure to locate B' and C'.

The coordinates of $\triangle A'B'C'$ are $A'(-3, 1)$, $B'(-3, 4)$, and $C'(-7, 4)$.

b. Draw $\triangle ABC \rightarrow \triangle A''B''C''$ by rotating $\triangle A'B'C'$ $90°$ or by rotating $\triangle ABC$ $180°$. The coordinates of $\triangle A''B''C''$ are $A''(-1, -3)$, $B''(-4, -3)$, and $C''(-4, -7)$. A'' is read *A double prime*.

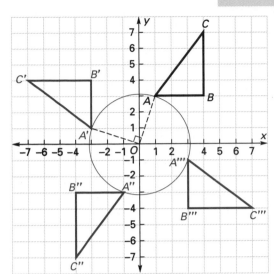

c. Draw $\triangle ABC \rightarrow \triangle A'''B'''C'''$ by rotating $\triangle A''B''C''$ $90°$ or by rotating $\triangle ABC$ $270°$. The coordinates of $\triangle A'''B'''C'''$ are $A'''(3, -1)$, $B'''(3, -4)$, and $C'''(7, -4)$. A''' is read *A triple prime*.

ONGOING ASSESSMENT

Graph $\overline{KL}$ with $K(2, 2)$ and $L(4, 6)$. Draw the image of $\overline{KL}$ after a $90°$, $180°$, and $270°$ rotation about the origin.

Critical Thinking In the Example and Ongoing Assessment, compare the coordinates of each image point with the original coordinates. Use the patterns in each rotation to complete the rotation rules.

For a $90°$ rotation: $(x, y) \rightarrow (\underline{\;?\;}, \underline{\;?\;})$

For a $180°$ rotation: $(x, y) \rightarrow (\underline{\;?\;}, \underline{\;?\;})$

For a $270°$ rotation: $(x, y) \rightarrow (\underline{\;?\;}, \underline{\;?\;})$

For a $360°$ rotation: $(x, y) \rightarrow (\underline{\;?\;}, \underline{\;?\;})$

A figure has **rotational symmetry** if every point on the rotated image is also a point on the original figure. For example, an equilateral triangle has rotational symmetry of $120°$.

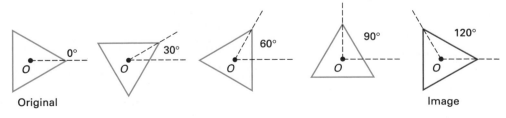

1 Draw rectangle *ABCD* with vertices as shown.

2 Rotate *ABCD* 90° about the origin.

3 Rotate *ABCD* 180° about the origin.

4 Rotate *ABCD* 270° about the origin.

5 Name the angle of rotation that gives a rectangle rotational symmetry.

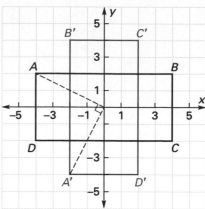

ONGOING ASSESSMENT

Name the angles of rotation that give a square rotational symmetry.

LESSON ASSESSMENT

Think and Discuss

1 Describe the path of a point as it rotates about a fixed point.

2 Suppose *P* and *Q* are two points on a bicycle wheel, and *P* rotates an angle of *x*° about the center of the wheel. What is the angle of rotation for *Q*?

3 When a polygon is rotated about a point, is the image congruent to the original figure?

4 Is the following *true* or *false*? Explain your reasoning.

Any figure has rotational symmetry of 360°.

Practice and Apply

Original figure

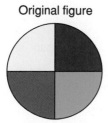

Each circle is an image formed by rotating the circle shown. What is each angle of rotation?

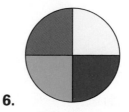

5.

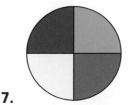

6.   **7.**

Draw the image of each figure after the given rotation about *O*.

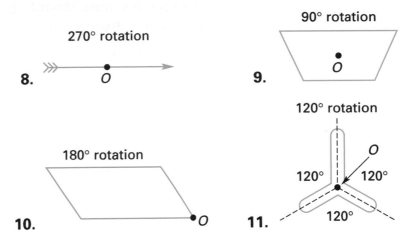

8. 270° rotation

9. 90° rotation

10. 180° rotation

11. 120° rotation

Plot each point on a coordinate plane. Plot the images formed by rotating each point the given number of degrees about the origin. Write the coordinates of each image point.

12. *A*(4, 2); 90°   **13.** *B*(−3, 5); 180°   **14.** *C*(−2, −3); 270°

15. Graph △*DEF* with vertices *D*(−7, 3), *E*(−4, 6), and *F*(−3, 1). Draw the three images formed by rotating △*DEF* 90°, 180°, and 270° about the origin.

16. Graph parallelogram *GHIJ* with vertices *G*(1, −1), *H*(5, −1), *I*(6, −3), and *J*(2, −3). Draw the three images formed by rotating *GHIJ* 90°, 180°, and 270° about the origin.

Use letters to name the location of *x* on the snowflake after each rotation about *O*.

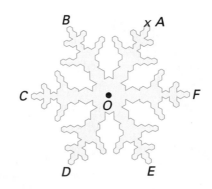

17. 120°   **18.** 180°   **19.** 300°

20. Name the rotational symmetries for the snowflake.

In Exercises 21–25, an original arrangement of pipes is shown on the left and its image after a transformation is shown on the right. Identify the transformation as a translation, reflection, or rotation.

21.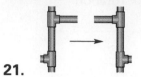

22.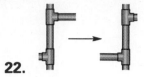

23.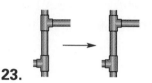

24.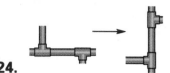

25.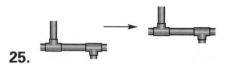

Mixed Review

In Exercises 26–29, use estimation to choose the most reasonable answer.

26. 49% of 76 is about _?_.

    a. 19   **b.** 38   **c.** 30

27. 66% of 90 is about _?_.

    a. 60   **b.** 30   **c.** 6

28. 124% of 160 is about _?_.

    a. 40   **b.** 4   **c.** 200

29. 79% of 125 is about _?_.

    a. 100   **b.** 10   **c.** 93

Solve each problem.

30. Juanita earns 6.5% commission on her weekly sales of telephone equipment. Juanita earned $292.50 last week. What was the total amount of her sales?

31. A painting is bought for $6000. The painting increases in value by 5% each of the next two years. What is the value of the painting after the second year?

32. The cost of a haircut increases from $8 to $9. What percent increase is this?

33. Thomas shoots 50 free throws after practice. He wants to make more than 75% of his shots. If Thomas makes 30 out of his first 40 shots, how many more must he make to reach his goal?

34. The value of an investment decreases 15% to $16,575. What was the original value of the investment?

Cumulative Problem Solving

In computer-aided manufacturing, the movement and assembly of parts are controlled by a computer. Each section of the manufacturing floor is modeled on a coordinate plane.

Suppose the entry point of one section is located at the origin. At the entry point, parts are placed on a conveyer belt and translated by the rule $(x, y) \rightarrow (x + 15, y + 5)$ where x and y are measured in meters.

35. Draw an xy-coordinate plane. Label point C the entry point for this section of the manufacturing floor. Locate and label point C', the image of C after translation by the conveyer. Show the coordinates of C' on the drawing.

36. At C', a robot arm picks up the part and reflects it across the line $y = 10$. Show the line of reflection on your drawing. Locate and label point C'', the image of C' after the reflection. Show the coordinates of C'' on your drawing.

37. From C'', the part is translated by a second conveyer by the rule $(x, y) \rightarrow (x + 6, y - 4)$. Locate and label point C''', the image of C'' after the translation. Show the coordinates of C'''.

38. Write a single translation rule for $C \rightarrow C'''$.

Polygon $ABCDEF$ is the basic figure for a quilt design.

39. Describe the line of symmetry for $ABCDEF$.

40. A pattern of identical polygons that covers a planar region without overlapping or leaving any gaps is called a **tessellation**. Describe how to use reflections and translations of $ABCDEF$ to tessellate a planar region for a quilt.

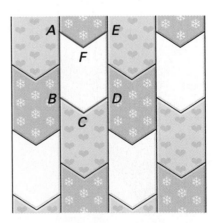

An emergency response team plots the location of an off-shore oil spill on an *xy*-coordinate plane. North is the positive *y*-direction. The spill occurs at *A*(13, 7), and spreads to the southwest.

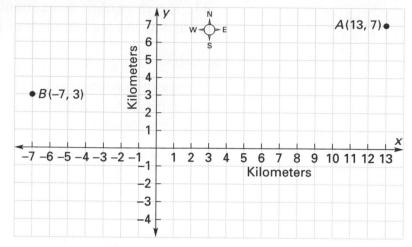

The leading edge of the spill is described by the translation rule $(x, y) \rightarrow (x - 2t, y - 3t)$ where *t* is the number of hours after the spill.

41. Complete the table of values for the leading edge of the spill for the values of *t* listed in the table. Draw an *xy*-coordinate plane, and plot the locations of the leading edge for these values of *t*.

t	(x, y)
0	(13, 7)
1	(11, 4)
2	
3	
4	
5	
6	

The emergency response team is on a ship with equipment to contain the spill. The ship leaves dock at *B*(−7, 3), and travels along a course given by the translation rule $(x, y) \rightarrow (x + 3t, y - 2t)$.

42. Complete a table similar to the one for the leading edge to show the ship's locations for the same values of *t*. Plot the ship's locations on the coordinate plane for these values of *t*.

43. How many hours after the spill does the ship arrive at the leading edge?

MATH LAB

Equipment
String (about 45 feet)
Tape measure
Marker
6 index cards
Masking tape

Problem Statement

You will use strings of different lengths as sides of triangles. Some combinations of lengths will form triangles, and other combinations will not.

Procedure

a Cut the string into 6 pieces 2, 4, 6, 8, 10, and 12 feet. Tie a knot at both ends of each string.

b Tape an index card to each string. Write the length of the string on each card.

c Assemble the first triangle as follows: Have three members of the group hold the ends of two strings together to form the vertices. Assemble the first triangle with the 10-, 6-, and 12-ft strings. Stretch the strings taut while holding the ends together.

Can you assemble a triangle with sides equal to these three lengths? If so, write Y for *yes* for the first triangle trial in a data table like the one shown.

Triangle Trial	Length of Sides (ft)			Can the triangle be assembled? (Y or N)	Is $b + c > a$? (Y or N)	$a + c > b$? (Y or N)	$a + b > c$? (Y or N)
	a	b	c				
1	10	6	12	Y			
2	10	6	8				
3	10	6	4				
4	10	6	2				
5	8	4	12				
6	8	4	10				
7	8	4	6				
8	8	4	2				

d Try to assemble each of the triangles using the lengths of sides listed in the table. Record Y or N for each trial.

e For each trial, compare the sum of the lengths $b + c$ to length a. Is the inequality $b + c > a$ *true* for the triangles you can assemble?

Is $a + c > b$?   Is $a + b > c$?

f Make a conjecture about the sum of the lengths of two sides of a triangle and the length of the third side. Test your conjecture for the triangles that you can assemble.

g Compare your conjecture to the **Triangle Inequality Property**.

The sum of the lengths of any two sides of a triangle is greater than the length of the third side.

Use the Triangle Inequality Property to predict three additional triangles that can be assembled from the lengths of the strings. Assemble the triangles to prove they are possible.

h Use the Triangle Inequality Property to predict three additional triangles that cannot be assembled from the lengths of the strings. Try to assemble the triangles to prove they are impossible.

Discussion Questions

1. Determine if a triangle can be constructed using sides of the following lengths.

    a. 3 ft, 5 ft, 7 ft   **b.** 5 m, 7 m, 1 m

    c. 3 cm, 3 cm, 5 cm   **d.** 10 in., 1 in., 9 in.

2. Suppose the base of an isosceles triangle measures $2x$. Let a represent the length of each leg, as shown in the diagram. Write an inequality to show the relationship between a and x.

3. An isosceles triangle has legs of length 10 cm. What are the possible lengths of the base of the triangle?

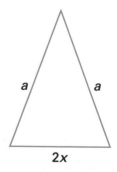

Equipment   Straightedge
                 Compass
                 Protractor
                 Ruler

Problem Statement

In this Activity, you will use a compass and a straightedge to construct geometric figures. In geometry, constructions are drawings made with a compass and straightedge only. A ruler and protractor can be used to check results, but not in creating the drawing.

Procedure

Copy a Line Segment

a Using the straightedge, draw a segment. Label the endpoints A and B.

b Draw a line and label it m. On m, label a point P.

c Set the compass point on A and adjust the compass so the pencil point is at B. Keep this adjustment and place the compass point on P. Draw an arc intersecting m. Label the point of intersection Q.

d Measure $\overline{PQ}$. Is $\overline{PQ} \cong \overline{AB}$?

Bisecting a Line Segment

e On another sheet of paper draw $\overline{PQ}$. Open the compass wider than half the length of $\overline{PQ}$. Place the compass point at P. Construct an arc above and below $\overline{PQ}$.

f Without changing the setting, place the compass point at Q. Construct an arc above and below $\overline{PQ}$ that intersects each arc you constructed in Step **e**. Label the points of intersection C and D.

g Use a straightedge to construct $\overleftrightarrow{CD}$. Label the intersection of $\overleftrightarrow{CD}$ and $\overleftrightarrow{PQ}$ point M.

h For $\overleftrightarrow{CD}$ to be the **perpendicular bisector** of $\overline{PQ}$, M must be the midpoint of $\overline{PQ}$ and m$\angle CMQ = 90°$. Use the ruler and protractor to measure. Does $PM = MQ$? Is m$\angle CMQ = 90°$? Have you constructed the perpendicular bisector of $\overline{PQ}$?

Copying an Angle

i Draw an angle and label it $\angle A$. Draw a ray with endpoint B.

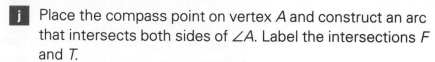

j Place the compass point on vertex A and construct an arc that intersects both sides of $\angle A$. Label the intersections F and T.

k Without changing the compass setting, place the compass on point B and construct an arc that intersects the ray and is at least as large as the arc in Step **j**. Label the point of intersection G.

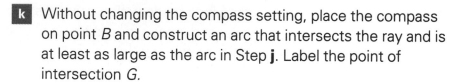

l Place the point of the compass on point T and adjust the compass until the pencil point touches F. Without changing the compass setting, place the compass point on G and construct an arc that intersects the arc you constructed in Step **k**. Label the intersection point P.

m Use a straightedge to construct $\overrightarrow{BP}$.

n Use the protractor to measure $\angle A$ and $\angle B$. Is $\angle A \cong \angle B$?

Bisecting an Angle

o Trace $\angle B$, constructed above.

p Place the compass point at vertex B and construct an arc that intersects both sides of $\angle B$. Label the intersections D and E.

q With the compass point at D and then at E, construct two intersecting arcs in the interior of $\angle B$. Use the same compass setting for both arcs. Label the intersection point F.

r Use the straightedge to construct $\overrightarrow{BF}$.

s If $\overrightarrow{BF}$ is the **bisector** of $\angle B$, then m$\angle DBF =$ m$\angle EBF$. Use the protractor to measure the angles. Have you constructed the bisector of $\angle B$?

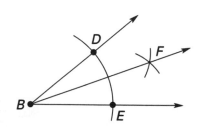

Parallel Lines Cut by a Transversal

A line that intersects two or more coplanar lines, each in a different point, is called a **transversal.** When a transversal intersects parallel lines, angles with special names are formed.

In the illustration, *t* is a transversal that intersects lines *m* and *n*.

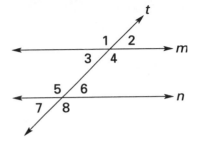

There are four pairs of **corresponding angles** formed.

∠1 and ∠5   ∠2 and ∠6

∠3 and ∠7   ∠4 and ∠8

When a transversal cuts parallel lines, corresponding angles are congruent. Since *m* and *n* are parallel, ∠1 ≅ ∠5, ∠2 ≅ ∠6, and so on.

Line Through a Point Parallel to a Given Line

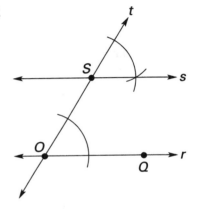

t Draw line *r*. Locate point *S* not on *r*.

u Draw transversal *t* through *S* and intersecting *r*. Label the intersection point *O*.

v Locate point *Q* on *r*.

w Copy ∠*SOQ*, so the vertex of the copy is at *S*, and one side of the copy lies along *t*. Extend the other side into a line. Label this line *s*.

Since the corresponding angles are congruent, *s* is parallel to *r*.

Discussion Questions

1. List the steps you could follow to construct an equilateral triangle. Follow your steps, and construct the triangle.

2. List the steps you could follow to construct a right triangle. Follow your steps, and construct the triangle.

3. Explain how you could construct an angle whose measure is 30°. An angle whose measure is 45°?

4. Explain how to use a transversal to tell if two lines are parallel.

Equipment   Graph paper
Scissors
Stiff paper or cardboard
Tape

Problem Statement

A **tessellation** is a design that completely covers a plane region with non-overlapping congruent shapes.

Tessellations are often used when designing patterns for wallpaper, fabrics, and flooring. M. C. Escher, a Dutch painter who lived from 1898 until 1972, created many works of art by tessellating regions with interesting shapes.

In this Activity, you will translate a part of a square to create a polygon. The polygon will then be used to tessellate a plane.

Procedure

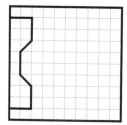

a A **square** is a quadrilateral that has four congruent sides and four right angles. Draw a square on a sheet of graph paper. Cut out the square.

b Draw a polygon on the square, using a portion of the left edge of the square as one side of the polygon. An example is shown.

c Cut out the polygon. Translate the polygon to the right, so its left side overlaps the right side of the square. Use tape to attach the polygon.

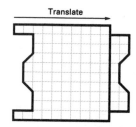

Translate

d Trace the final figure from Step **c** onto stiff paper or cardboard. Cut out the tracing.

e Trace the cardboard cutout on a sheet of paper. Translate the cutout to a new position and trace it again. Continue this process until you have tessellated an area on the paper.

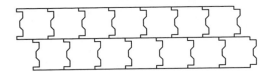

f Draw a polygon on the bottom edge of the figure from Step **d**, cut it out, and translate it to the top of the figure. Use this polygon to tessellate an area on a sheet of paper.

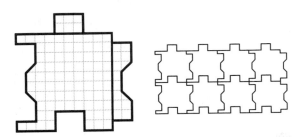

Discussion Questions

1. A rectangle tessellates because when the rectangle repeats around a common point *P*, the rectangles completely cover the region. What is the sum of the measures of all the angles about a common point in a tessallation?

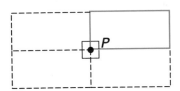

2. A tessellation that uses regular polygons is a **regular tessellation**. Which of the regular polygons shown can be used to tessellate a plane? (Hint: Repeat each polygon around a common point.)

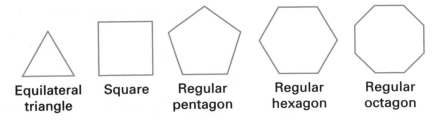

Equilateral   Square   Regular   Regular   Regular
triangle   pentagon hexagon octagon

CHAPTER 9   ASSESSMENT

Communicate

1. What geometric figure is the intersection of two lines? Of two planes? Of a line and a plane?

2. Explain why the sum of the measures of the two acute angles of a right triangle must equal 90°.

3. How do you find the sum of the measures of the angles of a polygon with *k* sides?

4. If two figures are congruent, what can you conclude about the figures?

5. List the steps you can follow to translate a triangle on a coordinate plane according to a translation rule.

Skills

For Exercises 6–9, use the figure shown.

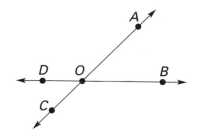

6. Name the two segments shown with endpoint *A*.

7. Name the two lines.

8. Name the vertex of ∠*AOB*.

9. Name the two acute angles shown.

Using a protractor, draw an angle of each of the following measures.

10. 80°   **11.** 135°

Find the missing angle measure for each triangle.

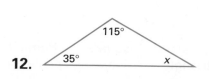

12.   **13.**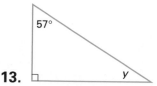

For Exercises 14–17, answer *always, sometimes,* or *never.*

14. An equilateral triangle has three congruent sides.

15. The diagonal of a polygon connects two adjacent sides.

16. Vertical angles are supplementary.

17. The image of a reflection is congruent to the original figure.

18. Point $A(-1, 5)$ is translated according to the translation rule $(x, y) \rightarrow (x + 1, y - 3)$. Find the coordinates of the image of A.

Applications

19. What is the perimeter of a regular hexagon with sides measuring 7 centimeters?

20. What is the sum of the measures of the angles of an octagon?

21. A roofing truss has the shape of an isosceles triangle. The angle at the apex is 122°. What is the measure of each base angle?

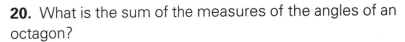

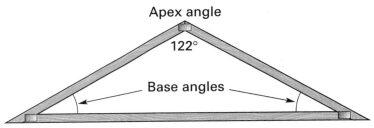

Apex angle

122°

Base angles

22. A computer graphics program reflects $B(-2, 3)$ over the y-axis. What are the coordinates of the image B'?

Math Lab

23. A landscape company submitted a bid for construction of a triangular flower bed that has sides of 8 feet, 7 feet, and 20 feet. Should you consider this a reliable bid? Explain your answer.

24. What two geometric constructions are required to construct an angle that measures 45°?

25. Show how a regular hexagon can be created by tessellations of an equilateral triangle.

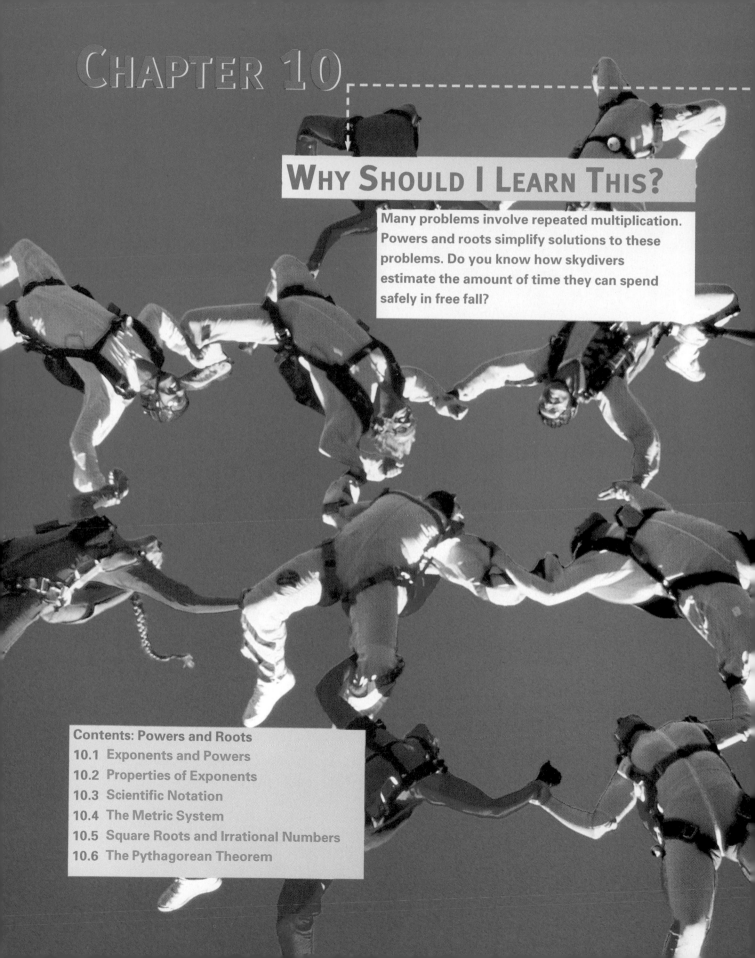

CHAPTER 10

WHY SHOULD I LEARN THIS?

Many problems involve repeated multiplication. Powers and roots simplify solutions to these problems. Do you know how skydivers estimate the amount of time they can spend safely in free fall?

POWERS AND ROOTS

LEARN HOW TO...

1. **Solve problems involving exponents using the rules of exponents.**
2. **Use scientific notation to represent very large or very small quantities.**
3. **Use appropriate units to estimate, measure, and solve problems in the metric system.**
4. **Identify and describe subsets of the real number system.**
5. **Use the Pythagorean Theorem to solve problems.**

Powers, roots, and scientific notation are shorthand methods for representing numbers. These methods simplify problem solving, recording, and computing when repeated multiplication or very large or very small quantities are involved.

For example, the volume of a sphere (such as a basketball) is computed from the formula $V = \frac{4}{3}\pi \cdot r \cdot r \cdot r$. This formula is easier to use (and remember) if it is written with an exponent: $V = \frac{4}{3}\pi r^3$.

Many scientists, engineers, and technicians use very large and very small numbers. In this chapter, you will learn how to use exponents to write these numbers in scientific notation. You will also see how powers of ten simplify measurements and calculations in the metric system. Most of the world uses the metric system to measure quantities in manufacturing, transportation, sales, and sports.

When a length is measured with a ruler, the result is a rational number. However, not all lengths can be represented by rational numbers. For example, you will use the Pythagorean Theorem to calculate the lengths of the sides of right triangles. Sometimes this calculation will result in a length that is an irrational number. In this chapter, you will learn the difference between rational numbers and irrational numbers.

LESSON 10.1 EXPONENTS AND POWERS

OBJECTIVES
- Evaluate exponential expressions.
- Use the order of operations to evaluate expressions.

Sky divers estimate their distance of free fall with the formula $d = 16t^2$. The variable d represents the free-fall distance in feet, and t represents the time in seconds. The expression t^2 is read *t to the second power* or *t squared*.

The variable t is called the **base**, and the number 2 is called the **exponent**. The exponent tells how many times the base is used as a factor. The exponent 2 means that t is used as a factor two times.

$$t^2 = t \cdot t$$

EXAMPLE 1   Using the Distance Formula

Estimate the distance a sky diver falls in 5 seconds.

SOLUTION

Substitute 5 for t in the formula $d = 16t^2$.

$$d = 16(5)^2$$
$$= 16(5 \cdot 5)$$
$$= 16(25) = 400$$

A sky diver falls about 400 feet in 5 seconds.

Exponential Form

For any number a and integer n, where $n \geq 1$,
$$a^n = \underbrace{a \cdot a \cdot a \cdot a \cdot \ldots \cdot a}_{n \text{ factors}}$$

The number 5^2, or 25, is called a **power** of 5. You read powers as shown below.

$5^1 \rightarrow$ *five to the first power*

$5^2 \rightarrow$ *five to the second power, or five squared*

$5^3 \rightarrow$ *five to the third power, or five cubed*

$5^4 \rightarrow$ *five to the fourth power*

Even and Odd Powers

1 Copy the following table.

Multiplication Equation	How Many Times is The Base Used as a Factor?	Exponential Form of the Equation
$5 = 5$	1	$5^1 = 5$
$5 \cdot 5 = 25$	2	$5^2 = 25$
$5 \cdot 5 \cdot 5 = ?$	?	?
$5 \cdot 5 \cdot 5 \cdot 5 = ?$	?	?
$-5 = -5$	1	$(-5)^1 = -5$
$(-5) \cdot (-5) = 25$	2	$(-5)^2 = 25$
$(-5) \cdot (-5) \cdot (-5) = ?$	?	?
$(-5) \cdot (-5) \cdot (-5) \cdot (-5) = ?$	?	?

2 Complete each multiplication equation in the table. Enter the number of times the base is used as a factor in each equation. Write the exponential form of each equation. Some of the rows are completed as examples.

3 Is 5^n a positive or negative number for any value of $n \geq 1$?

4 Is $(-5)^n$ a positive or negative number if n is even? If n is odd?

EXAMPLE 2 Evaluating Exponential Expressions

Find the value of each expression.

a. 8^4 **b.** $(-2)^3$ **c.** $\left(\dfrac{2}{3}\right)^2$ **d.** -0.3^4

SOLUTION

a. $8^4 = 8 \cdot 8 \cdot 8 \cdot 8 = 4096$

b. $(-2)^3 = (-2)(-2)(-2) = -8$

c. $\left(\dfrac{2}{3}\right)^2 = \dfrac{2}{3} \cdot \dfrac{2}{3} = \dfrac{4}{9}$

d. $-0.3^4 = -(0.3 \cdot 0.3 \cdot 0.3 \cdot 0.3) = -0.0081$

ONGOING ASSESSMENT

Find the value of each expression.

a. 4^5 **b.** $\left(-\dfrac{1}{2}\right)^3$ **c.** $(0.6)^2$ **d.** -3^4

To evaluate numerical expressions with exponents, you need an additional step for the Order of Operations you used in Chapter 1.

Order of Operations
1. Simplify expressions inside parentheses first.
2. Then find each power.
3. Then multiply and divide from left to right.
4. Then add and subtract from left to right.

EXAMPLE 3 Evaluating Expressions

Evaluate the following expressions for $a = 3$ and $b = 7$.

a. $(ab)^3$ **b.** $3(a - 2)^5 + b^2$ **c.** $\dfrac{a + 1}{(5 - b)^3}$

SOLUTION

a. $(ab)^3 = (3 \cdot 7)^3$

$= (21)^3$ Simplify expressions inside parentheses

$= 21 \cdot 21 \cdot 21$ Find each power

$= 9261$

b. $3(a - 2)^5 + b^2 = 3(3 - 2)^5 + 7^2$

$= 3(1)^5 + 7^2$ Simplify expressions inside parentheses

$= 3(1) + 49$ Find each power

$= 3 + 49$ Multiply left to right

$= 52$ Add left to right

c. $\dfrac{a + 1}{(5 - b)^3} = \dfrac{3 + 1}{(5 - 7)^3}$

$= \dfrac{4}{(-2)^3}$ Simplify expressions inside parentheses
The numerator implies parentheses

$= \dfrac{4}{-8}$ Find each power

$= -\dfrac{1}{2}$ Simplify

In Lesson 7.6, you learned how to find compound interest using a spreadsheet. You can also find compound interest using a formula.

$$A = P(1 + r)^n$$

P is the principal or initial amount of money invested.
r is the annual rate of interest as a decimal.
n is the number of years over which the money earns interest.
A is the total amount of money at the end of the period.

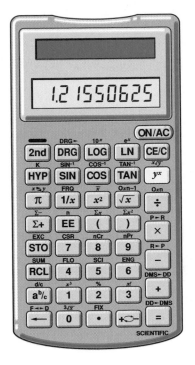

EXAMPLE 4 Computing Compound Interest

Shawna invests $1000 in a Certificate of Deposit that earns 5% interest compounded annually. How much will Shawna have in her account after 4 years?

SOLUTION

Substitute the values in the compound interest formula.

$$A = 1000(1 + 0.05)^4$$
$$= 1000(1.05)^4$$
$$\approx 1000(1.216)$$
$$\approx 1216$$

Shawna will have about $1216 in her account after 4 years.

Most scientific calculators have a $\boxed{y^x}$ that evaluates expressions with exponents. For example, to evaluate $(1.05)^4$, enter the following.

$$1.05 \boxed{y^x} 4 \boxed{=} 1.21550625$$

LESSON ASSESSMENT

Think and Discuss

1 Write $3x \cdot 3x \cdot 3x$ in exponential form. Write $3x \cdot x \cdot x$ in exponential form. What are the base and exponent for each expression?

2 Are $(-5x)^2$ and $25x^2$ equivalent expressions? Explain.

3 Are $\left(\dfrac{2}{3}\right)^4$ and $\dfrac{2^4}{3^4}$ equivalent expressions? Explain.

4 Does $(x + y)^2 = x^2 + y^2$? Choose values for x and y and evaluate both sides of the equation to verify your answer.

Use the formula $d = 16t^2$ to find the distance d in feet that an object falls in the given time t.

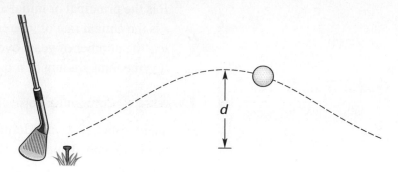

5. 8 seconds   **6.** 9 seconds   **7.** 20 seconds

Evaluate.

8. 4^3 **9.** 10^4 **10.** $(-3)^2$

11. $\left(\dfrac{1}{2}\right)^4$ **12.** $\left(-\dfrac{2}{5}\right)^3$ **13.** $3^2 + 1^4$

14. $(2-8)^2$ **15.** $(5 \cdot 2)^3 - 90$ **16.** $(12-9)^3 \div 9$

17. $4^2 - 6 \cdot 2^1$ **18.** $[1 - (3+2)^2] \div 4$

19. $\left[\left(\dfrac{20}{5}\right)^2 - 20\right] \cdot 2$ **20.** $(5 - 4 \cdot 3)^2$

21. $(12 \div 3 - 6)^3 - 5$ **22.** $\left[\left(\dfrac{1}{2}\right)^3 + \dfrac{7}{8}\right]^8$

Evaluate each expression for $s = 2$, $t = -3$, and $u = \dfrac{1}{3}$.

23. $(-5)^s$ **24.** $s^2 + 3tu^2$ **25.** $(s - tu)^4$

In Exercises 26 and 27, find the interest earned when compounded annually for each investment.

26. $20,000 at 8% for 6 years

27. $12,000 at 6.5% for 3 years

28. What is the sign of $(-1)^n$ when n is an odd integer?

29. Write *three-fifths to the fourth power* as an expression in exponential form.

30. Write $\left(-\dfrac{2}{3}\right)^3$ as a word phrase.

31. How is -4^2 different than $(-4)^2$?

Suppose a motorcycle is moving at an initial speed v_0 ft/s and accelerates at a rate of a ft/s per s for t seconds. The distance d in feet traveled by the motorcycle is

$$d = v_0 t + \frac{1}{2}at^2$$

32. How far does the motorcycle travel if its initial speed is 40 ft/s and it accelerates at 25 ft/s per second for 3 seconds?

33. What was the initial speed of a motorcycle that accelerates at 5 ft/s per second for 4 seconds and travels 320 feet?

Mixed Review

Replace each ? with $<$, $>$, or $=$ to make a *true* statement.

34. 3.59 _?_ 3.6

35. $-\frac{3}{5}$ _?_ $-\frac{9}{15}$

36. $\frac{5}{8}$ _?_ 0.62

Solve each equation.

37. $7(r - 9) = -2r$

38. $3c + 5 = c - 10$

39. $7.5 = 3d - 1.8$

40. $\frac{1}{5}m + \frac{1}{2} = \frac{3}{10}$

Use the Park Trails map to complete Exercises 41–43. Dionne hiked from the campsite to Buzzard Point and then on to Lookout Ridge. Warren hiked from the campsite to High Rock and then on to Lookout Ridge.

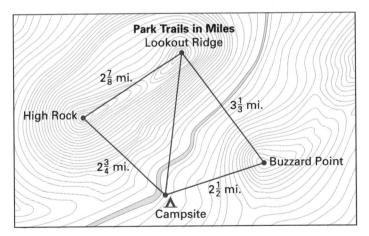

41. How far did Dionne hike?

42. How far did Warren hike?

43. How much farther did Dionne hike?

LESSON 10.2 PROPERTIES OF EXPONENTS

OBJECTIVES
- - - - - - - - - -
➤ Multiply and divide powers.
➤ Use the zero and negative exponents properties to simplify expressions.

A bit is the smallest unit of information that a computer can store. A bit can only have a value of 0 or 1.

Computers store or print data using sets of bits. For example, to print a single character of text (such as the letter A) a computer needs to process 8 bits of data. Eight bits is called a *byte*. How many different characters can be represented by 8 bits, or 1 byte, of data?

Start by representing a character with 1 bit and work up to 8. If there is only 1 bit in a set, two different sets are possible, (0) and (1). In this case, the computer can only represent two characters, for example, $A = (0)$ and $B = (1)$.

If there are 2 bits in a set, four different sets are possible. In this case, the computer can represent four characters, for example, $A = (00)$, $B = (01)$, $C = (10)$, and $D = (11)$.

Number of Bits in a Set	Sets	Number of Characters That Can Be Represented
1	(0) (1)	$2 = 2^1$
2	(00) (01) (10) (11)	$4 = 2 \cdot 2 = 2^2$
3	(000) (001) (010) (100) (011) (101) (110) (111)	$8 = 2 \cdot 2 \cdot 2 = 2^3$
4	?	$? = ? = 2^?$
⋮		⋮
8		$2^?$

How many different sets are possible with 4 bits? Notice the pattern that is developing. How many characters can be represented by 1 byte?

ACTIVITY 1 Multiplying Powers

Suppose a computer can print a one-byte character in one of four colors. How many different characters can be printed?

You found that 1 byte, or 8 bits, can represent 2^8 characters. You need to multiply $4 \cdot 2^8$. Use 2^2 for 4.

1 Write $2^2 \cdot 2^8$ in expanded form.

$$2^2 \cdot 2^8 = (2 \cdot 2)(2 \cdot 2 \cdot 2 \cdot 2 \cdot 2 \cdot 2 \cdot 2 \cdot 2)$$

How many factors of 2 did you write? Write the product as a power of 2.

2 If you add the exponents of $2^2 \cdot 2^8$, do you get the same result as in Step 1? Make a conjecture about how to find the product of powers with the same base.

3 Use your conjecture to find the following products. Check your answers by writing the powers in expanded form.

a. $2^3 \cdot 2^2$ **b.** $5^2 \cdot 5^3$ **c.** $x^5 \cdot x^2$

In Activity 1, you discovered the rule for multiplying powers.

How many seedlings are in four 8-packs?

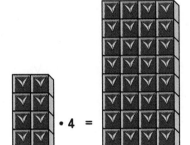

$$2^3 \cdot 2^2 = 2^{3+2} = 2^5 = 32$$

Product of Powers

To multiply powers that have the same base, add the exponents.

$$x^m \cdot x^n = x^{m+n}$$

EXAMPLE 1 Dividing Powers

Find the following quotients.

a. $\dfrac{2^3}{2^2}$ **b.** $(-3)^5 \div (-3)^3$ **c.** $\dfrac{y^4}{y}$

SOLUTION

Write the powers in expanded form.

a. $\dfrac{2^3}{2^2} = \dfrac{\cancel{2} \cdot \cancel{2} \cdot 2}{\cancel{2} \cdot \cancel{2}} = 2$

b. $(-3)^5 \div (-3)^3 = \dfrac{(-3)^5}{(-3)^3}$

$$= \dfrac{\cancel{-3} \cdot \cancel{-3} \cdot \cancel{-3} \cdot -3 \cdot -3}{\cancel{-3} \cdot \cancel{-3} \cdot \cancel{-3}} = (-3)^2$$

c. $\dfrac{y^4}{y} = \dfrac{\cancel{y} \cdot y \cdot y \cdot y}{\cancel{y}} = y^3$

Notice that the exponent of each quotient is the difference of the exponents in the fraction.

If an 8-pack of seedlings is divided into 4 groups, how many seedlings are in each group?

$$\frac{2^3}{2^2} = 2^{3-2} = 2^1 = 2$$

Quotient of Powers

To divide powers that have the same base, subtract the exponents (numerator minus denominator).

$$\frac{x^m}{x^n} = x^{m-n}, x \neq 0$$

ONGOING ASSESSMENT

Simplify.

a. $7^3 \cdot 7^{10}$ **b.** $\dfrac{10^8}{10^3}$ **c.** $x^{12} \div x^4$ **d.** $y \cdot y^9$

ACTIVITY 2   Zero Exponents

1 Choose any positive integer value for k and any nonzero value for x.

2 Substitute your values into the equation.

$$\frac{x^k}{x^k} = x^{k-k}$$

How do you know this equation is *true*?

3 Rewrite the numerator and denominator of $\dfrac{x^k}{x^k}$ using repeated multiplication. For example, if $k = 3$, $x^3 = x \cdot x \cdot x$. What is the numerical value of $\dfrac{x^k}{x^k}$?

4 Substitute your values into x^{k-k}. Simplify the exponent.

5 Compare your results with your classmates. What is the numerical value of x^0 for any nonzero value of x?

Activity 2 shows that

$$\frac{x^k}{x^k} = x^{k-k} = x^0 = 1$$

Zero Exponents

If x is any nonzero number,

$$x^0 = 1$$

Sometimes you will divide powers when the exponent in the denominator is greater than the exponent in the numerator. Example 2 shows two ways to represent negative exponents.

EXAMPLE 2 Negative Exponents

Simplify $\dfrac{a^2}{a^5}$.

SOLUTION

$$\frac{a^2}{a^5} = \frac{\cancel{a} \cdot \cancel{a}}{\cancel{a} \cdot \cancel{a} \cdot a \cdot a \cdot a}$$

$$a^{2-5} = \frac{1}{a \cdot a \cdot a}$$

$$a^{-3} = \frac{1}{a^3}$$

Negative Exponents

If x is any nonzero number,

$$x^{-n} = \frac{1}{x^n}$$

ONGOING ASSESSMENT

Simplify.

a. 6^{-2} **b.** $\dfrac{(-4)^5}{(-4)^7}$ **c.** $\dfrac{x}{x^6}$ **d.** $\dfrac{y^6}{y^6}$

LESSON ASSESSMENT

Think and Discuss

1 Someone simplifies $2^3 \cdot 2^2$ as 4^5. What mistake did they probably make? How would you show that it is incorrect?

2 In the expression, 4^n, what is the base and what is the exponent? If n is a negative integer, how many times do you use the base as a factor?

3 Explain why 6^{-1} is the reciprocal of 6.

Practice and Apply

Simplify.

4. $2^2 \cdot 2^3$ **5.** $a^2 \cdot a$ **6.** $(-1)^3(-1)^3$

7. $3^0 \cdot 3^2$ **8.** $\dfrac{5^4}{5^3}$ **9.** $10^6 \div 10^4$

10. $(-6)^2 \div (-6)^3$ **11.** 2^{-3} **12.** $(-3)^{-1}$

13. 4^{-2} **14.** $(-3)^0$ **15.** $4^{-5} \cdot 4^5$

Rewrite each expression using a positive exponent. Assume none of the variables equal zero.

16. $3x^{-2}$ **17.** ab^{-1} **18.** $5y^{-4}$

Rewrite each expression using a negative exponent. Assume none of the variables equal zero.

19. $\dfrac{2}{x^4}$ **20.** $\dfrac{1}{y^2}$ **21.** $\dfrac{4}{3a^2}$

Simplify each expression. Write each result with positive exponents. Assume none of the variables equal zero.

22. x^3x^5 **23.** $9b^2 \div 6b^6$ **24.** $\dfrac{8g^5}{4g^2}$

25. $\dfrac{m^4n^3}{mn^5}$ **26.** $\dfrac{x^{-4}y^2}{x^2y^3}$ **27.** $10st^2 \cdot s^2t^3$

Let $p = 2$, $q = -3$, and $r = -1$. Evaluate each expression.

28. 2^p2^r **29.** $(-3q)^{2p}$ **30.** $\dfrac{pq^2}{p^2q}$

31. p^2r^3 **32.** $q^2(p^3 + r^4)$ **33.** $\dfrac{4p^2}{p^4}$

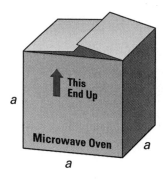

a

This End Up

Microwave Oven

a

a

A packaging company makes cardboard boxes in the shape of cubes. The amount of cardboard needed for each box is the surface area of the cube. If each side of the cube measures a, the surface area is $6a^2$ and the volume is a^3.

34. What is the ratio of the volume to the surface area of each box?

35. What is the ratio of the volume to the surface area for a box with sides measuring 36 inches? With 42 inches?

Mixed Review

36. Write $\dfrac{24}{60}$ in simplest form. **37.** Simplify $-2\dfrac{1}{2} \div -3\dfrac{1}{3}$.

38. Find 15% of $220. **39.** What percent of 12 is 4?

40. Reynaldo works at a furniture store. His salary is $2600 per month. He also earns a commission of 1.5% for all sales over $8000 each month. If Reynaldo's sales are $20,000 in March, what are his total earnings for the month?

A politician sends an e-mail letter to get votes. He mails copies to 5 people. The letter tells everyone receiving the letter to mail copies to 5 other people.

There are 5 copies of the letter in the first mailing. If each of these people mails 5 copies, there are $5 \cdot 5 = 5^2$ copies in the second mailing. Suppose the pattern continues for 10 mailings.

41. Let n represent the number of mailings. Construct a table of values for the number of copies for $n = 1$ through 10.

42. How many mailings are required for a *total* of 1 million people to receive copies of the letter?

The mass of the sun is approximately 10^{35} kilograms. The mass of the earth is approximately 10^{25} kilograms.

43. The earth's mass is about what percent of the sun's mass?

44. There are an estimated 10^{21} stars in the universe. If the sun is a star with an average mass, what is the total mass of the stars in the universe?

When handling food, proper hand washing is very important to prevent the spread of bacteria. For example, at room temperature, a certain bacteria can grow at a rate that doubles the bacteria population every 20 minutes.

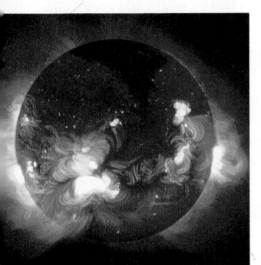

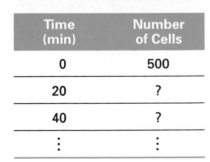

Time (min)	Number of Cells
0	500
20	?
40	?
⋮	⋮

45. Suppose a chicken salad is contaminated with 500 cells of this bacteria. Make a table of values for the population in 20-minute intervals, up to 120 minutes.

46. Plot the values on a coordinate plane, with *time* on the horizontal axis and *bacteria population* on the vertical axis. Is the relationship linear?

47. The bacteria population can be calculated with the following equation. What does n represent?

$$\text{number of cells} = \text{initial number of cells} \cdot 2^n$$

48. Suppose the chicken salad is contaminated with 5 bacteria cells. Use the equation to calculate the number of cells after 120 minutes.

49. Explain how this Exercise demonstrates the importance of proper hand washing when handling food.

LESSON 10.3 SCIENTIFIC NOTATION

OBJECTIVES
- Read and write numbers in scientific notation.
- Multiply and divide numbers in scientific notation.

Scientists, engineers, and technicians often work with very large or very small numbers. For example, astronomers use a very large number for the distance from the earth to the sun (about 93,000,000 miles). Medical lab technicians use a very small number for the diameter of a red blood cell (about 0.000007 meters).

Calculations are simplified by writing these numbers in *scientific notation.* A number in **scientific notation** is written as a product of two factors: the first factor is a number greater than or equal to 1 but less than 10, and the second factor is a power of 10.

Greater than or equal to 1 but less than 10 → 1×10^3 ← Powers of 10
→ 3×10^{-2} ←
→ 7.4×10^5 ←

ACTIVITY   Powers of Ten and Decimals

1 Study the powers of ten with positive exponents. Compare each exponent to the number of places the decimal point moves to the *right* of 1. For example,

$$1 \times 10^3 = 1\,\underbrace{0\,0\,0}.$$
How many places?

2 Continue the pattern, and write 10^4 as a decimal. How many places did you move the decimal point? If $m \geq 0$, how many places is the decimal point moved when you write 10^m as a decimal?

10^4	= ?
10^3	= $10 \cdot 10 \cdot 10 = 1000$
10^2	= $10 \cdot 10 = 100$
10^1	= 10
10^0	= 1
10^{-1}	= $\frac{1}{10} = 0.1$
10^{-2}	= $\frac{1}{10 \cdot 10} = 0.01$
10^{-3}	= $\frac{1}{10 \cdot 10 \cdot 10} = 0.001$
10^{-4}	= ?

3 Study the pattern for negative exponents. Compare each exponent to the number of places the decimal point moves to the *left* of 1 in decimal notation. For example,

$$1 \times 10^{-2} = 0.\underset{\text{How many places?}}{\underbrace{0\,1}}$$

4 Continue the pattern and write 10^{-4} as a decimal. How many places did you move the decimal point? If $m > 0$, how many places is the decimal point moved when you write 10^{-m} as a decimal?

EXAMPLE 1 Large Numbers and Scientific Notation

a. Write the distance in miles from the earth to the sun (93,000,000 miles) in scientific notation.

b. Write the distance in kilometers from the earth to the sun (1.5×10^8 km) in decimal notation.

SOLUTION

a. Move the decimal point to the left to get a number that is greater than or equal to 1 but less than 10. The number of places the decimal point is moved is the exponent.

$$\underset{\text{7 places}}{\underbrace{9\,3{,}0\,0\,0{,}0\,0\,0}} = 9.3 \times 10^7$$

In scientific notation, the distance from the earth to the sun is 9.3×10^7 miles.

b. A number in scientific notation is written in decimal notation by reversing the procedure.

Move the decimal point to the right. Add zeros as needed to fill the place value. The number of places the decimal point is moved is the exponent.

$$1.5 \times 10^8 = 1\,\underset{\text{8 places}}{\underbrace{5\,0{,}0\,0\,0{,}0\,0\,0}}$$

In decimal notation, the distance from the earth to the sun is 150,000,000 km.

ONGOING ASSESSMENT

a. Write 16,500 in scientific notation.

b. Write 9.5×10^2 in decimal notation.

EXAMPLE 2 Small Numbers and Scientific Notation

a. Write the diameter of a red blood cell (0.000007 m) in scientific notation.

b. Write 3.64×10^{-3} in decimal notation.

a. Move the decimal point to the right to get a number that is greater than or equal to 1 but less than 10.

$$0.\underbrace{0\,0\,0\,0\,0\,7}_{\text{6 places}} = 7 \times 10^{-6}$$

In scientific notation, the diameter of a red blood cell is 7×10^{-6} m.

b. Reverse the procedure to write a small number in decimal notation.

Move the decimal point to the left. Add zeros as needed to fill the place value.

$$3.64 \times 10^{-3} = 0.\underbrace{0\,0\,0}_{\text{3 places}}3\,6\,4$$

$$= 0.00364$$

a. Write 0.00062 in scientific notation.

b. Write 6.46×10^{-5} in decimal notation.

EXAMPLE 3 Multiplying Numbers in Scientific Notation

In orbit, the *Space Shuttle* travels about 18,000 miles per hour. How far does the *Space Shuttle* travel in a 4-day (96-hour) mission? Write the answer in scientific notation.

Use the rate formula $D = rt$. Multiply the rate by the time, with both numbers in scientific notation.

$$18{,}000 = 1.8 \times 10^4 \qquad\qquad 96 = 9.6 \times 10^1$$

$$D = (1.8 \times 10^4)(9.6 \times 10^1)$$

$$= (1.8 \times 9.6)(10^4 \times 10^1)$$

$$= 17.28 \times 10^5 \qquad\qquad \text{Not in scientific notation}$$

$$= 1.728 \times 10^1 \times 10^5 \qquad\qquad \text{Write 17.28 as } 1.728 \times 10^1$$

$$= 1.728 \times 10^6$$

You can also multiply the numbers using your calculator. Enter the numbers in scientific notation with the EXP or EE key.

$$1.8 \ \boxed{\text{EXP}} \ 4 \ \boxed{\times} \ 9.6 \ \boxed{\text{EXP}} \ 1 \ \boxed{=} \ \boxed{1.728^{06}}$$
or 1.728×10^6

The *Space Shuttle* travels about 1.7×10^6 miles, or about 1.7 million miles in a 4-day mission.

EXAMPLE 4 Multiplying and Dividing Numbers in Scientific Notation

Use your calculator to find the following. Round each answer to two places after the decimal point.

a. $(3.91 \times 10^{-6})(4 \times 10^{-3})$ **b.** $\dfrac{4.1 \times 10^5}{6.2 \times 10^8}$

SOLUTION

a. $3.91 \ \boxed{\text{EXP}} \ \boxed{+/-} \ 6 \ \boxed{\times} \ 4 \ \boxed{\text{EXP}} \ \boxed{+/-} \ 3 \ \boxed{=} \ \boxed{1.564^{-08}}$
or 1.56×10^{-8} (rounded)

b. $4.1 \ \boxed{\text{EXP}} \ 5 \ \boxed{\div} \ 6.2 \ \boxed{\text{EXP}} \ 8 \ \boxed{=} \ \boxed{6.612903226^{-04}}$
or 6.61×10^{-4} (rounded)

CULTURAL CONNECTION

Different forms of notation for very large numbers and small numbers were used before the 1600s. But the French philosopher and mathematician René Descartes is credited with developing the modern notation for exponents around the year 1637. Descartes' system of exponents came into wider use in the nineteenth and twentieth centuries when scientists studied astronomy (requiring very large numbers) and atomic particles (requiring very small numbers). The following Exercises demonstrate the efficiency of using powers of ten.

1. Write each of the following measurements as a power of ten.

Description	Approximate Size (meters)
Length of a soccer field	one hundred
Length of a DNA fragment	one millionth
Diameter of the earth	ten million
Diameter of a virus	one hundred-millionth
Height of a two-year-old	one
Diameter of a softball	one tenth
Diameter of the sun	one billion

2. List the measurements in order from least to greatest.

3. Is it easier to use the name of the number or the power of ten to order the numbers?

LESSON ASSESSMENT

1 Explain how to write a very large number in scientific notation. Is the exponent positive or negative?

2 Explain how to write a very small number (between 0 and 1) in scientific notation. Is the exponent positive or negative?

3 Write an algorithm for multiplying two numbers in scientific notation.

4 Explain how to use your calculator to divide two numbers written in scientific notation.

Practice and Apply

Is each number written in scientific notation? If not, explain why.

5. 9.8×10^2 **6.** 0.51×10^{-3} **7.** -6.2×2^5

Write each number in decimal notation.

8. 5.9×10^8 **9.** 3.75×10^{-4}

10. 3.5×10^{-3} **11.** 1.42×10^5

12. 8.75×10^{-6} **13.** 75.383×10^3

14. The distance to the nearest star, Alfa Centauri, is about 4.1×10^{12} kilometers.

15. The area of the Pentagon in Washington D.C. is about 3.7×10^6 square feet.

16. The thickness of a sheet of paper is about 8×10^{-5} meters.

17. It takes a light beam about 3×10^{-7} seconds to travel the length of a football field.

18. In one school year, you spend about 8.5×10^3 minutes in math class.

Write each number in scientific notation.

19. 88.5   **20.** 0.0000025

21. 57,300,000   **22.** 0.00001

23. 924,875   **24.** one trillion

25. The population of China is approximately one billion, two hundred million.

26. The width of a human hair is about 0.0008 inches.

27. The approximate land area of the United States is 3,500,000 square miles.

28. The wavelength of violet light is about 0.00004 centimeters.

29. Starfleet's U.S.S. Enterprise has a cargo capacity of 25,000,000 kg.

30. The time it takes for a TV signal to travel 15 miles is about 0.0000806 seconds.

Replace the ? with $<$, $>$, or $=$ to make a *true* statement.

31. 3×10^4 ? 3×10^2 **32.** 2.8×10^{-3} ? 2.8×10^{-2}

33. 4×10^6 ? 2×10^6 **34.** -3.2×10^{-12} ? -3×10^{-12}

Find each product or quotient using a calculator. Write the answer in scientific notation.

35. $(6.1 \times 10^4)(8 \times 10^9)$ **36.** $(8 \times 10^{-4})(3 \times 10^{-2})$

37. $\dfrac{8.9 \times 10^{-5}}{3.4 \times 10^3}$ **38.** $\dfrac{2.1 \times 10^6}{8.5 \times 10^{19}}$

39. The United States government spends approximately $1.9 trillion per year. The population of the United States is approximately 270 million. Estimate the amount spent by the government per person each year.

40. An atom of copper weighs 1.05×10^{-22} grams. Pennies minted before 1982 were pure copper and weighed about 3.1 grams. How many atoms of copper are in one of these pennies?

Choose the correct conversion factor. Then make the conversion.

41. 30 quarts to gallons   **a.** $\dfrac{1 \text{ gal}}{4 \text{ qt}}$ **b.** $\dfrac{4 \text{ qt}}{1 \text{ gal}}$

42. 6 feet to inches   **a.** $\dfrac{1 \text{ ft}}{12 \text{ in.}}$ **b.** $\dfrac{12 \text{ in.}}{1 \text{ ft}}$

43. 3.5 pounds to ounces   **a.** $\dfrac{1 \text{ lb}}{16 \text{ oz}}$ **b.** $\dfrac{16 \text{ oz}}{1 \text{ lb}}$

44. 30 minutes to hours   **a.** $\dfrac{1 \text{ hr}}{60 \text{ min}}$ **b.** $\dfrac{60 \text{ min}}{1 \text{ hr}}$

45. 15 quarts to pints   **a.** $\dfrac{1 \text{ qt}}{2 \text{ pt}}$ **b.** $\dfrac{2 \text{ pt}}{1 \text{ qt}}$

46. 126 days to weeks   **a.** $\dfrac{7 \text{ d}}{1 \text{ wk}}$ **b.** $\dfrac{1 \text{ wk}}{7 \text{ d}}$

47. 52 yards to feet   **a.** $\dfrac{3 \text{ ft}}{1 \text{ yd}}$ **b.** $\dfrac{1 \text{ yd}}{3 \text{ ft}}$

When Paul exercises on his treadmill, he sets the speed at 4 miles per hour. The distance D (in miles) he walks over a period of time t (in hours) can be determined by the formula $D = 4t$.

48. Make an input/output table to show how far Paul walks on the treadmill if he walks $\frac{1}{2}$ hour, 1 hour, and $1\frac{1}{2}$ hours.

49. Plot the ordered pairs for (t, D) on a coordinate plane and draw a line through the points.

50. What is the slope of the line you graphed?

51. What information in the problem does the slope describe?

LESSON 10.4 THE METRIC SYSTEM

OBJECTIVES

➤ Convert measurements within the metric system.
➤ Use dimensional analysis.
➤ Convert between U.S. units and metric units.

Taylor is a licensed practical nurse preparing flu vaccines. She has 0.25 liters of vaccine, and needs to fill syringes with 0.5 milliliters each. How many syringes can Taylor fill with vaccine?

The **liter** (L) is the basic measure of liquid capacity in the metric system of measurement. The **meter** (m) is the basic measure of length. The

gram (g) is the basic measure of mass. Other units are shown in the table. The most commonly used units are highlighted.

Metric System of Measurement

Prefix and Meaning			Length	Liquid Capacity	Mass
kilo-	1000	$= 10^3$	kilometer (km)	kiloliter (kL)	kilogram (kg)
hecto-	100	$= 10^2$	hectometer (hm)	hectoliter (hL)	hectogram (hg)
deka-	10	$= 10^1$	dekameter (dam)	dekaliter (daL)	dekagram (dag)
	1	$= 10^0$	meter (m)	liter (L)	gram (g)
deci-	0.1	$= 10^{-1}$	decimeter (dm)	deciliter (dL)	decigram (dg)
centi-	0.01	$= 10^{-2}$	centimeter (cm)	centiliter (cL)	centigram (cg)
milli-	0.001	$= 10^{-3}$	millimeter (mm)	milliliter (mL)	milligram (mg)

ACTIVITY   Metric Conversions Using Powers of Ten

Notice the metric system is based on powers of ten. Each unit is ten times larger than the unit below it. For example, 1 cm = 10 mm. This equation is a **conversion**.

You can write conversions using proportions. For example, start with the conversions 1 kg = 10^3 g and 1 mg = 10^{-3} g.

$$\frac{1\text{ kg}}{1\text{ mg}} = \frac{10^3\text{ g}}{10^{-3}\text{ g}} = 10^6$$

$$1\text{ kg} = 10^6\text{ mg}$$

Thus, a kilogram is 10^6 times larger than a milligram.

1 Complete the following equalities.

1 m = _?_ cm $\qquad$ 1 L = _?_ mL $\qquad$ 1 g = _?_ mg

1 km = _?_ m $\qquad\qquad\qquad\qquad$ 1 kg = _?_ g

2 To convert from a larger metric unit to a smaller metric unit, *multiply* by the appropriate power of ten. From the chart, you know that a centimeter is 10 times larger than a millimeter. Thus, to convert 0.83 cm to mm, multiply by 10.

$$(0.83 \text{ cm})\left(\frac{10 \text{ mm}}{1 \text{ cm}}\right) = 8.3 \text{ mm}$$

$$0.83 \text{ cm} = 8.3 \text{ mm}$$

Complete the following equalities.

0.52 m = _?_ cm $\qquad$ 0.033 L = _?_ mL $\qquad$ 1.2 g = _?_ mg

12.8 km = _?_ m $\qquad\qquad\qquad\qquad$ 0.7 kg = _?_ g

3 To convert from a smaller metric unit to a larger metric unit, *divide* by the appropriate power of ten. For example, to convert 48 mm to cm, divide by 10.

$$(48 \text{ mm})\left(\frac{1 \text{ cm}}{10 \text{ mm}}\right) = 4.8 \text{ cm}$$

$$48 \text{ mm} = 4.8 \text{ cm}$$

Complete the following equalities.

52 cm = _?_ m $\qquad$ 507 mL = _?_ L $\qquad$ 12 mg = _?_ g

1284 m = _?_ km $\qquad\qquad\qquad\qquad$ 79 g = _?_ kg

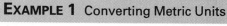

EXAMPLE 1 Converting Metric Units

How many 0.5-mL syringes can Taylor fill with 0.25 L of vaccine?

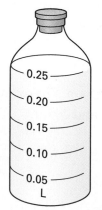

SOLUTION

Convert 0.25 L to mL. Since you need to convert a larger unit to a smaller unit, multiply by the appropriate power of ten.

$$(0.25 \text{ L})\left(\frac{1000 \text{ mL}}{1 \text{ L}}\right) = 250 \text{ mL}$$

$$0.25 \text{ L} = 250 \text{ mL}$$

Thus, Taylor has a total of 250 mL of vaccine.

Let x represent the number of syringes that can be filled. Each syringe will be filled with 0.5 mL of vaccine.

$$0.5x = 250$$

$$x = \frac{250}{0.5} = 500$$

Taylor can fill 500 syringes.

EXAMPLE 2 Using Dimensional Analysis

On page A2, the most common metric units are listed with the most common U.S. customary units. Suppose Taylor had 0.25 quart (qt) of vaccine. How many fluid ounces (fl oz) would she have?

SOLUTION

Use dimensional analysis.

$$0.25 \text{ qt} = \frac{0.25 \text{ qt}}{1} \cdot \frac{2 \text{ pt}}{1 \text{ qt}} \cdot \frac{2 \text{ c}}{1 \text{ pt}} \cdot \frac{8 \text{ fl oz}}{1 \text{ c}}$$

$$= \frac{(0.25)(2)(2)(8) \text{ fl oz}}{1} = 8 \text{ fl oz}$$

Taylor would have 8 fl oz of vaccine.

You can convert U.S. customary measurements to metric using conversion factors such as those listed in the table.

EXAMPLE 3 Converting U.S. Units to Metric Units

U.S. Customary to Metric Conversion
1 in. = 2.54 cm
1 yd = 0.91 m
1 mi = 1.61 km
1 lb = 0.454 kg
1 qt = 0.946 L

Metric wrenches are sized to the nearest millimeter. A bolt measures $\frac{1}{2}$ inch. Which metric wrench will come closest to fitting the bolt?

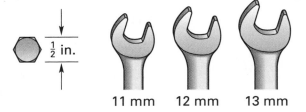

$\frac{1}{2}$ in.   11 mm   12 mm   13 mm

SOLUTION

Use the conversion factor to convert $\frac{1}{2}$ in. to cm.

$$\left(\frac{1}{2} \text{ in.}\right)\left(\frac{2.54 \text{ cm}}{1 \text{ in.}}\right) = 1.27 \text{ cm or } 12.7 \text{ mm}$$

Round to the nearest mm. $\left(\frac{1}{2} \text{ in.} \approx 13 \text{ mm}\right)$

The 13 mm wrench will come closest to fitting the $\frac{1}{2}$ inch bolt.

PROBLEM SOLVING

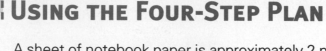

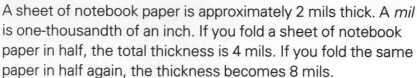

USING THE FOUR-STEP PLAN

2 mils

4 mils

8 mils

A sheet of notebook paper is approximately 2 mils thick. A *mil* is one-thousandth of an inch. If you fold a sheet of notebook paper in half, the total thickness is 4 mils. If you fold the same paper in half again, the thickness becomes 8 mils.

If you could fold a sheet of notebook paper 50 times, how thick would it be? Which of the following do you think best describes the thickness?

a. less than ten feet
b. more than ten feet, but less than a ten-story building
c. more than a ten-story building but less than Mt. Everest
d. more than the distance to the moon

Calculate the thickness of a sheet of notebook paper folded 50 times and compare it to your prediction.

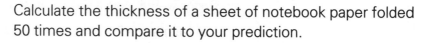

Number of Folds	0	1	2	3	4 ... 50
Thickness, mils	2	2·2	4·2	8·2	? ... ?

Understand the Problem

The problem uses repeated multiplication by 2. If you find the thickness in mils, how do you convert to inches?

Develop a Plan

Find a pattern. Make a table that shows the thickness after each fold. Then look for a pattern in the table.

Carry Out the Plan

Write the thickness in the table as powers of 2. Describe the pattern. Extend the pattern to 50 folds. Use your calculator to calculate 50 folds in mils. Convert the thickness to inches, feet, and miles.

Check the Results

Does the answer seem reasonable? Give a reason why your prediction may have been wrong.

LESSON ASSESSMENT

1 When converting a measurement from a larger unit to a smaller unit, what is the advantage of working with the metric system over the U.S. customary system?

2 Explain how to change milligrams to kilograms.

3 The prefix *micro-* means one-millionth. The prefix *nano-* means one-trillionth. Write 1 microsecond and 1 nanosecond in scientific notation. Which is greater? Explain your answer.

4 Computer speeds are measured in floating-point operations per second (flops). The prefix *mega-* means one million. The prefix *giga-* means one billion. Write 1 megaflops and 1 gigaflops in scientific notation. How many times faster is a gigaflop than a megaflop?

Practice and Apply

Replace each ? to make a *true* statement.

5. 15 km = _?_ m   **6.** 165 mL = _?_ L

7. 251 g = _?_ mg   **8.** 23 gm = _?_ kg

9. 213 cm = _?_ m   **10.** 0.4 L = _?_ mL

11. 17 mm = _?_ cm   **12.** 0.13 m = _?_ mm

13. 2500 mg = _?_ kg   **14.** 11 ft = _?_ in.

15. 12 pt = _?_ gal   **16.** 2.3 lb = _?_ oz

17. 1 L = _?_ oz   **18.** 10 mi = _?_ km

19. 10 kg = _?_ lb

For Exercises 20–25, choose the most reasonable estimate.

20. The length of a soccer field

     a. 110 cm   **b.** 110 m   **c.** 110 km

21. The capacity of a bathtub

     a. 150 mL   **b.** 150 L   **c.** 150 kL

22. The height of an average person

     a. 2 m   **b.** 2 cm   **c.** 2 km

23. The width of a $\frac{5}{8}$-inch wrench opening

    a. 16 mm   **b.** 16 cm   **c.** 16 m

24. The distance from San Francisco to Los Angeles

    a. 500 cm   **b.** 500 m   **c.** 500 km

25. The mass of a 12-oz soda

    a. 340 mg   **b.** 340 g   **c.** 340 kg

Replace each ? with <, >, or = to make a *true* statement.

26. 1.7 km _?_ 170 m   **27.** 35 g _?_ 0.35 kg

28. 0.61 L _?_ 610 mL   **29.** 3 km _?_ 2 mi

30. 6 in. _?_ 30.48 cm   **31.** 9.46 L _?_ 100 qt

32. A baker mixes 250 g of rye flour with 1.2 kg of bread flour. What percent of the mixture is rye?

33. How many 60-mL bottles of perfume can be filled from a 375-L container?

34. What is the weight in ounces shown on the scale?

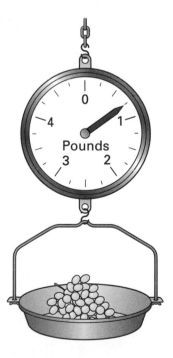

35. When you change the oil in a car, you drain all the old oil and replace it with new oil. An imported car's maintenance manual lists the oil capacity as 4.5 L. If you change the oil in this car, how many quarts of oil will you need?

36. What is the value of $5q + r$ when $q = -0.4$, and $r = 1.6$?

37. What is the value of $\dfrac{a + b}{a - b}$ when $a = 0.12$ and $b = 1.4$?

Rewrite each fraction as a decimal and as a percent.

38. $\dfrac{5}{8}$ **39.** $\dfrac{3}{5}$ **40.** $\dfrac{5}{2}$

Use the four-step problem-solving plan to solve Exercise 41.

41. A credit card company requires a minimum monthly payment of 10% of any unpaid balance. The company charges a 1.5% monthly finance charge for any unpaid balance and adds this amount in the following month's statement.

Suppose Mr. Jordan's May statement shows an unpaid balance of $240. What will be the balance for the June statement if Mr. Jordan makes the minimum payment in May?

Write the next two numbers in each sequence.

42. $3, -6, 9, -12, 15$ **43.** $\dfrac{1}{16}, \dfrac{1}{8}, \dfrac{1}{4}, \dfrac{1}{2}, 1$

Cumulative Problem Solving

For a planned mission to Mars, a spacecraft will travel approximately 78,300,000 km. The flight from Earth to Mars will take 259 days.

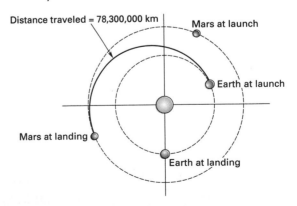

Distance traveled = 78,300,000 km

Mars at launch

Earth at launch

Mars at landing

Earth at landing

44. Write the distance traveled in scientific notation.

45. What is the spacecraft's average speed in kilometers per hour? What is the average speed in kilometers per second?

Trina is ordering supplies for Sunday's game. She expects to sell 2000 soft drinks and 1500 grilled burgers.

46. Each soft drink holds 12 fluid ounces. How many gallons of soft drink should Trina order?

47. Each burger patty weighs $3\frac{1}{2}$ ounces. How many pounds of meat should Trina order?

A computer's hard drive can store approximately 6 gigabytes of data. The prefix *giga-* means billion. A CD can store approximately 650 megabytes of data. The prefix *mega-* means million.

48. Write each of the storage capacities in scientific notation.

49. Suppose the computer's hard drive is completely filled with data, and you want to copy all the data onto CDs. About how many CDs will you need?

Estabon is a nurse adjusting the flow rate of an intravenous (IV) infusion set for a patient. An IV slowly injects fluid into the patient's vein. The doctor has ordered 500 mL of blood for the patient to be infused over 5 hours.

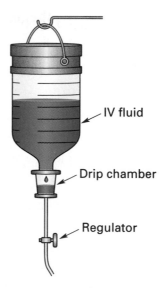

IV fluid

Drip chamber

Regulator

50. The *drop factor* is the number of drops per milliliter that an infusion set delivers. Estabon is using an infusion set that delivers 20 drops per milliliter (drops/mL). How many drops of blood must be delivered to the patient by this set? Write your answer in scientific notation.

51. To what flow rate, in drops per minute, should Estabon adjust the IV?

LESSON 10.5 SQUARE ROOTS AND IRRATIONAL NUMBERS

OBJECTIVES

➤ Identify perfect squares and compute square roots.
➤ Solve equation containing x^2.
➤ Estimate square roots that are irrational numbers.

Roberta makes baby quilts from scraps of material. She wants to make a square quilt and she has 25 square feet of material. How long should Roberta make the sides of the quilt?

ACTIVITY

Perfect Squares and Square Roots

1 Use Algeblocks to form four squares with 1, 2, 3, and 4 tiles along the sides of the squares.

1^2 tile 2^2 tiles 3^2 tiles   ?

2 The number of tiles in a square—its area—is the product of the number of tiles along each side. Since each side of a square has the same number of tiles, the product is a power. Copy and complete the table with the number of tiles in each square.

Number of Tiles Along the Side	1	2	3	4
Number of Tiles in the Square	? = 1^2	? = 2^2	? = 3^2	? = 4^2

3 The numbers you wrote in the table are *perfect squares*. A **perfect square** is a number that is the square of a whole number. Is 25 a perfect square? Explain.

4 List all the perfect squares less than 100.

5 The opposite of squaring a number is finding its **square root.** Since $16 = 4^2$, the square root of 16 is 4. The symbol $\sqrt{}$ indicates square root. You write $\sqrt{16} = 4$. Complete the following.

$$\sqrt{9} = \underline{\ ?\ } \qquad \sqrt{4} = \underline{\ ?\ }$$
$$\sqrt{1} = \underline{\ ?\ } \qquad \sqrt{25} = \underline{\ ?\ }$$

6 Notice that -4 is also a square root of 16, since $(-4)^2 = 16$. Every number greater than zero has a positive square root and a negative square root. Thus, the equation $x^2 = 16$ has two solutions, 4 and -4.

The $\sqrt{}$ symbol indicates the positive square root.

$$\sqrt{16} = 4 \text{ and } -\sqrt{16} = -4$$

Complete the following.

$$-\sqrt{81} = \underline{\ ?\ } \qquad -\sqrt{1} = \underline{\ ?\ }$$
$$-\sqrt{25} = \underline{\ ?\ } \qquad -\sqrt{100} = \underline{\ ?\ }$$

ONGOING ASSESSMENT

Write the squares of the whole numbers from 11 through 15. What is $\sqrt{169}$? What is $-\sqrt{225}$?

EXAMPLE 1 Solving Equations

Solve the equation $x^2 = 400$.

SOLUTION

The equation $x^2 = 400$ has two solutions, 20 and -20, since $20^2 = 400$ and $(-20)^2 = 400$. These two solutions can be expressed using the plus or minus symbol $\pm$.

$$\text{If } x^2 = 400, \text{ then } x = \pm 20.$$

ONGOING ASSESSMENT

Solve each of the following.

a. $x^2 = 49$ **b.** $y^2 = 256$

c. $z^2 = 0.25$ **d.** $t^2 - 100 = 0$

Can you make a perfect square using exactly 18 tiles? Even though 18 is not a perfect square, it has a square root.

EXAMPLE 2 Estimating Square Roots

Estimate $\sqrt{18}$ to the nearest tenth.

SOLUTION

18 lies between two perfect squares: 16 and 25. Therefore, $\sqrt{16} < \sqrt{18} < \sqrt{25}$, or

$$4 < \sqrt{18} < 5$$

First try the number halfway between 4 and 5.

$$4.5^2 = 20.25 \quad \leftarrow \quad \text{4.5 is too high}$$
$$4.4^2 = 19.36 \quad \leftarrow \quad \text{4.4 is too high}$$
$$4.3^2 = 18.49 \quad \leftarrow \quad \text{4.3 is too high}$$
$$4.2^2 = 17.64 \quad \leftarrow \quad \text{4.2 is too low}$$

$\sqrt{18}$ is between 4.3 and 4.2, but closer to 4.2. Therefore, to the nearest tenth, $\sqrt{18} \approx 4.2$.

Critical Thinking   Explain why $\sqrt{18}$ is closer to 4.2 than 4.3.

ONGOING ASSESSMENT

Estimate $\sqrt{30}$ to the nearest tenth.

The square root of 18 is an example of an *irrational number.*

Recall that a rational number can be written as a ratio of two integers. You can also write a rational number as a terminating or repeating decimal. For example,

$$\frac{3}{5} = 0.6 \qquad \frac{2}{9} = 0.\overline{2} \qquad \frac{9}{25} = 0.36 \qquad \frac{2}{11} = 0.\overline{18}$$

An **irrational number**, such as $\sqrt{18}$, is represented by a nonrepeating, nonterminating decimal. Use your calculator to find $\sqrt{18}$.

$$18 \;\boxed{\sqrt{x}} \quad \boxed{4.242640687}$$

The calculator displays the first ten digits. When you write the result, use ellipses (. . .) to show that the nonrepeating, nonterminating digits continue.

$$\sqrt{18} = 4.242640687 \ldots$$

To the nearest hundredth, $\sqrt{18} \approx 4.24$.

The square root of any positive integer that is not a perfect square is an irrational number. Write three square roots that are irrational numbers. Use your calculator to find the values of the square roots. Write the values to the nearest hundredth.

The set of **real numbers** consists of rational and irrational numbers. The Venn diagram below shows the subsets and relationships among the real numbers.

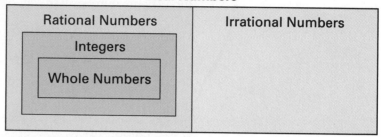

Real Numbers

Rational Numbers	Irrational Numbers
Integers	
Whole Numbers	

ONGOING ASSESSMENT

Give three examples of each of the following.

a. Whole numbers

b. Integers that are not whole numbers

c. Rational numbers that are not integers

d. Irrational numbers

Critical Thinking   Explain why $\sqrt{-16}$ does not exist in the real number system.

LESSON ASSESSMENT

Think and Discuss

1 Can you form a square with 121 Algeblocks? If so, how many tiles are along each side?

2 Write an algorithm for finding an estimate of $\sqrt{54}$ to the nearest hundredth.

3 Explain why every whole number greater than zero has two square roots.

4 Name the subsets of the real number system to which each of the following belong.

   a. -8 **b.** $\sqrt{6}$ **c.** $0.\overline{6}$ **d.** $\sqrt{81}$ **e.** $\sqrt{\dfrac{4}{9}}$

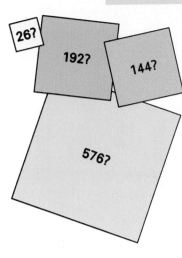

Which of the following are perfect squares? Write *yes* or *no*. For each perfect square, write its square roots.

5. 26

6. 144

7. 192

8. 576

Write two consecutive whole numbers that each square root is between.

9. $\sqrt{32}$

10. $\sqrt{45}$

11. $\sqrt{2}$

12. $\sqrt{98}$

Without using a calculator, find an approximation for each of the following to the nearest tenth.

13. $\sqrt{7}$

14. $\sqrt{19}$

15. $\sqrt{92}$

16. $\sqrt{159}$

Use a calculator to find each square root. Round to the nearest thousandth if necessary.

17. $\sqrt{89}$

18. $\sqrt{361}$

19. $\sqrt{500}$

20. $\sqrt{1024}$

21. $-\sqrt{631}$

22. $-\sqrt{35.3}$

23. $\sqrt{552.25}$

24. $-\sqrt{0.0036}$

Solve each equation.

25. $a^2 = 225$

26. $m^2 = 0.01$

27. $2x^2 = 7.22$

Use a calculator to find each product or quotient.

28. $\sqrt{20} \cdot \sqrt{5}$

29. $\sqrt{2} \cdot \sqrt{32}$

30. $\dfrac{\sqrt{125}}{\sqrt{5}}$

The area of a square is the square of the length of a side. The length of each side of a square is the square root of its area.

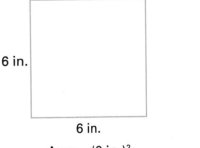

6 in.

6 in.

Area = (6 in.)^2
= 36 in.^{2}

9 in.^{2} d

d

$d^2 = 9$ in.^{2}
$d = \sqrt{9 \text{ in.}^2} = 3$ in.

31. The area of a square window is 1600 square inches. What is the length of each side of the window?

32. The area of a square garden is 225 square feet. What is the perimeter of the garden?

33. The garden in Exercise 32 is enclosed by a fence built 5 feet from each side of the garden. What area is enclosed by the fence?

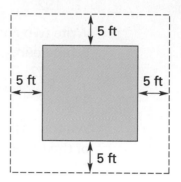

34. Find two different square roots that are irrational numbers, but whose product is a rational number. (Hint: see Exercises 28 and 29.)

35. Find two different square roots that are irrational numbers, but whose quotient is a rational number. (Hint: see Exercise 30.)

Mixed Review

Solve each equation.

36. $5x + 9 = 8x - 15$

37. $-15 = \frac{2}{3}(x - 1)$

Make a table of values for (x, y). Include 5 ordered pairs. Then graph the equation on a coordinate grid.

38. $y = 5x - 2$

39. $2x + 3y = -6$

40. A technician in a chemical analysis lab mixes 0.55 milliliters of solution A with 3.5 liters of solution B to make a new solution. How many liters does the new solution contain?

41. Shareka runs 3 miles around a track that is $\frac{1}{4}$ mile long. How many times around the track does Shareka run?

Rinji scored 89, 90, 91, 94, and 91 on five quizzes.

42. What is the range of Rinji's quiz scores?

43. What is the mean of Rinji's quiz scores?

44. What is the median of Rinji's quiz scores?

45. What is the mode of Rinji's quiz scores?

LESSON 10.6 THE PYTHAGOREAN THEOREM

OBJECTIVES

➤ Apply the Pythagorean theorem to find the unknown side of a right triangle.
➤ Determine if a triangle is a right triangle using the Pythagorean theorem.

Laina is a plumber's apprentice connecting two drain pipes of different heights. The horizontal distance between the ends of the pipes is 15 inches. The difference in height is 9 inches. What length should Laina cut the connecting pipe?

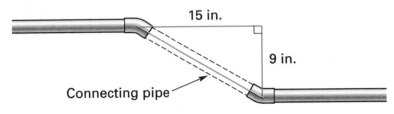

15 in.

9 in.

Connecting pipe

In a right triangle, the side opposite the right angle is called the **hypotenuse**. The two sides that form the right angle are called the **legs**.

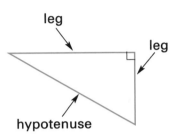

leg

leg

hypotenuse

ACTIVITY

A Right Triangle Relationship

1 From sheets of graph paper, cut out eight squares with sides of 3, 4, 5, 6, 8, 10, 12, and 13 units.

2 Use the sides of three squares to form a right triangle, with legs 3 and 4 units in length, and hypotenuse 5 units.

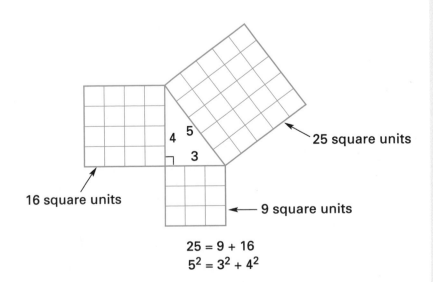

25 square units

16 square units

9 square units

$$25 = 9 + 16$$
$$5^2 = 3^2 + 4^2$$

3 Compare the area of the square containing the hypotenuse to the sum of the areas of the squares containing the two legs.

4 Use the squares to form a right triangle with legs 5 and 12 units. What is the length of the hypotenuse of this triangle?

Length of Legs	3	5	?
	4	12	?
Length of Hypotenuse	5	?	10

5 Use the squares to form a right triangle with hypotenuse 10 units. What are the lengths of the legs?

6 For each right triangle, compare the area of the square containing the hypotenuse to the sum of the areas of the squares containing the two legs.

7 Let c represent the length of the hypotenuse of a right triangle. Let a and b represent the lengths of the legs. Write an equation that describes the relationship between a, b, and c.

Over 2500 years ago, the Greek mathematician Pythagoras proved the relationship you found in the Activity is true for all right triangles. This relationship is called the Pythagorean Theorem.

8 Use the squares to form legs of three additional right triangles. Predict the length of the hypotenuse of each triangle. Measure each length and compare to your prediction.

Pythagorean Theorem
If c represents the length of the hypotenuse of a right triangle, and a and b represent the lengths of the legs, then

$$c^2 = a^2 + b^2$$

EXAMPLE 1 Using the Pythagorean Theorem

To the nearest tenth of an inch, what length should Laina cut the connecting drain pipe?

SOLUTION

The connecting pipe is the hypotenuse of a right triangle. Let c represent the length of the pipe. Use the Pythagorean Theorem and your calculator.

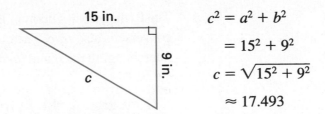

$$c^2 = a^2 + b^2$$
$$= 15^2 + 9^2$$
$$c = \sqrt{15^2 + 9^2}$$
$$\approx 17.493$$

To the nearest tenth, Laina should cut the length of the connecting pipe 17.5 inches.

EXAMPLE 2 Finding the Missing Leg

Find the length of the leg of the right triangle.

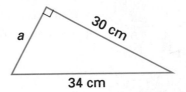

SOLUTION

$$c^2 = a^2 + b^2$$
$$34^2 = a^2 + 30^2$$
$$a^2 = 34^2 - 30^2$$
$$= 1156 - 900$$
$$= 256$$
$$a = \sqrt{256}$$
$$= 16$$

The length of the leg is 16 centimeters.

ONGOING ASSESSMENT

Find the missing lengths. Round to the nearest tenth, if necessary.

a. 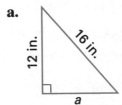 b. 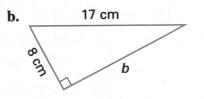 c.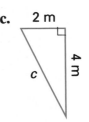

Critical Thinking   Which side of a right triangle is always longest? Explain your reasoning.

The Pythagorean Theorem is *true* for all right triangles. The converse is also *true*. The converse of a statement is obtained by interchanging the *if* and *then* parts.

> ### Converse of the Pythagorean Theorem
> If the sides of a triangle have lengths a, b, and c, where $c^2 = a^2 + b^2$, then the triangle is a right triangle.

EXAMPLE 3 A Right Triangle Test

A roof truss is designed as a triangle with sides 6 meters, 7 meters, and 8 meters. Is the roof truss a right triangle?

SOLUTION

If the truss is a right triangle, the longest side must be the hypotenuse.

$$c^2 = a^2 + b^2$$
$$8^2 \overset{?}{=} 6^2 + 7^2$$
$$64 \overset{?}{=} 36 + 49$$
$$64 \neq 85$$

The truss is not a right triangle.

ONGOING ASSESSMENT

Is a triangle with sides of the given lengths a right triangle?

a. 15 ft, 20 ft, 25 ft

b. 12 cm, 14 cm, 16 cm

LESSON ASSESSMENT

Think and Discuss

1 Write an algorithm for finding the length of a leg of a right triangle if you know the length of the hypotenuse and one leg.

2 Explain the difference between the Pythagorean Theorem and the Converse of the Pythagorean Theorem.

3 Does the relationship $c^2 = a^2 + b^2$ hold for an equilateral or acute triangle? Explain.

Name the hypotenuse and legs of each right triangle.

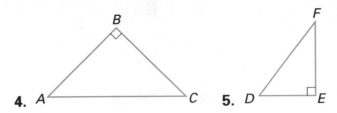

4. **5.**

Replace each ? with = or ≠ to make each of the following a *true* statement.

6. $15^2 + 20^2$ _?_ 25^2 **7.** $6^2 + 7^2$ _?_ 8^2

8. $39^2 - 36^2$ _?_ 15^2 **9.** $13^2 - 12^2$ _?_ 10^2

Find the missing side for each right triangle. If the side is not a perfect square, round the length to the nearest tenth.

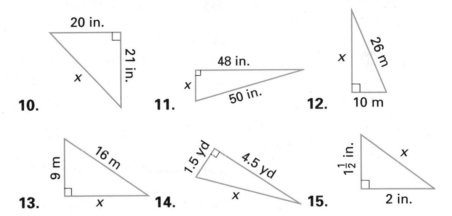

10. **11.** **12.**

13. **14.** **15.**

Determine if the following measures for the three sides of a triangle form a right triangle. Explain why or why not.

16. 8 in., 15 in. , 17 in. **17.** 15 ft, 62 ft, 65 ft

18. 6 m, 9.1 m, 10.9 m **19.** $\sqrt{10}$ yd, $\sqrt{12}$ yd, 18 yd

Find the unknown distance in each of the following. Round to the nearest tenth if necessary.

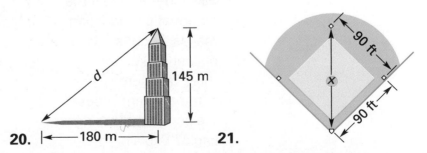

20. **21.**

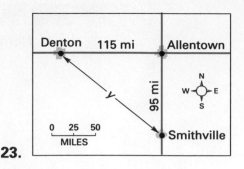

22. **23.**

24. A hiker walks 10 miles north from camp. Then he turns and walks 4 miles east. How far is the hiker from the camp?

25. The top of a 25-foot ladder reaches the edge of the roof. The base of the ladder is 12 feet from the building when the ladder leans against the building. How many feet above the ground is the point where the ladder touches the roof?

26. A radio broadcast tower is 200 feet high. One end of a wire is attached to the top of the tower. The other end of the wire is attached to the ground 150 feet away from the base of the tower. How long is the wire?

27. A swimming pool is 25 meters long and 15 meters wide. A rope is stretched along one diagonal of the pool. How long is the rope?

28. A rectangular warehouse floor has a diagonal walkway that is 91 feet long. One side of the warehouse floor is 72 feet long. How long is the other side of the warehouse floor?

29. A diver swims 30 feet from his boat to reach the anchor at the bottom of a buoy that is floating on the surface of the water. The rope connecting the buoy to the anchor is 25 feet long. How far is the buoy located from the boat?

30. To determine if the corner of a foundation makes a right angle, a builder makes the three measures shown in the diagram. Does the corner make a right angle? Explain.

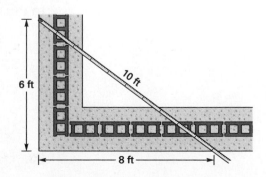

For Exercises 31 and 32, define a variable, write an equation, and solve.

31. The ninth-grade class has 565 students. There are two-thirds as many boys as girls. How many girls are in the ninth-grade class?

32. Together, Mary, Rhonda, and Raj earned $113. Mary earned $3 more than Rhonda. Raj earned $5 more than Rhonda. How much did each person earn?

Ramon can type 225 words in 5 minutes.

33. What is the unit rate in words per minute?

34. At this rate, how many words can Ramon type in 9 minutes?

Use the graph below that shows the profits of a company for 6 consecutive quarters for Exercises 35 and 36.

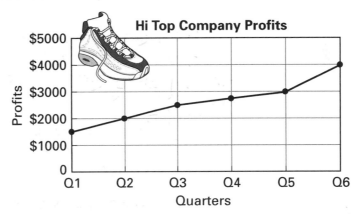

35. What is the profit in the fifth quarter?

36. How much more profit did the company make in the fourth quarter than in the second quarter?

37. Find the simple interest on a principal of $500 at 6.5% for 2 years.

38. Find the rate of interest if the simple interest paid on $1600 borrowed for $1\frac{1}{2}$ years is $192.

For Exercises 39–42, let $3x - 4y = 12$.

39. Write the equation in slope-intercept form.

40. Find the x- and y-intercepts of the graph of the equation.

41. What is the slope of the line?

42. What is the value of y when $x = 12$?

Officer Rodriquez is investigating the scene of an accident. As a part of her investigation, she measures the length of a skid mark left on the road by a car in the accident. Officer Rodriquez uses a formula to estimate the speed of the car at the beginning of the skid mark.

$$d = \frac{v^2}{30C}$$

d is the length of the skid mark in feet.
v is the estimated speed of the car in miles per hour.
C is the coefficient of sliding friction between the tire and the road surface.

Values for C are given in the table.

Coefficient of Sliding Friction

Road Surface	Dry Road	Wet Road
Concrete	0.90	0.60
Asphalt	0.85	0.65
Gravel	0.65	0.65
Packed snow	0.45	0.45

43. Use the formula to write an equation for v.

44. Officer Rodriquez measures a skid length of 215 feet. The accident occurred on wet asphalt. What speed should Officer Rodriquez report for the car that made the skid mark?

Dwana is ordering fencing material for a new playground. The playground is in the shape of an irregular pentagon, as shown in the figure.

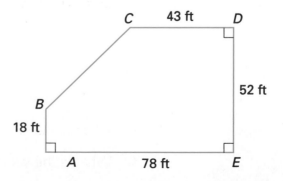

45. Draw or trace the outline of the pentagon. Draw a line through *B*, parallel to $\overline{AE}$. Draw a line through *C*, perpendicular to $\overline{AE}$.

46. $\overline{BC}$ is the hypotenuse of a right triangle. What are the lengths of the legs of the right triangle?

47. Calculate the length of $\overline{BC}$.

48. How many feet of fencing material should Dwana order?

Kyle is a lieutenant in the U.S. Navy. He is planning to fly to Norfolk to be in a friend's wedding. Since he cannot carry his ceremonial sword on the plane, Kyle will ship it through the mail. The sword is 38 inches long.

The Pac-n-Mail store has a box with the dimensions shown.

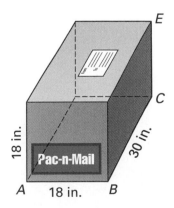

49. What is the length of the diagonal $\overline{AC}$ of the bottom of the box? Can Kyle ship the sword so that it lays flat on the bottom of the box?

50. What is the length of the diagonal $\overline{AE}$ in the box? (Hint: Use the legs $\overline{AC}$ and $\overline{EC}$.) Can Kyle ship the sword in the box?

MATH LAB

Activity 1: Pendulums and Square Root Equations

Equipment   Several large washers
String
Meterstick
Stopwatch
Graph paper

Problem Statement

A **pendulum** consists of a mass and a string. The mass is attached to one end of the string. The other end of the string, called the pivot, is fixed so the mass can swing back and forth. The **period** T of a pendulum is the time required to complete one swing, or round trip, of the motion.

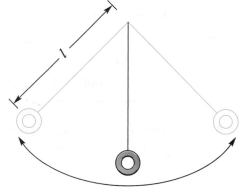

The period T of the pendulum is the time it takes for the mass to make one full swing.

In this Activity, you will measure the period of several pendulums. You will compare the measurements to values calculated from a formula.

Procedure

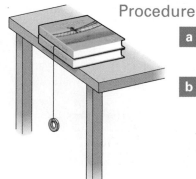

a   Tie the washers to the string. These washers are the mass of the pendulum.

b   Hang the mass over the side of a table or desk. Have a group member hold the string on top of the table, or place the string between books stacked on the table. To swing the pendulum, pull the mass to one side so it makes an angle of about 15° with the vertical. When you release the mass, it should swing in a vertical plane.

c Measure the length of the pendulum from the pivot to the center of the washer. For each length listed in the table below, measure and record the time for the pendulum to make 10 complete swings. For the longest pendulum, you may need to have a group member stand and hold the string.

Pendulum Length l, cm	Time for 10 Complete Swings, s	Average Period T, s
10		
20		
40		
80		
160		

d Calculate and record the average period for each length.

e Construct a coordinate plane on graph paper with *Pendulum Length* on the horizontal axis and *Period* on the vertical axis. Plot your measured data. Describe the relationship between l and T. Is the relationship linear?

f For a simple pendulum, the relation between l and T is a square root equation:

$$T = k \sqrt{l}$$

where k is a constant. When l is measured in centimeters, and T is measured in seconds,

$$k = \frac{2\pi}{\sqrt{981}}$$

Use the square root equation to make a table of values for l and T with at least ten values from $l = 0$ cm through 150 cm. Plot the (l, T) ordered pairs on the same coordinate plane from Step **e**. Draw a smooth curve through the points.

g Compare your measured values to the curve. If they are not the same, give some possible reasons.

h Predict the periods of a 60-cm and a 120-cm pendulum. Measure the periods and compare them to your predictions.

Discussion Questions

1. Explain why it is reasonable to expect measured periods for longer pendulums to be more accurate than for shorter pendulums. Does your data verify this statement?

2. Graph the square root equation $y = \sqrt{x}$ on a coordinate plane. Use $0 \le x \le 25$. Graph $y = -\sqrt{x}$ on the same coordinate plane. Are these linear equations? Why are negative square root equations not used when graphing the period of a pendulum?

Activity 2: Significant Figures and Scientific Notation

Equipment   Measuring tape, metric units
Measuring tape, U.S. customary units
Masking tape

Problem Statement

When you record measured data, you should write only figures for which the measurement is certain. For example, the smallest division on a centimeter ruler is one millimeter. Therefore, you can read the ruler to the nearest half-millimeter. The width of the blue stripe shown is 4.25 ± 0.05 cm.

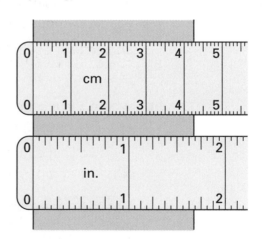

Similarly, you can read a ruler with units of fractions of an inch to the nearest one-half of the smallest fraction. The smallest fraction on the ruler shown is $\frac{1}{16}$ inch. Thus, you can read it to the nearest $\frac{1}{32}$ inch. The width of the stripe is $1\frac{22}{32} \pm \frac{1}{32}$ inches.

When you record a decimal measurement such as 4.25 cm, you are saying the measurement is precise to *three significant figures.* If you record the measurement with four significant figures—for example, 4.248 cm—you incorrectly imply the centimeter ruler has a greater precision than it really has. When you add or subtract measurements, round the result to the least precise value. For example, 4.25 cm ± 3.019 cm = 7.269 cm = 7.27 cm (rounded).

When you multiply or divide measurements, round the answer to the smallest number of significant figures in the measured values. For example, to calculate the width of $\frac{3}{4}$ of the 4.25-cm stripe, round to three significant figures.

$$\frac{3}{4}(4.25) = 3.1875 = 3.19 \text{ rounded}$$

This Activity demonstrates the use of significant figures and scientific notation. You will calculate the average step length of the members of your group in U.S. customary units and metric units. Then you will estimate the number of steps required to walk across the continental United States.

Procedure

a Mark a start line on the floor with masking tape. Have each group member place the tips of their shoes on the start line, and then walk 10 steps in a straight line. At the end of 10 steps, mark with a piece of masking tape the location of his or her shoe tip farthest from the start line.

b Measure the total distance walked by each group member in 10 steps, using the U.S. customary tape measure and the metric tape measure. Record the measurements, with the appropriate fraction or number of significant figures.

Group Member	Total Distance in 10 Steps, ft, in.	Total Distance in 10 Steps, m
1		
2		
3		
4		
5		

c Calculate the mean step length in inches for your group. Write your answer as a fraction.

d Using this mean, estimate the number of steps it would take to walk 2946 miles from New York City to San Francisco. Write your answer in scientific notation.

e Calculate the mean step length for your group, in centimeters. Write your answer as a decimal.

f Using this mean, estimate the number of steps it would take to walk 4743 kilometers from New York City to San Francisco. Write your answer in scientific notation.

g Compare your answers from Steps **d** and **f**. If they are not the same, in which significant figure are they different? Could rounding have caused the difference?

Discussion Questions

1. How many significant figures did you use to write your group's mean step length in centimeters? Explain why you used this number of significant figures.

2. How many significant figures did you use to estimate the number of steps to walk across the U.S.? Explain why you used this number of significant figures.

3. Convert your group's mean step length in inches (from Step **c**) to centimeters. Compare the result to that calculated in Step **e**. If they are not the same, in which significant figure are they different? Do you think the difference is due to rounding?

Activity 3: Minimum Cost for Highway Construction

Equipment   Spreadsheet computer program

Problem Statement

Brazos is 20 miles east and 7 miles south of Alban. An international trade agreement has greatly increased truck traffic between Brazos and Alban. To handle this traffic, the Highway Construction Board has proposed construction of a new highway.

The new highway will connect Brazos to I-60, which runs east and west through Alban. If the point of intersection of the new highway and I-60 is not at Alban, I-60 will have to be widened and resurfaced between the intersection point and Alban.

The cost of constructing the new highway is $180,000 per mile. The cost of widening and resurfacing I-60 is $120,000 per mile.

The Board has asked you to recommend the least expensive plan for constructing the new highway. You consider the following three options.

Option 1: Construct the new highway from Brazos perpendicular to I-60.

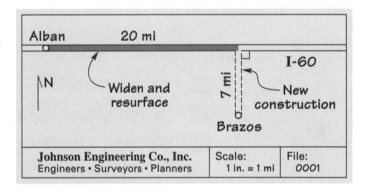

Option 2: Construct the new highway between Brazos and Alban. No widening or resurfacing of I-60 is required for this option.

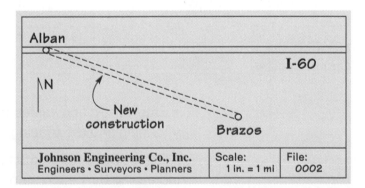

Option 3: Construct the new highway from Brazos to I-60, to a point between the perpendicular (Option 1) and Alban (Option 2). Let D represent the point of intersection of the new highway with I-60. For Option 3, you need to find the location of D which minimizes the total cost.

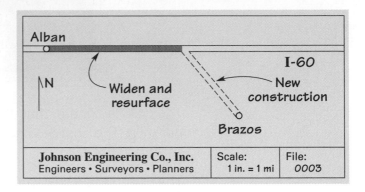

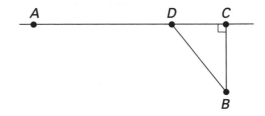

Procedure

a Find the total cost for Option 1.

b Find the total cost for Option 2.

c Construct a spreadsheet to calculate the costs of Option 3 for varying locations of point D.

	A	B	C	D	E	F	G
1	Cost to widen =	120,000		DC	AD Cost	BD Cost	AD+BD Cost
2	Cost of new constr =	180,000		0			
3				1			
4				2			
5	Option 1 cost =			3			
6	Option 2 cost =			4			

• Enter labels and values to display the costs per mile for widening and resurfacing, and for new construction.

• Enter values for lengths of $\overline{DC}$, from 0 to 20 miles, increasing by 1 each step.

- Enter a formula to calculate the cost of widening and resurfacing $\overline{AD}$ for each value of DC.

- Enter a formula to calculate the cost of new construction of $\overline{BD}$ for each value of DC. Most spreadsheet programs use the built-in function SQRT to calculate square roots. For example, the function =SQRT(12*3) returns the value 6.

- Enter a formula to calculate the total cost of widening and resurfacing $\overline{AD}$ plus new construction for $\overline{BD}$.

d What value of DC corresponds to Option 1? Compare the total cost calculated by the spreadsheet to the cost predicted for Option 1.

e What value of DC corresponds to Option 2? Compare the total cost calculated by the spreadsheet to the cost predicted for Option 2.

f Describe the trend in the data for total cost as DC increases from 0 to 20. What value of DC results in the lowest cost?

g Explain the construction plan you will recommend to the Highway Construction Board.

Discussion Questions

1. What is the longest possible new highway? Which option does this represent?

2. What is the shortest possible new highway? Which option does this represent?

3. Suppose the cost to widen and resurface is $180,000 per mile. Which option is the least expensive? Explain why this result makes sense.

CHAPTER 10 ASSESSMENT

Communicate

1. Explain what the exponent in the expression 2^3 means.

2. How do you multiply powers that have the same base? How do you divide powers that have the same base?

3. How can you tell if a number is written in scientific notation?

4. When you use your calculator to find $\sqrt{49}$ and $\sqrt{50}$, are the displays exact or approximate? Explain.

5. Describe how to find the length of the hypotenuse of a right triangle if the lengths of the two legs are known.

Skills

Simplify

6. $(-3)^2$

7. $(4-2)^3 + 5$

8. $4^5 \cdot 4$

9. $\dfrac{x^6}{x^3}$

10. $\left(-\dfrac{1}{2}\right)^0$

11. 6^{-6}

Write each number in decimal notation.

12. 2.5×10^{-4}

13. 1.654×10^6

Write each number in scientific notation.

14. 937,000

15. 0.0031

Replace each ? to make a *true* statement.

16. 37 m = ? cm

17. 46 g = ? kg

18. 6 L = ? qt   (1 qt = 0.946 L)

19. 12 in. = ? cm   (1 in. = 2.54 cm)

Find each square root. Round to the nearest thousandth if necessary.

20. $-\sqrt{189}$

21. $\sqrt{20}$

Find the missing side of each right triangle.

22. The legs measure 5 meters and 12 meters.

23. The hypotenuse measures 140 inches. One leg measures 100 inches.

Applications

24. Patti invests $1560 in a certificate of deposit that earns 5.9% interest compounded annually. How much will Patti have in her account after 3 years?

25. The area of a square garden is 324 yd². What is the length of each side of the garden?

26. A rectangular building is 77 feet long and 36 feet wide. Find the length of a walkway that is being built along one diagonal of the building.

Math Lab

27. The period of a pendulum T (in seconds) is given by the formula $T = 0.2\sqrt{l}$ where l is the length of the pendulum in centimeters. What is the length of a pendulum if its period is 1.8 seconds?

28. A granola bar weighs 5.78 ounces. Use significant figures to write the total weight of 1250 granola bars.

29. The cost of constructing a new highway is $1,800,000 per mile. The cost of widening and resurfacing the existing highway is $1,200,000. What is the total cost to build 12 miles of new highway and widen and resurface 17 miles of the existing highway?

CHAPTER 11

WHY SHOULD I LEARN THIS?

When geometric figures are enlarged or reduced, you can predict how their perimeters and areas change. How do artists use measurement, ratio, and proportion to make larger-than-life sculptures?

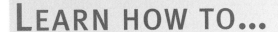

MEASUREMENT

LEARN HOW TO...

1. **Identify, describe, extend, and create geometric and numerical patterns and sequences.**
2. **Use ratio and proportion to solve problems involving similar figures.**
3. **Draw similar shapes using dilations.**
4. **Calculate distances from scale drawings and maps.**
5. **Find the perimeter, or circumference, and area of plane figures.**
6. **Describe the effects on perimeter and area when dimensions of a plane figure are changed proportionally.**

Everybody makes measurements at some time or other. For example, you can measure length, time, space, volume, and mass. Sometimes when you compare measurements, like lengths of geometric figures, you find patterns.

Useful patterns occur when the ratios of the lengths of corresponding sides of two figures are equal. These figures are called similar figures. Similar figures are important when you make scale drawings, enlarge or reduce photographs, build models, and read maps.

In Lesson 9.4, you learned the perimeter of a polygon is the measure of the distance around the polygon. Polygons also have area—the measure of the space enclosed by the polygon. In this chapter, you will derive and use formulas for the areas of rectangles, squares, parallelograms, and triangles. You will also discover a useful relationship between the ratios of perimeters and areas of similar polygons.

A circle is not a polygon, but it has a perimeter, called the circumference. Circles also enclose areas. You will use regular polygons to find the formula for the circumference and area of a circle.

LESSON 11.1 PATTERNS AND SEQUENCES

OBJECTIVES
- - - - - - - - - - - - - -
➤ Find the terms of a sequence.

One of the oldest known toys is the set of Russian Matryoshka nesting dolls. Many children have learned to count by playing with these dolls.

In one set, the height of the smallest doll is 12 mm, the second doll is 20 mm, the third doll is 28 mm, and so on. You can write the heights of these dolls as a *sequence*.

A **sequence** is a set of numbers arranged according to a pattern. Each number is called a **term** of the sequence.

ACTIVITY	An Arithmetic Sequence

1 Write the first four doll heights as a sequence.

$$12 \quad 20 \quad 28 \quad ?$$
$$+\underline{?} \quad +\underline{?} \quad +\underline{?}$$

2 What number is added to each term to get the next term in the sequence?

3 Continue the pattern, and write the next two terms. What is the height of the sixth Russian nesting doll?

Critical Thinking   In the Activity, you added the same number to each term to get the next term in the sequence. This number is called the *common difference*. Let d represent the common difference in a sequence. If you know the first term in the sequence, x_1, you can calculate the nth term, x_n, with a formula.

$$x_n = x_1 + d(n - 1)$$

Use the formula to calculate the seventh through the tenth terms of the sequence in the Activity.

In some sequences, you do not add the same amount each time.

The first four **triangular numbers** are shown.

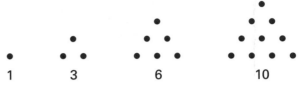

1   3   6   10

a. Draw the geometric figure for the fifth triangular number. What is the fifth term of this sequence?

b. What is the 8th triangular number?

a. For the fifth triangle, add a row of five to the bottom of the fourth triangle.

The fifth term of the sequence is 15.

b. Write the first five triangular numbers as a sequence.

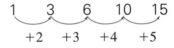

1   3   6   10   15
    +2   +3   +4   +5

The pattern is to add 2, add 3, add 4, and so on. The next three numbers in the sequence are 21, 28, 36. The eighth triangular number is 36.

Without drawing a picture, find the tenth triangular number in the sequence from Example 1.

Find the next three terms of each sequence.

a. $1, 3, 9, 27, \underline{?}, \underline{?}, \underline{?}$ **b.** $25x, 21x, 17x, 13x, \underline{?}, \underline{?}, \underline{?}$

a. Each term is three times the previous term.

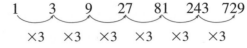

1   3   9   27   81   243   729
    ×3   ×3   ×3   ×3   ×3   ×3

The next three terms are 81, 243, 729.

b. Each term is $4x$ less than the previous term.

$$\underbrace{25x \quad 21x \quad 17x \quad 13x}_{-4x \qquad -4x \qquad -4x} \quad 9x \quad 5x \quad x$$

The next three terms are $9x$, $5x$, x.

Critical Thinking   Write a formula for the nth term of the sequence of Example **2a**.

$$x_n = \underline{?}$$

ONGOING ASSESSMENT

A house framer spaces 2-by-4 studs 16 inches apart. The drawing shows the first three studs. How far from the first stud are the next three?

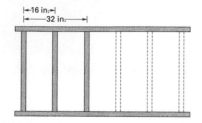

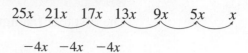

CULTURAL CONNECTION

Perfect numbers were studied by the ancient Egyptians and Pythagoras. But the first recorded use of perfect numbers was by Euclid in *The Elements,* written around 300 B.C.E. *The Elements* is history's best known geometry book. It also includes sequences and patterns.

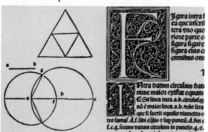

A **perfect number** is defined as a number that equals the sum of its factors (excluding the number itself). For example, 6 is a perfect number. The factors of 6 (excluding 6) are 1, 2, and 3. The sum of the factors is $1 + 2 + 3 = 6$.

1. Show that 10 is not a perfect number.

Euclid proved that the sequence of perfect numbers can be found from a formula. This is stated as Proposition 36 of Book IX of *The Elements.*

> If $k > 1$ and $2^k - 1$ is prime, then $2^{k-1}(2^k - 1)$ is a perfect number.

The first perfect number is found from $k = 2$.

$$2^2 - 1 = 4 - 1 = 3; \text{ 3 is prime.}$$
$$2^{2-1}(2^2 - 1) = 2^1(4 - 1) = 2(3) = 6$$

Therefore, 6 is the first perfect number.

2. Use Euclid's formula to find the next three perfect numbers in the sequence.

3. Show that 28 is a perfect number by adding its factors (excluding 28).

LESSON ASSESSMENT

Think and Discuss

1 Suppose the nth term of a sequence is given by the formula $x_n = (n - 2)^2$. Explain how to calculate the 12th term of the sequence.

2 The sum of the measures of the interior angles of a polygon is found from the expression $(n - 2)180°$. Explain how to use this expression to represent a sequence.

3 When finding a pattern for a sequence, explain how you decide whether addition, subtraction, multiplication, division, or an exponent is involved.

Practice and Apply

The first term in a sequence and the pattern are given. Write the next four terms of each sequence.

4. 3; add 5

5. 48; subtract 3

6. $8x + 5$; subtract $2x$

7. 144; divide by -2

8. $2a + 1$; subtract $a + 1$

9. $3g$; multiply by $2g$

Draw the next figure for each pattern.

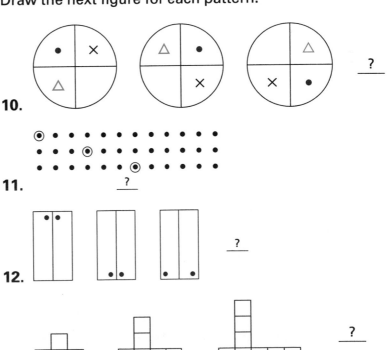

10.

11.

12.

13.

Find the next three terms of each sequence.

14. 20, 25, 30, 35, _?_, _?_, _?_　　**15.** 77, 67, 57, 47, _?_, _?_, _?_

16. 3, 6, 12, 24, _?_, _?_, _?_　　**17.** 2, 2, 4, 12, _?_, _?_, _?_

18. 1, −5, 25, −125, _?_, _?_, _?_　**19.** 5.8, 5.6, 5.4, 5.2, _?_, _?_, _?_

20. $\frac{1}{10}, \frac{1}{20}, \frac{1}{30}$, _?_, _?_, _?_　　**21.** 4, 5, 7, 10, _?_, _?_, _?_

22. 22, 2.2, 0.22, _?_, _?_, _?_

23. $k - 1, 2k - 1, 3k - 1$, _?_, _?_, _?_

24. $3d + 4, 3d + 2, 3d$, _?_, _?_, _?_

25. $20x - 5, 15x - 4, 10x - 3$, _?_, _?_, _?_

26. The first four **square numbers** are represented by this figure. Write a sequence showing the first ten square numbers.

27. Suppose your watch gains 2 minutes every day. How many minutes fast will your watch be after 30 days?

28. Suppose an investment in a mutual fund doubles in value every 6 years. If the initial investment is $2500, how long will it take for the investment to be worth $20,000?

Alyssa makes nylon kites. For one of her designs, Alyssa starts with a nylon panel in the shape of an isosceles right triangle. Then she adds congruent panels. The first three stages of the kite design are shown.

Stage 1

Stage 2

Stage 3

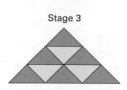

29. How many panels make up each stage?

Stage	Number of Panels
1	1
2	?
3	?
n	?

30. If Alyssa continues the pattern to eight stages, how many panels will she need in all?

The ages of the students in the chess club are shown below.

8 11 10 8 9 10 9 8 9 11 11 8

31. Find the mean of the data.

32. Find the median of the data.

33. Find the mode of the data.

Jamar earns $8 per hour at his job. He earns one-and-a-half times his regular rate for each hour he works over 35 hours in a week. This higher rate is called *overtime.*

34. How much will Jamar earn if he works 40 hours in one week?

35. What percent of this 40-hour week's pay is overtime?

A bag contains 6 chocolate chip cookies, 4 peanut butter cookies, and 5 raisin cookies.

36. One cookie is removed from the bag. What is the probability that it will be a chocolate chip cookie or a peanut butter cookie?

37. One cookie is removed from the bag. It is replaced, and another cookie is removed. What is the probability that both cookies will be raisin cookies?

38. Two cookies are removed from the bag. What is the probability that both cookies will be peanut butter cookies?

A department store is having a 30%-off sale.
39. What is the sale price of a pair of shorts that originally costs $24.50?

40. What is the original price of a shirt that is on sale for $18.20?

LESSON 11.2 SIMILAR FIGURES

OBJECTIVES

➤ Identify corresponding parts of similar polygons.
➤ Determine if polygons are similar.
➤ Find unknown parts of similar polygons including indirect measurement.

Jaclyn is an architect. Before construction begins on a building, she makes a scale model. Jaclyn's scale model is the same shape as the actual building, but it is much smaller. The scale model and the building are examples of **similar figures**.

Similar Figures

Similar figures have the same shape, but not necessarily the same size.

ACTIVITY

Corresponding Parts of Similar Polygons

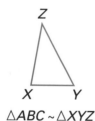

$\triangle ABC \sim \triangle XYZ$

$\triangle ABC$ and $\triangle XYZ$ are similar. The symbol ~ means *is similar to*.

1 Trace $\triangle ABC$ and $\triangle XYZ$.

2 There are three pairs of corresponding angles.

$\angle A$ and $\angle X$ $\qquad$ $\angle B$ and $\angle Y$ $\qquad$ $\angle C$ and $\angle Z$

Measure each pair of corresponding angles. What is the relationship between corresponding angles of the similar figures?

3 You can find pairs of corresponding sides between adjacent corresponding angles. There are three pairs of corresponding sides.

$\overline{AB}$ and $\overline{XY}$ $\qquad$ $\overline{BC}$ and $\overline{YZ}$ $\qquad$ $\overline{AC}$ and $\overline{XZ}$

Measure the lengths of the three pairs of corresponding sides.

4 Let AB represent the length of $\overline{AB}$, XY represent the length of $\overline{XY}$ and so on. Complete the following proportions.

$$\frac{AB}{XY} = \frac{?}{?} \qquad\qquad \frac{BC}{YZ} = \frac{?}{?} \qquad\qquad \frac{AC}{XZ} = \frac{?}{?}$$

If the lengths of corresponding sides have the same ratio, the sides are proportional. Are corresponding sides of the similar figures proportional?

The Activity demonstrates the following property of similar polygons.

> **Properties of Similar Polygons**
> Two polygons are similar if you can match their vertices so that
> - corresponding angles are congruent, and
> - corresponding sides are proportional.

EXAMPLE 1 Similar Polygons

Which of the following illustrates two similar polygons?

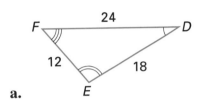
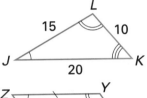

a.

b.

SOLUTION

a. The illustration shows the following pairs of congruent angles.

$$\angle J \cong \angle D \qquad \angle K \cong \angle F \qquad \angle L \cong \angle E$$

Find the ratios of the corresponding sides.

$$\frac{JK}{DF} = \frac{20}{24} = \frac{5}{6} \qquad \frac{KL}{FE} = \frac{10}{12} = \frac{5}{6} \qquad \frac{LJ}{ED} = \frac{15}{18} = \frac{5}{6}$$

The corresponding sides have the same ratio, and are therefore proportional. Since corresponding angles are congruent and corresponding sides are proportional,

$$\triangle JKL \sim \triangle DFE$$

b. The sides of ABCD and WXYZ are proportional, but the corresponding angles are not congruent. Therefore, ABCD and WXYZ are not similar.

EXAMPLE 2 Finding a Missing Measurement

Jaclyn is building a scale model of her newest design. On the blueprint, one wall has the dimensions shown. For the model, Jaclyn uses 14 inches for the 32-foot length of the wall.

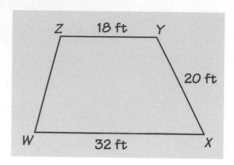

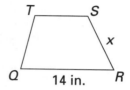

What length for $\overline{RS}$ should Jaclyn use in the model?

SOLUTION

Let x represent the unknown length. Since $QRST$ and $WXYZ$ are similar, corresponding sides are proportional.

$$\frac{WX}{QR} = \frac{32}{14} \qquad \frac{XY}{RS} = \frac{20}{x}$$

Write a proportion.

$$\frac{32}{14} = \frac{20}{x}$$

$$32x = 14(20)$$

$$x = \frac{14(20)}{32}$$

$$x = 8.75$$

Jaclyn should make the length of $\overline{RS}$ 8.75 inches.

ONGOING ASSESSMENT

Calculate the length of $\overline{ST}$ in Example 2.

LESSON ASSESSMENT

1 How can you tell if two polygons are similar?

2 Tell if each of the following statements is *true* or *false.* Explain your reasoning.

　　a. If two polygons are congruent, they are similar.

　　b. If two polygons are similar, they are congruent.

　　c. Two right triangles are always similar.

　　d. All regular quadrilaterals are similar.

3 Suppose the lengths of the sides of a polygon are given. The length of one side of a similar polygon is given. How can you find the unknown lengths of the second polygon?

Practice and Apply

Determine if the two figures are similar. Answer *yes* or *no.* If your answer is *no,* explain why.

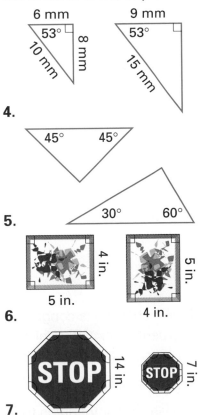

4.

5.

6.

7.

In Exercises 8–13, find each missing length.

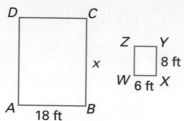

8.   ABCD ~ WXYZ

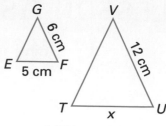

9.   △EFG ~ △TUV

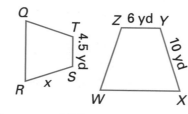

10.   HIJK ~ LMNO

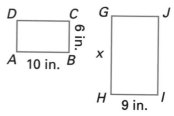

11.   ABCD ~ GHIJ

12.   QRST ~ WXYZ

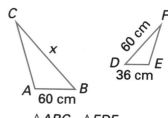

13.   △ABC ~ △EDF

To indirectly measure the distance *d* across a river, a surveyor makes the measurements shown. Use the drawing to answer Exercises 14–16.

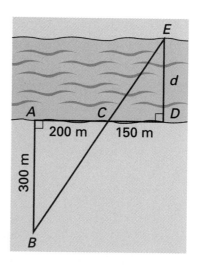

14. Which angle is congruent to ∠A? Which angle is congruent to ∠ACB? Which angle is congruent to ∠B? Explain your reasoning for each answer.

15. Which side corresponds to $\overline{AB}$? To $\overline{BC}$? To $\overline{AC}$?

16. Use similar triangles to find *d*.

17. The two right triangles shown in the diagram are similar. How tall is the antenna?

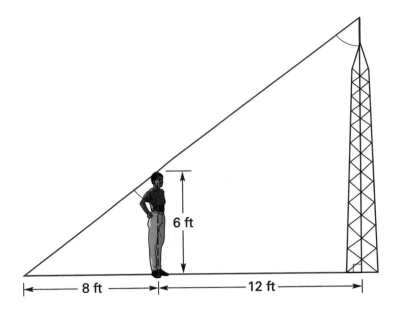

6 ft

8 ft

12 ft

18. The shadow of a flagpole is 47 feet long. At the same time, the shadow of a person 5 feet 6 inches tall is 7 feet long. How tall is the flagpole?

19. A person that is 1.67 meters tall casts a shadow 62 centimeters long. At the same time, a tree casts a shadow 5.8 meters long. How tall is the tree?

Use this figure to answer Exercises 20–25.

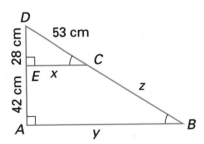

20. Name two right triangles in the figure.

21. Calculate x.

22. Name the congruent pairs of angles for the triangles.

23. Name the pairs of corresponding sides for the triangles.

24. The triangles are similar. Calculate y.

25. Calculate z.

26. The terms in the sequence 1, 5, 9, 13, . . . increase by fours. The terms in the sequence 2, 9, 16, 23, . . . increase by sevens. The number 9 is common to each sequence. What is the next number that is common to each sequence?

Solve each equation.

27. $12.9 = -4.8x + 6.9$

28. $2.5(x + 3) = 0.5x$

29. Two buses are loaded with 60 students each. If $\frac{3}{4}$ of the students get off the first bus and $\frac{2}{3}$ get off the second bus, which bus has more students remaining? How many more?

A bag contains 3 red marbles, 4 blue marbles, and 1 green marble. Find the probability of each of the following.

30. Drawing a red or blue marble in one draw

31. Drawing a red marble, replacing it, and drawing a green marble

32. Drawing a blue marble, keeping it, and then drawing a green marble

33. A square garden measures 8 feet on a side. The garden is surrounded by a walkway 2 feet wide. What is the total area of the garden and walkway?

34. Two of the angles of a triangular sail measure 90° and 55°. What is the measure of the third angle?

35. There are three stacks of dimes. One stack has 10 dimes and another has 18 dimes. If you double the dimes in each stack, there will be a total of 70 dimes. How many dimes are in the third stack before it is doubled?

36. This figure makes a half-turn about point P.

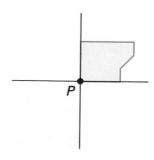

Which of these shows the result of the half-turn?

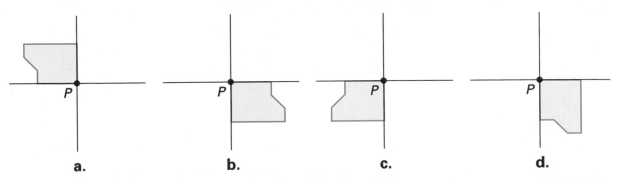

a.   b.   c.   d.

Cumulative Problem Solving

The cost for tuition, fees, books, room, and board at State University is approximately $11,000 this year. The cost is increasing 6% per year. Therefore, next year the cost will be $11,000 · 1.06 = $11,660.

37. Write a sequence showing the predicted cost for each of the next four years at SU. If you attend SU as a freshman four years from now, predict the cost for your freshman year.

38. Predict the total cost for four years at State University, if your freshman year is four years from now.

Fractals are geometrical figures that are created by using a rule to repeat (and grow) a simple pattern. Artists use computers to create interesting and lifelike images using fractals.

The **Sierpinski triangle** is a simple fractal. This pattern starts, at Stage 0, with a shaded equilateral triangle. The rule is to connect the midpoints of each side of the triangle. This creates four new triangles. The middle triangle is then erased. This leaves three triangles for stage 1.

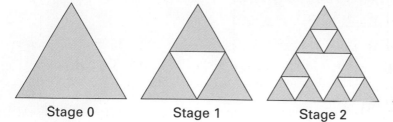

Stage 0   Stage 1   Stage 2   Stage 3   Stage 4

39. The rule is applied four times in the diagram. Copy and complete the table for the Sierpinski triangle.

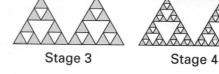

Stage	0	1	2	3	4
Number of Triangles					

40. Let *n* represent the number of a stage. Write an expression for the number of triangles in Stage *n*.

41. How many triangles will there be in Stage 10?

A fractal pattern is used to create a bush in a computer-generated landscape. The drawing on the left shows the bush after 6 stages.

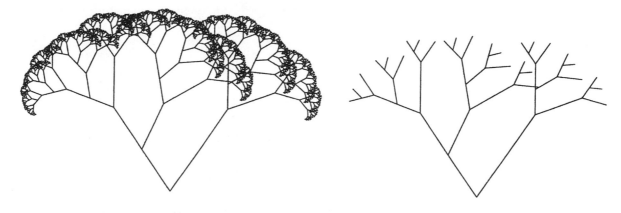

42. Draw Stage 0 of the pattern.

43. What is the number of this stage shown in the drawing on the right?

LESSON 11.3 DILATIONS

OBJECTIVES

- Identify the scale factor of a dilation.
- Use the center of dialation and scale factor to create a dialation of a polygon.
- Create a dilation on a coordinate plane.

In Chapter 9, you used translations, reflections, and rotations to transform geometric figures. These transformations are sometimes called *rigid motions* because the image is always *congruent* to the original figure.

A **dilation** is another kind of transformation. In a dilation, the image is *similar* to the original figure. This transformation is not a rigid motion since the image is not congruent to the original figure.

You can use the Properties of Similar Polygons to draw dilations. If the image is larger than the original figure, the dilation is an **enlargement**. If the image is smaller than the original figure, the dilation is a **reduction**.

ACTIVITY 1   Drawing Dilations

1 Draw △*ABC* with side lengths between 3 and 4 cm each.

2 Draw point *P* outside △*ABC*. This point is called the **center of dilation**. Draw rays from *P* that pass through each vertex of △*ABC*.

3 Set the compass width to *PA*. Mark *A'* along $\overrightarrow{PA}$ so that *AA'* = *PA*.

4 Repeat Step 3 for *B'* and *C'*. Connect the vertices of △*A'B'C'*.

5 Measure the angles of each triangle. Are corresponding angles congruent? Measure the sides of each triangle. Complete the following.

$$\frac{A'B'}{AB} = \underline{?} \qquad \frac{B'C'}{BC} = \underline{?} \qquad \frac{C'A'}{CA} = \underline{?}$$

Is △*ABC* ≅ △*A'B'C'*? Is △*ABC* ~ △*A'B'C'*?

6 In a dilation, the ratio of the length of a side of the image to the corresponding side of the original figure is called the **scale factor**. What is the scale factor of the dilation △*ABC* → △*A'B'C'*? Is this dilation an enlargement or a reduction?

Critical Thinking   On your drawing for Activity 1, what is the relationship between *PA* and *PA′*? Is this relationship *true* for *PB* and *PB′*? For *PC* and *PC′*? Describe how to draw an enlargement of △*ABC* using a scale factor of 3.

In Activity 1, the center of dilation was outside the original figure. It could also be inside or on the figure.

ACTIVITY 2   **A Reduction on a Coordinate Plane**

Tali is reducing the size of a photograph to use in a science project report. The original photograph has a length of 12 inches and a width of 8 inches. The report has space for a photograph 2 inches wide. What dilation scale factor should Tali use?

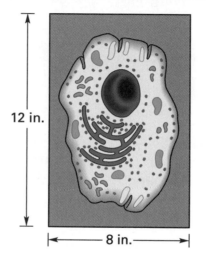

12 in.

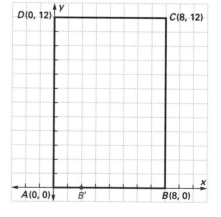

2 in.

|← 8 in. →|

1 Let *A, B, C,* and *D* represent the vertices of the original photograph. Draw *ABCD* on a coordinate plane with vertex *A* at the origin. Let the origin be the center of dilation.

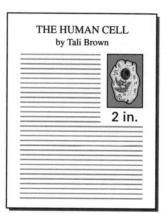

2 Draw the width of the reduced photograph *AB′* along the *x*-axis. Let *k* represent the scale factor for the dilation. Calculate the scale factor.

$$k = \frac{AB'}{AB} = \underline{?}$$

3 Use the scale factor to find the length of $\overline{AD'}$ in the reduced photograph.

$$\frac{AD'}{AD} = k \quad AD' = \underline{?}$$

Draw $\overline{AD'}$ along the *y*-axis.

4 Since corresponding angles of similar polygons are congruent, the image $AB'C'D'$ is a rectangle. Locate C'. Draw $AB'C'D'$. What are the coordinates of A, B', C', and D'?

5 What are the length and width of the photograph Tali should use in her report?

Critical Thinking Show that $\dfrac{AC'}{AC} = k$.

You can use a transformation rule to dilate a figure on a coordinate plane when the origin is the center of dilation. The coordinates of the image can be found from

$$(x, y) \rightarrow (kx, ky)$$

where k is the scale factor. If $k > 1$, the dilation is an enlargement. If $0 < k < 1$, the dilation is a reduction.

ONGOING ASSESSMENT

Use the transformation rule $(x, y) \rightarrow (\frac{1}{4}x, \frac{1}{4}y)$ for each vertex of $ABCD$ in Activity 2. Are the vertices you found using the transformation rule the same as those in the Activity?

EXAMPLE An Enlargement on a Coordinate Plane

A triangle has vertices $Q(1, 2)$, $R(4, 1)$, and $S(3, 4)$. What are the coordinates of the image $\triangle Q'R'S'$ after an enlargement with a scale factor of 3? Use the origin as the center of dilation.

SOLUTION

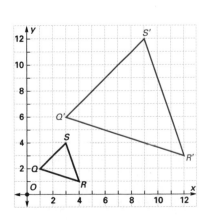

Transform each vertex for $k = 3$.

$$Q(1, 2) \rightarrow Q'(3 \cdot 1, 3 \cdot 2) \text{ or } Q'(3, 6)$$

$$R(4, 1) \rightarrow R'(3 \cdot 4, 3 \cdot 1) \text{ or } R'(12, 3)$$

$$S(3, 4) \rightarrow S'(3 \cdot 3, 3 \cdot 4) \text{ or } S'(9, 12)$$

Critical Thinking For the enlargement $\triangle QRS \rightarrow \triangle Q'R'S'$ in the Example, show the following for $O(0, 0)$.

$$OQ' = k \cdot OQ \qquad OR' = k \cdot OR \qquad OS' = k \cdot OS$$

LESSON ASSESSMENT

1 Explain why dilations are not rigid motions.

2 Suppose you are given a triangle and its image after a dilation. How can you find the scale factor of the dilation?

3 Use the origin as the center of dilation. How do you find the coordinates of the image on a coordinate plane?

Practice and Apply

Trace each figure and point *P.* Enlarge the figure so the image has sides twice as long as the figure. Use *P* as the center of dilation.

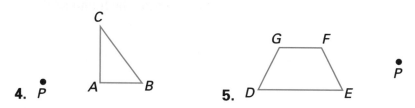

4. **5.**

Trace each figure and point *P.* Reduce the figure so the image has sides half as long as the figure. Use *P* as the center of dilation.

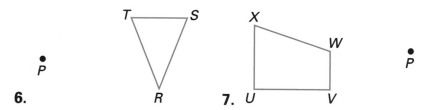

6. **7.**

Trace each figure. Enlarge or reduce the figure as indicated.

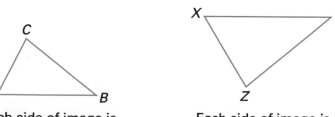

8. Each side of image is 3 times as long as the original. Use *A* as the center of dilation.

9. Each side of image is $\frac{1}{3}$ as long as the original. Use *Z* as the center of dilation.

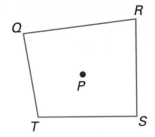

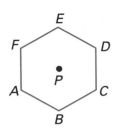

Each side of image is
$\frac{2}{3}$ as long as the
original. Use P as the
10. center of dilation.

Each side of image is
$\frac{5}{2}$ as long as the
original. Use P as the
11. center of dilation.

The vertices of a triangle are $A(0, 0)$, $B(0, 3)$, and $C(3, 0)$. Use the origin as the center of dilation.

12. What are the coordinates of $\triangle A'B'C'$ if it is a dilation of $\triangle ABC$, and the scale factor is $\frac{2}{3}$? Is the dilation an enlargement or reduction?

13. Draw $\triangle ABC$ and $\triangle A'B'C'$ on a coordinate plane.

The vertices of a rectangle are $W(-2, 0)$, $X(4, 0)$, $Y(4, 2)$, and $Z(-2, 2)$. Use the origin as the center of dilation.

14. What are the coordinates of $W'X'Y'Z'$ if it is a dilation of $WXYZ$, and the scale factor is $\frac{3}{2}$? Is the dilation an enlargement or reduction?

15. Draw $WXYZ$ and $W'X'Y'Z'$ on a coordinate plane.

16. Raul is a graphic artist who designs business cards. He creates a design on a rectangular template that measures 220 mm by 125 mm. To print the cards, he needs to reduce the size to 88 mm by 50 mm. What scale factor should Raul use in this dilation?

17. Trace each figure below. Draw an enlargement of △ABC using a scale factor of 2, and center of P, for each figure. Are the enlargements congruent? How are they different?

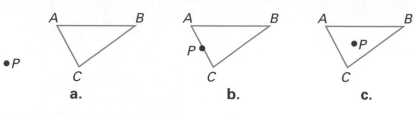

a.   b.   c.

Mixed Review

Solve for x.

18. $-\dfrac{2}{3}x + 5 = 1$ **19.** $\dfrac{3}{4}x - \dfrac{2}{3} = -\dfrac{11}{30}$

20. $\dfrac{15}{10} = \dfrac{18}{x}$ **21.** $\dfrac{x+4}{8} = \dfrac{3}{2}$

22. A pair of boots is on sale for $64. The original price of the boots is $80. What is the rate of discount for the sale?

Find the slope of the line through each pair of points.

23. (5, −2) and (−4, 2)   **24.** (−8, 3) and (0, 0)

25. (0, 0) and (7, −5)   **26.** $\left(9, \dfrac{1}{2}\right)$ and $\left(-5, \dfrac{3}{4}\right)$

27. A bicycle courier rides 9 miles to the east and then 16 miles to the south. How far is the courier from the starting point?

LESSON 11.4 SCALE DRAWINGS AND MAPS

OBJECTIVES
- Calculate the actual length from a scale drawing.
- Use the scale on a map.

Edward is drawing a floor plan of a new neighborhood healthcare clinic. He makes a *scale drawing* of the floor plan.

A **scale drawing** of an object is *similar* to the actual object. The **scale** shown on the drawing relates a length on the drawing to a corresponding length on the actual object. The scale factor is the ratio of these two lengths. Notice this scale factor is not the same as k in the dilation. The numerator and denominator do not have the same units.

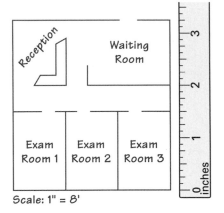

Scale: 1" = 8'

EXAMPLE 1 Actual Length from a Scale Drawing

What is the actual length of an exam room in the clinic?

SOLUTION

Let a represent the actual length of the exam room in feet. The scale factor is the ratio of a length on the drawing to the corresponding length on the actual building. Use this scale factor to write a proportion.

$$\frac{\text{Length on drawing (in.)} \rightarrow}{\text{Actual length (ft)} \rightarrow} \quad \frac{1}{8} = \frac{1\frac{1}{2}}{a}$$

$$1a = 8\left(1\frac{1}{2}\right)$$

$$a = 8\left(\frac{3}{2}\right) = 12$$

The actual length of an exam room is 12 feet.

ONGOING ASSESSMENT

What is the actual width of the waiting room in the clinic?

Critical Thinking   Edward needs to redraw one side of the receptionist's desk, so that it is 6 ft long. How long should he draw the desk on the scale drawing?

Suppose you own a business that distributes fresh fruit and vegetables to restaurants in Indianapolis, IN. You want to expand your business to cities within 100 miles of Indianapolis. You need to send advertising brochures to restaurants in these cities. Which cities should be included on your mailing list?

1 Maps are also scale drawings. The scale on a map is usually shown as a line segment. On this map of Indiana, what distance corresponds to 40 miles actual distance?

2 What distance on the map corresponds to 100 miles actual distance?

3 Measure the straight line distance of each city from Indianapolis. Which ones should you include on your mailing list?

EXAMPLE 2 Actual Distance from a Map

On a map of Canada, the scale shows 2.5 cm = 300 km. Vancouver and Edmonton are about 7.6 cm apart on this map. What is the actual distance between Vancouver and Edmonton?

SOLUTION

Let *d* represent the unknown distance. Use the scale to write a proportion.

$$\frac{\text{Distance on map (cm)}}{\text{Actual distance (km)}} \rightarrow \frac{2.5}{300} = \frac{7.6}{d}$$

$$2.5d = 300(7.6)$$

$$d = \frac{300(7.6)}{2.5} = 912$$

The actual distance between Vancouver and Edmonton is about 912 km.

ONGOING ASSESSMENT

Regina is 587 km from Winnipeg. What is the distance, in centimeters, between these two cities on the map in Example 2?

LESSON ASSESSMENT

1 Write the scale for a model ship that shows *every inch represents two feet.*

2 How do you determine the scale factor for a map?

3 Is a scale drawing a dilation? Explain.

Your class is building a diorama of the National Mall in Washington, D.C. using a scale of 1 in. = 100 ft.

4. The Washington Monument is 555 feet high. How tall should you build the monument in your diorama?

5. On the mall, the distance between the Washington Monument and the Lincoln Memorial is approximately $\frac{3}{4}$ mile. What distance should you use in your diorama?

A model car is built using a scale 1 in. = 1.5 ft.

6. If the model is 8.5 inches long, how long is the actual car?

7. If the diameter of each tire on the car is $2\frac{1}{2}$ feet, what is the diameter of each tire on the model?

8. On a hiking trail, the Hendersons follow a stream for 2.5 km. This distance corresponds to 5 cm on their trail map. What is the scale of the map?

You are helping design a float for a New Year's Day parade. The float will feature a butterfly and a kitten.

9. The kitten on the float is 21 ft from head to tail. If an average real kitten is 14 in. from head to tail, what scale factor should you use?

10. If an average butterfly wingspan is 3 in., how long should you make the wingspan of the butterfly on the float?

The walls of a doll house measure 14 inches. The walls of an actual house are approximately 10 feet high.

11. What scale factor was used in constructing the doll house?

12. What length bed should you put in the doll house if an actual bed is 6 feet long?

You are using this map to plan a trip.

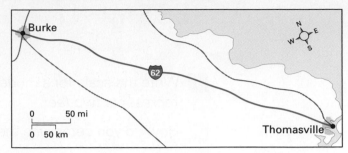

13. Estimate the actual distance between Burke and Thomasville.

14. Suppose you start at Burke and drive 400 miles. To find your location on the map, how many inches from Burke should you look?

The scale of the floor plan of an addition to an office building is 1 cm = 4 m. When complete, the addition will measure 12 m wide and 14 m long.
15. Find the width and length of the drawing of the addition.

16. A right triangle on the floor plan has legs that each measure 1.5 cm. Find the length of the hypotenuse of the right triangle on the building.

A sculptor makes the following animals for separate projects. Some are enlargements and some are reductions. Match each sculpture and its length with the scale factor used by the artist.

sculpture : actual
length : length

17. A falcon, 6 cm   **A.** 5 : 1

18. A crab, 3 m   **B.** 1 : 5

19. A dolphin, 10 cm   **C.** 20 : 1

20. A squirrel, 1m   **D.** 1 : 20

Mixed Review

The low temperatures in Chicago during one week in February were recorded as follows.

$-10°F$ $-14°F$ $-18°F$ $-15°F$ $-18°F$ $-5°F$ $0°F$

21. Find the mean of the data.

22. Find the median of the data.

23. Which of these is the longest time?

    A. 150,000 seconds   **B.** 1500 minutes

    C. 15 hours   **D.** 1.5 days

Write each of the numbers in scientific notation.
24. 3,590,000 miles   **25.** 0.0872 kilometers

Graph each inequality on a coordinate plane.
26. $y < 3x - 2$ **27.** $y \geq -5x + 1$

Use the four-step problem-solving plan to solve Exercises 28 and 29.
28. Wanda, Robert, Shawna, and Davon are walking in a line. Wanda is between Shawna and Davon. Davon is not leading the group. Robert is last. In what order is the group walking?

29. Eight girls are playing in an elimination badminton tournament. Each player is eliminated when she loses. How many games will the tournament take?

Cumulative Problem Solving

You just arrived at an airport to change planes. Your flight arrived late at Gate 7, and your next flight departs in 10 minutes from Gate 22. A map of the airport terminal is shown below.

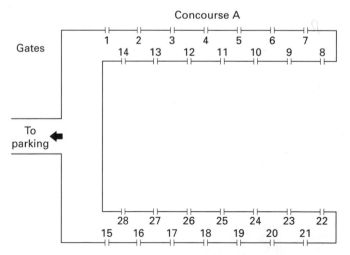

30. Gate 6 is approximately 100 feet from Gate 7. What is the scale of the terminal map?

31. Estimate the distance you must walk from Gate 7 to Gate 22.

32. If you can walk about 300 feet per minute, how many minutes will it take to reach Gate 22?

The illustration is based on an aerial photo taken with infrared film. It shows an area of forest after a fire. The dark spots are trees that survived the fire. The field of view in the illustration is 0.65 miles, from left to right.

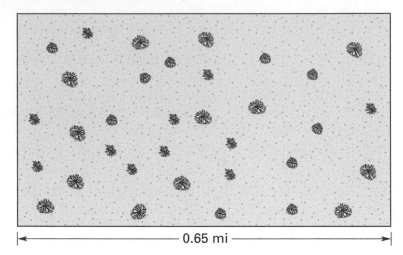

|←———————— 0.65 mi ————————→|

33. What is the scale factor of the illustration? Write the scale factor as a ratio.

distance on illustration : distance on ground

34. What is the distance on the ground shown in the illustration from top to bottom?

35. How many square miles of forest are in the illustration?

36. Estimate the average number of trees per square mile that survived the fire.

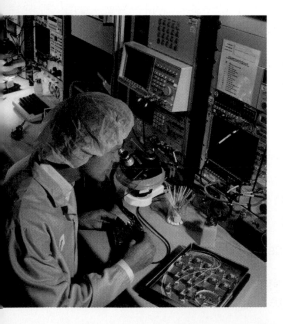

Paul is a computer chip design engineer. When he designs a circuit for a microchip, Paul draws the circuit on a large scale, and then uses photography to reduce the drawing to the actual size of the microchip.

For one design, Paul uses a 2 meter by 2 meter drawing. He draws a line to connect two transistors in a circuit. On the drawing, the line is 1 cm long. On the actual chip, the line will be 2.5 microns long. (1 micron = 10^{-6} m)

37. What is the scale factor of Paul's drawing?

38. What is the width of the actual part of the chip represented by the 2-meter wide drawing?

LESSON 11.5 AREA OF POLYGONS

OBJECTIVES
➤ Solve problems involving the area of polygons.

Petri is tiling a rectangular patio. Each tile measures 1 foot on a side. How many tiles will Petri need?

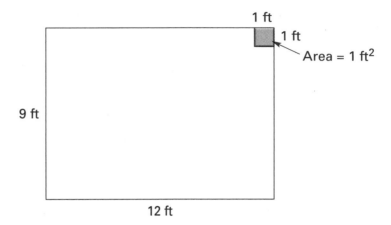

Each tile has an *area* of one square foot, abbreviated 1 ft². If the tile measured 1 cm on a side, its area would be 1 cm². The number of square units enclosed by a figure is the **area** of the figure.

ACTIVITY 1   Areas of Rectangles

1 Draw several squares and rectangles on grid paper. Some examples are shown.

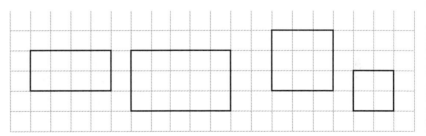

2 Find the area of each figure by counting the number of square units enclosed. Each grid square measures one unit on a side. Compare the area of each figure to the product of the lengths of its sides.

3 Describe how to find the area of a rectangle whose sides measure *l* and *w*.

4 Describe how to find the area of a square whose sides measure *s*.

Activity 1 demonstrates the formulas for the areas of rectangles and squares.

Area of a Rectangle

The area of a rectangle with length l and width w is

$$A = lw$$

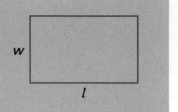

A square is a rectangle whose length and width are equal.

Area of a Square

The area of a square with sides s is

$$A = s^2$$

EXAMPLE 1 Finding the Number of Tiles

How many tiles does Petri need for the patio?

SOLUTION

The patio is a rectangle with length 12 ft and width 9 ft. The area is

$$A = lw = 12 \cdot 9 = 108$$

The area of the patio is 108 ft². Since the area of each tile is 1 ft², Petri needs 108 tiles.

ONGOING ASSESSMENT

Find the area of each rectangle.

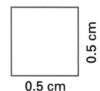

2.1 m

3.3 m

0.5 cm

0.5 cm

ACTIVITY 2   Area of a Parallelogram

Recall that a parallelogram is a quadrilateral with opposite sides parallel and congruent. The **bases** of a parallelogram can be either pair of parallel sides. The **height** is the perpendicular distance between the bases.

1 Draw a parallelogram on graph paper. How can you use the grid lines to make sure the opposite sides are parallel?

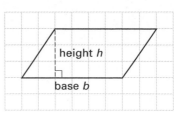

2 Cut off one end of the parallelogram, along a grid line. "Rearrange" the parallelogram as shown. What type of polygon is formed? What is the area of this polygon?

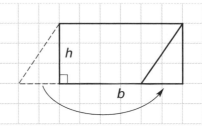

3 Write a formula for the area of a parallelogram.

The area of a parallelogram is the same as a rectangle with length b and width h.

Area of a Parallelogram

The area of a parallelogram with base b and height h is

$$A = bh$$

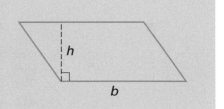

EXAMPLE 2 Finding the Missing Height

A zoo's new feline exhibit will be in the shape of a parallelogram. The total area of the exhibit should be approximately 3000 sq ft. What should be the height of the parallelogram?

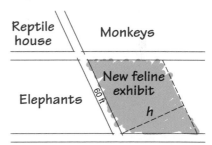

SOLUTION

The exhibit is a parallelogram.

$$A = bh$$
$$3000 = 60h$$
$$\frac{3000}{60} = h$$
$$h = 50$$

The height of the parallelogram is about 50 feet.

Find the area of each parallelogram.

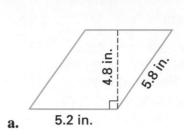

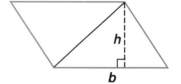

a. 5.2 in.

b. 3.8 cm

ACTIVITY 3   Area of a Triangle

1 Draw a parallelogram, or copy the one shown. The diagonal of a parallelogram divides it into two congruent triangles.

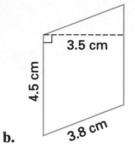

2 What is the sum of the areas of the two triangles?

3 What is the relationship between the area of each triangle?

4 Write a formula for the area of each triangle.

The base of a triangle can be any of its sides. The height is the perpendicular distance from the base to the opposite vertex.

Area of a Triangle
The area of a triangle with base *b* and height *h* is
$$A = \frac{1}{2}bh$$

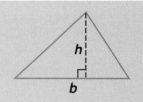

Find the area of each triangle.

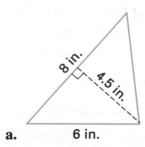

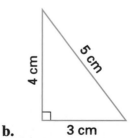

a. 6 in.

b. 3 cm

USING THE FOUR-STEP PLAN

To solve some types of problems, you need to supply facts not given in the problem statement. For example, suppose a problem gives the number of pages in a book and the time required to read the book in hours. You are asked to calculate the average number of minutes needed to read one page from the book. To solve this problem, you need to supply the fact that 1 h = 60 min.

Work through the four-step process, supply the missing fact, and solve the following problem.

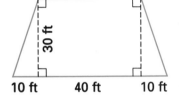

Kelsey is estimating the cost of carpeting the Hippodrome Theater. The shape and dimensions of the theater's floor are shown in the illustration.

A carpet installer provides a cost estimate of $25 per square yard. What is the total estimated cost for the carpet?

Understand the Problem

List the facts you are given. What is different about the dimensions of the theater floor and the estimated cost of the carpet?

Develop a Plan

Supply the missing facts. Find the area of the room in square feet. Supply the missing fact that $1 \text{ yd}^2 = ? \text{ ft}^2$. Convert the area to square yards. Calculate the cost of the carpet.

Carry Out the Plan

The theater floor is a composite of what two types of polygons? Use the formulas for their area to calculate the total area of the floor. Complete the calculations.

Check the Results

Which number is greater, the floor area in square feet or square yards? Do the answers seem reasonable?

LESSON ASSESSMENT

1 Explain how to find the length of the sides of a square if you know the area of the square.

2 What distance do you measure to determine the height of a parallelogram?

3 Which of the following quadrilaterals will have the larger area? Explain your reasoning.

a. A rectangle with sides of 6 inches and 12 inches

b. A parallelogram with no right angles and sides of 6 inches and 12 inches

4 Is the following statement *true* or *false*? Explain.

If one leg of a right triangle is the base, then the other leg is the height of the triangle.

Practice and Apply

Find the area of the following polygons.

5.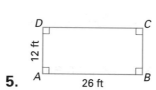

6.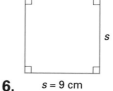
$s = 9$ cm

7.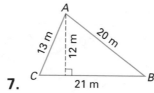

8.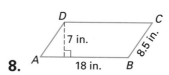

9.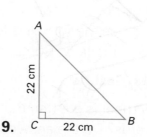

10.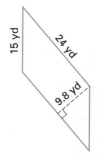

For Exercises 11–16, find the value of _x_ for each polygon.

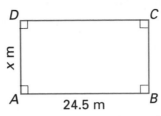

11. Area of _ABCD_ = 347.9 m²

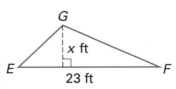

12. Area of △_EFG_ = 80.5 ft²

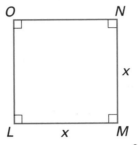

13. Area of _LMNO_ = 36 in.²

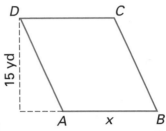

14. Area of _ABCD_ = 225 yd²

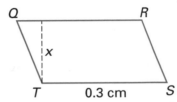

15. Area of _QRST_ = 0.045 cm²

16. Area of _HIJ_ = 21 m²

17. What is the area enclosed by the foundation of this house?

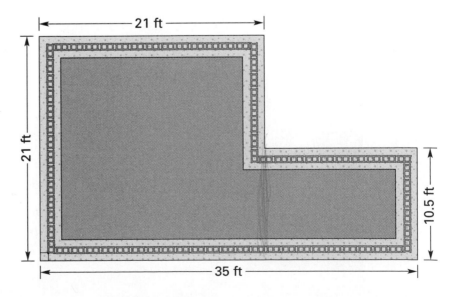

18. What is the area of *TUVWX*?

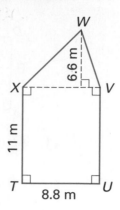

19. The rectangular cover for Sonya's swimming pool is 35 feet long and 18 feet wide. What is the area of the pool cover?

20. A parallelogram has an area of 636 in.² and a height of 12 in. Find the length of the base of the parallelogram.

21. What is the height of this parallelogram, if 26 ft² of paper are needed to make a banner that fits over the handrail?

22. The base of a triangular piece of plywood is 3.5 feet and the height is 2 feet. Find the area of the plywood.

A **rhombus** is a parallelogram with four congruent sides. This window in a restaurant door is in the shape of a rhombus. The sides of the window are 30 inches long. The perpendicular distance between one pair of parallel sides is $16\frac{1}{2}$ inches.

23. Find the area of the window.

24. Safety glass costs $7 per square foot. What would a piece of safety glass for the restaurant door window cost? (1 ft² = 144 in.²)

25. A rectangular-shaped solar panel will be 12 feet long. If the panel must have an area of 78 square feet, how wide should the panel be?

26. The length of a rectangle is twice its width. The area of the rectangle is 162 ft². What are the dimensions of the rectangle?

27. Marion is fencing a square field that contains 76 acres. How many feet of fence will Marion need? (1 acre = 43,560 ft²)

28. One piece of a quilt pattern is in the shape of a parallelogram as shown below. To make one quilt, 720 of these pieces are needed. How many square inches of material are needed to cut out the 720 pieces?

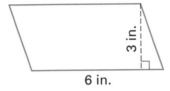

3 in.

6 in.

29. A basketball court is 90 feet by 50 feet. If a 4-foot wide strip is painted around the edge of the court, how many square feet of surface must be painted?

30. Two congruent parallelograms are cut from a rectangular piece of sheet metal as shown. What percent of the total amount of the sheet metal is wasted?

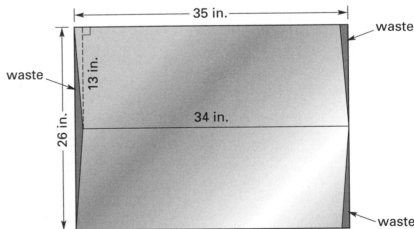

35 in.

waste

13 in.

waste

34 in.

26 in.

waste

31. A building lot is in the shape of a right triangle. The lengths of the two perpendicular sides of the property are 320 feet and 1843 feet. How many acres are in the property? (1 acre = 43,560 ft²)

Write each of the following as a decimal.

32. Eight hundred fifty thousand, six hundred twenty

33. Six hundred twenty-five millionths

Use the bar graph to complete exercises 34–36.

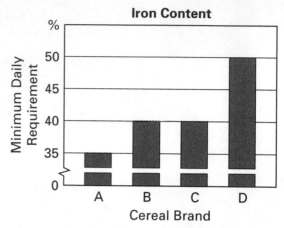

34. What percent of the minimum daily iron requirement is contained in Cereal B?

35. What percent of the minimum daily iron requirement is contained in Cereal D?

36. Explain how the graph can be used to mislead the consumer.

Solve each of the following for x.

37. $\frac{2}{3}x + 15 = 39$ **38.** $ax - b = c$ **39.** $\frac{8}{10} = \frac{x}{25}$

Solve each problem.

40. In March, Renaldo earned $120 babysitting. In April, he earned $80. What is the percent change in Renaldo's earnings from March to April 1?

41. The rate of discount at the Bargain Mart is 30%. Mary bought a hat for $24.50. What was the price of the hat before the discount?

42. A computer network is off-line for three quarters of an hour. If the network is taken off-line at 9:40, at what time will it be back on-line?

43. Paul, Anita, and their mother are assembling a jigsaw puzzle. Paul completes $\frac{1}{8}$ of the puzzle. Anita completes $\frac{3}{8}$ of the puzzle. Their mother completes $\frac{1}{2}$ of the puzzle. How much of the puzzle is left to complete?

LESSON 11.6 PERIMETER AND AREA OF SIMILAR POLYGONS

OBJECTIVES
- ➤ Find the perimeters of similar polygons.
- ➤ Find the areas of similar polygons.

In Lessons 11.2 and 11.3, you learned that in similar polygons, the lengths of corresponding sides have the same ratio. This ratio is called the scale factor. Is there also a relation between the perimeters of similar polygons? Is there a relation between the areas?

ACTIVITY 1   **Perimeters of Similar Rectangles**

1 Draw a pair of similar rectangles on graph paper.

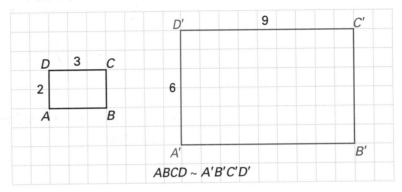

ABCD ~ A'B'C'D'

2 Record the lengths of the sides of each rectangle and the scale factor for the dilation.

| Original Figure | | | Image | | | Scale Factor | $\frac{P'}{P}$ |
l	w	P	l'	w'	P'		
3	2	10	9	6	30	3	$\frac{30}{10} = 3$

3 Calculate the perimeters P and P' of the rectangles. Calculate the ratio $\frac{P'}{P}$ of the perimeter of the image to the perimeter of the original rectangle. Record this ratio.

4 Draw two more pairs of similar rectangles. Use different scale factors and make one of the scale factors less than one. Repeat Steps 2 and 3 for these rectangles.

5 For each set of data, compare the ratio of the perimeters to the scale factor for the dilation. Make a conjecture about the ratio of the perimeters of two similar polygons.

Compare your conjecture to the following property.

> ### Perimeter of Similar Polygons
> If two polygons are similar with a scale factor $a : b$, then the ratio of their perimeters is $a : b$.

EXAMPLE 1 The Perimeter of Similar Triangles

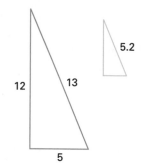

The red and blue triangles are similar. What is the perimeter of the blue triangle?

SOLUTION

Write the scale factor as the ratio of lengths Red:Blue.

$$\frac{\text{Red triangle} \rightarrow}{\text{Blue triangle} \rightarrow} \frac{13}{5.2}$$

The ratio of the perimeters is the same as the scale factor. The perimeter of the red triangle is $(5 + 12 + 13) = 30$. Let P represent the perimeter of the blue triangle.

$$\frac{\text{Red triangle} \rightarrow}{\text{Blue triangle} \rightarrow} \frac{13}{5.2} = \frac{30}{P}$$

$$13P = 5.2\,(30)$$

$$P = \frac{5.2(30)}{13} = 12$$

The perimeter of the blue triangle is 12.

ACTIVITY 2 Area of Similar Rectangles

1 Use the pairs of similar rectangles from Activity 1.

2 Record the lengths of the sides of each rectangle and the scale factor for its dilation.

Original Figure			Image			Scale Factor	$\frac{A'}{A}$	Scale Factor Squared
l	w	A	l'	w'	A'			
3	2	6	9	6	54	3	$\frac{54}{6} = 9$	$3^2 = 9$

3 Calculate the areas A and A' of the rectangles. For each pair of similar rectangles, calculate the ratio $\frac{A'}{A}$ of the area of the image to the area of the original rectangle.

4 For each set of data, compare the ratio of the areas to the square of the scale factor for the dilation. Make a conjecture about the ratio of the areas of two similar polygons.

Compare your conjecture to the following property.

Area of Similar Polygons
If two polygons are similar with a scale factor $a : b$, then the ratio of their areas is $a^2 : b^2$.

EXAMPLE 2 Areas of Similar Rectangles

Elaine is buying material for draperies. The material is sold in panels, as shown. If the smaller panel costs $79, what should Elaine expect to pay for the larger panel?

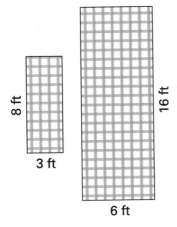

8 ft

3 ft

16 ft

6 ft

SOLUTION

The panels are similar if the ratios of corresponding sides are equal.

$$\frac{\text{Large panel} \rightarrow}{\text{Small panel} \rightarrow} \quad \frac{16}{8} = \frac{2}{1} \quad \text{and} \quad \frac{6}{3} = \frac{2}{1}$$

Therefore, the panels are similar with a scale factor of $\frac{2}{1}$. The ratio of the areas is $\frac{2^2}{1^2}$ or $\frac{4}{1}$.

The area of the larger panel is four times the area of the smaller panel. This means it takes four times as much material to make the larger panel. Thus, Elaine should expect the larger panel to cost four times as much as the smaller panel, or about 4($79) = $316.

ONGOING ASSESSMENT

The red and blue parallelograms are similar.

3

4.8

5

8

a. What is the scale factor?

b. What is the ratio of their perimeters?

c. If the area of the red parallelogram is 24, what is the area of the blue parallelogram?

Critical Thinking   If the ratio of the areas of two similar polygons is $\frac{9}{16}$, what is the ratio of their perimeters?

LESSON ASSESSMENT

1 Is the following statement *true* always, sometimes, or never? Explain your answer.

If the ratio of the perimeters of two rectangles is $a : b$, then the two rectangles are similar with a scale factor of $a : b$.

2 Is the following statement *true* always, sometimes, or never? Explain your answer.

If the ratio of the areas of two squares is $a^2 : b^2$, then the two squares are similar with a scale factor of $a : b$.

3 You are given $\triangle ABC \sim \triangle DEF$ with a scale factor of $\frac{\triangle ABC}{\triangle DEF} \to \frac{3}{2}$ and $\triangle DEF \sim \triangle STU$ with a scale factor of $\frac{\triangle DEF}{\triangle STU} \to \frac{4}{1}$. Is the following statement *true always, sometimes,* or *never*? Explain your answer.

The perimeter of $\triangle ABC$ is greater than the perimeter of $\triangle STU$.

Practice and Apply

Write a scale factor for each pair of similar polygons. Find the perimeter of each polygon.

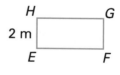

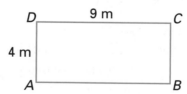

4.   Rectangles *ABCD* and *EFGH* are similar.

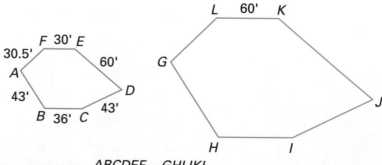

5.   ABCDEF ~ GHIJKL

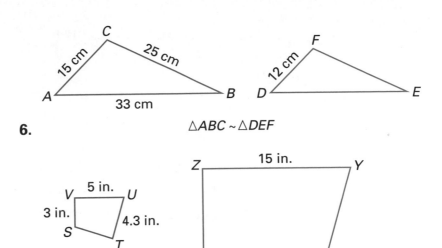

6. △ABC ~ △DEF

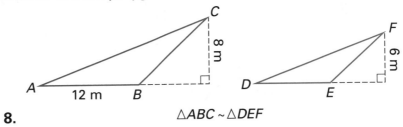

7. STUV ~ WXYZ

Write a scale factor for each pair of similar polygons. Find the area of each polygon.

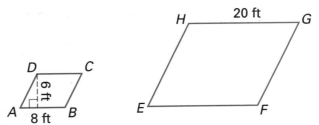

8. △ABC ~ △DEF

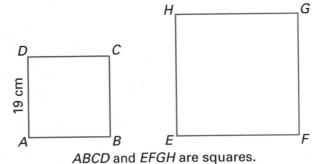

9. parallelogram *ABCD* ~ parallelogram *EFGH*

ABCD and EFGH are squares.
The scale factor for the dilation is 3:2.

10.

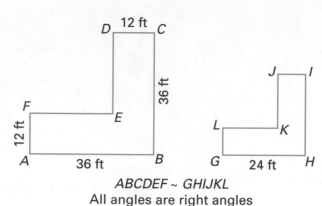

ABCDEF ~ GHIJKL

11. All angles are right angles

12. Two triangles are similar. The height of the smaller triangle is 6 inches and the corresponding height of the larger triangle is 15 inches. If the perimeter of the smaller triangle is 37.8 inches, what is the perimeter of the larger triangle?

13. If the area of the larger triangle in Exercise 12 is 318.75 in.², what is the area of the smaller triangle?

Fernando is making a scale model of a hexagon-shaped gazebo for a holiday exhibit. The dilation scale factor is 1 : 10. The area of the actual gazebo is 166.3 ft² and the perimeter is 48 feet.

14. How many square inches of material will Fernando need to make the floor of the model? (1 ft² = 144 in.²)

15. How many feet of material will Fernando need in order to make a railing around the model?

16. A 12-km bicycle race follows the route shown by the arrows on the illustration. The two right triangles are similar. What would be the length of the race if the route ran along Goliad instead of Crockett?

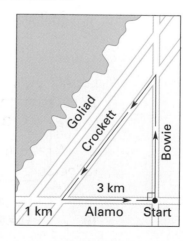

17. The building plans for a house call for 2350 ft² of insulation in the attic. Kareem uses these plans for a new home, but he enlarges the building by a scale factor of 4 : 3. How many square feet of insulation will Kareem need for the attic in his home?

18. A plot of land is in the shape of an irregular polygon. To determine the area of the plot, Demetria used a computer program to draw a dilation of the polygon using a scale factor of 1 : 10,000. The computer program calculated the area of the dilation as 3.86 in.². How many acres are in the plot of land? (1 ft² = 144 in.², 1 acre = 43,560 ft²)

19. A basketball court is a 90-foot-by-50-foot rectangle. A scale model of the court has an area of 5 ft². What scale factor should be used to make the backboards?

20. A dilation is used to make a 5-pointed star for a Texas display. The original star has a perimeter of 4 feet. The star in the display will be outlined with a 30-foot strand of lights. What scale factor should be used for the dilation?

Mixed Review

Graph each ordered pair on the same coordinate plane.

21. $A(-4, 0)$ **22.** $B(2, -3)$ **23.** $C(-1, 1)$ **24.** $D(5, 3)$

Solve each system by graphing.

25. $x - y = 3$ **26.** $y = 2x$
       $2x + y = 0$ $x - 2y = -6$

Let $A(-2, 3)$, $B(0, 5)$, and $C(3, 4)$ be the vertices of a triangle.
27. What is the image of each vertex for the translation $(x, y) \rightarrow (x + 3, y - 1)$?

28. What is the image of each vertex if the triangle is reflected over the *x*-axis?

Solve each equation for *x*.

29. $x^2 = 100$ **30.** $9x^2 = 4$

LESSON 11.7 CIRCLES

OBJECTIVES
- Calculate the circumference and area of a circle.

A center-pivot sprinkler irrigates a field by spraying water from a pipe that rotates around a fixed point. As the pipe rotates, its outside edge makes a *circle*. The part of the field irrigated by the center-pivot sprinkler is enclosed by the circle.

A **circle** is the set of all points in a plane that are the same distance from a given point. The given point is the **center** of the circle. A circle is named by its center. For circle *O*,

- $\overline{AO}$ is a *radius*. A **radius** is a line segment with one endpoint at the center of a circle and the other endpoint on the circle. Name two other radii of circle *O*.

- $\overline{BC}$ is a *diameter*. A **diameter** is a line segment that passes through the center of a circle and has both endpoints on the circle.

The length of the radius of circle *O* is *r*, and the length of the diameter is *d*. The words *radius* and *diameter* are also used for the lengths of the radius and diameter. The diameter of any circle is twice the radius.

$$d = 2r$$

Recall that the distance around a polygon is the perimeter. The distance around a circle is called the **circumference**.

ACTIVITY 1   What is the Value of π?

Use circular objects such as cans, drinking glasses, and wastepaper baskets to complete this Activity.

1 Measure the circumference of each circle.

2 Measure the diameter of each circle.

3 Divide each circumference by the corresponding diameter.

4 What average value did your class find for the ratio of each circumference to its diameter?

In every circle, the ratio of circumference C to diameter d is the same. For this reason, the ratio has a special name, *pi*. Pi is represented by the lower case Greek letter π.

$$\pi = \frac{C}{d}$$

Press the $\boxed{\pi}$ key on your calculator. What approximate value does your calculator display? Your calculator display is an approximation because π is an irrational number. When you do not have a calculator, you can approximate π to three significant figures as 3.14.

If you multiply both sides of $\pi = \frac{C}{d}$ by d, the result is the formula for the circumference of a circle.

Circumference of a Circle
The circumference C of a circle with diameter d and radius r is

$$C = \pi d \quad \text{or} \quad C = 2\pi r$$

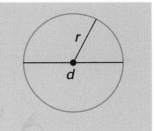

EXAMPLE 1   Calculating the Circumference

The pipe of a center-pivot sprinkler is 450 ft long. How far does the outside edge of the pipe travel in one revolution?

450 ft

SOLUTION

The outside edge moves in a circle. In one revolution, the outside edge travels the circumference.

$$C = 2\pi r$$
$$\approx 2(3.14)(450)$$
$$\approx 2826 \text{ ft}$$

Use a calculator.

$$2 \boxed{\times} \boxed{\pi} \boxed{\times} 450 \boxed{=} 2827.433388$$

In one revolution, the outside edge travels about 2827 ft.

Critical Thinking   Explain why there is a difference between the answers 2826 and 2827 in Example 1.

1 This circle has been cut into congruent pie-shaped wedges and rearranged to resemble a polygon. What type of polygon does the arrangement look like?

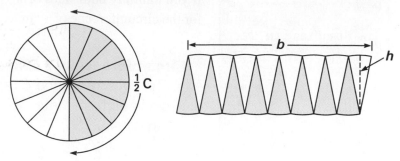

2 The area of the circle is the same as the area of the "rearranged polygon." Write an equation for the area *A* of this "polygon."

3 How is the height of the "polygon" related to the radius of the circle? Substitute *r* for *h* in the equation for *A*.

4 How is the base related to the circumference of the circle? Substitute $\frac{1}{2}(2\pi r)$ for *b* into the equation for *A*.

5 Simplify the equation. What is the equation for the area of a circle with radius *r*?

Area of a Circle
The area of a circle with radius *r* is

$$A = \pi r^2$$

EXAMPLE 2 Calculating the Area

How many acres are irrigated by a center-pivot sprinkler if the pipe is 450 feet long? (1 acre = 43,560 ft²)

SOLUTION

The size of the field irrigated is the area of the circle.

$$A = \pi r^2$$
$$\approx 3.14 \cdot (450)^2$$
$$\approx 6.36 \times 10^5$$

Use a calculator.

$$\boxed{\pi}\ \boxed{\times}\ 450\ \boxed{x^2}\ \boxed{=}\ 636172.5124$$

The area of the circle is approximately 6.36×10^5 ft^2.

Convert to acres.

$$6.36 \times 10^5 \text{ ft}^2 \cdot \frac{1 \text{ acre}}{43,560 \text{ ft}^2} \approx 14.6 \text{ acres}$$

The center-pivot sprinkler irrigates about 14.6 acres.

LESSON ASSESSMENT

Think and Discuss

1 Explain why the two formulas $C = 2\pi r$ and $C = \pi d$ give the same answer. Write a formula for the area of a circle using d.

2 What is measured by the circumference of a circle? What kinds of units are used?

3 What is measured by the area of a circle? What kinds of units are used?

4 Suppose the perimeter of a square is equal to the circumference of a circle. Which figure has the greater area? Explain why.

Practice and Apply

Find the circumference and area of each circle.

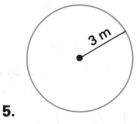

5.

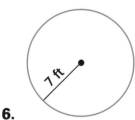

6.

7.

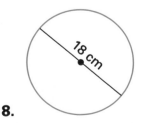

8.

Without using a calculator, estimate the circumference and area of each circle.

9. $r = 1$ m
10. $r = 3$ ft
11. $d = 2$ in.
12. $d = 10$ cm

Match the quadrilateral that has a perimeter approximately equal to the circumference of each circle.

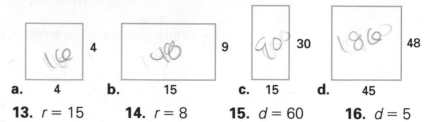

a. 4
b. 15
c. 15
d. 45

13. $r = 15$
14. $r = 8$
15. $d = 60$
16. $d = 5$

17. A **semicircle** is a half circle. What is the area of the semicircle below?

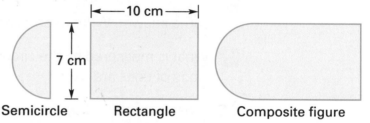

Semicircle   Rectangle   Composite figure

18. What is the area of the rectangle above?

19. What is the area of the composite figure made up of the semicircle and rectangle?

Find the area of each composite figure.

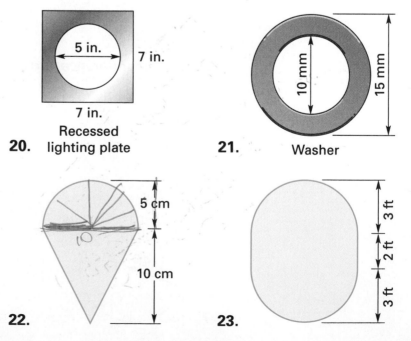

20. Recessed lighting plate

21. Washer

22.

23.

24. How many miles are in one lap around this race track?

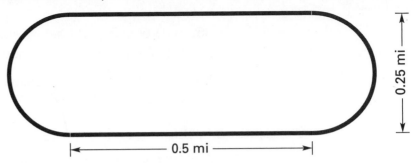

0.25 mi

0.5 mi

25. How many laps are in a 400-mile race?

26. A circular field has a radius of 550 m. One bag of fertilizer covers 1700 m². How many bags of fertilizer are needed to cover the field?

Find the radius and diameter of the circle with the given circumference or area.

27. $C = 1.5$ m

28. $C = 11.0$ in.

29. $A = 8$ ft²

30. $A = 7.5$ cm²

31. $C = 11.3$ mi

32. $A = 0.12$ mm²

You can buy circular beveled mirrors for $17 per sq ft. You can have a circular frame built for the mirror for $24 per ft.
33. What is the diameter of the largest mirror you can buy for $350?

34. How much will it cost to have a frame built for the mirror?

Mixed Review

The owner of a car dealership recorded his car and truck sales for one month.

Two-door cars	16	Four-door cars	28
Luxury cars	13	Small trucks	15
Half-ton trucks	9	One-ton trucks	6

Find the following to the nearest whole percent.
35. What percent of sales were small trucks?

36. What percent of sales were two-door cars?

37. What percent of sales were cars?

38. Suppose the total number of sales increases 11% the next month. How many vehicles are sold?

For Exercises 39–40, write an expression using integers and solve.

39. A diver is 35 feet below sea level. She descends another 22 feet. What is the diver's new position?

40. A water tank leaks 5 gallons per day. How many days will it take to leak 145 gallons?

Cumulative Problem Solving

A trundle wheel is a device for measuring distances too long for a measuring tape. When the wheel makes one complete revolution, it moves a distance equal to the circumference of the wheel.

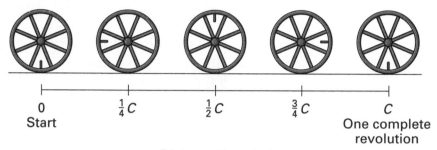

Distance Traveled
C = wheel circumference

Suppose you need to find the amount of fencing needed around the perimeter of a park. The diagram shows the number of revolutions the trundle wheel makes when it is pushed along each side of the park. The diameter of the wheel is 24 inches.

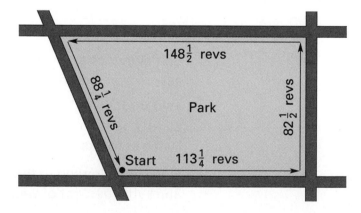

41. How many feet does the wheel move forward for each revolution?

42. What is the length around the park in feet?

43. What is the length in miles?

Stefani is planting Bermuda grass for the lawn around her new house. The house and lot are shown below.

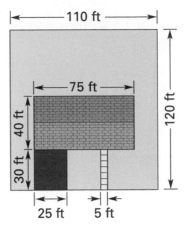

44. Two pounds of the grass seed covers 1000 square feet. How many pounds of seed does Stefani need?

An athletic club has an indoor running track, as shown. Each end of the track is a semicircle.

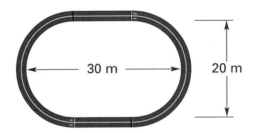

45. What is the total distance around the track?

46. How many laps would you need to complete to jog one kilometer?

Troy has volunteered to mow and line the soccer fields before a weekend tournament. The soccer complex has three sizes of fields.

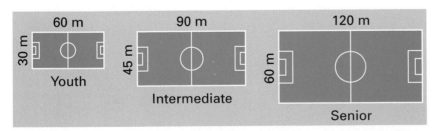

47. It takes Troy 30 minutes to mow an intermediate field. What is a reasonable estimate for how long it will take to mow a youth field? A senior field?

48. It takes Troy 20 minutes to line an intermediate field. What is a reasonable estimate for the time it will take to line a youth field? A senior field?

MATH LAB

Equipment Cardboard triangle, with sides
between 6 and 12 inches in length
Marking pen
Three strings (approximately 25 ft each)
One string (approximately 30 ft)
Golf tees (4)
Measuring tape
Protractor

Problem Statement

You will make a dilation of a triangle using string. To perform
the dilation, you will verify corresponding sides are
proportional and corresponding angles are congruent.

To perform the dilation, your teacher will assign your group a
scale factor *k* between 3 and 9 to use for the dilation.

Procedure

a Label the vertices of the cardboard triangle *A*, *B*, and *C*.

b Tie an end of each of the three strings together with a single
knot. This knot is the center of dilation, *P*. Fix *P* on the ground
with a golf tee.

c Place △*ABC* on the ground about 18 inches from *P*.

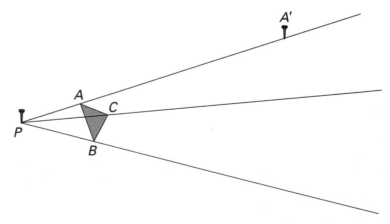

d Stretch one string so that it passes through *A*. Measure $\overline{PA}$.
Mark *A'* on the string so that $PA' = k \cdot PA$. Place a golf tee in
the ground at *A'*.

e Repeat Step **d** for B' and C'.

f Remove the strings, and pass a single string around A', B', and C' to form $\triangle A'B'C'$.

g What measurements are required to determine if $\triangle ABC \sim \triangle A'B'C'$? Use the tape measure and protractor to make the measurements. Record the values in your data table.

Discussion Questions

1. Is $\triangle ABC \sim \triangle A'B'C'$? What is the scale factor?

2. How would you change the procedures to dilate $\triangle ABC$ with a scale factor of 7 : 2?

3. Would the image $\triangle A'B'C'$ be different if the location of $\triangle ABC$ changed? Rotate $\triangle ABC$ so that P, A, and B are collinear. Repeat the procedures. Is $\triangle ABC \sim \triangle A'B'C'$? What is the scale factor?

Activity 2: Polynomials and Algeblocks

Equipment   Algeblocks or algebra tiles

Problem Statement

A **polynomial** is a variable expression containing one or more terms. Polynomials are named by the number of terms.

- A **monomial** has one term. These are monomials.

$$4x^2 \qquad -2y^3 \qquad 14a$$

- A **binomial** has two terms. These are binomials.

$$x - 8 \qquad y^2 + 4x \qquad d^3 - d^2$$

- A **trinomial** has three terms. These are trinomials.

$$3x^2 + x - 1 \qquad 2y^3 + 3x + y$$

To model a polynomial, let the long side of an Algeblock represent the variable x, and the short side represent the unit 1. The area of a block models x^2, x, or 1.

Algeblocks

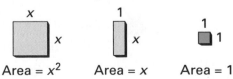

Area = x^2 Area = x Area = 1

Procedure

a You can model the trinomial $x^2 + 2x + 3$ with the following Algeblocks.

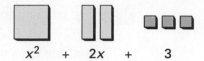

$$x^2 \quad + \quad 2x \quad + \quad 3$$

What polynomial is modeled by the following?

Use Algeblocks to model $3x^2 + x + 2$.

b You can model addition of polynomials by combining Algeblocks. The area of a composite figure is the sum of the areas of the figures that are combined. To add $(2x^2 + x + 3) + (x^2 + 3x + 2)$, combine the Algeblocks.

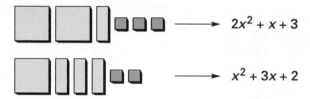

Group blocks with the same area. What polynomial is modeled by the new arrangement of blocks? This is the sum of the polynomials above.

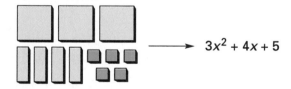

What two polynomials are modeled by the following? Write the sum of the polynomials.

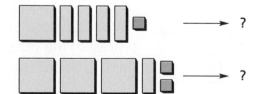

c Explain how the Algeblocks in Step **b** demonstrate the rule for adding polynomials.

To add polynomials, combine like terms.

Use the rule to find the sum $(5x^2 + 3x - 8) + (-x^2 + x)$. You can align like terms.

$$\begin{array}{r} 5x^2 + 3x - 8 \\ -x^2 + x + 0 \\ \hline 4x^2 + 4x - 8 \end{array}$$

Find the following sums.

$$(-2x^2 + x - 3) + (-x^2 + 3x + 1) = \underline{?}$$

$$(x^2 - 4x - 9) + (-3x^2 + 2) = \underline{?}$$

d You can model multiplication of polynomials by arranging Algeblocks in rectangles. The area of a rectangle is length · width.

The product $2x(x + 2)$ is modeled in the following diagram.

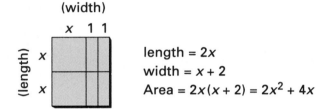

length = 2x
width = x + 2
Area = $2x(x + 2) = 2x^2 + 4x$

The composite rectangle has two x^2 blocks and four x blocks. Thus, $2x(x + 2) = 2x^2 + 4x$.

Each diagram models the product of a monomial and binomial. Write the products modeled.

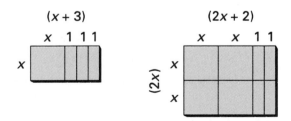

e The products modeled in Step **d** can also be found using the Distributive Property. For example,

$$2x(x + 2) = 2x(x) + 2x(2)$$
$$= 2x^2 + 4x$$

Use the Distributive Property to find the following.

$$x(x - 5) \qquad 4x(3x + 1) \qquad 9x(-x + 2)$$

f The diagram below models the product of two binomials. What is the product?

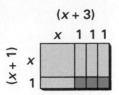

The composite rectangle has one x^2 block, four x blocks, and three unit blocks. Thus, $(x + 1)(x + 3) = x^2 + 4x + 3$.

Write the product modeled by each of the following.

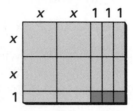

g The products modeled in Step **f** can also be found using the Distributive Property. For example,

$$(x + 1)(x + 3) = x(x + 3) + 1(x + 3)$$
$$= x^2 + 3x + x + 3$$
$$= x^2 + 4x + 3$$

Use the Distributive Property to find the following.

$(x + 3)(x - 2)$ $(4x + 1)(x + 1)$ $(2x - 3)(x + 2)$

Discussion Questions

1. Find the sum.

$$(y^3 - 2y^2 + 6y - 3) + (3y^3 + y^2 - 2y)$$

2. What type of polynomial results when you multiply two monomials? A monomial and a binomial? Two binomials?

3. Find each product using Algeblocks.

$3x(x + 2)$ $(x + 2)(3x + 2)$ $(2x + 1)(2x + 1)$

4. Find each product using the Distributive Property.

$5y(2y - 1)$ $(y - 2)(3y + 7)$ $(2y - 4)(2y + 4)$

Equipment Compass
Metric ruler
Protractor

Problem Statement

Archimedes was a Greek mathematician who lived during the third century B.C.E. Among his contributions to mathematics was an early method for approximating π.

Archimedes used regular polygons constructed inside and outside of circles. The perimeter of each polygon approximates the circumference of the circle. Thus, π is approximately the polygon's perimeter divided by the circle's diameter.

Your teacher will assign each group a different regular polygon. Your group will use this regular polygon and Archimede's method to approximate π.

Procedure

a Use the compass to draw a circle with a diameter of 5 cm to 10 cm.

b Follow these steps to draw a regular *n*-sided polygon *inscribed* in the circle.

• A circle contains 360°. Divide the circle into *n* congruent sections. For example, if you are drawing a pentagon, divide the circle into 5 sections, each measuring $\frac{360°}{5} = 72°$. Use the protractor to draw *n* congruent, adjacent angles. Make the sides of the angles radii of the circle. Use the center of the circle as the common vertex.

• Draw the sides of the inscribed polygon by connecting the endpoints of adjacent radii.

• An **inscribed polygon** is drawn completely within a circle with each vertex on the circle.

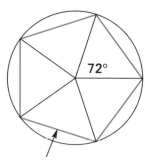

Inscribed pentagon

c Follow these steps to draw a regular *n*-sided polygon *circumscribed* about the circle.

• At the endpoint of each radius on the circle in Step **b**, draw a perpendicular line using a protractor. Each line intersects the circle at exactly one point. These lines are **tangent** to the circle.

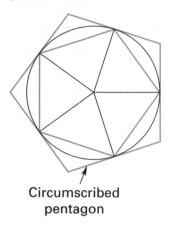

Circumscribed pentagon

• Each point of intersection of adjacent tangent lines is a vertex of the polygon that circumscribes the circle.

• A **circumscribed polygon** is drawn around the circumference of a circle with each side of the polygon intersecting the circle at exactly one point.

d Find the perimeter P_i of the inscribed polygon, the perimeter P_c of the circumscribed polygon, and the diameter d of the circle. Calculate the ratios $\frac{P_i}{d}$ and $\frac{P_c}{d}$.

e Combine your data with the rest of the class, and complete a table similar to the one shown. For the pentagon, measure the perimeters and diameter on the illustrations in Steps **b** and **c**.

Regular Polygon	Inscribed $\frac{P_i}{d}$	Circumscribed $\frac{P_c}{d}$
Triangle		
Quadrilateral		
Pentagon		
Hexagon		
Octagon		
Decagon		

Plot the data values on a coordinate plane similar to the one shown. You should plot two values, $\frac{P_i}{d}$ and $\frac{P_c}{d}$, for each regular polygon.

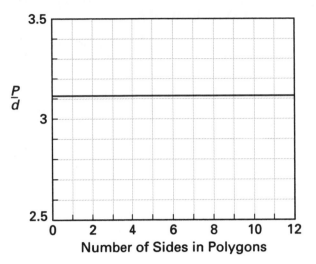

Discussion Questions

1. Describe the trend of the values for the inscribed polygons. Which inscribed polygon gave the closest approximation to π?

2. Describe the trend of the values for the circumscribed polygons. Which circumscribed polygon gave the closest approximation to π?

3. Why is it reasonable to expect $\frac{P_i}{d} < \pi$ for each inscribed polygon? Why is it reasonable to expect $\frac{P_c}{d} > \pi$ for each circumscribed polygon?

4. How did Archimedes get closer and closer approximations to π using this method? π is an irrational number. Can anyone ever obtain an exact value? Explain.

CHAPTER 11 ASSESSMENT

Communicate

1. How can you use the lengths of the sides of two rectangles to determine if the rectangles are similar?

2. The scale factor of a dilation is 2 : 1. How does the size of the image compare to the size of the original figure?

3. What is the relationship between the area of a parallelogram and the area of two triangles formed by a diagonal of the parallelogram?

4. What is the relationship between the scale factor of two similar polygons and the ratio of their perimeters? What is the relationship between the scale factor of two similar polygons and the ratio of their areas?

5. How do you find the circumference of a circle?

Skills

Find the next three terms of each sequence.

6. 8, 12, 16, 20, . . .   7. 1600, 800, 400, 200, . . .

Find the missing length for each pair of similar figures.

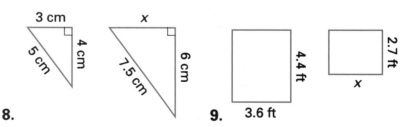

8.   9. 3.6 ft

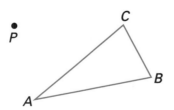

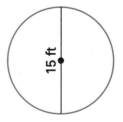

10. Trace the figure and point *P.* Enlarge the figure so that each side of the image is 3 times as long.

11. Find the circumference and area of the circle.

Find the area of each figure.

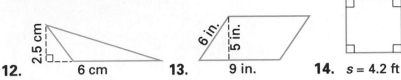

12. **13.** **14.** $s = 4.2$ ft

Write the scale factor for each pair of similar polygons. Write the ratios of the perimeter and the ratio of the areas.

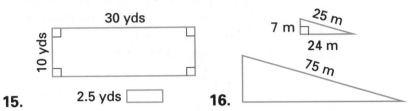

15. **16.**

Applications

17. An 8-inch-by-10-inch photograph will be reduced to fit a space that is 3.2 inches by 4 inches. What is the scale factor for the reduction?

18. The scale on a map is 2 cm = 50 miles. The distance on the map between Lincoln, Nebraska and Des Moines, Iowa is 7 cm. What is the actual distance in miles between the two cities?

19. A section of a football field must be resodded after a game. The rectangular section is 25 yards long and 20 yards wide. How many square yards of turf are needed?

20. The circular, plastic cap of a can of tennis balls has a diameter of 3 inches. How many square inches of plastic are needed to make the cap?

Math Lab

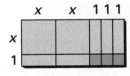

21. The dilation of a triangle is formed with string. The center of dilation is *P* and one vertex of the triangle is *A*. If $PA = 2.5$ cm and the scale factor is 4, what is the length of PA'?

22. Find the product of $(x + 1)(2x + 3)$ shown by the Algeblocks model.

23. A regular hexagon is inscribed in a circle with diameter 4 centimeters. The length of each side of the hexagon is 2 centimeters. What is the ratio of the perimeter of the hexagon to the diameter of the circle? What value does this ratio approximate?

CHAPTER 12

WHY SHOULD I LEARN THIS?

Geometric figures are not usually confined to a plane—most are three-dimensional. There are five basic three-dimensional figures. Several of them were used in the design of the Rock and Roll Hall of Fame.

Contents: Surface Area and Volume

SURFACE AREA AND VOLUME

LEARN HOW TO...

1. **Make orthographic projections, isometric drawings, and one-point perspective drawings of three-dimensional figures.**
2. **Find the surface areas of prisms, cylinders, pyramids, and cones.**
3. **Find the volumes of prisms, cylinders, pyramids, and cones.**
4. **Solve problems using the ratios of the areas and volumes of similar solids.**

The world is filled with three-dimensional objects, commonly called solids. The five basic solids are prisms, cylinders, cones, pyramids, and spheres. A book is a rectangular prism. A soda can is a cylinder. You eat ice cream from a cone. The Transamerica building is a pyramid. A basketball is a sphere. You will begin this chapter by identifying the five basic solids and drawing some of them with orthographic projections, isometric drawings, and perspective drawings.

Solids have surface area and volume. The surface area is the total area on the surface of the solid. The volume is the space enclosed inside the solid. Architects, artists, builders, electricians, plumbers, and others use the formulas for surface area and volume to solve problems in their occupations.

There are useful relationships between the scale factor, surface area, and volume of similar solids. In this chapter, you will use these relationships to determine surface area and volume of similar solids.

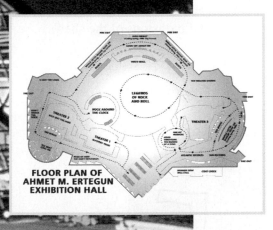

FLOOR PLAN OF
AHMET M. ERTEGUN
EXHIBITION HALL

LESSON 12.1 DRAWING THREE-DIMENSIONAL FIGURES

OBJECTIVES

➤ Draw an orthographic projection of a given figure.
➤ Create an isometric drawing.
➤ Create a one-point perspective drawing.

In Chapters 9 through 11, you studied two-dimensional figures in a plane. But most of the figures you will encounter in the world are not confined to a plane. They are three-dimensional figures, or **solids.** Five basic solids are shown.

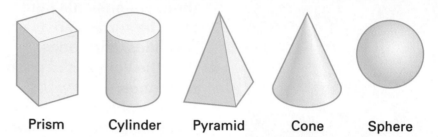

Prism   Cylinder   Pyramid   Cone   Sphere

Architects, designers, engineers, and artists often use two-dimensional drawings to model solids. These drawings are made on paper or computer screens. Three types of drawings are commonly used.

- orthographic projections

- isometric drawings

- perspective drawings

An **orthographic projection** shows the top, front, and side views of an object separately. These views appear as if your line of sight is perpendicular to the object's top, front, and side.

For example, if you were building a storage shed, an orthographic projection would show the shape and dimensions of the shed.

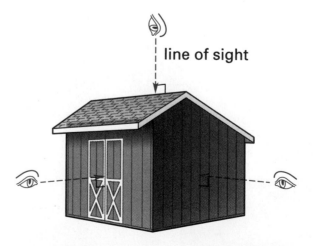

line of sight

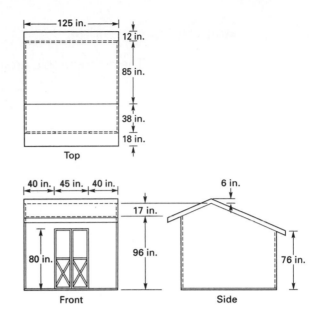

Top

40 in. 45 in. 40 in.

17 in.

6 in.

80 in.

96 in.

76 in.

Front   Side

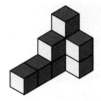

EXAMPLE 1 Drawing an Orthographic Projection

Draw the orthographic projection of the figure at the left.

SOLUTION

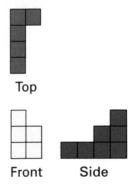

Top

Front   Side

ONGOING ASSESSMENT

Draw the orthographic projection of the figure at the right.

An orthographic projection shows all the lines and dimensions of an object, but not its three-dimensional nature. An **isometric drawing** shows what an object looks like when you view it at an angle.

In this isometric drawing of a prism, how many faces can you see? How many are hidden?

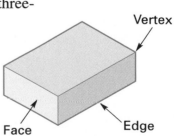

Vertex

Face   Edge

The orthographic projections of a rectangular prism are shown.

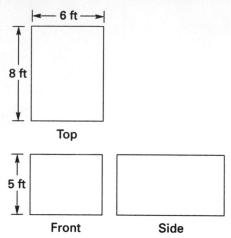

Top

Front   Side

Use isometric dot paper to make an isometric drawing of the prism. Let one unit between each pair of dots equal one foot.

1 Draw a vertical line segment 5 units long to represent the edge where the front and side faces intersect. Draw two segments to represent top edges of the prism. What are the lengths of these edges on the prism?

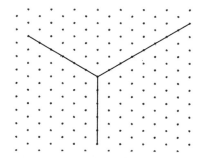

2 Draw two more segments to represent the bottom edges of the prism. How can you make sure the edges are parallel to the ones you drew in Step 1?

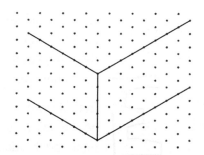

3 Complete the top, front, and side of the prism.

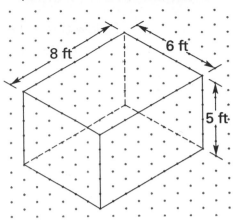

4 Finish the prism by drawing hidden segments as dashed lines. Label the dimensions.

An orthographic projection of a set of steps is shown. Make an isometric drawing of the steps.

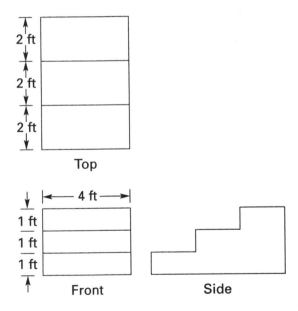

A **perspective drawing** makes a two-dimensional drawing look more like the actual three-dimensional object. This is done by making lines appear to meet at a point on the horizon. By having lines meet at the horizon, the drawing gains a distance perspective.

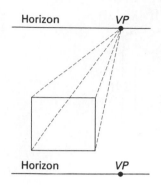

Follow these steps to make a one-point perspective drawing of the rectangular prism from Activity 1.

1 First draw a line for the horizon, and select a vanishing point (*VP*).

2 Draw the front face of the prism. Connect each vertex to the vanishing point with *perspective lines*.

3 Draw the back face of the prism. Make sure corresponding edges are parallel. Draw the remaining edges by connecting corresponding vertices. Erase the perspective lines that are not part of the prism.

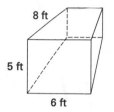

Critical Thinking   When you make a perspective drawing, some line segments are not parallel on the drawing even though they are parallel on the actual object. Which segments in the drawing for Activity 2 are like this?

CULTURAL CONNECTION

In the 14th and 15th centuries, Renaissance painters developed the techniques of using perspective to make paintings look more realistic. In the 1480s, the early Renaissance artist Piero della Francesca wrote about the mathematics of perspective in his book *De Prospectiva Pingendi.*

One of Piero's paintings, *Ideal City,* is shown. Where did Piero locate the vanishing point in his *Ideal City?*

LESSON ASSESSMENT

Think and Discuss

1 What does an orthographic projection show? Is an orthographic projection three-dimensional? Explain.

2 Make an isometric drawing of an object for which the top, front, and side views are the same.

3 Railroad tracks are parallel. Describe how they appear in a one-point perspective drawing.

4 On a perspective drawing, why is the point on the horizon called the vanishing point?

Practice and Apply

Create an orthographic projection showing top, front, and side views of each of the following.

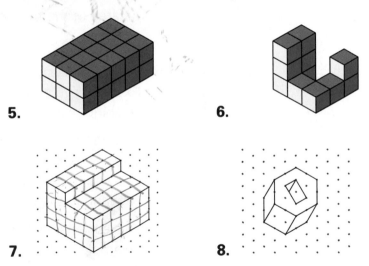

5.

6.

7.

8.

Create an isometric drawing of the stack of blocks using each set of orthographic projections.

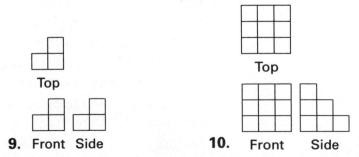

9. Front Side

10. Front Side

Use the following orthographic projection of a rectangular box for Exercises 11–14.

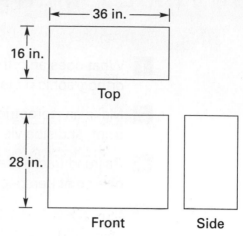

Top

Front   Side

11. Create an isometric drawing of the rectangular box. Label the dimensions on your drawing. Use dashed lines to show the hidden lines.

12. Find the area of the top of the box.

13. Find the area of the front of the box.

14. Find the area of a side of the box.

Use this one-point perspective drawing of a rectangular prism for Exercises 15 and 16.

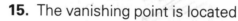
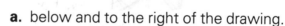

15. The vanishing point is located

    a. below and to the right of the drawing.
    b. above and to the right of the drawing.
    c. above and to the left of the drawing.
    d. below and to the left of the drawing.

16. The three-dimensional prism has six rectangular faces. For example, *ABCD* is a face. Which faces in the perspective drawing are similar to the actual faces on the prism?

VP
•

17. Trace onto a sheet of paper the block letter E and vanishing point shown. Create a one-point perspective drawing of the letter. Make the depth of the drawing appear to be about the same as the length across the top.

Solve each equation.

18. $\frac{2}{3}y + 8 = -7$

19. $7.0 - 0.5a = -1.9a$

20. $-x + \frac{1}{4} = 2x$

21. $c + \frac{1}{2}c = 3$

22. $0z - 0.2z = 3.6$

23. $\frac{12}{10} + \frac{a}{5} = -a$

Write each number as a percent.

24. $\frac{3}{8}$

25. 0.025

26. $3\frac{2}{3}$

27. 1.75

28. A gas tank is filled with 12 gallons of gasoline. This is two-thirds of its capacity. Find the capacity of the gas tank.

29. The sum of the page numbers of two facing pages of a text book is 193. What are the page numbers?

30. When a ball is released from a certain height, it bounces back to $\frac{5}{8}$ the height. The second bounce of the ball is 15 feet high. From what height was the ball released?

31. The value of a new car drops 20% during the first year of ownership. A new car is purchased for $24,500. What is the value of the car one year later?

The vertices of a scale drawing of a rectangular garden gate have the coordinates $A(-3, 3)$, $B(4, 3)$, $C(4, -5)$, and $D(-3, -5)$.

32. Draw the gate on a coordinate plane.

33. Find the perimeter of the gate.

34. Find the area of the gate.

35. Find the length of a diagonal of the gate.

36. If the drawing is translated by the function rule $f(x, y) \rightarrow (2x + 1, y - 1)$, what are new coordinates of the vertices of the image?

LESSON 12.2 SURFACE AREA OF PRISMS

OBJECTIVES

➤ Compute the surface area of a prism.

Carly is a packaging designer for a cereal manufacturer. When she designs a new cereal box, she must report the amount of material that will be required to make the box. What amount should Carly report for the design shown?

10 in.

8 in.

3 in.

ACTIVITY

Surface Area from a Net

A **net** is a flat pattern that can be folded, without any gaps or overlap, into a three-dimensional figure. The net for Carly's cereal box is shown.

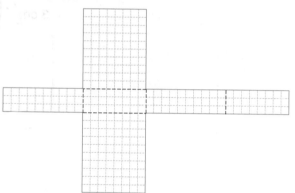

1 Copy the net on graph paper. Cut out the net. Fold along the dotted lines to form a three-dimensional figure.

2 The figure you have assembled is a **prism.** The flat surfaces that form the prism are called **faces.** Name the polygons that form the faces of this prism.

3 The top and bottom faces are congruent. What is the total area of these polygons?

4 The front and back faces are also congruent. What is the total area of these polygons?

5 The right and left faces are also congruent. What is the total area of these polygons?

6 The **surface area** of the box is the sum of the areas of the top, bottom, front, back, and sides. What is the surface area?

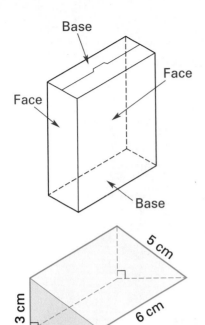

Base

Face

Face

Base

The top and bottom faces of the cereal box are called the **bases** of the prism. The bases of a prism are congruent and parallel. A prism is named by the polygons that form the bases. Since the bases of the cereal box are rectangles, it is a *rectangular prism.*

Surface Area of a Prism
The surface area of a prism is the sum of the areas of the bases and faces.

EXAMPLE 1 The Surface Area of a Triangular Prism

Find the surface area of this triangular prism.

5 cm

3 cm

4 cm

6 cm

SOLUTION

Make a sketch of the net showing the bases and faces.

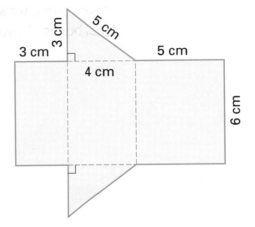

The surface area of the triangular prism is the sum of the areas of its bases and faces.

$$\text{surface area} = \text{area of bases} + \text{area of faces}$$
$$= 2\left[\frac{1}{2}(3)(4)\right] + 3 \cdot 6 + 4 \cdot 6 + 5 \cdot 6$$
$$= 12 + 18 + 24 + 30$$
$$= 84$$

The surface area of the triangular prism is 84 cm^2.

Critical Thinking Explain why the triangles are the bases in Example 1, and the rectangles are the faces.

Find the surface area of this rectangular prism.

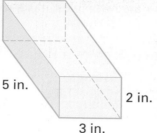

5 in.

2 in.

3 in.

PROBLEM SOLVING

USING THE FOUR-STEP PLAN

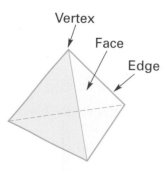

Vertex

Face

Edge

Regular tetrahedron

The Renaissance painter Piero della Francesca (see page 646) also studied and wrote short books about geometry and applied mathematics. One of his books, *De Quinque Corporibus Regularibus,* written in the 1480s, describes the five regular *polyhedra.*

A **polyhedron** is any three-dimensional figure that is bounded by polygons. A prism is an example of a polyhedron. A regular polyhedron has congruent regular polygons for all its faces. The simplest example is a tetrahedron.

There are only five regular polyhedra. Copy the following table.

The Five Regular Polyhedra

Name	Face	Number of Faces	Number of Vertices	Number of Edges
Tetrahedron	Triangle	4	4	6
Cube	Square	6	8	12
Octahedron	Triangle	8	?	?
Dodecahedron	Pentagon	12	20	30
Icosahedron	?	?	?	?

A net for an icosahedron is shown. Use the net to fill in the last row of the table.

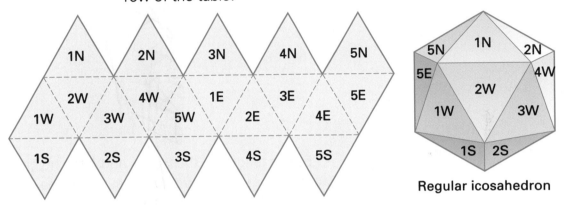

Regular icosahedron

Complete the table for the octahedron.

Understand the Problem

Each face of a regular octahedron is a polygon. Name the polygon. How many faces are there?

Develop a Plan

Build a model of a regular octahedron.

Carry Out the Plan

Draw a net. Cut out the net and assemble the octahedron. Tape the sides. How many vertices and edges are in an octahedron?

Check the Results

Is your model a polyhedron? Is it a regular polyhedron? Is it an octahedron?

LESSON ASSESSMENT

1 How is a triangular prism different from a rectangular prism? How are they alike?

2 A donut is a three-dimensional object that you cannot unfold into a net. Describe another object for which there is no net.

3 Explain why the illustration below on the right is not a net for the prism on the left.

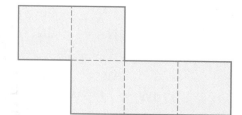

4 Let l be the length, w the width, and h the height of a rectangular prism. Show that the surface area of the prism can be found with this formula.

$$\text{surface area} = 2lw + 2lh + 2wh$$

For Exercises 5–7, tell which three-dimensional object is not a prism.

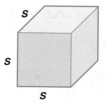

5. A   B   C   D

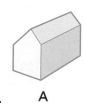  

6. A   B   C   D

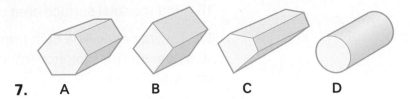

7.   A   B   C   D

Draw a net for each of the prisms in Exercises 8–9. Find the surface area of each prism.

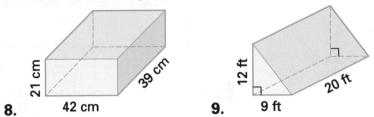

8. 21 cm, 39 cm, 42 cm

9. 12 ft, 20 ft, 9 ft

Find the surface area of each prism.

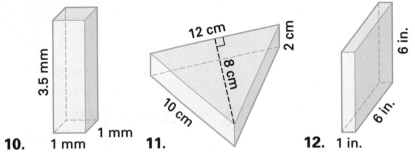

10. 3.5 mm, 1 mm, 1 mm

11. 12 cm, 2 cm, 8 cm, 10 cm

12. 6 in., 6 in., 1 in.

The Bosque County Fair is building six stands to display model cars entered for competition in the Youth Division. Use this illustration of one of the stands to answer Exercises 13–17.

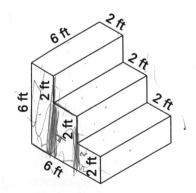

6 ft, 2 ft, 2 ft, 2 ft, 2 ft, 6 ft, 2 ft, 6 ft, 2 ft

13. Two congruent polygons form the right and left faces of each stand. Name the polygons.

14. Is the stand a prism?

15. The other polygons are rectangular faces. How many rectangular faces are there?

16. Find the total surface area of each stand.

17. The stands will be built from plywood. If plywood costs $0.55 per square foot, how much will the plywood cost for all six stands?

18. This tent is a triangular prism. All faces of the tent including the floor are made of canvas. How many square feet of canvas are needed to make the tent?

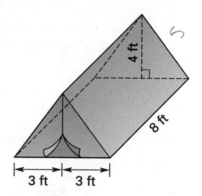

19. You are having a pool built with the dimensions shown. It costs $3.50 per square foot to have gunnite sprayed for the sides and floor of the pool. How much will the gunnite cost?

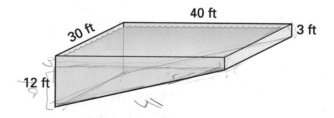

Mixed Review

20. In a carton of scarves, $\frac{1}{8}$ are blue, $\frac{1}{16}$ are yellow, $\frac{1}{2}$ are red, and $\frac{5}{16}$ are green. If you take a scarf from the carton without looking, what color is it most likely to be?

21. A box contains 24 spools of thread of various colors. The probability of randomly selecting a spool of black thread is $\frac{3}{8}$. How many spools of black thread are in the box?

Write each number in scientific notation.

22. Light travels about 16,095,000,000 miles in 1 day.

23. There are about 31,536,000 seconds in 365 days.

24. It takes about 0.0028 seconds for sound to travel 3 feet.

LESSON 12.3 SURFACE AREA OF CYLINDERS

OBJECTIVES
→ Calculate the surface area of a cylinder.

Sometimes cereals are not packaged in rectangular prisms. For example, this oatmeal container is a *cylinder.*

A **cylinder** has two circular bases that are congruent and parallel.

ACTIVITY   Surface Area of a Cylinder

The net for the cylindrical container is shown.

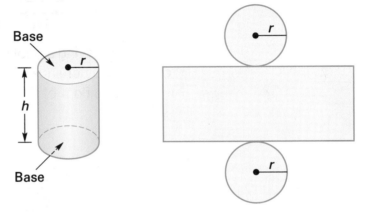

Base

Base

1   Write the formula for the area of each base of the cylinder. What is the total area of the bases?

2   Write the formula for the circumference of each base of the cylinder.

3   When the curved surface of the cylinder is flattened out, what type of figure is produced? How is the length of this figure related to the circumference of the base of the cylinder? How is the width of this figure related to the height of the cylinder?

4   Write a formula for the area of the curved surface of the cylinder.

5   The surface area of a cylinder is the total area of the bases plus the area of the curved surface. Write a formula for the surface area of a cylinder with radius *r* and height *h*.

Compare your formula to the following.

Surface Area of a Cylinder

The surface area S of a cylinder is the sum of the areas of the bases and the curved surface.

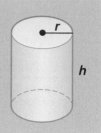

$$S = 2\pi r^2 + 2\pi rh$$

EXAMPLE Surface Area of a Cylindrical Container

Calculate the surface area of the oatmeal container.

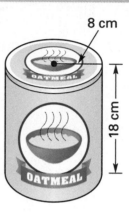

8 cm

18 cm

SOLUTION

$$S = 2\pi r^2 + 2\pi rh$$

$$\approx 2(3.14)(8)^2 + 2(3.14)(8)(18)$$

$$\approx 401.9 + 904.3$$

$$\approx 1306.2$$

You can also use a calculator.

2 ⊗ π ⊗ 8 x² ⊕ 2 ⊗ π ⊗ 8 ⊗ 18 ⊜ 1306.902544

The surface area of the cylinder is approximately 1307 cm².

Critical Thinking   What part of the oatmeal container in the Example has an area approximately 904.3 cm²?

ONGOING ASSESSMENT

Find the surface area of the cylinder at the left.

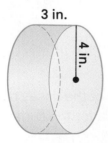

3 in.

4 in.

LESSON ASSESSMENT

Think and Discuss

1 How is a cylinder like a prism? How is it different?

2 What geometric figures are used to make a net for a cylinder?

3 Suppose the radius and height of a cylinder are given in centimeters. What is the most convenient unit of measure for the surface area of the cylinder?

4 Suppose you use the length of a 10- by 10-inch sheet of paper to form the curved surface of a cylinder. Explain how you can calculate the diameter of the bases of the cylinder.

Practice and Apply

Find the surface area of the cylinder formed by each net.

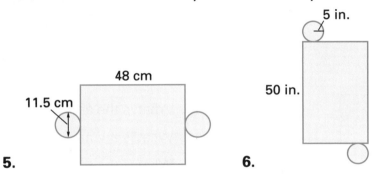

5.

6.

Find the surface area of each cylinder.

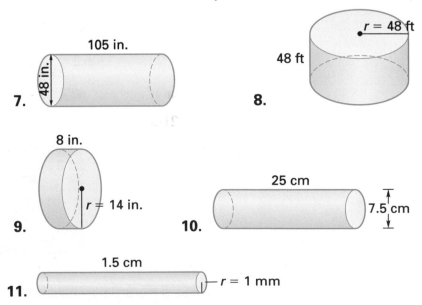

7.

8.

9.

10.

11.

The outside curved surface of a cylindrical water tank must be painted. The tank has a diameter of 12 feet and a height of 12 feet.

12. What is the surface area to be painted?

13. Assume you can only buy paint in one-gallon cans. How many gallons of paint are needed if one gallon covers 400 square feet?

14. If you can buy paint in one-gallon and one-quart cans, what is the least amount of paint you can buy to complete the job?

A napkin ring is manufactured in the shape of a hollow cylinder. The ring is to be silver plated.

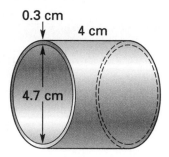

0.3 cm

4 cm

4.7 cm

15. What is the area of the outside surface of the ring?

16. What is the area of the inside surface?

17. What is the total area of the ends of the ring?

18. What is the total surface area to be silver plated?

19. The soup can below has a diameter of 6.5 cm and a height of 9.5 cm.

6.5 cm

9.5 cm

TOMATO SOUP

What is the area of the label around the can?

Suppose a cylinder's radius is equal to its height.

20. Write a formula for the cylinder's surface area.

21. If the surface area of the cylinder is 24 cm², what is the radius of the cylinder?

Find the surface area of each composite figure.

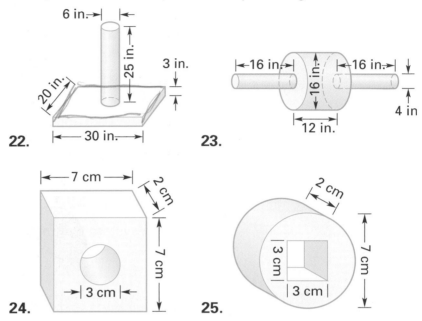

22.   **23.**

24.   **25.**

It costs $500 to set up equipment to manufacture gears. The cost to manufacture a gear is $4.50.

26. What is the total cost for producing 30 gears?

27. How many gears can be produced if you spend a total of $1500?

28. An inspector rejects finished gears at a ratio of 3 to 150. Write the rejection ratio as a percent.

29. During one summer, the number of people applying for unemployment dropped from 900 to 800. What was the percent decrease for unemployment applications?

30. During one year, the number of housing starts increased by 3% to 11,640. Find the number of housing starts the year before.

31. Tamara decreased the time required to complete a company's payroll from 20 hours per week to $17\frac{1}{2}$ hours per week. By what percent did Tamara decrease the time required?

32. The Bureau of Labor Statistics estimates a 22.2% increase in the number of jobs between 1996 and 2006 for people with an Associates Degree. If the number of jobs in 1996 was approximately 4.122 million, what is the estimated number of jobs in 2006?

Solve each system by graphing.

33. $y = x - 1$
$y = 2x + 3$

34. $2x + 2y = 6$
$y = 2x$

Cumulative Problem Solving

Janine is buying paint for a post-and-rail fence that completely encloses a field. Each section of the fence has one post and three rails. The dimensions of a section are shown. The fence contains 25 sections.

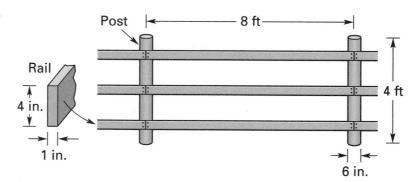

35. What is the surface area to be painted for each post?

36. What is the surface area to be painted for each rail? What is the surface area for three rails in a section?

37. What is the total area Janine must paint for the fence?

38. If one gallon covers 200 square feet, how many gallons should Janine buy?

Orthographic projections of the top, front, and side views of a birdhouse are shown. The birdhouse will be constructed from a cedar board 6 inches wide.

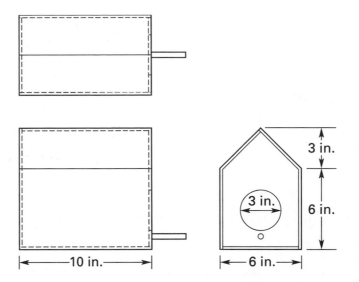

39. Make an isometric drawing of the birdhouse.

40. How many rectangles are needed to construct the birdhouse? What is the area of each rectangle?

41. How many pentagons are needed to construct the birdhouse? What is the area of each pentagon?

42. What is the total surface area, in square inches, of the cedar board needed to construct the birdhouse?

43. Draw the cedar board on graph paper, using the scale shown. Show how you would cut the board to get the seven pieces for the birdhouse. Use shading to show the parts of the board not used or removed. What is the minimum length of board needed?

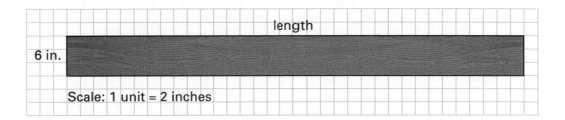

LESSON 12.4 VOLUMES OF PRISMS AND CYLINDERS

In the last two lessons, you found the surface area of three-dimensional figures. Surface area is measured in square units; for example, square inches (in.^{2}), square centimeters (cm^2), or square meters (m^2).

The **volume** of a three-dimensional figure is the amount of space it encloses. Volume is measured in *cubic units;* for example, cubic inches (in.^{3}), cubic centimeters (cm^3), or cubic meters (m^3).

A **cube** is a rectangular prism with congruent square faces. A cube that measures 1 cm on each edge has a volume of 1 cm^3.

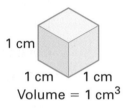

1 cm
1 cm   1 cm
Volume = 1 cm^3

ACTIVITY 1   Volume of a Prism

Follow these steps to find the volume of the prism shown.

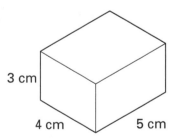

3 cm
4 cm   5 cm

1 Cover the base of the prism with a layer of cubes of 1 cm^3. How many cubes are required?

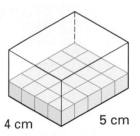

4 cm   5 cm

2 Add layers of cubes to fill the volume. How many layers are required in all?

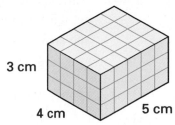

3 cm

4 cm   5 cm

3 How many cubes are required to fill the space enclosed by the prism? What is the volume of the prism in cm³?

4 What is the area of the base of the prism? Multiply the area of the base by the height of the prism. How does this result compare to the volume found in Step 3?

5 Make a conjecture about how to calculate the volume of a prism.

Compare your conjecture to the following.

Volume of a Prism

The volume *V* of a prism is the product of the area of the base *B* and the height *h*.

$$V = Bh$$

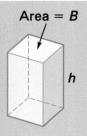

Area = *B*

h

EXAMPLE 1 The Volume Formula

Suppose a rectangular prism has a height *h*, and base with length *l* and width *w*. Show that its volume is given by the formula $V = lwh$.

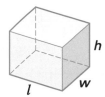

h

l   *w*

SOLUTION

The base of the prism is a rectangle whose area is length times width.

$$B = lw$$
$$V = Bh$$
$$\quad = lwh$$

EXAMPLE 2 Volume of a Hexagonal Aquarium

Philip builds aquariums. A customer asks for a hexagonal aquarium with the same volume as the rectangular aquarium shown. What is the area of the base of the hexagonal aquarium?

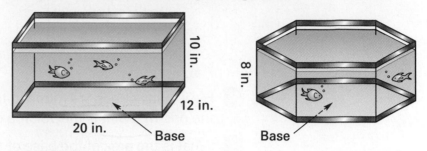

SOLUTION

Both aquariums are prisms. The base of the rectangular aquarium is a rectangle whose area is

$$B = \text{length} \cdot \text{width} = (20 \text{ in.})(12 \text{ in.}) = 240 \text{ in.}^2$$

The volume of the rectangular aquarium is

$$
\begin{aligned}
V &= Bh \\
&= (240 \text{ in.}^2)(10 \text{ in.}) \\
&= 2400 \text{ in.}^3
\end{aligned}
$$

The volume of the hexagonal aquarium is the same.

$$V = Bh$$

$$2400 \text{ in.}^3 = B(8 \text{ in.})$$

$$B = \frac{2400 \text{ in.}^3}{8 \text{ in.}}$$

$$= 300 \text{ in.}^2$$

The area of the base of the hexagonal aquarium is 300 in.^{2}

ONGOING ASSESSMENT

Find the volume of each solid.

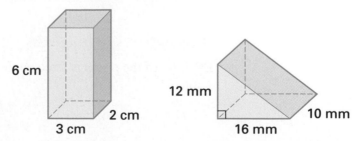

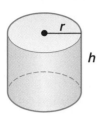

Like a prism, the volume of a cylinder is the product of the area of the base and the height.

1 What figure is the base of a cylinder? What is the area of the cylinder's base?

2 Write a formula for the volume of a cylinder with radius *r* and height *h*.

Compare your formula to the following.

Volume of a Cylinder

The volume *V* of a cylinder is the product of the area of the base *B* and the height *h*.

$$V = \pi r^2 h \quad \text{or} \quad V = Bh$$

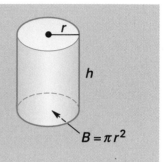

$B = \pi r^2$

EXAMPLE 3 Amount of Juice in a Glass

Jelani is a dietitian recording the amount of food for a client. The client drinks a glass of juice at breakfast. The dimensions of the glass are shown. How many grams of juice should Jelani record for her client?

$$(1 \text{ g juice} \approx 1 \text{ cm}^3)$$

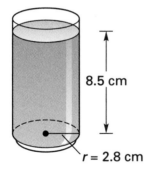

8.5 cm

r = 2.8 cm

SOLUTION

The glass is in the shape of a cylinder.

$$V = \pi r^2 h$$
$$\approx 3.14(2.8)^2(8.5)$$
$$\approx 209.2 \text{ cm}^3$$

Or you can use a calculator.

$\boxed{\pi}\;\boxed{\times}\;2.8\;\boxed{x^2}\;\boxed{\times}\;8.5\;\boxed{=}\;209.3557344$

The volume is approximately 209.4 cm³.

$$\text{weight} \approx \frac{1\text{g}}{\text{cm}^3} \cdot 209.4 \text{ cm}^3 \approx 209.4 \text{ g}$$

There are approximately 209.4 g of juice in the glass.

LESSON ASSESSMENT

Think and Discuss

1 Show that the volume V of a cube with edges of length s is given by the formula $V = s^3$.

2 Explain why the volume of a cube with sides twice as long as a smaller cube has eight times the volume of the smaller cube.

3 How are finding the volume of a prism and a cylinder the same? How are they different?

4 Suppose you need to double the volume of a cylinder by doubling one of its dimensions. Should you double the cylinder's height or radius? Explain your answer.

Practice and Apply

Find the volume of each solid.

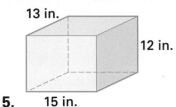

5. 13 in., 12 in., 15 in.

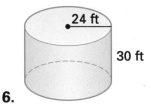

6. 24 ft, 30 ft

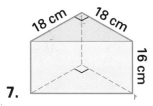

7. 18 cm, 18 cm, 16 cm

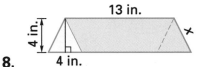

8. 13 in., 4 in., 4 in.

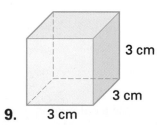

9. 3 cm, 3 cm, 3 cm

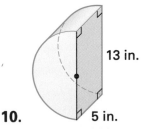

10. 13 in., 5 in.

11. Find the volume of a hexagonal prism that has a base area of 113 square meters and a height of 2 meters.

12. A pipe with diameter 3.5 in. and height 6 in. is replaced by a pipe that has the same volume. The new pipe has diameter 4.2 in. What is its height?

A water-filled lawn roller is shaped like a cylinder. It has a diameter of 21 inches and a length of 4 feet.

13. What surface area can be covered by the roller in one complete turn?

14. How many gallons of water will it take to fill the roller? (1 ft³ of water = 7.48 gallons)

15. What is the weight of the water in the roller when full? (1 ft³ of water weighs 62.5 pounds)

16. A rectangular tank has a square base with sides of 3 feet. How tall is the tank if it holds 100 gallons of water when full? (1 ft³ of water = 7.48 gallons)

17. What is the weight of this gold ingot? (1 in.³ of gold weighs 0.7 pounds.)

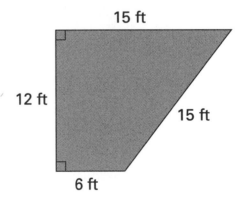

A garden is in the shape of a quadrilateral as shown. It is covered with 6 inches of topsoil.

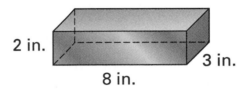

18. How many cubic feet of topsoil are needed?

19. How many cubic feet are in one cubic yard?

20. Topsoil costs $45 per cubic yard. How much will the topsoil for the garden cost?

21. A plastic case in the shape of a rectangular prism has outside measurements of 45 cm × 15 cm × 15 cm. The inside measurements are 43 cm × 13 cm × 13 cm. How many cubic centimeters of plastic were used to make the case?

22. A cylindrical beaker with a diameter of 3 inches has 6 inches of water in it. When a rock is placed in the beaker, the height of the water is raised to 8 inches. What is the volume of the rock?

23. What is the volume of metal in this machine nut?

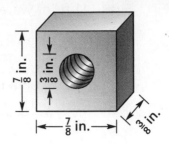

24. A car engine has six cylinders. Each cylinder has a height of 8.4 cm and a diameter of 8.8 cm. The total volume of the six cylinders is called the *displacement* of the engine. Find the engine's displacement in liters. (1 L = 1000 cm^3)

25. You can make a cylinder by rolling an 8 × 11-inch sheet of paper. You can use the long side of the paper as the height of the cylinder, or you can use the short side. Which way results in the greater volume? By how much?

Mixed Review

Solve each equation.

26. $-3x + 4 = 25$

27. $\frac{2}{3}y - \frac{1}{2} = -2\frac{1}{4}$

Graph each inequality on a number line.

28. $5x - 7 \leq 20$

29. $-4x + 15 < -9$

30. There are 3 blue marbles, 5 red marbles, and 2 green marbles in a bowl. One marble is drawn from the bowl at random. What is the probability that the marble will be blue or green?

31. Explain the difference between an acute, obtuse, and right angle.

32. The sum of two angles of a triangle is 120°. Find the measure of the third angle.

33. The legs of a right triangle measure 10 inches and 12 inches. Find the length of the hypotenuse to the nearest tenth of an inch.

LESSON 12.5 PYRAMIDS AND CONES

Architects have designed structures with *pyramid* shapes for centuries. The ancient Egyptians and Mayan Indians built pyramids as monuments to their kings. In 1989 a new entrance to the Louvre museum in Paris was completed. This glass structure, designed by I. M. Pei, is a pyramid.

A **pyramid** has a base that is a polygon. The faces of a pyramid are triangles that have a common vertex.

Pei's structure is a **square pyramid,** since its base is a square. A net of a square pyramid is shown. Since the base has four sides, there are four faces in a square pyramid.

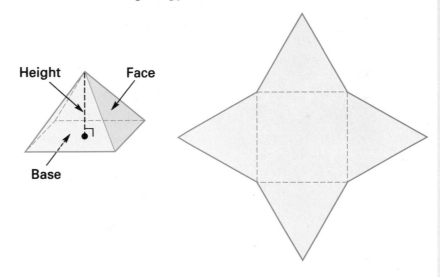

ACTIVITY 1   The Surface Area of a Square Pyramid

1. To calculate the area of the base of a square pyramid, what formula do you use?

2. To calculate the area of each face of the pyramid, what formula do you use? To calculate the total surface area of the pyramid, you only need to use this formula once. Explain why.

Surface Area of a Pyramid
The surface area of a pyramid is the sum of the areas of the base and faces.

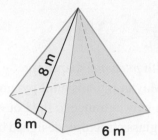

EXAMPLE 1 Finding the Surface Area of a Pyramid

Find the surface area of the pyramid at the left.

SOLUTION

pyramid surface area = 4(area of each face) + area of base

$$= 4\left[\frac{1}{2}(6)(8)\right] + (6)(6)$$

$$= 96 + 36$$

$$= 132$$

The surface area of the pyramid is 132 m².

A **cone** has a circular base and a vertex that is not in the same plane as the base. The surface area of a cone is also the sum of the areas of the base and face. The curved face is the *lateral surface* of the cone.

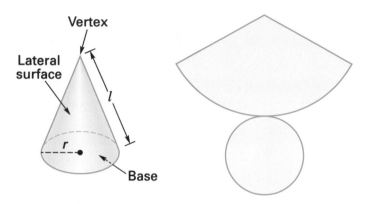

The **slant height** l of a cone is the distance from the vertex to the base, along the lateral surface. The area of the lateral surface is πrl.

Surface Area of a Cone

The surface area S of a cone is the sum of the areas of the base and lateral surface.

$$S = \pi r^2 + \pi rl$$

Critical Thinking Find the slant height of this cone. Find the surface area of the cone.

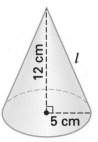

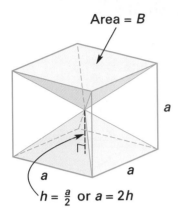

Area = B

a

a   a

$h = \frac{a}{2}$ or $a = 2h$

The diagram at the left shows a cube with sides of length *a*. The cube is divided into six congruent square pyramids by connecting opposite diagonals.

Supply the missing reasons for the steps to find a formula for the volume of one of the pyramids.

Steps	Reasons
1. Volume of the cube $= Ba$	?
2. Volume of a pyramid $= \frac{1}{6} \cdot$ Volume of the cube	Given
3. $\qquad = \frac{1}{6}Ba$	?
4. $\qquad = \frac{1}{6}B(2h)$	?
5. $\qquad = \frac{1}{3}Bh$	?

Activity 2 shows that a square pyramid has one-third the volume of a prism with a congruent base and the same height.

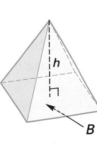

h

B

$V = \frac{1}{3}Bh$

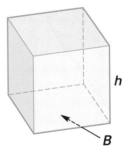

h

B

$V = Bh$

This relationship is true for any pyramid and prism with congruent bases and the same height.

Volume of a Pyramid

The volume *V* of a pyramid with base area *B* and height *h* is

$$V = \frac{1}{3}Bh$$

There is a similar relationship between cones and cylinders. A cone has one-third the volume of a cylinder with a congruent base and the same height. For the cylinder and cone, $B = \pi r^2$.

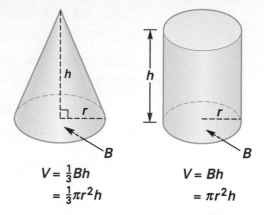

$V = \frac{1}{3}Bh$ $V = Bh$

$= \frac{1}{3}\pi r^2 h$ $= \pi r^2 h$

Volume of a Cone

The volume V of a cone with base area B and height h is

$$V = \frac{1}{3}Bh \quad or \quad V = \frac{1}{3}\pi r^2 h$$

EXAMPLE 2 Finding an Unknown Dimension

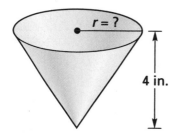

You are designing a cone-shaped paper cup. The height of the cup is 4 inches. The cone must hold 30 cubic inches of water. What radius should you make the base of the cone?

SOLUTION

$$V = \frac{1}{3}\pi r^2 h$$

$$30 = \frac{1}{3}\pi r^2(4)$$

$$\frac{3(30)}{4\pi} = r^2$$

$$r^2 \approx 7.162$$

$$r \approx \sqrt{7.162} \approx 2.676$$

You should make the radius approximately 2.7 inches.

ONGOING ASSESSMENT

A pyramid-shaped paper cup has the same height and volume as Example 2. If the base is a square, what is the length of each edge?

LESSON ASSESSMENT

1 What type of polygon forms the faces of a pyramid? What formula do you use to calculate the area of this polygon?

2 Suppose you are given the radius of the base of a cone and its slant height in meters. What is the most convenient unit of measure for the surface area of the cone? For the volume?

3 Suppose a prism and a pyramid have the same volume. The bases of the prism and pyramid are congruent squares. How are the heights related?

4 Can the height and slant height of a cone be equal? Explain.

Practice and Apply

Find the surface area and volume of each solid.

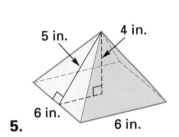

5. (5 in., 4 in., 6 in., 6 in.)

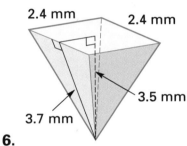

6. (2.4 mm, 2.4 mm, 3.5 mm, 3.7 mm)

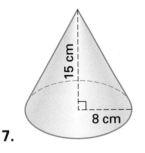

7. (15 cm, 8 cm)

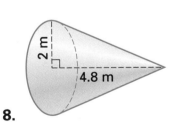

8. (2 m, 4.8 m)

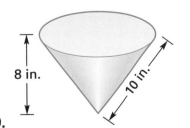

9. (8 in., 10 in.)

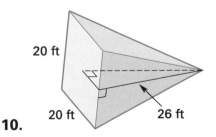

10. (20 ft, 20 ft, 26 ft)

The linear dimensions of the cone and pyramid are the same.

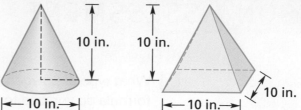

11. Calculate the area of the base of the cone.

12. Calculate the area of the base of the pyramid.

13. Without calculating, predict which solid has the greatest volume. Why did you choose this solid?

I. M. Pei's glass pyramid in Paris has a square base with sides measuring 116 ft. The height of the pyramid is 71 ft.

14. Calculate the slant height l of each face of the pyramid.

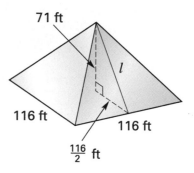

15. Approximately how many square feet of glass were required to build the pyramid? (The base is not glass.)

16. Approximately how many cubic feet are enclosed by the pyramid?

A **tetrahedron** is a pyramid with four triangular faces. A net for a tetrahedron is shown.

17. What is the area of the base?

18. What is the area of each face?

19. What is the surface area of the tetrahedron?

20. What is the volume of the tetrahedron below?

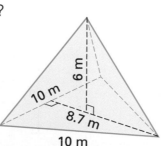

21. Devon uses this funnel to pour oil into his car. Will the funnel hold one quart of oil? (4 qt = 231 in.³)

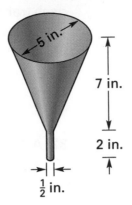

5 in.

7 in.

2 in.

$\frac{1}{2}$ in.

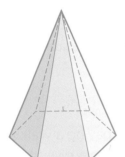

22. What is the name of the solid shown at the left?

23. Sketch a net of the solid.

24. This silo is 65% full. What is the volume of the grain in the silo?

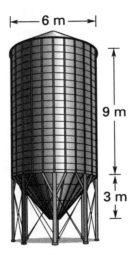

6 m

9 m

3 m

Mixed Review

Write an inequality to describe each graph.

25.

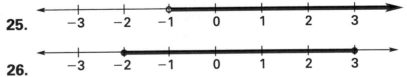

26.

Solve each system by graphing.

27. $y = 2x - 1$

   $y = -2x + 7$

28. $y = -x - 1$

   $y = \frac{1}{2}x + 2$

For Exercises 29–32, plot A(0, 2), B(2, 4), and C(4, 2) on a coordinate plane. Draw the original figure and image after each transformation. Show the coordinates of the image vertices after each transformation.

29. $(x, y) \rightarrow (x + 1, y - 3)$

30. Reflection over the *x*-axis

31. Reflection over the *y*-axis

32. A dilation with scale factor $\frac{1}{2}$

Rectangle *ABCD* is composed of 5 congruent squares. The area of *ABCD* is 245 cm².

33. Find the area of one square.

34. Find the length of one side of one square.

35. Find the perimeter of *ABCD*.

Cumulative Problem Solving

Shaneka is comparing the cost of paving a walkway around a garden. A sketch of the garden and walkway are shown at the left. She is considering using pavers or concrete.

36. Calculate the total area of the walkway to be paved.

37. *Pavers* are like bricks, with the dimensions shown. What is the area of the top surface of each paver? How many pavers are required to cover the walkway?

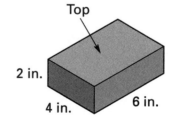

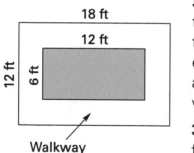

Walkway

38. A contractor will complete the walkway with pavers for $1.50 each. What is the cost of using pavers for the walkway?

39. If concrete is used, it will be poured to a depth of 6 inches. How many cubic feet of concrete are required to pave the walkway? How many cubic yards are required?

40. A contractor will complete the walkway with concrete for $145 per cubic yard. What is the cost of using concrete for the walkway?

41. Will Shaneka spend less money if she uses pavers or concrete?

The basement of a school building floods to a depth of 18 inches. The basement floor is a rectangle that measures 48 feet by 40 feet. For water, 1 ft³ = 7.48 gallons.

42. How many gallons of water are in the basement?

43. If a pump can remove 20 gallons per minute, how long will it take to remove the water from the basement?

You are designing a cone-shaped paper cup to hold 4 fl oz of water. The height of the cup is $3\frac{1}{2}$ inches.

44. What diameter should you use for the cup?
(1 fl oz = 1.805 in.³)

Logan is designing a package for a new bubble gum flavor for market testing. The new package will contain the same amount of bubble gum as the current package. The current package has 10 pieces.

45. How many cubic centimeters of bubble gum are in the current package?

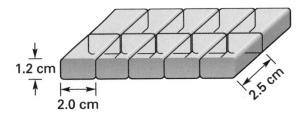

46. Logan's design is a long, thin tape. The width of the tape is 2 cm, and the thickness is 0.1 cm. Calculate the length l of the tape, if it has the same volume as the current package.

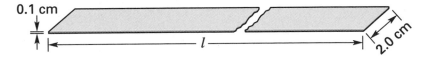

47. The tape is wound into a cylinder. The new package must be large enough to contain this cylinder. What is the approximate radius r of the cylinder?

LESSON 12.6 SIMILAR SOLIDS

In Chapter 11, you learned that similar polygons have the same shape, but not necessarily the same size. In similar polygons, the ratios of all corresponding sides are equal.

Similar solids are solids that have the same shape, but not necessarily the same size. In similar solids, the ratios of all corresponding linear measures (such as edge length, radius, and height) are equal.

These cones are similar because the ratio of the radii equals the ratio of the heights.

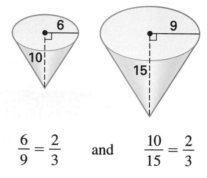

$$\frac{6}{9} = \frac{2}{3} \quad \text{and} \quad \frac{10}{15} = \frac{2}{3}$$

ONGOING ASSESSMENT

Tell if the following pairs of solids are similar. Explain your answer.

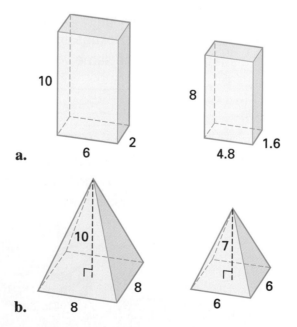

a.

b.

Prism A is a rectangular prism with length l, width w, and height h. Prism B is similar to Prism A.

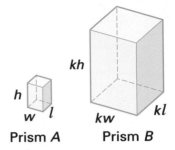

Prism A Prism B

1. What is the ratio of the length of a face of Prism B to the length of the corresponding face of Prism A? This ratio is the scale factor.

2. Write expressions for the surface area and volume of each prism. Simplify the expressions. Record the expressions in a table similar to the one shown. Prism A is recorded as an example.

Length	Width	Height	Surface Area	Volume
l	w	h	$2(hw + wl + hl)$	?
kl	kw	kh	?	?

3. Let S_A and S_B represent the surface areas of Prisms A and B. What is $\frac{S_B}{S_A}$?

4. Let V_A and V_B represent the volumes of Prisms A and B. What is $\frac{V_B}{V_A}$?

5. Repeat Steps 2–4 for similar Cylinders A and B.

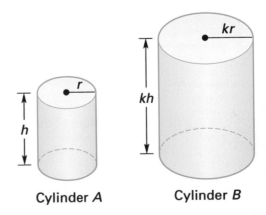

Cylinder A Cylinder B

6. Make a conjecture about the ratio of the surface areas of two similar solids. Make a conjecture about the ratio of the volumes of two similar solids.

Compare your conjectures to the following.

> **Area and Volume of Similar Solids**
> If two solids are similar with a scale factor of $a : b$, then
>
> - the ratio of their surface areas is $a^2 : b^2$
> - the ratio of their volumes is $a^3 : b^3$

EXAMPLE Finding Surface Area and Volume

These detergent boxes are similar rectangular prisms.

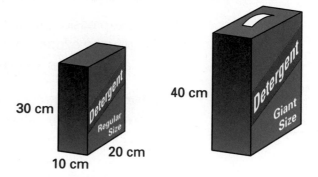

a. What is the scale factor?

b. What is the surface area of the regular-size box?

c. What is the surface area at the giant-size box?

d. What is the volume of the giant-size box?

SOLUTION

a. The scale factor is the ratio of corresponding sides.

$$\frac{\text{Regular size} \rightarrow a}{\text{Giant size} \rightarrow b} = \frac{30}{40} \quad \text{or} \quad \frac{3}{4}$$

b. Let S_R represent the surface area of the regular-size box. S_R is the sum of the areas of the faces.

$$S_R = 2(30 \cdot 10) + 2(10 \cdot 20) + 2(30 \cdot 20)$$
$$= 2(300) + 2(200) + 2(600)$$
$$= 600 + 400 + 1200$$
$$= 2200 \text{ cm}^2$$

The surface area of the regular-size box is 2200 cm².

c. Let S_G represent the surface area of the giant-size box. The ratio of the surface areas $\dfrac{S_R}{S_G}$ is $\dfrac{a^2}{b^2}$.

$$\dfrac{a^2}{b^2} \to \dfrac{3^2}{4^2} = \dfrac{2200}{S_G}$$

$$S_G(3^2) = 2200(4^2)$$

$$S_G = \dfrac{2200(4^2)}{3^2}$$

$$\approx 3911 \text{ cm}^2$$

The surface area of the giant-size box is about 3911 cm^2.

d. Let V_R represent the volume of the regular-size box. V_R is the area of the base times the height.

$$V_R = 10(20)(30)$$

$$= 6000 \text{ cm}^3$$

Let V_G represent the volume of the giant-size box. The ratio of the volumes $\dfrac{V_R}{V_G}$ is $\dfrac{a^3}{b^3}$.

$$\dfrac{a^3}{b^3} \to \dfrac{3^3}{4^3} = \dfrac{6000}{V_G}$$

$$V_G = \dfrac{6000(4^3)}{3^3}$$

$$\approx 14{,}222 \text{ cm}^3$$

The volume of the giant-size box is about $14{,}222 \text{ cm}^3$.

LESSON ASSESSMENT

Think and Discuss

1 Is the following statement *true* or *false*? Explain your answer.

Two prisms are similar if the ratio of the areas of their bases is $a^2 : b^2$.

2 Suppose Cylinder $A \sim$ Cylinder B with a scale factor $A : B$ of $1 : 2$, and Cylinder $B \sim$ Cylinder C with a scale factor $B : C$ of $1 : 3$. Is Cylinder $A \sim$ Cylinder C? If so, what is the scale factor?

3 Can a pyramid be similar to a prism? Explain why or why not.

Match each prism with its similar prism. Write the scale factor (of the numbered prism to the lettered prism) as a ratio, *a* : *b,* and as a decimal.

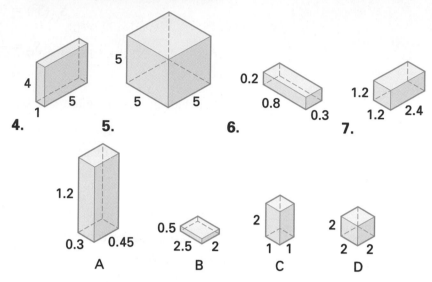

4.   **5.**   **6.**   **7.**

For Exercises 8 and 9, solid *A* ~ solid *B.* Find the surface area and volume of *A.* Then use the scale factor to find the surface area and volume of *B.*

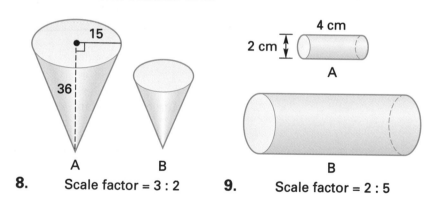

8.   Scale factor = 3 : 2   **9.**   Scale factor = 2 : 5

10. Two waste-water pipes are similar cylinders with a scale factor *A* : *B* of 3 : 2. Pipe *A* can hold 9 gallons of water. How many gallons can Pipe *B* hold?

Darlene is buying a cake for her parents' anniversary party. She has two to choose from. The cakes are similar prisms.

11. What is the scale factor of the smaller cake to the larger cake?

12. The smaller cake costs $40. What is a reasonable price for the larger cake if the price increase is due to surface area increase?

For Exercises 13–18, write *true* or *false*.

13. $7.601 < 7.061$

14. $0.24 < 0.024$

15. $0.37 = 0.3700$

16. $8.7 + 2.6 < 17$

17. $6.38 - 1.38 > 6.38 + 1.38$

18. $3.8 + 5.8 = 4.8 + 4.8$

Margo received the following quiz scores for a nine-week period.

82 87 79 93 82 90 86 88 96

19. Find Margo's mean quiz score.

20. Find Margo's median quiz score.

21. The scale for a model house is 15 feet = 2 inches. If the living room of the house is 20 feet by 30 feet, what will its dimensions be in the model?

22. A bag contains 6 red marbles, 3 blue marbles, and 1 green marble. If you pull one marble from the bag at random, what is the probability that it will be blue or green?

A triangle has vertices at $A(1, 1)$, $B(2, 4)$, and $C(3, 1)$. Give the coordinates of the vertices of the image after each of the following transformations.

23. $(x, y) \rightarrow (x + 2, y - 1)$

24. A reflection over the *x*-axis

25. A dilation with a scale factor of 3 with the center of dilation at the origin

26. The guy wire on a 100-foot tower is anchored 75 feet from the base of the tower. How long is the guy wire?

An S-gauge model train is a reduction of an actual train using a scale factor of 1 : 64.

27. A triple-bay coal car, model HTe, built by the Reading Company, is 45 feet long. How long is the S-gauge model of the HTe coal car?

28. The HTe coal car has a capacity of 3422 cubic feet. What is the capacity of the model?

A civil engineer designs an elevated-highway support. She sketches a design for the support on isometric dot paper, using a scale of 1 grid unit = 5 feet.

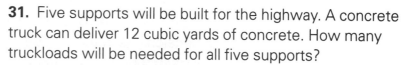

29. Make an orthographic drawing showing the top, front, and side views of the support.

30. Calculate the volume, in cubic yards, of concrete needed for each support.

31. Five supports will be built for the highway. A concrete truck can deliver 12 cubic yards of concrete. How many truckloads will be needed for all five supports?

A museum has a temporary display of ancient Egyptian artifacts. To advertise the display, you have been asked to construct a scale model of the Great Pyramid of Egypt for the entrance to the museum. The model should be 40 feet high.

32. The Great Pyramid has a height of 480 feet, and a square base measuring 755 feet on a side. What scale factor should you use for the model?

33. If you use plywood for the faces of the model, how many square feet of plywood will you need?

MATH LAB

Activity 1: Packaging Softballs

Equipment   Softball
Compass
Tape
Centimeter ruler
Scissors
Cloth tape measure
Two sheets of poster board

Problem Statement

Manufacturers design efficient packages that are the right size for their products. The less wasted volume in a package, the more money a company saves. Packaging material is expensive, and it usually ends up in a landfill or a recycling plant. Therefore, reducing the amount of material required is good economics and good for the environment.

In this Activity, you will construct two types of packaging for a softball. One package has the shape of a cube. The other has the shape of a cylinder or a tube. You will construct the minimum size of each package for a softball. You will also determine which of the two types of packages uses less material.

Should a ball be packaged in a box or a tube?

A softball has the shape of a
sphere. A **sphere** is the set of all
points in space that are the
same distance from a given
point, called the **center.**

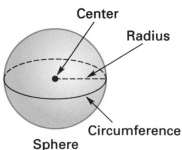

Center
Radius
Circumference
Sphere

Procedure

a Measure the circumference of the softball. Calculate the diameter. Record this value in a data table similar to the one shown.

Softball Packaging Data

Measurement/Calculation	Values
Diameter of the softball	
Edge of the box	
Diameter of the tube	
Height of the tube	
Circumference of the tube	
Surface area of the box	
Surface area of the tube	

b To allow for size variation in manufacturing, add 0.2 cm to the diameter of the softball. Use this length for the edge of the box, the diameter of the tube, and the height of the tube. Record these values in the data table.

c On one sheet of poster board, draw the net for the box.

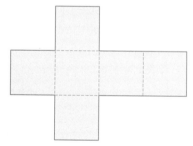

d Cut out the box. Fold the net along the dotted lines. Tape the edges together. Leave one side of the box open for a lid.

e Calculate and record the circumference of the tube.

f On the other sheet of poster board, draw the net for the tube.

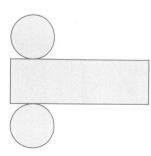

g Cut out the tube. Tape the edges together. Leave one end of the tube open for a lid.

h Put the softball in the box and then in the tube. Does the ball fit in both containers with little wasted space?

i Calculate and record the surface areas of the box and the tube.

Discussion Questions

1. Which container uses less material, the box or the tube?

2. If you use the container with the smallest surface area to package 100,000 softballs, how many square centimeters of packaging material will you save over the other container?

3. The volume V of a sphere is given by the formula $V = \frac{4}{3}\pi r^3$. What is the volume of the softball? Calculate the volume of the box and the tube. If the box and tube each hold a softball, which container has the smallest unoccupied volume?

4. List reasons a company might choose to package softballs in cubical rather than cylindrical containers.

Activity 2: Volume Relationships

Equipment   Open-top cylindrical can
Paper (construction paper or
    notebook paper)
Ruler
Cloth tape measure
Compass
Protractor
Tape
Peas, beans, popcorn, or similar-sized
    objects (enough to fill the
    cylindrical can)

Problem Statement

You will construct a cone whose base and height match those of a given cylinder. You will determine the relationship between the volumes of the cone and cylinder.

Procedure

a Measure the circumference and height of the cylindrical can. Calculate the radius. Record the values in a table similar to the one on the next page.

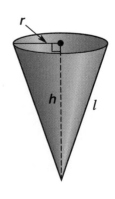

Measurement/Calculation	Values
Diameter, d	
Radius, r	
Height, h	
Slant height, l	
Central angle, x	

b You will construct a cone with the same radius and height. Calculate the slant height l of the cone. Record the value.

c The net for the lateral surface of the cone has a central angle, x. This angle is a sector of a circle whose radius is l. The length along the curved part of the sector (called the **arc length**) is the circumference of the cone's base, $2\pi r$. To calculate the value of x in degrees, use a proportion.

$$\frac{\text{Sector}}{\text{Full circle}} \begin{array}{c} \rightarrow \\ \rightarrow \end{array} \frac{x}{360°} = \frac{2\pi r}{2\pi l}$$

$$x = 360° \cdot \frac{r}{l}$$

d Draw the net for the lateral surface of the cone on a piece of notebook paper or construction paper.

e Cut out the net. Fold the paper into a cone, so that the edges just touch. Tape the edges together.

f Fill the cone with peas, level to the top. Pour the peas into the cylinder. Repeat until the cylinder is full. How many full cones are required to fill the cylinder?

g Write the relationship between the volume of the cone V_{cone} and the volume of the cylinder V_{cyl}.

h Compare your results with the rest of the class.

Discussion Questions

1. Did the size of the can affect the results of Steps **g** and **h**?

2. The volume of a cylinder is given by this formula.

$$V_{cyl} = \pi r^2 h$$

Write a formula for the volume of a cone.

$$V_{cone} = \underline{\ ?\ }$$

Equipment   Spreadsheet computer program

Problem Statement

Two solids are similar if the ratios of corresponding dimensions are the same. This ratio is the scale factor. For example, two similar prisms are shown, with a scale factor of 2 : 1.

In this Activity, you will use a spreadsheet to calculate the ratio of surface areas and volumes of similar solids. You will also see how these ratios are related to the scale factor.

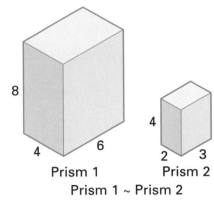

Prism 1   Prism 2

Prism 1 ~ Prism 2

Procedure

a   Set up a spreadsheet with labels as shown.

= D2*B2

	A	B	C	D	E	F	G	H
1	**Prism 1**					**Prism 2**		
2	Length =		$k =$			Length =		
3	Width =		$k^2 =$			Width =		
4	Height =		$k^3 =$			Height =		
5								
6		**Surface Area**	**Volume**		**SA 2 : SA 1**	**Vol 2 : Vol 1**		
7	Prism 1							
8	Prism 2							
9								
10								

= 2*B2*B3 + 2*B2*B4 + 2*B3*B4   = B8/B7

b   You will enter given dimensions for Prism 1, and calculate the dimensions of Prism 2 so that Prism 2 ~ Prism 1. Let k be the scale factor, or the ratio of corresponding dimensions of Prism 2 to Prism 1. The value of k will be entered in cell D2. Enter formulas to calculate k^2 and k^3.

c   Enter formulas to calculate the dimensions of Prism 2. The first is shown as an example.

d   Enter formulas to calculate the surface areas of the prisms. The first is shown as an example.

e Enter formulas to calculate the volumes of the prisms.

f Enter a formula to calculate the ratio of the surface areas and another formula to calculate the ratio of the volumes of the prisms.

g Use the toolbar commands *Format / Cells / Number / Fraction* so that cells D2–D4 and E7–F7 display entries as fractions up to three digits.

h Copy the table.

Trial	Prism 1 l	w	h	k	k^2	k^3	SA 2 : SA 1	Vol 2 : Vol 1
1	2	3	4	2				
2	2	3	4	3				
3	9	6	12	2				
4	9	6	12	$\frac{1}{2}$				
5	9	6	12	$\frac{4}{3}$				
6								
7								
8								

i Enter values from the spreadsheet for the dimensions of Prism 1 and k shown in the table for Trial 1. Record the values calculated by the spreadsheet for k^2, k^3, SA 2 : SA 1, and Vol 2 : Vol 1.

j Repeat Step **h** for Trials 2–5 listed in the table. Add three additional trials using your own values.

k Change the spreadsheet, and prepare a new data table to compare the surface area and volume of two similar cylinders, cones, or square pyramids.

Discussion Questions

1. What is the relationship between k^2 and SA 2 : SA 1?

2. What is the relationship between k^3 and Vol 2 : Vol 1?

3. Suppose the ratio between corresponding dimensions of two similar solids is 4 : 1. What is the ratio of their surface areas? What is the ratio of their volumes?

CHAPTER 12 ASSESSMENT

Communicate

1. How are orthographic projections used to show a three-dimensional object?

2. How do you find the surface area of a prism?

3. What geometric figures form the net for a cylinder?

4. How are the formulas for the volume of a prism and the volume of a cylinder similar?

5. Two similar solids have a scale factor of $\frac{a}{b}$. What is the ratio of their surface areas?

Skills

6. Create an isometric drawing from the orthographic projections shown.

7. Use isometric dot paper to draw a cube with edge lengths of 5 units.

8. Create a one-point perspective drawing of a three-dimensional block letter T.

Top

Front

Side

Find the surface area of each solid.

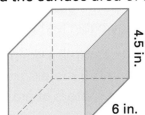
4.5 in.
6 in.
9. 5 in.

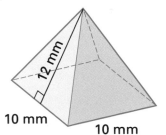
12 mm
10 mm   10 mm
10.

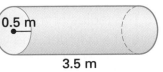
0.5 m
3.5 m
11.

25 cm
12. 15 cm   15 cm

Find the volume of each solid.

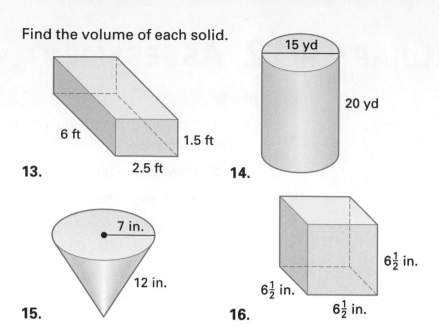

13.

14.

15.

16.

17. The scale factor of two similar rectangular prisms is 2 : 1. The volume of the larger prism is 60 cm³. What is the volume of the smaller prism?

Applications

18. A cardboard container has the shape of a rectangular prism. How many cubic feet of cardboard are needed to make the box if its length is 2.5 feet, its width is 4 feet, and its height is 3 feet?

19. An outdoor light post has a cylindrical concrete base. The diameter of the base is 2.5 feet and the height is 3.5 feet. How many cubic feet of concrete are needed for the base?

20. The bottom of a grain silo is cone-shaped. The diameter of the cone is 5 meters and the height is 5.75 meters. How many cubic meters of grain will this part of the silo hold?

Math Lab

21. The diameter of a softball is 9.71 cm. What are the dimensions of a box that will just hold the softball? What is the volume of this box?

22. The radius of the base and the height of a cone match those of a cylinder. The volume of the cone is 100 in.³ What is the volume of the cylinder?

23. Each side of a prism is increased by a factor of 1.5. Describe the surface area of the enlargement.

Bridges

to Algebra and Geometry

Second Edition

Mathematics In Context

Reference Section

Tables of Measures

TIME

60 seconds (s)	1 minute (min)
60 minutes	1 hour (h)
24 hours	1 day
7 days	1 week
4 weeks (approx.)	1 month
365 days 52 weeks (approx.) 12 months	1 year
10 years	1 decade
100 years	1 century

METRIC LENGTH

10 millimeters (mm)	1 centimeter (cm)
100 cm 1000 mm	1 meter (m)
1000 m	1 kilometer (km)

U. S. CUSTOMARY LENGTH

12 inches (in.)	1 foot (ft)
36 in. 3 ft	1 yard (yd)
5280 ft 1760 yd	1 mile (m)

METRIC AREA

100 square millimeters (mm^2)	1 square centimeter (cm^2)
10,000 cm^2	1 square meter (m^2)
10,000 m^2	1 hectare (ha)

U. S. CUSTOMARY AREA

144 square inches (in^2)	1 square foot (ft^2)
9 ft^2	1 square yard (yd^2)
43,560 ft^2 4840 yd^2	1 acre (A)

METRIC VOLUME

1000 cubic millimeters (mm^3)	1 cubic centimeter (cm^3)
1,000,000 cm^3	1 cubic meter (m^3)

U. S. CUSTOMARY VOLUME

1728 cubic inches (in^3)	1 cubic foot (ft^3)
27 ft^3	1 cubic yard (yd^3)

METRIC LIQUID CAPACITY

1000 milliliters (mL)	1 liter (L)
1000 L	1 kiloliter (kL)

U. S. CUSTOMARY LIQUID CAPACITY

8 fluid ounces (fl oz)	1 cup (c)
2 c	1 pint (pt)
2 pt	1 quart (qt)
4 qt	1 gallon (gal)

METRIC MASS

1000 milligrams (mg)	1 gram (gm)
1000 g	1 kilogram (kg)
1000 kg	1 metric ton (t)

U. S. CUSTOMARY WEIGHT

16 ounces (oz)	1 pound (lb)
2000 lb	1 ton (t)

Glossary

Absolute value The distance of a number from zero on a number line. (131)

Acute triangle A triangle with three angles whose measures are between 0° and 90°. (473)

Addition equation An equation that models the addition of one or more quantities. (186)

Addition Property of Equality When you add the same quantity to both sides of an equation, the equation stays equal and balanced. (189)

Additive identity Zero is called the additive identity because when you add zero the value of the original quantity remains unchanged. Example: 5 + 0 = 5 (26)

Adjacent angles Two angles in the same plane that share a common side and a common vertex but have no interior point in common. (468)

Algebraic expression A mathematical sentence involving at least one variable. (16)

Angle The figure formed by two rays with a common endpoint. (462)

Angle-Sum Property of Triangles The sum of the measures of the angles in a triangle is 180°. (474)

Approximate An estimate that is close to a solution but not exact. (11)

Area The amount of space inside a flat shape, such as a triangle or a circle. (605)

Associative Property of Addition When you add several terms, you can change the way they are grouped without changing the answer. Example:
5 + (3 + 17) = (5 + 3) + 17 (25)

Associative Property of Multiplication When you multiply several terms, you can change the way they are grouped without changing the answer. Example:
5 · (3 · 17) = (5 · 3) · 17 (37)

Axis Two perpendicular number lines that are used to locate points on a coordinate plane. (400)

Base Whenever a number is raised to a power, that number is called the base.
Example: in $2^3 = 8$, 2 is the base (524)

Base of a parallelogram Either pair of parallel sides. (606)

Base-ten system The number system in which numbers are written in decimal notation. (4)

Binomial The sum of two monomials. (631)

Bisector A ray, line, or plane that divides a geometric figure into two congruent figures, each having one-half the measure of the original. (516)

Box-and-whisker plot A type of diagram or graph that shows the quartiles and extreme values of data. (85)

Center of dilation The point about which a transformation is mapped. (593)

Circle The set of all points in a plane equidistant from a given point. (622)

Circle graph A graph in which information is represented using a circle that is cut into sectors to show values of a particular category. Also called *pie chart*. (357)

Circumference The distance around a circle, starting at one point, going around the circle once, and ending up at the same point you started. (622)

Collinear points Points that lie on the same line. (463)

Common denominator A multiple of all the denominators in a problem. (248)

Common factors Whole numbers that divide into each number in a set of two or more numbers with no remainder. (238)

Commutative Property of Addition When you add several terms, you change the order of addition without affecting the final answer. Example: $23 + 6 = 6 + 23$. (24)

Commutative Property of Multiplication When you multiply several terms, you can change the order of multiplication without affecting the final answer. Example: $23 \cdot 6 = 6 \cdot 23$. (36)

Complementary angles Two angles whose measures have a sum of 90°. Each angle is called the complement of the other. (468)

Complements When the sum of two percents is 100%, the percents are called complements. (376)

Compound interest Interest computed using both the principal and any previously accrued interest. (382)

Cone A three-dimensional figure that consists of a circular face, called the *base*, a point called the *vertex* that is not in the plane of the base, and a *lateral surface* that connects the vertex to each point on the boundary of the base. (671)

Congruent figures Two geometric figures that have the same size and shape. (473)

Congruent polygons Two polygons are congruent if their corresponding parts are congruent. (489)

Conjecture A guess based on several observations. (474)

Conversion factor A factor by which one unit can be converted to another. (300)

Coordinate A number that is used to tell where a point is located on a graph. The ordered pair $(7, 2)$ gives two coordinates that locate a unique point in the Cartesian coordinate system. (130)

Coordinate plane The plane containing the x- and y-axes. (400)

Corresponding angles A pair of angles in similar locations in relation to a transversal intersecting parallel lines. When a transversal cuts parallel lines, the corresponding angles are congruent. (489)

Corresponding sides Any pair of sides in the same relative positions in two similar figures. (489)

Counting Principle To find the number of possible outcomes for an event that has different stages, multiply the number of choices in each stage of the event. (318)

Cross-Products Property If $\frac{a}{b} = \frac{c}{d}, b \neq 0, d \neq 0$, then $ad = bc$. (295)

Cylinder A three-dimensional figure that consists of two parallel congruent circular regions, called *bases*, and a *lateral surface* that connects the boundaries of the bases. (656)

Data set A group of related facts expressed as numbers. (70)

Decimal A number that uses place value and a decimal point to show values less than one, such as tenths and hundredths. (4)

Decimal percent A percent written as a decimal. Example: $60\% = 0.6$ (354)

Degree A unit of measurement equal to $\frac{1}{360}$ of a complete revolution. (466)

Dependent event Two events are dependent if the outcome of the first event affects the second event. (322)

Diagonal of a polygon A segment joining two nonconsecutive vertices. (482)

Diameter A line segment passing through the center of a circle and has both endpoints on the circle.(622)

Dilation A dilation with center at the origin and positive scale factor k, is a transformation in which every point (a, b) has an image point (ka, kb). The mapping is $(a, b) \rightarrow (ka, kb)$. (593)

Distributive Property The distributive property states that $a(b + c) = ab + ac$ for all values of $a, b,$ and c. Example: $5(3 + 2) = 5 \cdot 3 + 5 \cdot 2$. (38)

Division equation An equation that models the division of one or more quantities. (193)

Division Property of Equality When you divide both sides of an equation by the same nonzero quantity, the equation stays balanced. (192)

Domain The set of all input values for a function; the allowable values of the independent variable. (439)

Enlargement A dilation with scale factor k such that $k > 1$. (593)

Equal ratios Ratios that represent the same comparison. (295)

Equiangular triangle A triangle with three congruent angles. (473)

Equilateral triangle A triangle with three congruent sides. (473)

Equivalent fractions Two or more fractions that name the same amount. Example: $\frac{2}{4}$ and $\frac{1}{2}$ name the same amount. (236)

Estimate A number which is near another number. Also called *approximation*. (11)

Event A collection of possible outcomes of an experiment. (311)

Experimental probability A probability calculation based on the collection of data. (327)

Exponent A quantity representing the power to which a base is raised. Example: in $2^3 = 8$, 3 is the exponent; it means $2 \cdot 2 \cdot 2$, or 8. (524)

Faces The sides of a solid. (649)

Formula An equation that expresses a relationship between at least two variables. (217)

Fraction A number that names part of a whole or part of a group. (236)

Frequency The number of times an event or data value occurs. In a frequency table, the sum of the tally marks in each row is the frequency of the counts. (77)

Frequency polygon A line graph formed by drawing a fitted line through the midpoints of the tops of each bar in a histogram. (102)

Frequency table A table that shows the frequency and the cumulative frequency of data. (76)

Function A relation between two variables such as x and y where there is one and only one possible value of y for any given value of x. (441)

Function rule A way of describing a function in words, in arrow notation, or in function notation. (443)

Greater than When comparing two numbers, the number with the higher value is greater. Example: $4 > 3$ (7)

Greatest common factor (GCF) The greatest common factor of two or more integers is the greatest number that is a factor of all the integers. (238)

Height of a parallelogram The perpendicular distance between bases. (606)

Histogram A bar graph that shows the frequency of data from the heights of the bars. (93)

Hypotenuse In a right triangle, the side opposite the right angle. It is always the longest side. (557)

Identity An equation whose solution is the set of all numbers. (213)

Identity Property of Addition The sum of any number and zero is the original number. Example: $5 + 0 = 5$ (26)

Identity Property of Multiplication The product of any number and one is that number. Example: $5 \cdot 1 = 5$ (37)

Image The figure resulting from a transformation. (495)

Improper fraction A fraction that has a numerator greater than or equal to its denominator. (254)

Independent event Two events are independent if the outcome of the first event does not affect the second event. (322)

Inequality A sentence comparing unequal quantities with one of the following symbols: $\neq, <, >, \leq, \geq$. (273)

Input A value of the domain of a function. (443)

Integer A number with no fractional part. The numbers $\ldots -2, -1, 0, 1, 2 \ldots$ represent the set of integers. (129)

Irrational number A number whose decimal representation never terminates, or repeats. (553)

Isometric drawing A drawing of a three-dimensional object in which parallel edges of the object are shown as parallel line segments in the drawing. (643)

Isosceles triangle A triangle with two congruent sides. (473)

Least common denominator (LCD) The least common multiple of the denominators of two or more fractions. (248)

Leg Either of the two sides of a right triangle adjacent to the right angle. (557)

Less than When comparing two numbers, the number with lower value is less. Example: $4 < 5$. (7)

Like terms Terms that contain exactly the same variables raised to the same exponents. Example: $3x^2$ and $-2x^2$ are like terms (203)

Line graph A graph that uses a line to show how data change over a period of time. (100)

Line of reflection The line over which a transformation of a figure is reflected. (501)

Line plot Numerical data displayed on a number line. (76)

Linear equation An equation written in the form $y = mx + b$, where m and b are constants. The graph of a linear equation is a straight line. (406)

Literal equation An equation in which the constants are represented by letters. Example: $ax + b = c$ (219)

Magnitude The numerical value or length of a vector. (154)

Mean The sum of the data values in a data set divided by the number of data values. (70)

Measures of central tendency Numbers used to describe sets of data because they represent a centralized, or middle, value. (70)

Median The middle value of an ordered set of data. For an even number of values, the median is the average of the two middle values. (34, 70)

Mode The number(s) that occurs most often in a data set. (70)

Monomial A monomial is a number, a variable, or a product of a number and one or more variables. (631)

Multiple A number that is the product of a given number and another whole number. (248)

Multiplication equation An equation that models the multiplication of one or more quantities. (192)

Multiplication Property of Equality When you multiply both sides of an equation by the same quantity, the equation remains balanced. (194)

Multiplication Property of Inequality You can multiply both sides of an inequality by a positive number without changing the inequality sign. But if you multiply both sides by a negative number, you must reverse the inequality sign. (279)

Multiplicative identity One is the multiplicative identity because when you multiply any quantity by one, the result is the same quantity. Example: $5 \cdot 1 = 5$ (37)

Net A two-dimensional pattern you can form into a three-dimensional figure. (649)

Numerical expression A mathematical expression that contains no variables. (16)

Obtuse angle An angle whose measure is between 90° and 180°. (473)

Opposites Two numbers are opposite if they are the same distance from zero.
Example: 5 and −5 are opposites (130)

Ordered pair A pair of numbers enclosed by parentheses and separated by a comma. The ordered pair represents a unique point in the Cartesian coordinate plane. Example: (2, 1) is an ordered pair; it is represented by the point 2 units to the right and 1 unit up from the origin (120, 400)

Origin The point in the Cartesian coordinate system where the axes cross and where the values of both x and y are zero. (400)

Orthographic projection A projection that depicts a three-dimensional object by detailing three views of the object. (642)

Outcome Outcomes are all possible combinations of a counting problem. (311)

Outlier A value of a data set that is much greater or much less than the rest of the data and thus affects the mean of the data. (72)

Output A value of the range of a function. (443)

Parallelogram A quadrilateral with both pairs of opposite sides parallel. (497)

Percent Part of 100. Example: 60% is 60 out of 100; 60% = 0.60 = 0.6 (348)

Percent change The ratio of the amount a quantity changes to its original amount. (374)

Perfect square A rational number whose square root is a rational number. (551)

Perimeter The distance around a figure. (217)

Perimeter of a polygon The sum of the measures of the sides of a polygon. (481)

Perpendicular Lines that intersect to form right angles are perpendicular. (501)

Perpendicular bisector A line, ray, or segment that is perpendicular to the given segment at its midpoint. (516)

Perspective drawing A drawing that makes a two-dimensional image look like a three-dimensional object. (644)

Polygon A plane figure formed by three or more consecutive segments. The segments form the sides of the polygon. Each side intersects exactly two other sides at its endpoints. The intersections are the *vertices* of the polygon. No three consecutive vertices of a polygon are collinear. (480)

Polyhedron A three-dimensional figure that is bounded by polygonal faces that enclose a region of space. (652)

Positive sign A plus in front of a number that shows that the number's value is greater than zero. Example: +3 (128)

Power When you multiply the base b by itself n times, the product is the nth power of b. Example: the third power of 2 is 2^3, or 8 (524)

Prime number A positive integer whose only positive integer divisors are itself and 1. (286)

Prism A polyhedron with two polygonal faces lying in parallel planes and with the other faces parallelograms. (649)

Probability of Dependent Events If A and B are dependent events, $P(A$ and $B) = P(A) \cdot P(B \mid A)$. (324)

Probability of Independent Events If A and B are independent events, $P(A$ and $B) = P(A) \cdot P(B)$. (323)

Proportion A mathematical sentence stating that one ratio is equal to another. Example: $\frac{a}{b} = \frac{c}{d}$, where $b \neq 0$ and $d \neq 0$ (295)

Pyramid A polyhedron with a polygon for its base and triangles with a common vertex as its faces. (670)

Pythagorean Theorem In a right triangle, the square of the length of the hypotenuse equals the sum of the squares of the lengths of the two legs. (558)

Quadrants The Cartesian coordinate plane is divided into four regions by the axes; these regions are called quadrants. (400)

Radius A line segment with one endpoint at the center of the circle and the other endoint on the circle. (622)

Random numbers Numbers chosen without preference to ensure outcomes are unbiased. Random numbers are listed in many books and can be generated by calculators or computer spreadsheets. (328)

Range The set of all outputs for a function; the possible values of the dependent variable. The interval in which all the data lie, found by calculating the difference between the data points with the largest and the smallest values. (76, 439)

Rate A ratio that compares two unlike quantities. Example: miles per hour (299)

Ratio The quotient of two quantities with the same units. (294)

Rational number Any number that can be written as a ratio of two integers with the second integer not equal to zero. Integers, terminating decimals, and repeating decimals are all rational numbers. (247)

Real numbers The set of all rational and irrational numbers combined is called the set of real numbers. (554)

Reciprocal If the product of two numbers is one, the numbers are reciprocals. A number's reciprocal is also called its multiplicative inverse. (266)

Reciprocal Property If a and b are nonzero whole numbers, the reciprocal of $\frac{a}{b}$ is $\frac{b}{a}$ and $\frac{a}{b} \cdot \frac{b}{a} = 1$. (266)

Reduction A dilation with scale factor k such that $0 < k < 1$. (593)

Reflection A reflection over a line l is a transformation that maps every point P to a point P' such that: (1) if P is not on l, then l is the perpendicular bisector of PP'; (2) if P is on l, then P' is P. Line l is the *line of reflection*, and P' is the reflection image of P. (501)

Regular polygon A polygon that is both equilateral and equiangular. (481)

Regular tessellation A tessellation in which each shape is a regular polygon and all the shapes are congruent. (519)

Repeating decimal A decimal that, after some point, consists of an infinite number of repetitions of the same number sequence. Example: $2\frac{2}{3} = 2.666\ldots$ (242)

Resultant The one vector that represents the combination of two or more vectors. (155)

Right angle An angle whose measure is 90°. (469)

Rigid motion A transformation that does not change the size or shape of a figure. (496)

Rise The vertical change in a line between two points, found by calculating the difference between the y values of the points. (413)

Rotation A rotation through $a°$ about a point O is a transformation that maps every point P to a point P' such that : (1) if point P is different from point O, then $OP' = OP$ and m$\angle POP' = a°$; (2) if point P is point O, then P' is P. Point O is the *center of rotation*, $a°$ is the *angle of rotation*, and P' is the rotation image of P. (506)

Rounding To make an estimate to a particular decimal place by either rounding up or down depending on which estimate the exact value is closest to. (11)

Run The horizontal change in a line between two points, calculated as the difference between the x values of the points. (413)

Sample A part of a statistical population whose properties are studied to gain information about the whole. (333)

Sample space The set of all possible outcomes of an event. (316)

Scale A ratio called a scale is used when making a model to represent something that is too large or too small to be conveniently drawn at actual size. (599)

Scale drawing A reduced or enlarged drawing of an object. (599)

Scale factor The ratio by which the original dimensions of a figure are multiplied to enlarge or reduce the figure. (593)

Scalene triangle A triangle with no congruent sides. (473)

Scatter plot Two sets of data plotted as ordered pairs in a coordinate plane. (121)

Scientific notation A shorthand way of writing very large or small numbers such that they are represented by a number greater than or equal to one and less than ten multiplied by a power of ten written in exponential form. Example: $3{,}700{,}000 = 3.7 \times 10^6$ (536)

Second quartile The median of a data set. (85)

Sequence A set of numbers or objects arranged in a pattern. (578)

Side One of the segments that make up a polygon; one of the rays of an angle; one of the faces of a solid. (462)

Similar figures Figures that have the same shape, but not necessarily the same size, are similar. (584)

Similar solids Solids that have the same shape, but not necessarily the same size. (679)

Simple interest Interest calculated only on the original principal. (381)

Simulation When it is very difficult or impossible to calculate the probability of an event, a similar event can be created or simulated and tested to represent the actual event. (328)

Slant height On a cone, the distance from the vertex to the base, along the lateral surface. (672)

Slope The ratio of the rise of a line to its run; slope can be thought of as the "steepness" of the line. (414)

Slope-intercept form The graph of a linear equation written in the form $y = mx + b$ has m as its slope and b as its y-intercept. (420)

Solution A value of a variable that makes an open sentence true. (250)

Sphere The set of all points in a space that are a given distance from a given point. The given point is the *center* of the sphere, and the given distance is the *radius*. (686)

Square number A number raised to the second power. Example: 5^2 is five squared (582)

Square pyramid A pyramid with a square base. (670)

Square root The square root of a is a number which multiplied times itself gives a. The square root of a is written $\sqrt{a}$. Example: the square root of 25, $\sqrt{25}$, is 5 (552)

Stacked-bar graph A graph that compares two similar data sets with stacked bars. (98)

Statistics The branch of mathematics that deals with collecting, organizing, and analyzing data. (69)

Stem-and-leaf plot A method to display data in which each data value is separated into two numbers that are used to form a stem and leaf. (80)

Subtraction equation An equation that models the subtraction of one or more quantities. (188)

Subtraction Property of Equality If the same quantity is subtracted from both sides of an equation, then the equation stays balanced. (187)

Supplementary angles Two angles whose measures have a sum of 180°. Each angle is called the supplement of the other. (468)

Surface area The sum of the areas of the faces of a solid. (650)

Term A number in a sequence. A quantity combined as a whole with other quantities by addition. Example: in $5x^3 - 4$, $5x^3$ and 4 are terms. (203, 578)

Terminating decimal A decimal in which the sequence of digits after the decimal point comes to an end.
Example: $\frac{3}{4} = 0.75$ (242)

Tessellation A design that completely covers a plane region with nonoverlapping shapes. (511)

Tetrahedron A pyramid with four triangular faces. (675)

Theoretical probability A ratio comparing the number of ways a successful outcome can occur to the total number of possible outcomes. (311)

Transformation A correspondence between one figure, called a preimage, and a second figure, its image, such that each point of the preimage is paired with exactly one point of the image, and each point of the image is paired with exactly one point of the preimage. (495)

Translation A slide of a figure from one location to another. (495)

Translation rule A rule for finding the coordinates of a translated image based on the fact that every point on the original image slides the same number of units. (496)

Transversal A line that intersects two or more coplanar lines each in a different point. (517)

Triangle Inequality Property The sum of the lengths of any two sides of a triangle is greater than the length of the third side. (514)

Triangular numbers A sequence of numbers starting with 1 and adding 2, then 3, then 4, and so on. Example: The first five triangular numbers are 1, 3, 6, 10, 15. (579)

Unit fraction A fraction with 1 in its numerator and a positive integer in its denominator. (262)

Unit rate A comparison to one unit. (299)

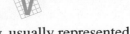

Variable A quantity, usually represented by a letter, that can take on different values. (16)

Vector A quantity having both magnitude and direction, often represented by an arrow. (154)

Vertex The point two sides of a polygon have in common. The point of intersection of the sides of an angle. (462)

Vertical angles Two angles whose sides form two pairs of opposite rays. (488)

Volume The amount of space enclosed by an object. (663)

Whole number Any of the numbers 0, 1, 2, 3, ... (4)

X-axis The horizontal axis of the Cartesian coordinate system. (400)

X-coordinate The first number in an ordered pair. It tells how far to the right or left of the origin a point is located. (400)

X-intercept The x-coordinate of the point at which a line crosses the x-axis. (419)

Y-axis The vertical axis of the Cartesian coordinate system. (400)

Y-coordinate The second number in an ordered pair. It tells how far up or down from the origin a point is located. (400)

Y-intercept The y-coordinate of the point at which a line crosses the y-axis. (419)

Zero pair Since the sum of opposites is zero, they are called a zero pair. You can add or subtract zero pairs without altering values of an equation. (142)

Selected Answers

This section contains selected answers to the **Practice and Apply** and **Mixed Review** Sections.

Chapter 1 Decimals and Problem Solving

Lesson 1.1, Pages 4–10

5. 3.356 **7.** hundredths **9.** ten-thousandths **11.** >
13. > **15.** > **17.** fifteen ten-thousandths
19. 0.625 **21.** Tuesday
22.–25.

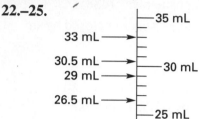

33 mL →
30.5 mL →
29 mL →
26.5 mL →

35 mL
30 mL
25 mL

27. Mei, Lana, Nancy, Mary **29.** 682 **31.** 744.44
33. $157.19 **35.** 90 **37.** $1827 **39.** $4704

Lesson 1.2, Pages 11–15

5. a. 13.0 **b.** 13.05 **7. a.** 0.4 **b.** 0.36 **9. a.** 8.5
b. 8.49 **11.** hundred-thousandths **13.** 170.18;
170.2 **15.** 18.9695 s; 19.0 s **17.** 136.4 kg
19. thousandths **21.** ten-thousandths **23.** <

Lesson 1.3, Pages 16–23

5. $p + 8$ **7.** $\$18 + s$ **9.** 46 **11.** $18 \div (4 + 5) \cdot 7 + 6$
13. 11 **15.** 10 **17.** 12 **19.** 16 **21.** 36 **23.** 18
25. $\frac{96}{12}$; 8 cartons **27.** $\$74.99 \cdot 0.085 = \$6.37$
29. hundredths **31.** 2.301 **33.** 12.52; 12.45; 12.42

Lesson 1.4, Pages 24–28

5. 5 **7.** 0 **9.** Associative Property of Addition
11. Identity Property of Addition **13.** Associative
Property of Addition **15.** Associative Property of
Addition **17.** 28 **19.** 40 **21.** 200 **23.** 38 grams
25. 0 grams **27.** 216.3 **29.** 7.83 **31.** 119.08
33. 54 **35.** 2 **37.** 6 **39.** 0

Lesson 1.5, Pages 29–35

5. $60 **7.** $160 **9.** 11,700 **11.** $1800 **13.** $6.00
15. $1 **17.** $7.00 (rounding to nearest dollar)

19. about $80; $74.89; reasonable **21.** about $3;
$2.45; reasonable **23.** 0.000001 **25.** 17.018,
17.088, 17.108 **27.** 108 **29.** Identity Property of
Addition **31.** Commutative Property of Addition

Lesson 1.6, Pages 36–41

5. 3 **7.** 1 **9.** Associative Property of Multiplication
11. Identity Property of Multiplication
13. Associative Property of Multiplication
15. Distributive Property **17.** 72 **19.** $40q$ **21.** 193
23. $7(10 + 8) = 126$ **25.** $3(40 + 8) = 144$
27. $5(400 + 50 + 2) = 2260$ **29.** $39.57
31. 648 cubic feet **33.** hundredths **35.** about 3000
feet; 3349 feet

Lesson 1.7, Pages 42–48

5. about 2 **7.** about $1200 **9.** about $10
11. $1866.97; about $1790 **13.** $3162.20; about
$3200 **15.** 273; about 200 or 300 **17.** $1.35;
about $1.50 **19.** 190 years; about 190 years
21. 196.85 in.; about 200 in. **23.** $378.18; about
$330 **25.** nine and seventy-eight hundredths
27. 149,000,000, 263,000,000, 937,000,000,
1,203,000,000 **29.** Associative Property of
Multiplication **31.** Distributive Property
33. Identity Property of Multiplication

Lesson 1.8, Pages 49–58

5. $282 **7.** 10 months **9.** $3962.25 **11.** $90.95
13. purchase **15.** $91.35 **17.** 61 **19.** 720
21. < **23.** 48.24 cm; 48.78 cm; 49.36 cm;
49.45 cm **25.** 46.0 m; 45.97 m **27.** 5
29. about $5 per h; $5.43 per h

Chapter 2 Working with Data

Lesson 2.1, Pages 70–75

5. mean: 86.3; median: 86.5; mode: 88
7. mean: 5.45; median: 5.4; mode: 5.4.

9. mean: 86.6; median: 86; mode: none
11. 95 **13.** median **15.** Mean: 17.3; median: 17.5; mode: 18 **17.** 13 **19.** 2 **21.** about $1000; $1256.64 **23.** 2 quarters; 1 quarter, 2 dimes, and 1 nickel; 1 quarter, 1 dime, and 3 nickels; 4 dimes and 2 nickels **25.** about $800 **27.** C, B, A
29. 1500, 1900, or 2000 miles

Lesson 2.2, Pages 76–79

5.

	x			
x	x	x	x	
x	x	x	x	x
x	x	x	x	x
7	8	9	10	11

mean: 9.13; median: 9; mode: 9

7.

Ages	Talley	Frequency (f)	nf
13	⊞	5	65
14	⊞ |||	8	112
15	⊞ ||	7	105
16	⊞	5	80

mean: 14.48; median: 14; mode: 14

9.

Distances (km)	Talley	Frequency (f)	nf
4			1	4
5		0	0
6						4	24
7	⊞		6	42
8			1	8
9					3	27
10						4	40
		$\Sigma f = 19$	$\Sigma nf = 145$

mean: 7.63 km; median: 7 km; mode: 7 km
11. Answers will vary. **13.** 0.00004 **15.** >
17. 8h **19.** 0.45 **21.** 23 **23.** 31.5 **25.** 16ab

Lesson 2.3, Pages 80–84

5. ones **7.** 113

9.

Grayson Stem	Leaves
5	1 3 8
6	0 2 5 5 8
7	0 3 3 4

Key: 5|3 means 53

Martin Stem	Leaves
4	1 9
5	0 2 9
6	0 2 4 5
7	8 9
8	2

Key: 4|1 means 41

11. Grayson

13. Ages of Employees

Stem	Leaves
2	6 7 7 8 9 9
3	0 2 3 3 3 8 8
4	0 1 6 7 8
5	0 4 4 4 5 6 7
6	0 2 2 3 8

Key: 4|1 means 41

15. 43.5 **17.** 130; 159 **19.** mean: 144.1; median: 145; mode; 145 **21.** 7 hundred-thousandths.
23. 0.0005, 0.0045, 0.005 **25.** about 5600 miles; 5460 miles

Lesson 2.4, Pages 85–90

5. 18 and 35; 22, 25, 32; none **7.** 70 and 88; 70, 75, 83; none

9.

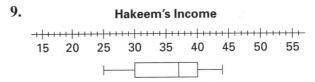

Hakeem's Income

11. Kevin; $46 **13.** Kevin; $40 **15.** One possible answer; There is a $10 range in the middle half of the income for Hakeem and a $7 range for Kevin.

16.–17.

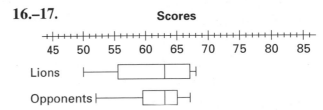

Scores

19. Lions: 31; Opponents: 15 **21.** 23,079, 23,508, 23,753 **23.** 7.9 **25.** 7 **27.** 32; 64

Lesson 2.5, Pages 91–99

5. Monday **7.** 8.5 hours **9.** The bars become shorter. **11.** mean: 5.8; median: 5.5; mode: 5
13. They do not last as long as the alkaline, but last longer than the other two in high-rate and low-rate use. **15.** Alkaline and heavy duty
17. Number of installations that required that time period to complete **19.** 20 **21.** 4

23.

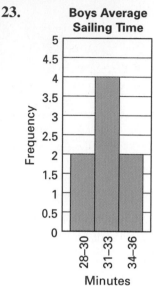
Boys Average Sailing Time

25.

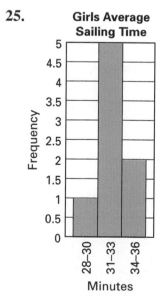
Girls Average Sailing Time

27. 9 ten-thousandths **29.** 3 ten-thousands
31. Identity Property for Multiplication
33. Distributive Property

Lesson 2.6, Pages 100–107

5. increasing **7.** Annual profits for 1996 through 2000 **9.** Vertical scale is not constant. **11.** $22,000
13. $23,500 **15.** 4th and 6th **17.** 8 weeks
19. mean: 52.0; median: 52; mode; 50 and 57

21.

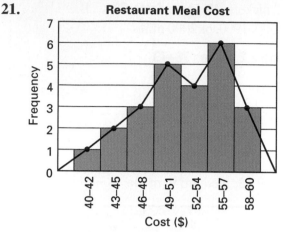
Restaurant Meal Cost

23. Thursday, Friday, and Saturday
25. Freshmen; $15 **27.** No; There are no two days that have the same amount of sales. **29.** Fr: $165; Soph: $155 **31.** 731 miles **33.** 2412.5 miles

Lesson 2.7, Pages 108–116

3. Increasing **5.** Graph B has the steeper slope.
7. Mean **9.** Mode **11.** Answers will vary.
13. Answers will vary.

15.

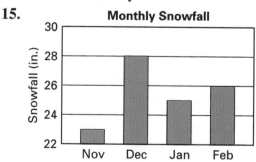
Monthly Snowfall

17. 56.9 **19.** $220.00 **21.** 4 **23.** 250 **25.** about $190

Chapter 3 Integers

Lesson 3.1, Pages 128–133
Lesson Assessment
5. 3 points **7.** $-7°$ **9.** 8 in. **11.** $-$55 **13.** -18
15. -4 **17.** 0 **19.** 23 **21.** 19 **23.** 0

25.

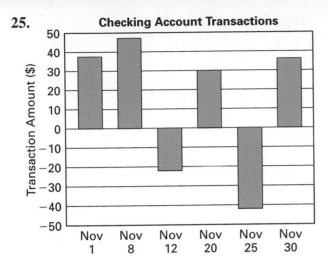

Checking Account Transactions

27. > **29.** tens **31.** $29 **33.** 13 **35.** $38

Lesson 3.2, Pages 134–139

5. > **7.** < **9.** > **11.** = **13.** > **15.** >
17. −6, −5, −3, 2, 4, 8 **19.** 15°F > 10°F
21. −10°F < −5°F **23.** 30 **25.** 7 **27.** about
1000; 1151 **29.** about 1500; 1484.8
31. about 30.58 **33.** 603.4 **35.** 80.8

Lesson 3.3, Pages 140–147

5. −8 + (−3) = −11 **7.** 4 + (−1) = 3
9. −3 + (−7) = −10 **11.** −15 **13.** −96
15. −39 **17.** 27 **19.** 183 **21.** −129 **23.** −345
25. −159 **27.** Always true **29.** Not always true;
Could be positive and negative addends with the
absolute value of the positive addend greater than
the absolute value of the negative addend
31. −7 + 4 = −3; 3 less MB **33.** $25 + (−$8) +
$4 + (−$3) + $0 = $18; $18 **35.** −2 + 8 + (−4)
= 2; gain of 2 yd **37.** 26 **39.** 19 **41.** 1.5 **43.** about
20 mpg **45.** about 87.7 **47.** 86

Lesson 3.4, Pages 148–153

5. −9 **7.** 0 **9.** −9 **11.** 6 **13.** −49 **15.** −5
17. 5 − 8; −3 **19.** 20,320 ft − (−12,925 ft);
33,245 ft **21.** −2; −16 **23.** 270 **25.** Option I;
Option I pays $250 and Option II pays $225.
27. Option II

Lesson 3.5, Pages 154–161

5. −6 + 10 = 4 **7.** −4 + 10 + (−10) = −4
9. 2 **11.** 6 **13.** 0 **15.** −1 **17.** −10
19. Commutative Property of Addition
21. −3; 2; −1 **23.** −3 + 2 + (−1) = −2
25. $13 **27.** 7 **29.** 0 tenths **31.** 8 millions **33.** 6
35. 67.57 in. **37.** 67 in.

Lesson 3.6, Pages 162–167

5. −54 **7.** 45 **9.** 0 **11.** 280 **13.** Always true
15. Not always true; One of the integers may be
0. **17.** −16 **19.** −5 **21.** −10 ft per second;
6(−10); −60 ft **23.** none; 150(4); $600
25. −10 ft per min, −8 min; (−8)(−10); 80 ft
forward **27.** 74 **29.** 76

31.

```
  +--+--+--+--+--+--+--+--+--+--+--+--+--+--+--+--+
  58 60 62 64 66 68 70 72 74 76 78 80 82 84 86 88
      |---[        |        ]------|
```

Lesson 3.7, Pages 168–175

5. −3 **7.** −4 **9.** 4 **11.** −25 **13.** 3 **15.** 3
17. 151 **19.** $\frac{20}{4}$; 5 months **21.** $\frac{-220}{11}$;
−20 ft per min **23.** 0.505, 0.515, 0.550, 0.551
25. 0.651, 0.650, 0.615 **27.** 14 kg **29.** $154

Chapter 4 Solving Equations

Lesson 4.1, Pages 186–191

7. 4.3 **9.** 14 **11.** 24 **13.** 137 **15.** 3 **17.** −151
19. −1.8 **21.** $x − 64 = 25$; $89 **23.** $x − 21 =$
190; 211 trees **25.** $x − 36 = 144$; $180
27. 23,465; 23,546; 23,654 **29.** 5 **31.** about 2.83

Lesson 4.2, Pages 192–197

5. −56 **7.** −90 **9.** −32 **11.** −0.1 **13.** 0 **15.** −18
17. 12 **19.** $6p = 900,000$; about 150,000 people
21. $250t = 6$; 0.024 cm **23.** $2n = 450$; 225 cars
25. 4 hundred thousands **27.** 23,900 **29.** −20
31. −2.7

Lesson 4.3. Pages 198–202

5. 2 **7.** -5 **9.** 74.4 **11.** $4\frac{1}{3}$ **13.** -14 **15.** -25.6 **17.** 74 **19.** $3c + 55 = 190$; $45

21. $\frac{x}{6} - 115 = 35$; $900 **23.** $3c - 45 = 270$; $105 **25.** $4(m - 3)$ **27.** about 61,500 **29.** -29 **31.** -6.4

Lesson 4.4, Pages 203–210

5. $15e$ **7.** $16n$ **9.** -2 **11.** 10 **13.** 10 **15.** -9.22 (rounded) **17.** -4 **19.** $16x + 20x = 315$; $8.75 **21.** $x + x - 26 = 560$; 293 girls **23.** $x + 2x - 15 = 315$; 110 shares **25.** $42x + 56x = 34.30$; $0.35 **27.** $x + 2x + (x + 2) = 50$; 12 minutes **29.** $<$ **31.** $>$ **33.** -30

Lesson 4.5, Pages 211–216

5. 2.5 **7.** $-3\frac{1}{3}$ **9.** 5 **11.** 1.2 (rounded) **13.** -2 **15.** -3 **17.** -6.3 (rounded) **19.** $2000 + 50x = 1500 + 75x$; 20 cars **21.** $x + 150 = 3x$; 75 stamps **23.** Commutative Property of Multiplication **25.** Identity Property of Addition **27.** 135 **29.** 15, 21 **31.** -23 **33.** 6:05 P.M.

Lesson 4.6, Pages 217–223

5. $r = \frac{D}{t}$ **7.** $a = 180 - b - c$ **9.** $p = \frac{I}{rt}$ **11.** $x = m$ **13.** $x = -s$ **15.** $x = 2.5e$ **17.** $x = 2t + 8$ **19.** $x = 2 - a$ **21.** $m = \frac{F-1}{2}$; 3 miles **23.** 33 feet **25.** 3 **27.** 6 **29.** 6.5 **31.** positive

Chapter 5 Rational Numbers

Lesson 5.1, Pages 236–240

5. $\frac{5}{7}$ **7.** $\frac{3}{8}$ **9.** c. $\frac{2}{7}$ **11.** 1, 2, 3, 6; 6 **13.** 1, 2; 2 **15.** $\frac{1}{3}$ **17.** $\frac{3}{10}$ **19.** $\frac{7}{30}$ **21.** $\frac{7}{15}$ **23.** True **25.** False **27.** -5 **29.** 8

Lesson 5.2, Pages 241–246

5. 0.8 **7.** -0.125 **9.** -0.15 **11.** -0.175 **13.** -0.5625 **15.** $-\frac{5}{8}$ **17.** $-\frac{1}{4}$ **19.** $-\frac{1}{3}$ **21.** $\frac{2}{3}$; $0.\overline{6}$ **23.** $\frac{1}{4}$; 0.25 **25.** $\frac{13}{20}$ **27.** Deshaun: 2; Miliani: 2; Heath: 1 **29.** Test 2 and Test 3 **31.** Boys: 88; Girls: 90 **33.** 0 **35.** -26

Lesson 5.3, Pages 247–253

7. $<$ **9.** $\frac{3}{8} < 0.4 < \frac{4}{9}$ **11.** $-\frac{1}{2} < -\frac{1}{5} < \frac{1}{4} < \frac{1}{3}$

13.

15.

17. Less than **19.** Walt

21.

23. False **25.** True **27.** -7 **29.** -8

Lesson 5.4, Pages 254–260

5. $2\frac{1}{5}$ **7.** $4\frac{1}{2}$ **9.** $-\frac{17}{3}$ **11.** $\frac{64}{5}$ **13.** $\frac{1}{3}$ **15.** $-\frac{1}{3}$ **17.** $1\frac{13}{20}$ **19.** $\frac{3}{8}$ **21.** $4\frac{9}{10}$ **23.** $x - \frac{3}{4} = 2\frac{9}{16}$; $3\frac{5}{16}$ inches **25.** $P = \frac{2}{3} + \frac{2}{3} + \frac{3}{4} + \frac{3}{4}$; $2\frac{5}{6}$ yards **27.** $x + 3\frac{1}{2} = 6\frac{1}{6}$; more; $\frac{5}{6}$ cup **29.** 95; 95.037 **31.** Fill the 3-gallon can twice and pour into the 7-gallon can. Fill the 3-gallon can again. Pour into the 7-gallon can until it is full. This leaves 2 gallons in the 3-gallon can. Pour the water out of the 7-gallon can. Pour the 2 gallons out of the 3-gallon can into the empty 7-gallon can. Fill the 3-gallon can and pour it into the 7-gallon can. There are now 5 gallons of water in the 7-gallon can.

Lesson 5.5, Pages 261–265

5. $-\frac{2}{3}$ **7.** $13\frac{1}{3}$ **9.** $2\frac{2}{5}$ **11.** -12 **13.** $27\frac{1}{25}$ **15.** $249 **17.** $90; $36 **19.** $179\frac{2}{3}$ km **21.** 2 **23.** 4 **25.** 6 **27.** 3 **29.** May **31.** April, May, and June **33.** 5 cars **35.** about 4.9 cars

Lesson 5.6, Pages 266–272

5. $-\frac{8}{7}$ **7.** -1 **9.** $\frac{8}{9}$ **11.** $-\frac{2}{15}$ **13.** $-1\frac{1}{5}$ **15.** -36 **17.** -20 **19.** $1\frac{7}{9}$ **21.** $9x = 58\frac{1}{2}$; $6\frac{1}{2}$ feet **23.** $\frac{3}{8}x = 132$; 352 students **25.** 30°C **27.** False **29.** False **31.** 4

Lesson 5.7, Pages 273–277

5. $c < -18$ **7.** $10 \geq z$ **9.** $t > -\frac{5}{8}$ **11.** $m \leq -2\frac{7}{12}$
13. $x - 38.50 < 5.50$; $\$38.50 \leq x < \$44.00$
15. $x + 381 \leq 400$; $\$0 \leq x \leq \$19$; $\$19$ or less
17. $x + 23.50 \leq 75$; $\$0 \leq x < \$51.50$; $\$51.50$ or
less **19.** $w - \frac{3}{4} < 5\frac{1}{2}$; less than $6\frac{1}{4}$ pounds
21. 830,000 **23.** 30,000 **25.** 19.184
27. 1,000,000 **29.** -755.5 **31.** 94 **33.** 94

Lesson 5.8, Pages 278–284

5. $p < -8$ **7.** $-4 \leq y$ **9.** $z < -40$ **11.** $-25 \geq b$
13. $q \geq 1\frac{1}{3}$ **15.** $33.66 \leq \frac{2}{3}x$; $\$50.49$ **17.** $\frac{x}{6} \geq 4$;
24 inches **19.** $75 + 7.5h \geq 160$; $11\frac{1}{3}$ hours
21. 78.48 **23.** 18.4 **25.** 9 **27.** -1 **29.** 13 gallons

Chapter 6 Ratio, Proportion, and Probability

Lesson 6.1 Pages 294–298

5. $\frac{4}{5}$ **7.** $\frac{18}{1}$ **9.** $\frac{2}{3}; \frac{2}{3}; \frac{2}{3}$; all equal **11.** $\frac{7}{2}; \frac{14}{3}; \frac{7}{2}$;
not all equal **13.** Yes **15.** Yes **17.** Yes **19.** No
21. $\frac{1}{3}$ **23.** Lareef: $\frac{12}{15}$; Rahmen: $\frac{16}{20}$ **25.** 25
27. Sample answer: (5, 8), (10, 16), (15, 24)
29. 24 **31.** -49 **33.** -4 **35.** 409.736 **37.** -4
39. 129.6 **41.** 3 **43.** $f \geq 10$

Lesson 6.2 Pages 299–303

5. 2.7 ounces per cubic centimeter **7.** 1.465 feet
per second **9.** 4 fish per hour; 5 hours **11.** 2.15
bulbs per minute; about 29.8 minutes
13. $\frac{10}{35} \overset{?}{=} \frac{15}{51}$; $510 \neq 525$; no **15.** $\frac{150}{5} \overset{?}{=} \frac{256}{8}$;
$1200 \neq 1280$; no **17.** 7 pounds **19.** 600 feet
21. $\$94.50$ **23.** about 90.9 minutes
25. $80.\overline{6}$ feet per second **27.** $-15°F + (-8°F)$
29. $1\frac{3}{8} + (-\frac{3}{4}) + \frac{1}{2}$ **31.** $\$3.25$ **33.** $\$1.625$; $\$1.50$

Lesson 6.3 Pages 304–310

5. 10 **7.** 15 **9.** 24 **11.** 5 **13.** -4 **15.** -27
17. 6 **19.** $\frac{16}{12} = \frac{48}{x}$; $\$36$ **21.** $\frac{4}{120} = \frac{x}{180}$;
6 houses **23.** $\frac{2}{5} = \frac{x}{100}$; 40 students **25.** $\frac{8}{3} = \frac{792}{x}$;
297 pounds **27.** $\frac{x}{6840} = \frac{1}{400}$; about 17 families

29. $\frac{1}{5} = \frac{x}{20}$; 4 cm **31.** $\frac{x}{12} = \frac{3}{8}$; 4.5 in. **33.** 4 **35.** 7
37.

Stem	Leaves
5	5
6	5 8
7	0 0 0 6 6
8	0 2 2
9	0

Key: 6|5 means 65

39. -5.25 **41.** -2 **43.** -6

Lesson 6.4 Pages 311–315

5. $\frac{1}{4}$ **7.** $\frac{1}{2643}$ **9.** $\frac{1}{3}$ **11.** $\frac{1}{2}$ **13.** $\frac{1}{2}$ **15.** $\frac{1}{2}$ **17.** $\frac{3}{4}$ **19.** $\frac{1}{5}$
21. $\frac{3}{10}$ **23.** $\frac{1}{4}$ **25.** $\frac{2}{3}$ **27.** brown; $\frac{1}{2}$ is the greatest
fraction **29.** $\frac{1}{4}$ **31.** Commutative Property of
Addition **33.** $-m - n$ **35.** 6.2r **37.** $9.94 \leq x \leq 10.06$

Lesson 6.5 Pages 316–321

3. H, 1; H, 2; H, 3; H, 4; H, 5; H, 6; T, 1; T, 2;
T, 3; T, 4; T, 5; T, 6 **5.** $\frac{1}{12}$ **7.** $\frac{1}{3}$ **9.** 16 **11.** 0 **13.** 1
15. 20 **17.** 216 **19.** 4, 435, 236 **21.** False
23. True **25.** False **27.** $6\frac{7}{12}$ **29.** $4\frac{3}{8}$

Lesson 6.6 Pages 322–326

5. $\frac{1}{4}$ **7.** $\frac{1}{2}$ **9.** $\frac{1}{2}$ **11.** $\frac{1}{9}$ **13.** $\frac{1}{8}$ **15.** $\frac{1}{12}$ **17.** $\frac{15}{56}$ **19.** $\frac{1}{10}$
21. $\frac{1}{6}$ **23.** $\frac{4}{5}$ **25.** $\frac{1}{5}$ **27.** 3.7 **29.** -10 **31.** 6

Lesson 6.7 Pages 327–332

5. $\frac{13}{665}$ **7.** $\frac{2}{125}$ **9.** One possible answer could be to
toss three coins. Let H represent a correct answer
and T an incorrect answer. Record the results of the
toss of each coin (for example: H, H, T). A recorded
result with three heads is a favorable outcome.
11. Answers depend on simulation chosen. **13.** $\frac{3}{5}$
15. $\frac{3}{10}$ **17.** Sample answer: generate a pair of
random numbers between 1 and 5. Let 1 and 2
represent shots made and 3, 4, and 5 shots not
made. If both shots are made it is a favorable
outcome. **19.** Answers depend on simulation
chosen. **21.** $\frac{6}{43}$ **23.** $\frac{3}{86}$ **25.** 6 rows, 12 columns;
8 rows, 9 columns; 9 rows, 8 columns; 12 rows,
6 columns **27.** 120 **29.** 124

Lesson 6.8 Pages 333–337

3. 656 students **5.** about 141,657 people **7.** yes
9. no **11.** 0.298 **13.** 0.132 **15.** 1194 **17.** 1352
19. 561 **21.** 7 million **23.** 0 thousandths
25. 0.0067 **27.** Divide by 2; 0.25, 0.125, 0.0625
29. -8

Chapter 7 Percent

Lesson 7.1, Pages 348–353

7. 35% **9.** 83.3% **11.** 46.7% **13.** 87.5% **15.** $\frac{4}{25}$
17. $\frac{3}{5}$ **19.** $\frac{1}{6}$ **21.** $\frac{1}{200}$ **23.** 1 **25.** $66\frac{2}{3}$% **27.** $16\frac{2}{3}$%
29. $\frac{7}{25}$ **31.** 75% **33.** $\frac{9}{20}$ **35.** 121% **37.** -2
39. $6 \le m$ **41.** B: $\frac{2}{5}$ **43.** C: $\frac{5}{9}$

Lesson 7.2, Pages 354–361

5. 60 **7.** 1.05 **9.** 60 **11.** 6.45 **13.** 59.36
15. 1330 students **17.** $562.50 **19.** 65 rings
21. 56 students **23.** 156 **25.** about 53 **27.** 0.222
29. $7\frac{1}{12}$ **31.** $1\frac{5}{18}$ **33.** $\frac{1}{4}$

Lesson 7.3, Pages 362–366

5. $2.40 **7.** $6.30 **9.** 24 **11.** 560 **13.** 216
15. 1218 **17.** 2250 **19.** 37.5% **21.** 87.5%
23. 91 **25.** 550 **27.** $\frac{1}{4}$ of $2700; $675 **29.** Round
7.65% to 8%. Use 1% · 8 = 8%. Find 1% of
$858.76 and round to the nearest dollar.
Multiply by 8.; $72 **31.** Round 3.9% to 4%.
Use 1% · 4 = 4%. Find 1% of 1026 miles and
round to the nearest mile. Multiply by 4.;
40 miles **33.** Find 10% of $32.38. Round to
nearest 10 cents. Divide by 2 and add to the
rounded value. Divide this sum by 3.; $1.60
35. 4 **37.** -17 **39.** -1

Lesson 7.4, Pages 367–373

5. 50% **7.** 108 **9.** 250 **11.** $133\frac{1}{3}$%
13. 8.5% · $70 = x; $5.95 **15.** $4.80 = 15% · x;
$32 **17.** $4250 = 85% · x; $5000
19. $\frac{60}{100} = \frac{480}{x}$; 800 **21.** $\frac{0.3}{100} = \frac{x}{120}$; 120.36 cm;
119.64 cm **23.** -2 **25.** $-2\frac{8}{9}$ **27.** 12
29. Repair the old one.

Lesson 7.5, Pages 374–380

5. $30 **7.** $49.20 **9.** $73.50 **11.** $112.50
13. 882 students **15.** 12.5% **17.** about 14.3%
19. $10,200 **21.** 7.5% **23.** about 6.6%
25. about 2395.6 volts **27.** $6.25
29. 96% of the pre-May 1 price **31.** $-\frac{1}{4}$
33. -3 **35.** $\frac{11}{2} = \frac{x}{9}$; $49.50 **37.** $\frac{1}{12}$

Lesson 7.6, Pages 381–388

5. $51.56 **7.** $3250 **9.** about 8.86% **11.** $27.50
13. 25% **15.** $5300 **17.** 1% **19.** $56 **21.** *ABC*: $38;
XYZ: $36 **23.** *ABC*: $32 *XYZ*: $32 **25.** $\frac{6}{90} = \frac{36}{x}$;
540 cal **27.** $\frac{1.50}{12} = \frac{x}{21}$; about $2.63 **29.** $\frac{1}{4}$

Chapter 8 Graphing on the Coordinate Plane

Lesson 8.1, Pages 400–404

5. $(-4, 4)$ **7.** $(3, -4)$ **9.** $(-5, -2)$ **11.** $(4, 4)$
13. *G* **15.** *E* and *F* **17.** *B* **19.** $-$ **24.**

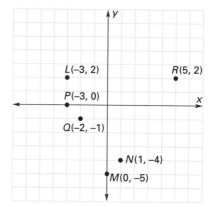

25. 2 units

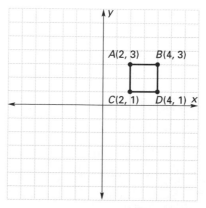

27. −, + **29.** +, − **31.** 0, + or − **33.** 0.005
35. Identity Property of Addition **37.** 4

Lesson 8.2, Pages 405–412

5. Sample Answer: $(-1, 0), (0, 1), (1, 2)$
7. Sample Answer: $(-1, -3), (0, -1), (1, 1)$

9.

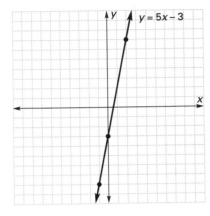

11.

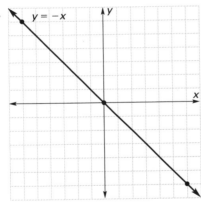

13.

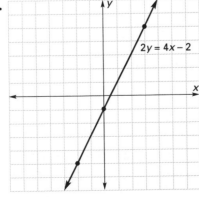

15.

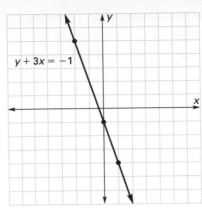

17.

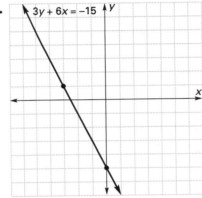

19. 6 minutes; 10 minutes; 16 minutes **21.** $45;
$85; $125 **23.** 32°F; 122°F; 212°F
25. 8 centimeters **27.** $P = 2n + 2$ **29.** $\frac{2}{5}$ **31.** $\frac{3}{4}$
33. 6.4 **35.** 1 **37.** $33 **39.** 90

Lesson 8.3, Pages 413–418

5. $\frac{2}{7}$ **7.** $\frac{2}{3}$ **9.** $-\frac{3}{8}$ **11.** $\frac{3}{7}$ **13.** $\frac{1}{56}$ **15.** 2
17. Sample Answer: $(0, 0), (1, 12), (2, 24)$

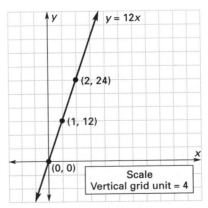

19. Same as the coefficient of x.; There are 12 inches per foot.

21. Sample answer: (0, 0), (1, 8), (2, 16)

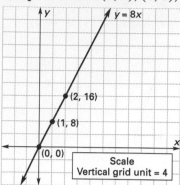

23. Same as the coefficient of x.; The speed of the airplane. **25.** Any solution to the equation $y = -\frac{1}{2}x$ is correct. **27.** $3\frac{1}{6}$ feet **29.** 1.25

31. $x < -2$ **33.** 200% **35.** $\frac{65}{24}$ **37.** $\frac{23}{12}$

Lesson 8.4, Pages 419–427

5. -1; 1; $y = -x + 1$ **7.** 4, 4; $y = 4x + 4$

9. -2; 3; $\frac{3}{2}$;

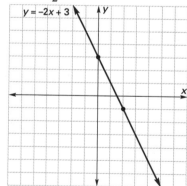

11. $-\frac{2}{3}$; 1; $\frac{3}{2}$;

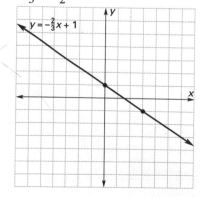

13. $\frac{1}{3}$; 0; 0;

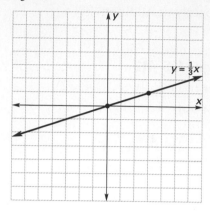

15. 3; 2; $-\frac{2}{3}$;

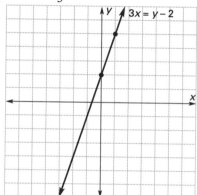

17. $y = -40x + 680$ **19.** 680; Pounds of food supply on hand at the beginning

21.

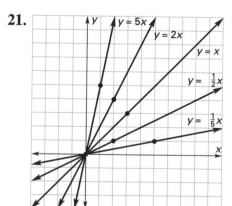

The lines have the same intercept but the slope of the line becomes steeper. **23.** $y = 5x + 10$

25. 10; cost of instruction **27.** $>$ **29.** -10 **31.** $\frac{1}{8}$

Lesson 8.5, Pages 428–432

5. d. **7.** a. **9.** (2, 10) **11.** (1, 2) **13.** (7, 3)
15. $t + c = 300$ **17.** $(c, t) \rightarrow (200, 100)$;
Mrs. Vanderpool needs 200 square feet of carpet
and 100 square feet of tile. **19.** $5c + 7b = 1500$
21. w = width; l = length **23.** $(w, l) \rightarrow (60, 120)$
25. b. **27.** $x \geq 11$ **29.** $\frac{1}{3}$

Lesson 8.6, Pages 433–438

5. $y \geq -\frac{3}{2}x - 2$ **7.** $y > 1$ **9.** yes; yes; no

11.

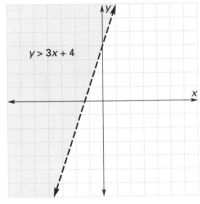

13.

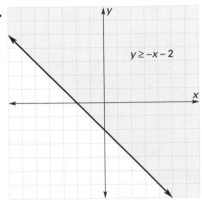

15.

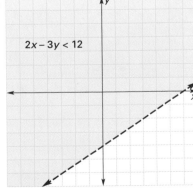

17. $10b + 5t \geq 150$ **19.** Quadrant 1;
Negative amounts of the herbs have no meaning.
21. $6x + 4y \leq 100$ **23.** Quadrant 1.
A negative number of cables has no meaning.

25.

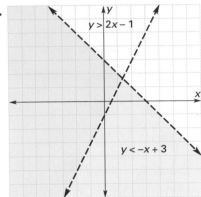

27. It is the region that is above the graph of
$y = 2x - 1$ and below the graph of $y = -x + 3$.

29.

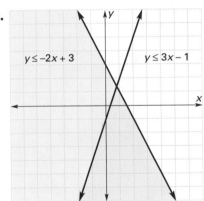

31.

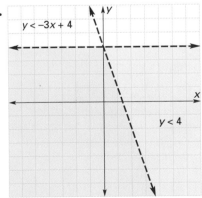

33. 2 hundredths **35.** 500; 457.10 **37.** 34,600;
34,581.96

Lesson 8.7, Pages 439–448

5. Domain: {0, 1, 2, 3}; Range: {0, 1, 2, 8}
7. Domain: {3}; Range: {−1, 0, 1} **9.** yes **11.** no
13. yes **15.** yes

17.

Input x	Output $f(x)$
−2	12
0	4
2	−4

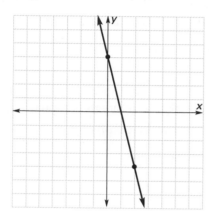

19.

Input x	Output $f(x)$
−1	$3\frac{1}{3}$
0	4
3	6

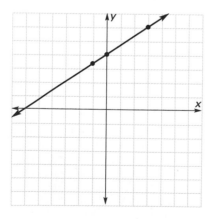

21. $-3 \le y \le 7$ **23.** $f(x) = x - 3$; 3
25. $f(x) = 3x$; 18

29. $f(t) = 150t$
31.

Input x	Output $f(x)$
−10	14
0	32
10	50

33. yes; Each domain value is paired with only one range value. **35.** 44.15 **37.** $\frac{7}{8}$ **39.** 7.5 **41.** $\frac{1}{2}$ **43.** $\frac{1}{4}$

Chapter 9 Introduction to Geometry

Lesson 9.1, Pages 460–465

5. $\angle RST$ **7.** $\overrightarrow{YX}$ **9.** $\angle ABC$
11. point R **13.** $\overrightarrow{ST}$ **15.** Sample answers: $\overline{RT}, \overline{ST}, \overline{RS}$ **17.** 4; $\angle X, \angle WXY, \angle YXW, \angle 2$

19.

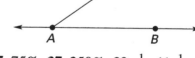

21.

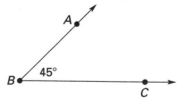

23.

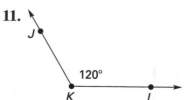

25. M **27.** J **29.** impossible

33.

35. 75% **37.** 250% **39.** $\frac{1}{25}$ **41.** $\frac{1}{4}$

Lesson 9.2, Pages 466–472

5. 40°; acute **7.** 90°; right
9.

11.

13. complementary **15.** complementary
17. 180° **19.** They are supplementary.

21.

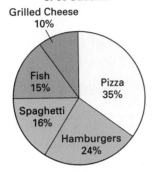

Preferred Cafeteria Meals
of 80 Sudents

Grilled Cheese 10%
Fish 15%
Pizza 35%
Spaghetti 16%
Hamburgers 24%

23.

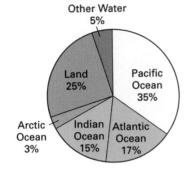

Coverage of the Earth's Surface

Other Water 5%
Land 25%
Pacific Ocean 35%
Arctic Ocean 3%
Indian Ocean 15%
Atlantic Ocean 17%

25. $-\frac{7}{12}$ **27.** $-\frac{3}{2}$
29. $40 = x \cdot 160$; 25% **31.** $x = 37.5\% \cdot 680$; 255

Lesson 9.3, Pages 473–479

5. isosceles; acute **7.** scalene; obtuse
9. isosceles; right

11.

13. The sum of the measures of an obtuse angle and a right angle would be greater than 180°.

15.

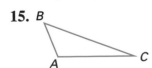

17. 20° **19.** 58° **21.** 57.5° **23.** 45° **25.** $-\frac{1}{3}$
27. 6 **29.** $p > 3$ **31.** $\frac{1}{2}$ **33.** $\frac{7}{10}$

Lesson 9.4, Pages 480–487

5. octagon; yes **7.** quadrilateral; no **9.** triangle; no

11. 10 m **13.** 32 cm **15.** 1080° **17.** 2340°
19. $128\frac{4}{7}°$ **21.** 125° **23.** 60° **25.** 90° **27.** 33.7°
29. 11 sides **31.** 22 sides **33.** 4° **35.** 0°
37. $T = 1500 + 1500 \cdot 0.08 \cdot \frac{2}{3}$; $1580
39. -27; -17; 3 **41.** 0; 0; 216 **43.** 7; 9; $\frac{41}{5}$

Lesson 9.5, Pages 488–494

5. I and III, II and VIII **7.** $\angle RQP$ **9.** $\overline{RS}$
13. 2.3 mm **15.** 8.4 mm
17. $\triangle FEB$ **19.** 40 **21.** 60° **23.** $M(4, -7)$
25. < **27.** > **29.** 1200 s **31.** $822

Lesson 9.6, Pages 495–500

5. Four units left and seven units up.
7. B **9.** C **11.** $(-4, 8)$ **13.** $(2, 4)$

15.

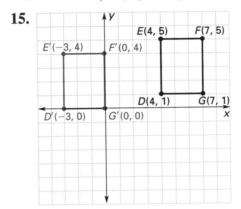

19. $(x, y) \rightarrow (x + 5, y)$ **21.** $y = -3x + 6$ **23.** 1.9
25. $\frac{4}{3}$ **27.** 144 yards **29.** 81 inches **31.** 150% **33.** $220

Lesson 9.7, Pages 501–505

5. A and H, B and G **7.** $(-4, -5)$ **9.** $(0, -3)$
11. $(4, 5)$ **13.** $P'(-4, -5)$, $Q'(-1, -2)$,
$R'(-3, -1)$ **15.** $P'(-4, -7)$, $Q'(-1, -4)$,
$R'(-3, -3)$

17.–18.

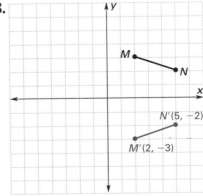

19. The coordinates were reflected over the x-axis. **21.** The coordinates were translated to the left 3 units and reflected over the x-axis. **23.** The x-coordinate of E is the y-coordinate of F and the y-coordinate of E is the x-coordinate of F. **25.** $85.5 = x + 81$; 4.5 inches **27.** $w + w + 9 + w + w + 9 = 42$; 6 feet **29.** 2; 4; 8;

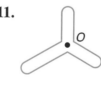

Lesson 9.8, Pages 506–512

5. 180° **7.** 270°

9.

11.

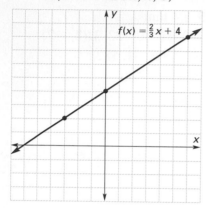

17. C **19.** F **21.** reflection **23.** translation **25.** translation **27.** a. 60 **29.** a. 100 **31.** $6615 **33.** at least 8

Chapter 10 Powers and Roots
Lesson 10.1, Pages 524–529

5. 1024 feet **7.** 6400 feet **9.** 10,000 **11.** $\frac{1}{16}$ **13.** 10 **15.** 910 **17.** 4 **19.** -8 **21.** -13 **23.** 25 **25.** 81 **27.** $2495.40 **29.** $(\frac{3}{5})^4$ **31.** -4^2: base is 4; $(-4)^2$: base is -4 **33.** 70 ft per s **35.** $=$ **37.** 7 **39.** 3.1 **41.** $5\frac{5}{6}$ miles **43.** $\frac{5}{24}$ mile

Lesson 10.2, Pages 530–535

5. a^3 **7.** 9 **9.** 100 **11.** $\frac{1}{8}$ **13.** $\frac{1}{16}$ **15.** 1

17. $\frac{a}{b}$ **19.** $2x^{-4}$ **21.** $\frac{4a^{-2}}{3}$ **23.** $\frac{3}{2b^4}$ **25.** $\frac{m^3}{n^2}$ **27.** $10s^3t^5$ **29.** 6561 **31.** -4 **33.** 1 **35.** 6:1; 7:1 **37.** $\frac{3}{4}$ **39.** $33\frac{1}{3}$ %

Lesson 10.3, Pages 536–542

5. yes **7.** no; factor is a power of 2 and not 10 **9.** 0.000375 **11.** 142,000 **13.** 75,383 **15.** 3,700,000 sq ft **17.** 0.0000003 seconds **19.** 8.85×10^1 **21.** 5.73×10^7 **23.** 9.24875×10^5 **25.** 1.2×10^9 **27.** 3.5×10^6 square miles **29.** 2.5×10^7 kg **31.** $>$ **33.** $>$ **35.** 4.88×10^{14} **37.** about 2.6×10^{-8} **39.** about $7000 **41.** a; 7.5 gal **43.** b; 56 oz **45.** b; 30 pt **47.** a; 156 ft

49.

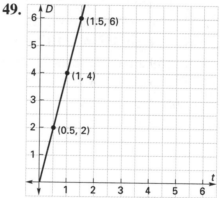

51. walking speed on treadmill

Lesson 10.4, Pages 543–550

5. 15,000 m **7.** 251,000 mg **9.** 2.13 m **11.** 1.7 cm **13.** 0.0025 kg **15.** 1.5 gal **17.** about 33.83 oz **19.** about 22 lb **21.** b. **23.** a. **25.** b. **27.** $<$ **29.** $<$ **31.** $<$ **33.** 6250 bottles **35.** about 4.8 quarts **37.** -1.1875 **39.** 0.6; 60% **41.** $219.24 **43.** 2, 4

Lesson 10.5, Pages 551–556

5. no **7.** no **9.** 5 and 6 **11.** 1 and 2 **13.** 2.6 **15.** 9.6 **17.** 9.434 **19.** 22.361 **21.** -25.120 **23.** 23.5 **25.** ± 15 **27.** ± 1.9 **29.** 8 **31.** 40 inches **33.** 625 square feet **35.** Sample answer: $\sqrt{24} \div \sqrt{6} = 2$ **37.** -21.5

39.

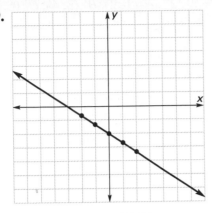

41. 12 times **43.** 91 **45.** 91

Lesson 10.6, Pages 557–565

5. hypotenuse: $\overline{DF}$; legs: $\overline{DE}, \overline{EF}$ **7.** ≠ **9.** ≠
11. 14 in. **13.** 13.2 m **15.** 2.5 in. **17.** no;
$65^2 \neq 15^2 + 62^2$ **19.** no; $18^2 \neq \sqrt{10}^2 + \sqrt{12}^2$
21. 127.3 ft **23.** 149.2 mi **25.** about 21.9 feet
27. about 29.2 meters **29.** about 16.6 feet
31. $x + \frac{2}{3}x = 565$; 339 girls **33.** 45 words per
minute **35.** about $3000 **37.** $65 **39.** $y = \frac{3}{4}x - 3$
41. $\frac{3}{4}$

Chapter 11 Measurement

Lesson 11.1, Pages 578–583

5. 45, 42, 39, 36 **7.** $-72, 36, -18, 9$ **9.** $6g^2, 12g^3,$
$24g^4, 48g^5$

11.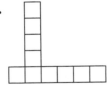

13.

15. 37, 27, 17 **17.** 48, 240, 1440 **19.** 5.0, 4.8, 4.6
21. 14, 19, 25 **23.** $4k - 1, 5k - 1, 6k - 1$
25. $5x - 2, -1, -5x$ **27.** 60 minutes **29.** 4; 9; n^2
31. $9\frac{1}{3}$ **33.** 8 **35.** about 17.6% **37.** $\frac{1}{9}$ **39.** $17.15

Lesson 11.2, Pages 584–592

5. no; The angles are not congruent. **7.** yes
9. 10 cm **11.** 15 in. **13.** 100 cm **15.** $\overline{DE}; \overline{EC}; \overline{DC}$
17. 15 feet **19.** about 15.6 m **21.** 45 cm
23. $\overline{DE}, \overline{DA}; \overline{DC}, \overline{DB}; \overline{EC}, \overline{AB}$ **25.** 79.5 cm

27. $-1\frac{1}{4}$ **29.** second bus; 5 students **31.** $\frac{3}{64}$
33. 144 square feet **35.** 7

Lesson 11.3, Pages 593–598

5.

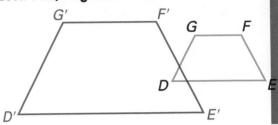

7.

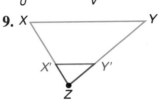

9.

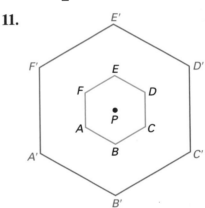

11.

15.

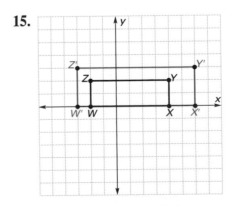

17. a.

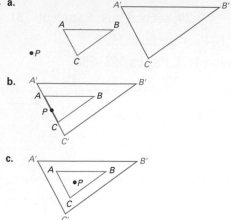

b.

c.

Yes they are congruent.; The position of the image triangle in relation to the original triangle is different.

19. $\frac{2}{5}$ **21.** 8 **23.** $-\frac{4}{9}$ **25.** $-\frac{5}{7}$ **27.** about 18.4 miles

Lesson 11.4, Pages 599–604

5. 39.6 inches **7.** $1\frac{2}{3}$ inches **9.** 18 : 1 **11.** 7 : 60
13. about 425 miles **15.** 3 cm wide and 3.5 cm long
17. B **19.** D **21.** about $-11.4°$F **23.** A
25. 8.72×10^{-2}

Lesson 11.5, Pages 605–614

5. 312 ft² **7.** 126 m² **9.** 242 cm² **11.** 14.2 m
13. 6 in. **15.** 0.15 cm **17.** 588 ft² **19.** 630 ft²
21. $3\frac{1}{4}$ft **23.** 495 in² **25.** 6.5 ft **27.** about 7278 feet
29. 1184 ft² **31.** about 6.8 acres **33.** 0.000625
35. 50% **37.** 36 **41.** $35 **43.** none

Lesson 11.6, Pages 615–621

5. 2 : 1 or 1 : 2; 242.5 ft; 485 ft **7.** 3 : 1 or 1 : 3;
16.3 in.; 48.9 in. **9.** 5 : 2 or 2 : 5; 48 ft²; 300 ft²
11. 2 : 3 or 3 : 2; 720 ft²; 320 ft² **13.** 51 in²
15. 4.8 feet **17.** 4178 ft² **19.** 1 : 30 **21.–24.**

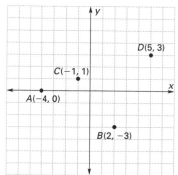

25. $(1, -2)$ **27.** A' $(1, 2)$, B' $(3, 4)$, C' $(6, 3)$
29. ± 10

Lesson 11.7, Pages 622–629

5. about 18.8 m; about 28.3 m² **7.** about 39.6 in.;
about 124.7 in² **9.** Sample answers: 6 m; 3 m²
11. Sample answers: 6 in.; 3 in² **13.** C **15.** D
17. about 19.2 cm² **19.** about 89.2 cm²
21. about 98.2 mm² **23.** about 40.3 ft²
25. about 224 labs **27.** about 0.24 m; about 0.48 m
29. about 1.60 ft; about 3.2 ft **31.** about 1.80 mi;
about 3.6 mi **33.** about 5.1 ft **35.** 17% **37.** 66%
39. -35 ft $+$ -22 ft; -57 ft

Chapter 12 Surface Area and Volume

Lesson 12.1, Pages 642–649

5.

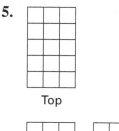

Top

Front   Side

7.

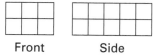

Top

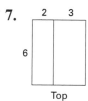

Front   Side

9.

11.

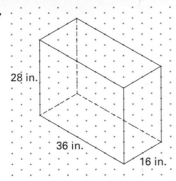

13. 1008 in² **15.** b.
19. −5 **21.** 2 **23.** −1 **25.** 2.5% **27.** 175%
29. 96 and 97 **31.** $19,600 **33.** 30 **35.** about 10.63

Lesson 12.2, Pages 650–656

5. B **7.** D
9. 828 ft²

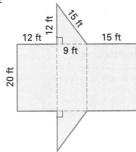

11. 160 cm² **13.** octagons **15.** 8 **17.** $633.60
19. $7980 **21.** 9 spools **23.** 3.1563 × 10⁷;
3.65 × 10²

Lesson 12.3, Pages 657–663

5. about 1941.9 cm² **7.** about 19,452.7 in²
9. about 1935.2 in² **11.** about 100.5 mm²
13. 2 gallons **15.** about 66.6 cm² **17.** about 9.4 cm²
19. about 194 cm² **21.** about 1.38 cm
23. about 1407.4 in² **25.** about 127.0 cm²
27. 222 gears **29.** 11.1% **31.** 12.5% **33.** (−4, −5)

Lesson 12.4, Pages 664–670

5. 2340 in³ **7.** 2592 cm³ **9.** 27 cm³ **11.** 226 m³
13. about 22 ft² **15.** about 600 pounds
17. 33.6 pounds **19.** 27 ft³ **21.** 2858 cm³
23. about 0.25 in³ **25.** $C = 11$ and $h = 8$;
about 21 in³ **27.** $-\frac{21}{8}$ **29.** $x > 6$ **31.** acute
angle < 90°, obtuse angle > 90°, right angle = 90°
33. 15.6 in.

Lesson 12.5, Pages 671–679

5. $S = 96$ in²; $V = 48$ in³ **7.** $S =$ about 628.3 cm²;
$V =$ about 1005.3 cm³ **9.** $S =$ about 301.6 in²;
$V =$ about 301.6 in³ **11.** about 78.54 in²
13. pyramid; The base area of the pyramid is
greatest and heights are the same. **15.** 21,270 ft²
17. 15.6 cm² **19.** 51.6 cm² **21.** no
25. $x > -1$ **27.** (2, 3)
29.

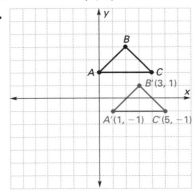

33. 49 cm² **35.** 84 cm

Lesson 12.6, Pages 680–686

5. D; 2.5 : 1; 2.5 **7.** C; 1.2 : 1; 1.2
9. $S_A =$ about 31.4 cm²; $V_A =$ about 12.6 cm³;
$S_B =$ about 196.3 cm²; $V_B =$ about 196.3 cm³
11. 1 : 1.5 **13.** false **15.** true **17.** false **19.** 87
21. $2\frac{2}{3}$ in. by 4 in. **23.** A' (3, 0), B' (4, 3), C' (5, 0)
25. A' (3, 3), B' (6, 12), C' (9, 3)

Index

A

Absolute values, 131
  comparing, 136–137
Acute triangle, 473
Addition
  of algebraic expressions, 203–205
  equations, solving, 186–188
  of integers, 140–147, 155–156
  of mixed numbers, 257
  of rational numbers, 254–260
  solving inequalities with, 273–277
  of zero pairs, to subtract, 149
Addition Property of Equality, 189
Addition Property of Inequality, 273–275
Addition Property of Opposites, 142
Additive identity, 26
Adjacent angles, supplementary and
  complementary, 469
Algeblocks
  to add integers with like signs,
    140–141
  to add and subtract expressions,
    203, 205
  perfect squares and square roots,
    551–552
  polynomials and (Math Lab),
    631–634
Algebra
  basic properties of, 25
  mobiles with (Math Lab), 228–231
Algebraic expression, 16–17
  adding, 203–205
Algorithms, 141
  percent–to–fraction, 350
Angle(s), 462, 466–472
  copying and bisecting (Math Lab),
    516
  corresponding, 489, 517
  drawing, 467
  measuring, of polygon, 482
  vertical, 488–489
  See also Headings
Angle–Sum Property for Polygons, 483
Angle–Sum Property for Triangles, 474
Approximation, 11
Arc length, 689
Area
  of circle, 624
  distribution over (Math Lab),
    389–390
  perimeter and, of similar polygons,
    615–621
  of polygons, 605–614
  and volume, of similar solids,
    679–680
  See also Surface area
Arrays, factoring with (Math Lab),
  285–286
Associative Property of Addition,
  25–26
Associative Property of Multiplication,
  37–38
Assumed mean method, 170
Axes, 400

B

Balance, 381
  credit card, paying off (Math Lab),
    393–395
Bar graphs, 91–99
  and histograms, 93–99
  See also Circle graphs
Base(s)
  and exponent, 524
  parallelogram, 606
  prism, 650
Base–ten system. See Decimal system
Basic properties of algebra, 25
Binomial, 631
Bisector, 516
Blocks. *See* Algeblocks
Boundary, 434
Box–and–whisker plots, 85–90
Break–even point, 197

C

Cancellation, 263
Cell, 100
Center
  of circle, 622
  of dilation, 593
  of sphere, 686
Central angle, 470
Central tendency, measures of,
  70–75, 77
  misleading, 110
Circle graphs, 357
  constructing, 470
Circles, 622–629
  area of, 624
  circumference of, 623
Circumference, 449, 622–623
Circumscribed polygon, 636
Coefficient, 205
Collinear points, 463
Common denominators, 248
  fractions with, adding and
    subtracting, 255
Common factors, 238
Commutative Property of Addition,
  24–25, 157
Commutative Property of Multiplication,
  36
Complement, of percent, 376
Complementary angles, 468–469
  acute, 475
Composite number, 286
Compound interest, 382–383
  computing, 527
Cones, 670–678
Congruence, 473, 488–494, 593
Conjecture, 330, 474
Converse of the Pythagorean Theorem,
  560
Conversion, 543
  factor, 300
  of metric units, 544–545
Coordinate plane, 400
  enlargement on, 595
  parallel lines on, 430
  reduction on, 594–595
  solutions on, 434
Coordinates
  on number line, 130–131
  of points, 400–401
Corresponding angles, 517
  and sides, 489
Corresponding parts, of similar
  polygons, 584
Counting Principle, 318
Cross–Products Property, 295–296
Cube, 663
  as polyhedron, 652
  See also Number cube
Cubic units, 663
Cultural Connection
  ball and urn experiments, 330
  Descartes' system of exponents, 539
  Egyptian and Roman census, 111
  Fibonacci sequence, 484
  history of zero, 171
  lattice method for simplifying
    multiplication, 45
  Mayan vigesimal system, 351
  measuring musical notes, 244
  perfect numbers, 580
  Piero della Francesca's perspective,
    645
  Rhind Papyrus, 214
  using coordinate systems for
    murals, 402
Cylinder(s)
  and prisms, volumes of, 663–669
  surface area of, 656–662

D

Data, 69
  analyzing, 109–110
  comparing, with box–and–whisker
    plot, 87–88
  containing negative values,
    128–129
  set, 70
  value, 70
Decagon, 480

R

Radius, 622
Random numbers, 328
Random sample, 333
Range, 76, 439–440
Rate, 299
Ratio, 235
    finding rise to run, 413
    and proportion, 294–298
        to make scale drawings
          (Math Lab), 338–339
    selecting correct, 305
Rational number(s)
    adding and subtracting, 254–260
    dividing, 266–272
    equations, 257
    and inequalities, 247–253
    multiplying, 261–265
Ray, 462
Real numbers, 553
Reciprocal Property, 266
Rectangles
    area of, 605–606
    similar
        area of, 616–617
        perimeters of, 615–616
Rectangular prism, 650
Reduction, 593
Reflections, 495, 501–505
Regular polygon, 481
Regular tessellation, 519
Relation, 439
Repeating decimal, 242
    as fraction, 243
Rhind Papyrus, 214
Right triangle, 473, 475
    test, 560
    See also Pythagorean Theorem
Rigid motions, 496, 593
Rise, finding, to run ratio, 413
Rotation, 495, 506–512
Rotational symmetry, 507–508
Rounding, decimals, 11–15
Rules
    function, 443
    translation, 496–497
Run, 413

S

Sample space, 316–321
Sampling, 333–337
    biased, 334
Scale drawings
    and maps, 599–604
    using ratios and proportions
        to make (Math Lab), 338–339
Scale factor, 593
Scalene triangle, 473
Scatter plot, 121
Scientific notation, 536–542
    significant figures and (Math Lab),
        568–570
Second quartile, 85
Segment. See Line segment
Semicircle, 626
Sequences, patterns and, 578–583
Shapes. *See* Geometric figures

Sides
    of angle, 462
    corresponding, 489
    of polygon, 480
Sierpinski triangle, 592
Sigma Σ, 77
Significant figures, 568–570
Similar figures, 584–592
    polygons, perimeter and area of,
        615–621
Similar solids, 679–685
    with spreadsheet (Math Lab),
        690–691
Simple interest, 381–382
Simulations
    birthday (Math Lab), 341–343
    experimental probability and,
        327–332
Slant height, 671
Slope, 413–418
Slope–Intercept Form of Equation,
    419–420
    for spring (Math Lab), 451–453
Solids, 642
    similar, 679–685
        with spreadsheet (Math Lab),
        690–691
Solution, 187, 250, 274
    of the equation, 405
    of inequalities, 433
Spec length, 178
Sphere, 686
Spreadsheet
    birthday simulations (Math Lab),
        341–343
    break–even point with (Math Lab),
        453–455
    figuring proportions in, 306
    for paying off credit card balance
        (Math Lab), 393–395
    similar solids with (Math Lab),
        690–691
    solving equations with (Math
        Lab), 226–228
    solving inequalities with (Math
        Lab), 288–289
    statistics calculations (Math Lab),
        118–120
Square, 518
    area of, 606
Square numbers, 582
Square pyramid, 670
Square root equations, pendulums and
    (Math Lab), 566–568
Square roots, and irrational numbers,
    551–556
Stacked bar graph, 98
Statistics, 69
    misuses of, 108–116
    of produce (Math Lab), 117–118
Stem–and–leaf plots, 80–84
Step–by–step, averaging steps and
    estimating distance (Math Lab),
    63–65
Subtraction
    adding zero pairs for, 149
    equations, solving, 188–189

    of integers, 148–153
    of rational numbers, 254–260
    solving inequalities with, 273–277
Subtraction Property of Equality,
    187–188
Subtraction Property of Inequality,
    273–275
Sums, estimating, 29–35
Supplementary angles, 468–469
Surface area
    cone, 671
    cylinder, 656–662
    prism, 649–655
    pyramid, 670–671
    and volume, finding, 681
Symmetry
    lines of, 503
    rotational, 507–508
Systems of equations, 428–432

T

Table, using, to graph linear equation,
    406–407
Tally mark, 77
Tangent, 636
10%, estimating with, 362–363
Terminating decimal, 242–243
Terms, 203, 578–580
    rearranging, 205
Tessellations, 511, 518–519
Tetrahedron, 652, 675
Theoretical probability, 311
Third quartile, 85
Three–dimensional figures, drawing,
    642–648
Transformations, 495
Translations, 495–500
Transversal, 517
Trapezoid, 503
Tree diagram, 316
Trend, 101
Triangle(s) , 473–479
    area of, 608
    inequalities (Math Lab), 513
    reflection of, graphing, 502
    Sierpinski, 592
    similar, perimeter of, 616
    translating, 496
Triangle Inequality Property, 514
Triangular numbers, 579
Triangular prism, surface area of, 651
Trinomial, 631
Two–step equations, 198–202

U

Unfavorable outcomes, 329
Unit fraction, multiplying by, 262–263
Unit rate, 299
Units, in formulas, 218–219

V

Value
    absolute, 131
    comparing, 136–137
    negative, data containing, 128–129
Vanishing point, 645
Variables

Credits

Chapter 1
Courtesy of NASA: pp. 2, 3, 53; © Photodisc: pp. 4, 7, 9, 11, 15, 16, 21, 23, 24, 34, 36, 39, 40, 42, 46, 48, 49, 51, 54, 57, 67; © CORD: pp. 59, 63.

Chapter 2
© Photodisc: pp. 68, 69, 70, 74, 76, 78, 82, 85, 95, 100, 104, 107, 111, 113, 116, 125; © CORD: pp. 118, 120.

Chapter 3
© John Curry/Habitat for Humanity International: p. 174; © Photodisc: pp. 126, 127, 132, 134, 145, 148, 150, 153, 158, 160, 165, 167, 168, 171, 173, 183; ©CORD: pp. 176, 180.

Chapter 4
© Photodisc: pp. 184, 191, 192, 200, 202, 204, 207, 209, 211, 214, 232; © CORD: pp. 224, 226.

Chapter 5
© Eyewire: p. 253; © Photodisc: pp. 234, 235, 242, 244, 245, 256, 258, 260, 261, 268, 272, 273, 276, 281, 291; CORD: pp. 285, 287.

Chapter 6
Courtesy of NASA: p. 308; © Photodisc: pp. 292, 293, 297, 299, 300, 302, 304, 306, 311, 314, 321, 327, 332, 336; © CORD: pp. 339, 341.

Chapter 7
© Photodisc: pp. 346, 347, 348, 352, 354, 356, 358, 361, 366, 370, 372, 379, 387, 397; © CORD pp. 389, 391.

Chapter 8
© Photodisc: pp. 398, 402, 403, 405, 409, 410, 417, 420, 424, 432, 439, 439, 447; © Weatherstock: p. 427; © CORD: pp. 449, 451.

Chapter 9
© Photodisc: pp. 458, 459, 472, 475, 476, 483, 484, 487, 493, 497, 503, 505, 510, 512; © CORD: pp. 513, 518.

Chapter 10
© Digital Vision: p. 523; © Photodisc: pp. 522, 529, 535, 536, 542, 543, 548, 550, 551, 556, 566, 575; © CORD pp. 567, 568.

Chapter 11
© Photodisc: pp. 576, 577, 583, 590, 598, 600, 604, 613, 615, 621, 622; © CORD: pp. 630, 631

Chapter 12
© Photodisc: pp. 645, 652, 661, 664, 669, 672, 685, 686; Courtsey of Rock and Roll Hall of Fame: pp. 640, 641; © CORD: pp. 687, 689.